Fundamentals of Sport and Exercise Science

SPRT1025

Compiled by:

Dr Paul Castle
Claire-Marie Roberts
Chris Hughes
Dr Dan Eastough
Dr Nicola Gerrett

UNIVERSITY OF WORCESTER
Institute of Sport and Exercise Science

ISBN 13: 9781121944237

McGraw-Hill Custom Publishing

www.mcgrawhillcreate.co.uk

Published by McGraw-Hill Education (UK) Ltd an imprint of McGraw-Hill Education, 2 Penn Plaza, New York, NY 10121.

ISBN: 9781121944237

Fundamentals of Sport and Exercise Science

Contents

Credits

Fundamentals of Sport and Exercise

Introduction

Sport and exercise science is crucial in analysing human behaviour, movement and performance and the purpose of the module is to enable students to gain a holistic understanding of the nature of sport and exercise through scientific investigation.

SPRT1025 provides students with an introduction to the science of sport and exercise, encompassing the traditional disciplines of psychology, physiology and biomechanics. These disciplines will be combined to showcase multidisciplinary approaches to sport or exercise-specific situations and the ways in which data/information is integrated to examine such situations. This textbook has been compiled in order to provide the reader with appropriate supporting material for SPRT1025: Fundamentals of Sport and Exercise. Additional journal readings will be provided to further enhance an understanding of these disciplines.

With tutor guidance and support from this text, students should be able to achieve the following learning outcomes, by the end of the module:

LO1

Explain how movement is produced during performance of a skill in sport and exercise (psychological; physiological; biomechanical);

LO2

Evaluate selected psychological factors that influence behaviour in sport and exercise;

LO3

Evaluate selected physiological factors that influence behaviour in sport and exercise;

LO4

Evaluate selected biomechanical factors that influence behaviour in sport and exercise.

Setting the Scene

The Introductory chapter of this compilation will provide an overview of the fundamentals of sport and exercise. The module requires you to consider issues that can be examined from biomechanics, psychology and physiology. Importantly, you should remember that these disciplines should be viewed in an integrated, rather than an isolated way. The data collected in any one discipline may influence, or be influenced by factors appearing in other disciplines. For example, in a competition, a poorly executed long jump (biomechanics) may be influenced by increased heart rate (physiology) which may be influenced by increased anxiety (psychology). Although the data collected in each discipline is distinct, the interrelationship between the disciplines remains. In order to help guide you, in selecting an issue for examination, you should reflect on the issue from the perspective of each discipline.

Section 1: Biomechanics

Biomechanics can be considered to be how the body interacts with the world around it. Biomechanics focusses on the **Centre of Gravity**

When you move, what you move is your centre of gravity. The body may move around this point but it is the centre of mass that determines any movement you make. Where your centre of mass is and how you control it is key to any sporting performance, it affects all aspects of balance, movement and skill and those people who are good at any sort of skill that requires large body movements are good at controlling their centre of mass.

To read more about these topics see chapters by: Hamilton, et al (2012) – Kinesiology: Scientific Basis of Human Motion.

Kinematics is movement. In biomechanics you need to be able to understand measure and describe movement, since all skill or performance is about managing the movement that you want and the movement that you don't want. This section looks at the theory behind movement, how it is described, how it is controlled and the theoretical concepts behind it. As always an understanding of how the theory is applicable to practice is fundamental to grasping the topic area.

To read more about these topics see chapters by: Hamilton, et al (2012) – Kinesiology: Scientific Basis of Human Motion.

Force causes changes in movement. Understanding how forces work and how this is converted into movement allows sports performers and coaches to understand how skill works. More effective control of the force required for sports techniques makes for more effective skill. However the concepts of momentum, impulse and inertia mean that skill is not just about generating more force – it is about controlling the force that is present effectively. Elite performers manage the forces required for skilled actions more effectively and efficiently, so understanding the theoretical concepts and being able to apply these to human movement allows us to analyse and understand what is required in sport.

To read more about these topics see chapters by: Hall (2012) – Basic Biomechanics.

Any **movement** in sport takes place **within a fluid environment**. Understanding how the fluid a sport takes place affect the movements is critical; how the water has a direct impact on swimming, sailing or kayaking, or how the air affects how fast you can run or how far you can throw a ball. Any movement in a fluid environment is subject to drag and drastically affects the outcome from what is theoretically possible. Sports performers need to understand how to control this to their advantage, whether by reducing drag to increase maximum speed or increasing drag to reduce velocity. Any sport involving a projectile needs to understand how this drag affects the flight path but also how introducing spin can alter the movement of the projectile to their advantage.

To read more about these topics see chapters by: Hall (2012) – Basic Biomechanics.

Section 2: Psychology

Psychological foundations of sport and exercise could be construed as being 'two sides of a coin'. Sport and Exercise Psychologists may engage in research, which can then be used to inform practical application with performers. Some Chartered or Accredited Sport and Exercise Psychologists work solely with sports performers, others work in the area of physical activity and/or exercise. Others combine research with teaching and consultancy.

Studying this section of the module will help you explore questions such as "Can sport performance be predicted by personality?", "How can coaches facilitate athletes' motivation?" and "Can pre-competitive anxiety enhance sporting performance?" The Sport & Exercise Psychologist's role is to understand the relationship between these factors and to offer solutions to challenges associated with fluctuations between them.

To read more about these topics see chapter by: Wuest & Fisette (2012) – Sport & Exercise Psychology.

Personality

In general terms personality is an individual's unique psychological make-up and denotes consistent characteristics of individual differences in behaviour. Defining and understanding personality more specifically depends upon which perspective you choose to adopt. For example, behaviourists suggest that the individual is conditioned to respond in certain ways whereas, social learning theorists suggest one learns from observing others succeeding in particular environments. Personality is seen as a relatively stable response to a variety of situations and can help us understand, for example, why some people enjoy competing in sport while others may seek to avoid it. Ultimately, by understanding more about an individual's personality, we can predict sport and exercise behaviour including reactions to specific events or competitive environments. Personality is most commonly measured by questionnaires developed specifically to determine levels of different personality traits possessed by an individual.

.

To read more about this topic, see chapter by Cox (2012) – Personality as a Core Characteristic of the Individual

Arousal and Anxiety

The concepts of arousal and anxiety are pervasive in both modern life and in sport. There are many examples of athletes succeeding in sport, yet others choke under the pressure and stress of competition. It is important to understand both concepts as they are closely related.

Arousal is a general term regarding the physiological components of the intensity of alertness and readiness of an individual. It can vary on a continuum from extremely low (e.g. sleep), to extremely high (e.g. excitement). Changes in arousal levels can occur in different sporting environments and relate to the individual's perception of the situation. Moreover, an individual will have an optimum level of arousal required for producing peak sports performance. Different levels of arousal are also required for different sports and different activities within a sport. For example, compare the optimum level of arousal required for archery (low) to rugby (high). Furthermore, within the sport of rugby, consider the difference in arousal required for tackling or the scrum (high) compared to taking penalty kicks (lower).

Anxiety is generally considered as a consequence of higher states of physiological arousal, which produce feelings of discomfort and worry. In sport,

it is commonplace for athletes to experience the negative effects of anxiety. In line with personality theory, anxiety can be categorised into trait and state anxiety. Consequently, individuals with a high level of trait anxiety will be prone to experience more frequent and more intense levels of state anxiety in certain situations. The extent of the state anxiety reaction will also depend upon the individual's interpretation and appraisal of the situation, as illustrated in the example below.

Consider two athletes both competing in County level ladies hockey trials.

- Athlete A has a very high expectation of performance and has set a very high goal for herself. However, she does not feel that her previous performances are at a high enough level and does not feel quite ready for the trials.

- Athlete B has also set high goals for herself, but feels that she has been very successful in performances running up to the trials, is really focused and ready for the event.

It is likely that athlete A will experience and exhibit a greater state anxiety reaction than athlete B. This reaction is based on the athlete's assessment of a variety of factors including:

- performance expectations;
- ability;
- previous performances;
- perceived readiness for the event;
- information regarding the opposition.

To read more about this topic, see chapter by Cox (2012) – Anxiety, Stress and Mood Relationships.

Motivation

Motivation is responsible for: the *selection* and *preference* for an *activity*, the *persistence* at the activity, the *intensity* and *effort* put into performance. There are many theories of motivation including:

- need achievement theory;
- goal achievement theory;
- hierarchy of needs;
- cognitive evaluation theory;
- self-determination theory.

One of the more recent theoretical developments for motivation is the hierarchical model of motivation, which derives from self-determination theory and looks at intrinsic motivation, extrinsic motivation and amotivation across three levels; global, contextual and situational.

Motivation is possibly one of the most vital psychological components for sport and exercise performance as it determines participation or dropout. It has an integrated effect on mood, confidence, anxiety and competence and without motivation for an activity, participation would not take place. Novice performers tend to focus their motivation around internal factors including effort and enjoyment whilst at the more elite level, athletes value the feedback from peers and significant others.

Motivation is measured by self-report, either through psychometric measures derived from specific theories, or through interviews/ focus groups, to ascertain the reasons 'why' performance manifests itself in the way it does. It is such an intangible concept that using other forms of measurement is extremely difficult and often unreliable, lacking validity and credibility.

To read more about this topic, see chapter by Williams (2010) – Motivational Processes and the Facilitation of Quality Engagement in Sport.

Section 3: Physiology

Control of Exercise & Fuels for Exercise

All energy comes from the sun and exists in many forms (heat, chemical, electrical etc). Energy cannot be created nor destroyed but is simply transferred from one form to another. The human body obtains energy from food sources such as carbohydrates, fats and protein, which are broken down and stored in the body or is used for cellular function. The breakdown of energy is known as metabolism and the only useable source of energy in the body is adenosine triphosphate (ATP). To ensure that there is a continual supply of energy three energy pathways exist; ATP-PC, glycolysis and oxidative phosphorylation.

ATP-PC is an anaerobic energy system as it does not require oxygen to release energy. Therefore, it is able to supply an immediate release of ATP which is often required for explosive actions such as standing up from a sitting position and a javelin throw. However, this energy system only provides energy for 8-15 seconds. Once this is depleted, glycolysis will be the predominant energy supplier and again through a series of chemical reactions releases a large amount of energy without the need for oxygen, thus is known as anaerobic metabolism. A bi-product of this energy system is lactate and hydrogen ions,

and if too much accumulates can impair muscle function and hinder performance. Anaerobic glycolysis can provide energy for approximately 3 minutes and typically used in sports such as the 800m.

Aerobic metabolism is the most complex of the three energy systems and it incorporates glycolysis, the Krebs cycle and the electron transport chain. It releases a large amount of energy for a long time but very slowly. It is typically used for endurance events such as a marathon.

To ensure that there is a continual supply of energy these three energy systems do not work in isolation but as an integrated system known as the energy continuum. This means that all system work at the same time but one system is the predominant fuel provided. Understanding the process required to release energy in each three systems is essential knowledge for basic physiology of exercise and performance. More in-depth knowledge is required to understand which energy system is the utilised in a variety of sports and what the bi-products that may limit performance are.

To read more about this topic, see chapters by:

Powers & Howley - Bioenergetics

Cardiorespiratory Responses to Exercise

As explored in the previous Chapter, the need for fuel is essential for basic bodily functioning from sleeping to exercise. To ensure that all cells have the energy provision to function it is essential that fuels, nutrients, oxygen and water are circulated around the body. Of these, it is imperative that oxygen is transported around the body to sustain life. The major challenge to the human body during exercise is the increased demand for oxygen. The primary purpose of the cardiorespiratory system is to transport sufficient oxygen around the body through a tightly regulated circuit. To meet the oxygen demands, the body makes adjustments to the cardiovascular system (e.g. heart and blood vessels) and the respiratory system (lungs). These two systems will be consider independently and conjointly to understand the design and function of each system, how they are regulated and the responses to various types of exercise.

To read more about this topic, see chapters by:

Robergs & Keteyian - Pulmonary adaptations to exercise

Robergs & Keteyian - Cardiovascular function and adaptation to exercise

Cardiovascular Responses to Exercise

The role of the cardiovascular system is to transport oxygen to tissues and remove waste, to transport nutrients around the body and to regulated temperature. The structure of the heart and blood vessels enables these three functions to work efficiently; the heart as a two pumps in one and a rich network of blood vessels distributed around the body.

The role of the heart is to pump oxygenated blood around the body (otherwise known as the systemic circuit) and via the pulmonary system (otherwise known as the pulmonary circuit). During exercise, the heart rate must increase to meet the demands for oxygen and facilitate the removal of waste products such as carbon dioxide. During exercise, blood vessels will vasodilate or vasoconstrict in order to distribute blood from inactive organs to working muscles. However during exercise body temperature rises and to prevent over heating blood must also be distributed to the skin to allow for the dissipation of heat via evaporation and convection. In addition, the brain cannot be denied blood. As a result there is competition between for oxygenated blood from the brain, the working muscles and the skin. Regulation of heart rate, blood flow and blood pressure is essential to meet the demands of the body. It is essential that students have an understanding of the structure and function of the cardiovascular system and the responses to exercise.

To read more about this topic, see chapters by:

Robergs & Keteyian - Cardiovascular function and adaptation to exercise

Respiratory Responses to Exercise

As covered in the previous two chapters, the need for oxygen is essential for human function. The pulmonary system is the vehicle that delivers that oxygen from the environment to the body. The pulmonary system comprises the nose, naval cavity, pharynx, larynx, trachea, bronchial tree and the lungs, which all serve a purpose in filtering and preparing the oxygen for gas exchange in the lungs. This is known as pulmonary respiration where the exchange of oxygen and carbon dioxide takes place. Oxygen enters the blood stream and is delivered to cells around the body where another form of respiration occurs; cellular respiration; whereby oxygen is utilised by the body and carbon dioxide produced. The diffusion of gas from the environmental into the body and from the blood into the cells is regulated via the partial pressure of oxygen and carbon

dioxide at each stage during the respiratory process.

During exercise there is an increased demand for oxygen and an increased production of waste products that must be removed via the lungs. To meet these demands, pulmonary ventilation (the movement of gas in and out of the lungs) must increase via increased breathing frequency. Therefore the mechanism of breathing and the muscles involved in inspiration and expiration needs to be understood. In addition , an understanding of how breathing frequency is regulated is essential to a full understanding of the respiratory system and its responses to exercise.

To read more about this topic, see chapters by:

Robergs & Keteyian- Pulmonary adaptations to exercise

Dr Paul Castle

Claire-Marie Roberts

Chris Hughes

Dr Dan Eastough

Dr Nicola Gerrett

July 2013

CHAPTER

14

THE CENTER OF GRAVITY AND STABILITY

OBJECTIVES

At the conclusion of this chapter, the student should be able to:

1. Define the term *center of gravity,* and explain the basis for its location in the human body.
2. Estimate the location of the center of gravity of individuals in any position.
3. State the principles of equilibrium, and explain and demonstrate applications of each.
4. Discuss the factors that affect the stability and energy cost of the erect posture.
5. Explain the effects that the postural adaptations have on static and dynamic postures.
6. Explain the value of both anticipatory and compensatory postural adjustments.
7. Locate the center of gravity of an individual using either the reaction board or the segmental method.

CENTER OF GRAVITY

Definition of Center of Gravity

The **center of gravity** of a body is sometimes described as its balance point or that point about which a body would balance without a tendency to rotate. For this reason, the center of gravity is often identified as the point where all the weight of the body or object is concentrated. More accurately, it is the point where the weight of the body may be said to act.

The ability to locate the center of gravity of a body is based on the knowledge of what it takes for a system to be balanced, or in equilibrium. Two conditions must be met:

1. All the linear forces acting on the body must be balanced.

2. All the rotary forces (torques) must be balanced.

Another way of expressing these necessary conditions for equilibrium is to say that the sum of all the forces acting on the body must equal zero. If there is a downward-directed linear force, there must be an equal upward force so that the vector sum of these forces equals zero. If there is a negative clockwise torque, it must be canceled out by a positive counterclockwise torque of equal magnitude (Figure 14.1).

In this illustration it is represented as the intersection of the *x*-, *y*-, and *z*-axes. It may be located by application of the principle of torques.

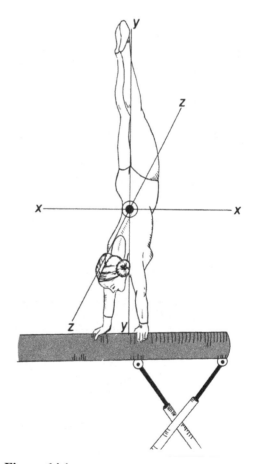

Figure 14.1   The center of gravity of a body is the point where all forces acting on the body equal zero.

A simple experiment to locate the center of gravity, or balance point, consists of suspending an irregularly shaped object by a string and letting it hang until it ceases to move (Figure 14.2). A vertical line is drawn on the object from the point of suspension in a line that is a continuation of the string. The object is then suspended from another point, and the vertical string continuation line is drawn again. This procedure is repeated one more time. The point at which the three drawn lines intersect is the center of gravity. If the object is suspended from this point, it will hang in whatever position it is placed because the weight of the object is equally distributed about this point and no unbalanced forces (torques) exist.

The location of the center of gravity of any object remains fixed as long as the body does not change shape. In rigid bodies of homogeneous mass, the center of gravity is at the geometric center. Where the density of a rigid body varies, the center of gravity is not at the geometric center but is shifted toward the more weighted section. If an object's shape or position changes, the location of the center of gravity will also change. This happens in the human body (Figure 14.3). It is a segmented structure, capable of numerous positions, and the location of its center of gravity changes

accordingly. This is an important consideration in the execution of sports skills. The evolution of the technique for the high jump shows how the change of placement of the center of gravity in the body increased the height of the bar over which the jumper could project himself (Figure 14.4). As one changes the relationship of the body segments to each other, the center of gravity may even be located completely outside the body itself.

Placement of Center of Gravity in Humans

The location of the center of gravity of a human being in the normal standing position varies with body build, age, and sex. It is generally accepted that in the transverse plane the center of gravity in females is located at approximately 55% of the standing height, whereas in males the center of gravity is at approximately 57% of standing height. The center of gravity will be higher in infants, whose head size is still quite large in relation to the rest of the body. As the infant body grows and changes, the center of gravity descends to the adult position, a point level with the first sacral segment, which is approximately behind the navel and about 6 inches above the crotch.

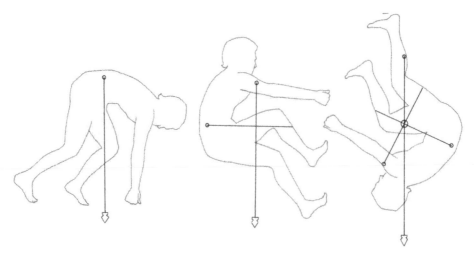

Figure 14.2 Location of the center of gravity in an irregularly shaped object.

CHAPTER 14   The Center of Gravity and Stability | www.mhhe.com/hamilton12e   **363**

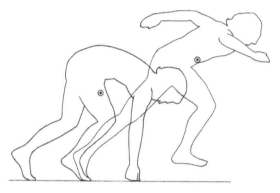

Figure 14.3   A shift in segment configuration results in a relocation of the body's center of gravity.

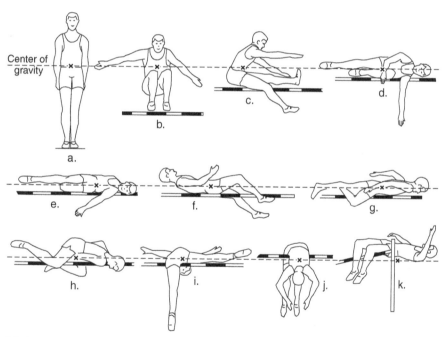

Figure 14.4   Effect of shift in center of gravity on high jump performance. *Source:* From *The Mechanics of Athletics*, by G. H. G. Dyson. Copyright © 1970, University of London Press, London. Reproduced by permission of Hodder & Stoughton, Ltd./ New English Library, Ltd.

In quiet standing, the center of gravity of the body can be considered to be held almost directly over the *center of pressure*. The center of pressure is that point at which the force vector for ground reaction force can be said to be applied. During normal standing, there will be some motion in the head region, which will in turn produce a pendulum-like motion in the center of gravity. As the center of gravity shifts slightly, the center of pressure will also shift slightly in the foot–ground interface. This slight motion is referred to as postural sway. Postural sway is normally measured in both the sagittal plane (anteroposterior or AP sway) and the frontal plane (mediolateral or ML sway). AP sway has been found to average 2 to 3 cm, whereas ML sway averages 1 to 2 cm (Raymakers et al., 2005).

Postural sway magnitude and velocity can be affected by a number of factors. Age, fatigue, injury, bracing, obesity, and the stability of the external environment have all been found to influence postural sway. Increased postural sway has been found to be related to falling in the elderly and in some pathological conditions. The presence of excessive postural sway should be viewed as an indication that there may be problems with stability.

STABILITY AND EQUILIBRIUM

All objects at rest are in equilibrium. All the forces acting on them are balanced; the sum of all linear forces equals zero, and the sum of all torques equals zero. However, all objects at rest are not equally stable. If the position of an object is slightly altered and the object tends to return to its original position, the object is in stable equilibrium. *Stable equilibrium* occurs when an object is placed in such a fashion that an effort to disturb it would require its center of gravity to be raised. Thus it would tend to fall back into place (Figure 14.5a). The more its center of gravity has to be raised to upend it, the more stable it is. A brick on its side is more stable than one on end because its center of gravity needs to be raised higher to upend it. The wrestler and defensive lineman both know the value of shifting body position to increase stability

by lowering the center of gravity. In fact, if for any reason the equilibrium is too precarious, assuming a crouching, kneeling, or sitting position will lower the center of gravity and increase stability.

Unstable equilibrium exists when it takes only a slight push to destroy it. This is the situation when the center of gravity of the object drops to a lower point when the object is tilted (Figure 14.5b). A pencil on end or a tightrope walker displays unstable equilibrium because the center of gravity is bound to be lowered if either loses its balance. Swimmers standing on the starting block poised for the start of a race or sprint runners at the start of their race are in unstable equilibrium, as are toe dancers on point or balance beam performers. In each instance, the center of gravity will be lowered if the individual is perturbed so that rotation occurs around the point of support.

The third classification of equilibrium is called *neutral equilibrium* and exists when an object's center of gravity is neither raised nor lowered when it is disturbed (Figure 14.5c). A ball lying on a table is in neutral equilibrium. Objects in neutral equilibrium will come to rest in any position without a change in level of the center of gravity. Upon receiving a slight push, such objects fall neither backward nor forward.

Because people ordinarily hold themselves in an upright position and because the effect of gravity is always in operation on this earth, the problems of stability are ever present. Probably the only time the human body is not adjusting itself in response to gravitational force is when it is in a position of complete repose. Either consciously or unconsciously, human beings spend most of their

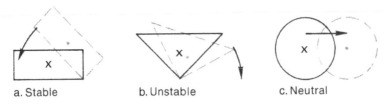

a. Stable   b. Unstable   c. Neutral

Figure 14.5   Types of equilibrium.

waking hours adjusting their positions to the type of equilibrium best suited to the task.

Factors Affecting Stability

The ability to maintain one's balance under unfavorable circumstances is recognized as one of the basic motor skills. Standing on tiptoe or on one foot without losing one's balance or maintaining a headstand or a handstand for an appreciable length of time is such a skill. These particular feats are examples of static balance, and the mark of skill is to accomplish them with a minimum of motion. Familiarity with the following factors affecting the stability of a performer's equilibrium state should make the analysis of balance easier and may suggest means for improvement of the skill with which the technique is executed.

The three most critical factors affecting stability are the size of the base of support, the relation of the line of gravity to the base of support, and the height of the center of gravity. Other factors such as mass of the body, friction, segmental alignment, visual and psychological factors, and physiological factors may also play a role in stability.

Size and Shape of the Base of Support

The size of the base of support is a primary factor in the stability of an object. Much of the difficulty experienced in balancing on one leg on a balance beam, a tightrope, or another small surface is due to the narrow base of support. The problem is to keep the center of gravity over the base of support, a requisite for maintaining equilibrium. The wider the base, the easier this is.

The base of support includes the part of a body in contact with the supporting surface and the intervening area (Figure 14.6). In a person whose weight is supported entirely by the feet, the base of support includes the two feet and the space between. If the feet are separated, the base is widened and the equilibrium improved. The person supported by crutches in Figure 14.7 has a base of support that encompasses the area bounded by the feet and crutches. He will be more stable if he places the crutches forward, making a triangular base instead

of a linear one. There is another factor, however, that must not be overlooked. If one takes a stride position that is wider than the breadth of the pelvis, the legs will assume a slanting position. This introduces a horizontal component of force that, if accompanied by insufficient friction between the feet and the supporting surface, as when standing on ice, does not make for greater stability. In fact, the wider the stance, the less one can control the sliding of the feet. From this we see that we must observe all the principles that apply to a situation. Observance of only one may not bring the results expected.

In addition to the size of the base of support, the shape is also a factor in stability. To resist lateral external forces, the base should be widened in the direction of the oncoming force. In Figure 14.7c, the position provides great stability for lateral forces from the side but very little from the front or back. Where the forces are known to be coming from a forward-backward direction, as when catching a swift ball or spotting a performer in gymnastics, a forward-backward stance is recommended. A similar adjustment is made when one stands in a bus or a subway train. The tendency to be thrown backward when the vehicle starts up is resisted either by standing sideways with the feet in a moderately wide stance, or by facing forward and leaning forward with one foot placed forward. These automatic reactions to external forces are for one purpose only—namely, to enable one to keep the center of gravity over the base of support in spite of the perturbing external forces. When the direction of oncoming force cannot be predicted, a slight oblique stance is probably best.

Height of the Center of Gravity

Ordinarily, the center of gravity in an adult human being is located approximately at the level of the upper third of the sacrum, but *only* during the normal standing position. If the arms are raised or if a weight is carried above waist level, the center of gravity shifts to a higher position, and it becomes more difficult to maintain one's equilibrium. Activities and stunts such as walking on stilts, canoeing, and balancing a weight on the head are difficult or dangerous

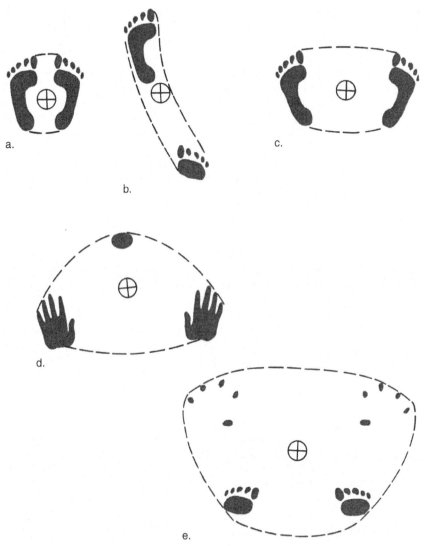

Figure 14.6   The base of support includes the part(s) of the body in contact with the supporting surface and the intervening area. What can you conclude about the stability of the base of support in these illustrations? In (a), (b), and (c) the weight is supported by the feet; in (d) it is supported by the forehead and hands during a headstand; in (e) the weight is supported by the hands and feet while the body is in a squat position. Circled crosses indicate point of intersection of line of gravity with base of support.

because of the relatively high center of gravity. Lowering the center of gravity will increase the stability of the body because it allows greater angular displacement of the center of gravity within the bounds of the base of support (Figure 14.8).

Relation of the Line of Gravity to the Base of Support

An object retains its equilibrium only so long as its line of gravity falls within its base of support. When the force that the body is resisting is the

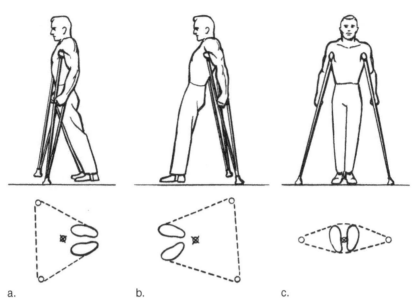

a.   b.   c.

Figure 14.7 Bases of support with varying degrees of stability. Can you rank these from most stable to least stable? The subject in (a) and (b) is secure primarily in the anteroposterior direction; the position in (c) provides greater stability in the frontal plane than in the sagittal plane. *Source: From Williams and Lissner: Biomechanics of Human Motion* (2nd ed.), by B. Leveau. Copyright © 1977, W. B. Saunders, Orlando, FL. Reprinted by permission.

a.   b.   c.

Figure 14.8 The height of the center of gravity changes with a change in body position. X = center of gravity. As the center of gravity moves closer to the base of support, more angular displacement of the center of gravity can occur before it goes beyond the vertical line marking the edge of the base of support. The angle in (a) is greater than that in (b), and the angle in (b) is greater than that in (c). Thus, a > b > c with respect to lateral stability.

downward force of gravity, the nearer the line of gravity to the *center* of the base of support, the greater the stability (Figure 14.9); and, conversely, the nearer the line of gravity to the *edge* of the base of support, the more precarious the equilibrium (Figure 14.10). Positions of instability occur when gravity can "pull us over." This occurs when the force of gravity changes from a linear force to a rotational force, or torque. Consider a brick standing on its end. If this brick is tilted and balanced on one of the edges, the line of force from the center of gravity acts through the base of support, or in this case, the axis of rotation. The brick is stable, and the lever arm of the force of gravity is zero. However, any shift in the location of the center of gravity of the brick will produce a lever arm, and the brick will rotate and fall. This is what happens to humans. When the center of gravity gets outside the base of support, the force of gravity immediately has a lever arm, and the human begins to rotate about the axis of rotation (the feet). For example, consider someone performing a trust fall (in which you close your eyes

Figure 14.10   Position of the body in which the line of gravity falls near the anterior edge of the base of support. This position is less stable than the one shown in Figure 14.9.

and someone stands behind you and promises to catch you). As you lean back, you feel yourself getting less and less stable as your center of gravity approaches the edge of your base of support. Once your center of gravity passes outside your base of support, a lever arm is established through which the force of gravity can produce a torque and cause you to rotate about your feet as you fall backward. This factor constitutes the major problem in some dance techniques, balance stunts, tightrope walking, and pyramid building.

To develop the neuromuscular control necessary to acquire such skills as these, there is no substitute for repeated practice. There are, however, a few methods that help keep the center of gravity centered over the base of support. One of these we do almost unconsciously. If we carry a heavy weight at one side of the body (e.g., a suitcase or a pail of water), *this constitutes a unilateral load* that, if uncompensated, would shift the center of gravity to that side, bringing it dangerously close to the edge of the base of support. By raising the opposite arm sideways, by bending or leaning to

Figure 14.9   Position of the body in which the line of gravity falls approximately through the center of the base of support. This is a stable position.

Figure 14.11   Compensating for a unilateral load by inclining the entire body to the opposite side.

Figure 14.12   Compensating for a unilateral load by bending to the opposite side.

the opposite side, or by a combination of these, we counterbalance the external load and keep the line of gravity close to the center of the base of support (Figures 14.11 and 14.12). Another application of the principle of keeping the line of gravity over the center of the base of support is seen in the tight-rope walker who carries a balancing pole or, to a lesser degree, in the gymnast walking on a balance beam with arms extended sideward.

    When the external force acting on a body is a lateral one, stability is increased if the line of gravity is placed so that it will continue to remain over the base even when forced to move by the external force. Leaning into the wind (Figure 14.13) or pushing a heavy chest are examples of when the line of gravity should be close to the edge of the base of support nearest the oncoming force. Pulling in a tug-of-war is an example of having the gravity line near the edge of the base of support farthest away from the external force. When one is not certain from which direction an external force may be applied, equilibrium is most stable when the line of gravity is in the center of the base of support.

Figure 14.13   Leaning into the wind to balance the effect of its force on the body.

Mass of the Body

The mass or weight of an object is a factor in equilibrium only when motion or an external force is involved. Then, as Newton's second law states, $F = ma$. The amount of force needed to effect a change in motion (acceleration) is proportional to the mass being moved. The greater the mass (inertia), the greater the stability. It is a matter of common observation that an empty cardboard carton is more likely to blow down the street than one filled with canned goods. Likewise, a lineman weighing 120 kg is less likely to be brushed aside than one weighing 60 kg. In all sports involving physical contact, the heavy, solid individual stands a better chance of keeping his or her footing than does the lighter one. Recall that mass is a measure of an object's inertia, and inertia is a measure of resistance to change in motion state (Newton's first law). Therefore, the greater the mass, the greater the resistance to change in position or motion. When all factors are considered, however, mass is less a factor in stability than are the location of the line of gravity and the height of the center of gravity.

Friction

Friction as a factor in stability has already been suggested in relation to the size of the base of support. It has even greater influence when the body is in motion or is being acted on by an external force. Inadequate friction is what makes it difficult to keep one's equilibrium when walking on icy pavement, particularly if an active dog tugs unexpectedly on its leash. When the supporting surface presents insufficient friction, the footgear can make up for it. The person who must walk on icy pavement can wear "creepers" on the shoes, the golfer and the soccer player can wear cleats, and the basketball player can wear rubber-soled shoes.

Segmental Alignment

If, instead of being in one solid piece, an object consists of a series of segments placed one above the other, the problem of retaining its equilibrium is a multiple one. Maximum stability of a segmented body is ensured when the centers of gravity of all the weight-bearing segments lie in a vertical line that is centered over the base of support. In a column of blocks, this means that each block must be centered over the block beneath. In a jointed column, as in the human body, one segment cannot slide off another, but it is quite possible for the segments to be united in a zigzag alignment. Such is all too often the case in human standing posture. In fact, the alignment of the body segments is a widely used criterion for judging standing posture. When the segments are aligned in a single vertical line, the posture is not only more pleasing in appearance to most of us, but there is less likelihood of strain to the joints and muscles. When one segment gets out of line, there is usually a compensatory misalignment of another segment in order to maintain a balanced position of the body as a whole. (For every "zig" there is a "zag.") At every point of angulation between segments, there is uneven tension thrown on the ligaments and uneven tension in opposing muscle groups. This causes fatigue, if not actual strain.

The addition of an external weight to the body, as when one carries books, babies, or suitcases, may be thought of as the addition of a segment. The additional segment will add mass to the body and change its stability somewhat. More important, though, is the effect on the height of the center of gravity and the location of the line of gravity. The center of gravity will be displaced in the direction of the added weight, and the line of gravity will shift accordingly. Its new location will be governed by the nature of compensation made to accommodate the additional weight (see Figures 14.11 and 14.12).

Visual and Psychological Factors

Factors that belong in this category are less easily explained than the others but are familiar to everyone. Consider how difficult it is to stand on one foot with eyes closed versus eyes open. The giddiness that many experience when walking close to an unprotected edge high above the ground or when crossing a swirling river on a footbridge is a real detriment to one's equilibrium. Even if the supporting surface is entirely adequate, the sense of balance may be disturbed. A common means of preserving the balance, both in this type of situation and when walking on a narrow rail, is to fix the eyes on a stationary spot above or beyond the "danger area." This seems to facilitate neuromuscular control by reducing the disturbing stimuli.

Physiological Factors

In addition to the visual and psychological factors, there are also physiological factors related to the physical mechanism for equilibrium—namely, the semicircular canals. In addition to actual lesions of this mechanism, any disturbance of the general physical condition is likely to affect the sense of balance. Feelings of dizziness accompanying nausea or any form of debility reduce one's ability to resist other factors that threaten the equilibrium. Colds, viruses, and other problems that affect the inner ear may also interfere with balance. These physiological factors are largely beyond our control. One principle that can be derived from them, however, is that it is better to avoid situations likely to threaten the equilibrium when there is a temporary physiological disturbance. The same would be true of any decrease in proprioception, as often occurs with injury.

Principles of Stability

The principles of stability are stated here as simply and concisely as possible, and several examples are suggested in each case.

1. Other things being equal, the lower the center of gravity, the greater will be the body's stability.

Examples   *a.* When landing from a jump, one usually flexes at the knees, both to absorb force and to lower the center of gravity in order to regain one's balance.

b. In canoeing, the kneeling position represents a compromise position that combines the advantages of stability and ease of using the arms for paddling. Kneeling is preferable to sitting on the seat because the lowering of the center of gravity makes the position a more stable one. Although it is less stable than sitting on the floor of the canoe, it is a more convenient position for paddling. A position frequently recommended is kneeling and sitting against a thwart or the edge of a seat.

c. A performer on a balance beam quickly squats when he or she feels as if balance is being lost.

d. A wrestler tries to remain as stable as possible by lowering the center of gravity.

2. Greater stability is obtained if the base of support is widened in the direction of the line of force.

Examples   *a.* This helps an individual keep from being thrown off balance when punching with force, pushing a heavy object, or throwing a fastball. It also enables the puncher to "put the full body weight behind the punch" because, with a relatively wide forward-backward stance, the weight can be shifted from the rear foot to the forward foot as the force is delivered.

b. In pushing and pulling heavy furniture, the whole body can be put into the act without loss of balance.

c. When catching a fast-moving object such as a baseball, or a heavy one such as a medicine ball, widening the base in line with the direction of the force enables the catcher to "give" with the catch and, in this way, to provide a greater distance in which to reduce or stop the motion of the object. It also ensures greater accuracy by reducing the likelihood of rebound.

d. The military "at ease" is more stable than the position of "attention."

e. Keeping one's balance when standing on a bus or train that is accelerating or decelerating is facilitated by widening the stance in the direction that the vehicle is moving, that is, in a forward-backward direction in relation to the vehicle.

3. For maximum stability, the line of gravity should intersect the base of support at a point that will allow the greatest range of movement within the area of the base in the direction of forces causing motion.

Examples   *a.* A football player knowing he will be pushed from in front should lean forward so that he can "give" in a backward direction without losing his balance.

b. A person in a tug-of-war line leans backward in preparation for absorbing a strong forward pull from the opponent.

c. A tennis player anticipating the opponent's return will keep the line of gravity centered so that the center of gravity can be shifted quickly in any direction without loss of balance.

d. Dragging a heavy box forward on a high shelf and then lifting it down is an activity in the home to which this principle applies. Assuming a forward-backward stance and leaning forward for this act gives the individual a wider distance to receive the weight of this forward-moving object. This decreases the likelihood of being thrown off balance when the box suddenly comes free of the shelf. It also enables one to take a step backward, which makes it easier to lower the box in front and to keep control of it. With a sideward stance, one would be more likely to be thrown off balance as the box comes free. There is also the danger of exerting so much horizontal force that, instead of lowering the box in front, the individual swings back overhead, hyperextending the spine and running the risk of straining the back.

e. Basketball and other team games involving running often require sudden reversals of direction. If the player tries to turn while the feet are close together, the momentum is likely to throw the runner off balance. This can be prevented by spreading the feet to check the forward motion and leaning back so that the line of gravity will be toward the rear. The runner can then quickly pivot to reverse direction.

4. Other things being equal, the greater the mass of a body, the greater will be its stability.

Example   *a.* In sports in which resistance to impact is a factor, heavy, solid individuals are more likely to maintain their equilibrium than lighter ones. This provides one basis for selecting linemen in football.

5. Other things being equal, the most stable position of a vertical segmented body (such as a column of blocks or the erect human body) is one in which the center of gravity of each weight-bearing segment lies in a vertical line centered over the base of support or in which deviations in one direction produce torques that must be balanced by deviations producing torque in the opposite direction.

Examples   *a.* This principle applies to postural adjustments for achieving a well-balanced alignment of the body segments, both with and without external loads.

b. In balance stunts in which one person (or group of persons) supports the weight of another person or persons, the chief problem is one of either aligning or balancing the several centers of gravity over the center of the base of support.

6. Other things being equal, the greater the friction between the supporting surface and the parts of the body in contact with it, the more stable the body will be.

Example   Wearing cleats and rubber-soled shoes for sport activities not only aids in locomotion but also serves to increase one's stability in positions held momentarily between quick or forceful movements, as in basketball, fencing, football, field hockey, lacrosse, and other sports.

7. Other things being equal, a person has better balance in locomotion under difficult circumstances when the vision is focused on stationary objects rather than on disturbing stimuli.

Example   Beginners learning to walk on a balance beam or to perform balance stunts, and others who for any reason have difficulty in keeping their balance, can minimize disturbing visual stimuli by fixing their eyes on a stationary spot in front of them, either at eye level or somewhat above eye level.

8. There is a positive relationship between one's physical and emotional state and the ability to maintain balance under difficult circumstances.

Example   Persons should not be permitted to attempt dangerous balance stunts or activities requiring expert balance ability when their physical or emotional health is impaired.

9. Regaining equilibrium is based on the same principles as maintaining it.

Examples   *a.* After an unexpected loss of balance, such as when starting to fall or after receiving impetus when off balance, equilibrium may be more quickly regained if a wide base of support is established and the center of gravity is lowered.

b. Upon landing from a downward jump, stability may be more readily regained if the weight is kept evenly distributed over both feet or over the hands and feet, and if a sufficiently wide base of support is provided.

c. Upon landing from a forward jump, the balance may be more readily regained if one lands with the weight forward and uses the hands, if necessary, to provide support in the direction of motion.

From this emphasis on stability, it might seem that one should seek maximum stability in all situations. This is not true regarding certain stunts and gymnastic activities that are designed for the purpose of testing and developing body control under difficult circumstances. In many gymnastic vaults, for instance, "good form" stipulates that the performer land with the heels close, the knees separated, the arms extended sideward, and the trunk as erect as possible while the knees bend slightly to ensure a light landing. In teaching beginners, it seems wiser to postpone emphasis on form from the point of view of appearance and to stress good mechanics and safety.

Mobility

There is an inverse relationship between stability and mobility. The greater the stability of a given body, the more difficult it will be to start the body moving. Conversely, the greater the mobility of the body, the less stability it possesses. A critical point in this relationship is the change from a position of stability to a state of mobility and eventually back to a position of stability. An example of this transition is seen in walking. The stationary standing position is a stable position with the line of gravity centered over the base of support. To initiate the step, a force is exerted downward and backward against the ground. The ground reaction force acts to move the center of gravity slightly up and to shift the line of gravity forward of the base of support, initiating the forward step. The swing leg then moves forward to reestablish a base of support either to regain stability or to initiate the next step.

Often in sport and physical activity, it is necessary to alter stability intentionally to become mobile. To initiate forward motion, swimmers and runners waiting for the start of a race assume a position in which they may lose balance rapidly (Figure 14.14a). A football lineman in a three-point stance is also in a position to lose balance and apply forward force quickly. In many instances the ability to start, stop, or change direction quickly depends on manipulating the stability of the body.

Both the speed and the direction of the desired mobility are used to determine the nature of the change in stability required to initiate the motion. To enhance the speed of a start in a given direction, the line of gravity should be as close as possible to the edge of the base of support in the direction of the desired motion. The opposite is true if a performer is attempting to stop quickly. A quick stop requires that stability be established quickly. To accomplish this, the performer must enlarge the base of support, lower the center of gravity, and move the line of gravity away from the leading edge of the base of support (Figure 14.14b).

CENTER OF GRAVITY AND POSTURE

When we speak of posture, we are speaking of the shape or configuration of the body. Of primary concern is the way in which the parts of the body relate to each other and to the external environment. For all practical purposes, no individual's posture can be described completely. Posture means position, and a multisegmented organism such as the human body cannot be said to have a single posture. It assumes many postures and seldom holds any of them for an appreciable time. We look at posture as being either static or dynamic. In reality, all postures are dynamic, involving muscle activity for the maintenance of position.

a.

b.

Figure 14.14 (a) Becoming unstable in order to move quickly. (b) Reestablishing stability to stop motion.

Because dynamic postures should be of greater concern than static postures to those who specialize in human movement, it may be well to say a word in defense of the practice of examining static posture. It is admitted that the posture in a static position is of little importance in itself, unless this posture must be maintained for long periods of time. In reality, all posture is somewhat dynamic. Even when standing still, the body is in motion, undergoing postural sway. The motion of the center of gravity—and the center of pressure—is used as a measure of postural stability. The alignment of the body when maintaining the erect standing posture becomes important in controlling and maintaining the appropriate level of postural sway. It also becomes significant when taken as the point of departure for the many postural patterns assumed by the individual, both at rest and in motion. Because there is an almost endless variety of active postures and because these are extremely difficult to judge, a convenient

custom is to accept the standing posture as the individual's basic posture from which all other postures stem. Hence, as a reflection of the individual's characteristic postural patterns, the standing posture takes on an importance it would not otherwise have.

Static posture by definition implies a state of equilibrium. In quiet standing, for example, one assumes that the body is balanced within itself. In reality, this is not completely true. To maintain a static posture such as standing, each segment of the body must be balanced with respect to the inferior, supporting segments. Given the irregular, nonrigid shapes of the body and the segments, this is not feasible. For this reason, even in quiet standing, there must be muscular activity in order to maintain segmental balance. Evidence of this can be seen in the postural sway described earlier. In postural sway, projection of the center of gravity (line of gravity) moves slightly within the base of support. The magnitude of this motion reflects to a large extent the stability of the body. The larger the magnitude of the postural sway, the less stable the static posture. A less stable posture requires a greater level of muscular activity, although there is no clear-cut point at which postural sway becomes detrimental. The reasons why the body produces this sway are unclear. Postural sway may have its origins in the postural reflexes that aid in the maintenance of upright posture (Visser et al., 2008). Measures of sway have been used to quantify static balance and to distinguish the existence of neurological disorders, load-carrying demands, aging, or attentional demands. Postural sway is measured in many ways, the most popular being computerized dynamic posturography. More recently, several researchers (Forth et al., 2007; Haddad et al., 2006) have demonstrated that the "time to contact" (TtC) method appears to provide greater clinical sensitivity. This measure includes the velocity as well as location of the center of mass.

Slight perturbations in static postures will produce changes in the pattern of postural sway.

For example, lifting the arm forward (shoulder flexion) will produce a torque in the forward and/or downward direction. This will necessitate that an equal and opposite torque be produced in order to maintain equilibrium. To accomplish this, the body weight (center of gravity) will be shifted slightly backward. This will increase the magnitude of the postural sway in the AP plane somewhat. An example of this can be seen in the center of pressure traces presented in Figure 14.15. Any variation in the standing posture will affect sway in some manner.

Postural Adaptation

A number of conditions necessitate postural adjustment if one is to maintain a reasonably balanced standing position. These include standing on either an uphill or a downhill slope; standing on the level but wearing high heels; standing on a moving surface, such as a bus, streetcar, subway, or train; holding a heavy bundle against the front of the body; pregnancy; and standing on one foot.

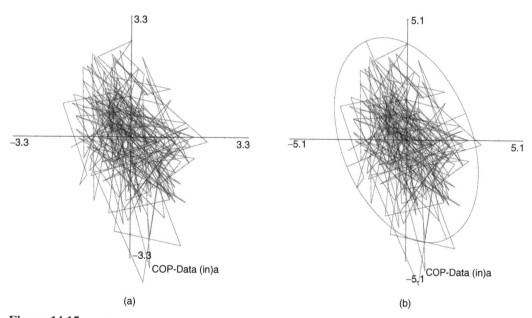

(a)   (b)

Figure 14.15   (a) Center of pressure during quiet standing. (b) Center of pressure as arms are raised.

In all of these conditions, the body can be relied upon to adjust automatically through the function of proprioceptors and the feedback mechanism.

Maintaining postural control in various environments and under varying surface conditions requires adaptations by the body. Researchers have identified two main strategies that help negotiate specific threats to balance. The hip strategy is used to navigate slippery surfaces, and the ankle strategy is used to navigate uneven surfaces. It is probable that these strategies exist on a continuum with the hip strategy on one end and the ankle strategy on the other. The different challenges to balance lie along this continuum and usually require a combination of responses to maintain upright posture (Bardy et al., 2002).

The hip strategy is easily observable when someone is walking across a slippery surface. Adjustments made to maintain the center of gravity over the base of support are achieved through trunk flexion–extension and hip flexion–extension. Based on a review of previous literature, Blackburn et al. (2003) concluded that the hip plays a substantial role for balance in the sagittal plane.

The ankle strategy is more subtle and is observable as a person walks over gravel or moves the head suddenly. While navigating these surfaces, the ankle/foot adopts a position that allows the person walking to maintain a level gaze. The knee may bend slightly; however, the hip and knee joint angles remain relatively static when the ankle strategy is employed.

The ability to remain upright, in quiet stance, is a complicated process that requires integration of the information from the visual, vestibular, and proprioceptive systems.

Consider trying to get a skeleton to remain upright just by balancing the bones one on top of another. Next, think about how the skeleton would lean if the left arm were raised and how the muscular system would have to respond to this shift. Now, think about how unstable the skeleton would become if it were standing on one leg, which happens with each step we take. The human body must interpret threats to remaining upright, devise a plan to counteract these threats, and implement that plan in time to prevent a fall.

When standing in a moving bus, streetcar, or train, one should be prepared to make three adjustments: acceleration, deceleration, and side-to-side sway. The same principle applies to all three—namely, establishing a comfortably wide stance in the direction of motion (forward-backward for acceleration and deceleration, and sideward for a steady speed, especially if there is a pronounced sway). During sudden acceleration, especially, the person tends to be thrown toward the back of the vehicle, in keeping with Newton's first law of motion.

The foot toward the rear, therefore, should be well braced, and more weight should be borne by the forward foot in anticipation of the jerk. The reverse is true during deceleration and stopping. In both acceleration and deceleration, the body is less likely to be thrown off balance if the knees are slightly flexed; doing so shortens the lever upon which the vehicle's motion acts and also lowers the center of gravity of the body.

The adjustment to standing on one foot is a delicate one but is usually managed automatically by the muscle, joint, and labyrinthine proprioceptors, and by the reflex response. The adjustment consists of a shift in the body weight to the single supporting limb and in the support of the pelvis on the side of the free limb. The latter adjustment requires additional effort by the quadratus lumborum and the abductors (gluteus medius and minimis, tensor fasciae latae, and oblique abdominal muscles on the support side). The iliopsoas, which is continuously active during all standing, increases its activity in steadying the lumbar spine (Basmajian & DeLuca, 1985). In addition, there is probably a continuous interplay of the deep muscles of the lumbar spine and possibly of many of the lower extremity muscles. The alternating action of the foot and ankle muscles, especially the tarsal pronators and supinators, is quite pronounced in their effort to keep the center of gravity over the narrow base of support. This problem can be helped somewhat by turning the toes slightly outward (i.e., rotating the thigh slightly outward) before assuming the one-legged stance.

Dynamic Posture

Movements of the body will cause a disruption, or perturbation, to the static posture. As illustrated earlier with the raising of the arm, any motion perturbs the static posture. When this perturbation occurs, the posture becomes dynamic. In dynamic postures, we must remember Newton's law of action and reaction. Every motion of a body segment produces an instantaneous reaction throughout the kinetic chain. These reactions also are transmitted to the supporting surface. This implies that there must be some muscular activity to counteract these reaction forces and torques. As more segments are added to the motion, the perturbations become greater. When the point is reached where the body moves from a state of stability to one of mobility, the posture is completely dynamic, or constantly changing. In this dynamic state, postural stability depends on the motion of both the center of pressure and the center of gravity. If both are aligned in relation to one another, static postural stability might be attained at the conclusion of the motion. If these two constructs are not aligned, balance may be lost. The more critical factor, however, is the relationship between center of pressure, center of mass, and momentum. If the motion vectors of the center of pressure and the center of gravity are not in the same direction as the momentum vector of the system (body), the regaining of static balance may be difficult if not impossible.

Postural Adjustments

During movement activities, postural adjustments take place almost continuously. Some of these adjustments are in response to proprioceptive feedback and help to maintain posture during the motion. Other postural adjustments are anticipatory in nature. These adjustments take place before the motion occurs. The purpose of these anticipatory postural adjustments is to prepare the body to maintain a dynamic equilibrium when the motion starts. A good example of an anticipatory postural adjustment might be the slight backward lean that occurs in preparation for lifting a weight in front of the body. Postural adjustments occur throughout the course of the movement. These adjustments, both feedback and feedforward in nature, rely on information from the neuromuscular system, as discussed in Chapter 4.

Postural adjustments, therefore, occur before, during, and after movement. Anticipatory postural adjustments prepare the body to move while maintaining dynamic balance. Postural adjustments during the motion (compensatory adjustments) act to keep the body in a state where stability is possible at the conclusion of the voluntary movement.

Principles Applied to Posture

By this time, the reader should understand that posture influences all we do and that it is not a static but a dynamic configuration. It should also be understood that no single ideal postural model is appropriate for all individuals. Instead, there must be an understanding of the principles that govern efficient posture. These principles must then be applied to each individual.

1. The weight-bearing segments of the body are so aligned in good standing posture that angles of inclination in the trunk and in the pelvic girdle are within "normal" limits. These limits are based on an erect posture of the pelvic girdle (lack of either posterior or anterior tilt) and the maintenance of normal spinal curves.
2. To be stable, the intersection of the line of gravity with the base of support will be close to the geometric center of the base. Maximum postural stability usually occurs when the line of gravity is over the center of pressure.
3. Standing posture is a position of extension of the weight-bearing joints. This should be an easy, balanced extension and should not be accompanied by strain or tension (Figure 14.16).

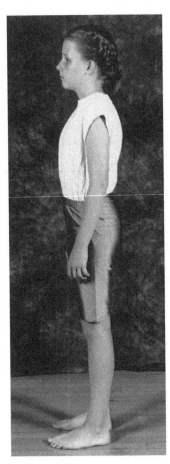

Figure 14.16 Except for a slightly forward head, the subject shows good alignment and extension without strain.

4. From the viewpoint of energy expenditure, efficient posture would seem to be a position that requires a minimum expenditure of energy *for the maintenance of good alignment.* Excess energy expenditure indicates hypertonicity, poor neuromuscular coordination, or both.

5. Efficient posture, both static and dynamic, requires a minimum of muscle force. This implies adequate development of the antigravity muscles to resist the pull of gravity successfully and to maintain alignment without excessive effort or tension. It also implies a balance between antagonistic muscle groups. There is no indication, however, that "the stronger the muscles, the better the posture."

6. Posture, both static and dynamic, requires sufficient flexibility in the structures of the weight-bearing joints to permit good alignment without interference or strain. Poor flexibility may be caused by tight ligaments or fasciae, short muscles, or hypertrophied muscles. The flexibility should not be so great, however, that excessive muscular effort is needed to keep the weight-bearing joints in alignment.

7. Posture requires coordination. This implies neuromuscular control and well-developed postural reflexes.

8. Adjustments in posture can be made more readily by individuals who have a good kinesthetic awareness of the postures they assume and of the degree of tension in their muscles.

9. The characteristics of normal posture change with age. Young children typically have a protruding abdomen and hollow lower back. Loss of muscle strength, inactivity, and balance problems in older persons show up in a wider stance, forward head, and rounded upper back, and limited flexibility in the trunk, hips, and knees.

Finding the Center of Gravity in the Human Body

The location of the center of gravity in human beings is of interest to scientists in many areas. Anatomists, kinesiologists, orthopedists, physical therapists, space engineers, and equipment design engineers have all shown interest in methods of determining the location of the center of gravity. Early experiments located the center of gravity by balancing the body over a wedge. Various other methods have since been developed to estimate the location of the center of gravity, either at rest or in motion. Two of these procedures, easily replicated with a minimum of equipment, are described here.

Reaction Board Method

It is a fairly simple matter to find an estimate of the center of gravity of a motionless body by using the *reaction board method*. Making use of the principle of moments, this procedure relies on the fact that the sum of the moments acting on a body in equilibrium is zero. Using this information, the location of the gravitational line is found for each plane. The center of gravity of the body becomes the intersection of the values for each of these three planes. Directions for locating the center of gravity in three planes follow.

Apparatus (Figure 14.17)
1. Scales: preferably either the Toledo or the spring balance type.
2. A stool or block the same height as the platform of the scales.
3. A board about 40 cm wide and 200 cm long. A knife edge should be attached to the underside of each end so that when the board is placed in a horizontal position, it rests on the knife edges. To simplify the calculations,

the distance from knife edge to knife edge should measure exactly 200 cm. The front edge of the board should be marked in centimeters. The board should be tested with a level to make certain it is horizontal.

Directions (Refer to Figure 14.17)
1. Find the subject's total weight, **W.**
2. Put one knife edge of board on the scale platform and the other edge on the box platform. Use a spirit level to make sure the board is horizontal. Note the reading on the scales. This is the partial weight of the board, **B.**
3. Have the subject lie supine on the board with the heels against the footrest at the end of the board away from the scales. The position the subject assumes should be as similar to the standing position as possible. Record the reading on the scales. This is the partial weight of the subject and board, **S.**
4. For equilibrium to exist about the pivot point **P,** the counterclockwise torques must equal the clockwise torques. If **W** is the total weight of the subject; **B,** the partial weight of the board; **S,** the partial weight of the subject and board; **L,** the length of the

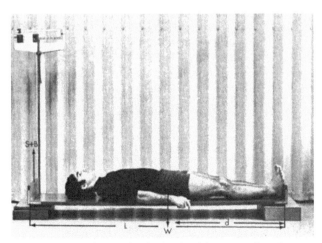

Figure 14.17 Reaction board method for locating the height of the center of gravity.

board; and *d,* the perpendicular distance from *P* to *W;* then

$$d \times W = (S - B)L$$

(clockwise torques = counterclockwise torques)

$$d = \frac{(S - B)L}{W}$$

Rearranged, the distance between the subject's feet and center of gravity is *d.* This is comparable to the distance between the ground and the center of gravity when the subject is standing but must be viewed as an estimate because of shifts in body organs and tissues when lying down.

5. The percentage height of the center of gravity with respect to the subject's total height is found by dividing the value of *d* in the transverse plane (supine lying position)

by the subject's total height and multiplying by 100.

$$Percent = \frac{d \text{ in transverse place}}{\text{subject's height}} \times 100$$

6. To locate the center of gravity in the frontal or sagittal planes, the procedure must be repeated with the subject standing on the board (preferably near the middle). For the sagittal plane, the subject stands with the side to the scales (Figure 14.16) and for the frontal plane location, the subject stands facing the scales. Use the same formula

$$d = \frac{(S - B)L}{W}$$

to solve for *d.* The value of *d* represents the distance from the knife edge *P* to the plane in which the subject's center of gravity is located.

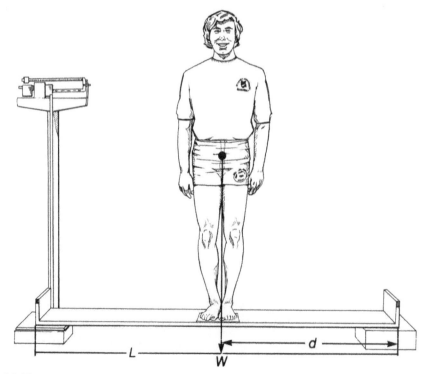

Figure 14.18   Reaction board method for locating the line of gravity in the sagittal plane.

7. To find the single point representing the spot where the line of gravity intersects the base of support, a piece of paper should be placed under the subject's feet for the side-view measurement. The outline of the feet is traced on the paper. When the first *d* is found, the distance is measured and marked on both the left and right sides of the paper. The paper should then be removed and the points connected by a straight line. When the subject faces forward for the second measurement, the paper should be placed on the board so that the subject's feet will fit in the footprints. When the second *d* is found, the distance should be measured and marked on both edges of the paper, and the place where two lines intersect represents the approximate position of the point where the line of gravity strikes the base of support. This is a crude method of locating this point and is not strictly accurate, because the subject may not be standing in exactly the same posture for both measurements. Furthermore, the element of swaying always introduces a source of error.

A modification of the reaction board method involves the use of a large triangular board supported by scales on two corners and a platform of equal height under the third corner (Waterland & Shambes, 1970). Each corner makes contact with its support through a pointed bolt. Again, it is important that the board be horizontal. If this triangle is equilateral, the moments are taken about lines forming two sides of the triangle, and the perpendicular distance from each line to the center of gravity is determined as follows:

$$d_1 = \frac{(S_Y - B_Y)L}{W}$$

$$d_2 = \frac{(S_X - B_X)L}{W}$$

where

d_1 = distance between XP and center of gravity
d_2 = distance between YP and center of gravity
S_X = partial weight of subject and board on scale X
S_Y = partial weight of subject and board on scale Y
B_X = partial weight of board recorded on scale X
B_Y = partial weight of board recorded on scale Y
W = weight of subject
L = altitude of triangle (perpendicular distance from scale to line about which moment is being taken)

Segmental Method

Experiments using the reaction board are convincing in showing how the body automatically compensates for external loads and segmental adjustments. It is revealing also to see how the body adjusts for the sideward raising of an arm, the forward bending of the trunk, a briefcase carried in one hand, or a load of books carried on the hip. Such analysis, however, is limited to the body in a stationary position. The location of the center of gravity of someone in action requires the use of another method. A highly useful procedure is one called the *segmental method*. This technique makes use of a photograph of the subject and involves finding the location of the center of gravity of each of the body segments, the position of these individual gravity points with respect to arbitrarily placed *x*- and *y*-axes, and knowledge of the ratio between the individual segment weights and the total body weight.

Considerable research has been done to determine values for the proportionate weights of body segments and the locations of the segmental centers of gravity. These data have been obtained through the weighing and suspension of cadaver segments, determination of the weight of segments of living subjects through the amount of water displaced by the immersed segment, and formation of mathematical models. Among the most commonly used data today are those of Dempster (1955). He weighed eight elderly male cadavers, dismembered them, weighed the segments, and determined the proportion of total weight for each segment. In addition, he located the center of gravity and specific gravity for each segment.

Using the same definitions of joint center used by Dempster, and using the segmental water volume values determined by Clauser (as cited in Plagenhoef et al., 1983), Plagenhoef and colleagues (1983) immersed the various segments of 135 subjects in water to determine segment weights as a percentage of total body weight (Figure 14.19). These data are presented in Figure 14.20 and Table 14.1. This research team

then selected a smaller sample and again used the segmental immersion technique to locate the segmental centers of gravity as a percentage of the total segment length. These data are presented in Table 14.2.

With information on the proportionate mass of body segments and the location of the center of gravity of each segment, the center of gravity of the whole body in any plane may now be determined by making use of the principle of torques. The sum of the torques of the individual segments about arbitrarily placed *x*- and *y*-axes will produce the location of the center of gravity of the whole body with respect to the *x*- and *y*-axes. This is because the total body weight acting at the center of mass is the resultant of the combined segment weights acting at their mass centers, and the resultant moment of the total body weight about the *x*-, *y*-axes is the sum of the individual segment torques about the same axes.

The segmental method for determining the center of gravity requires a considerable amount of measurement and calculation and therefore can be time consuming. The use of computer programs speeds up the process considerably, as does the use of motion analysis systems with built-in *x*-, *y*-coordinate systems.

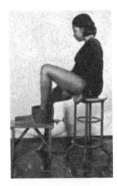

Figure 14.19 Immersion tanks for determination of segmental weights. Using segment landmarks as defined by Dempster, the segment is immersed in water. The displaced water is weighed and multiplied by the specific gravity of the segment to obtain the segmental weight. *Source:* From *Scientific Bases of Human Movement* (3rd ed.), by B. Gowitzke & M. Milner. Copyright © 1988, Williams & Wilkins, Baltimore, MD.

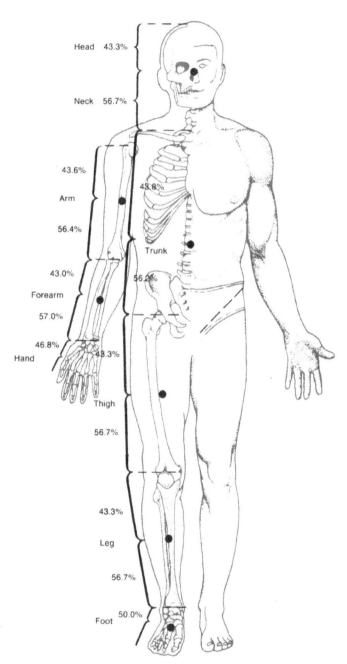

Figure 14.20   Joint centers and percentage distance of centers of gravity from joint centers in males. *Source:* Compiled from data in Plagenhoef et al., 1983; Hinrichs, 1990; and Dempster, 1955.

TABLE 14.1	Location of the Segment Center of Gravity as a Percentage of the Segment Length			
	Men (N = 7)		Women (N = 9)	
	Proximal	Distal	Proximal	Distal
Hand	46.8	—	46.8	—
Forearm	43.0	57.0	43.4	56.6
Upper arm	43.6	56.4	45.8	54.2
Foot	50.0	—	50.0	—
Shank	43.4	56.6	41.9	58.1
Thigh	43.3	56.7	42.8	57.2
Whole trunk[a]	63.0	37.0	56.9	43.1
Pelvis[b]	5.0	95.0	5.0	95.0
Abdomen	46.0	54.0	46.0	54.0
Thorax[c]	56.7	43.3	56.3	43.7
Head and neck[d]	55.0	45.0	55.0	45.0
Abdomen and pelvis[e]	44.5	55.5	39.0	61.0

[a]Hip joint to shoulder joint = 100%.
[b]Hip joint to plane of umbilicus = 100%.
[c]Pectoral line to shoulder joint (glenohumeral) = 100%.
[d]Top of the head to seventh cervical = 100%.
[e]Hip joint to T-11 = 100%.

Source: From "Anatomical Data for Analyzing Human Motion," by S. Plagenhoef, F. Evans, & T. Abdelnour, *Research Quarterly,* 54(2), 172, 1983. Copyright © 1983, American Alliance for Health, Physical Education. Recreation, and Dance, Reston, VA.

TABLE 14.2	Body Segment Percentages of Total Body Weight for Living Men and Woman	
Segments	Men	Women
Hands	1.3	1.0
Forearms	3.8	3.1
Upper arms	6.6	6.0
Feet	2.9	2.4
Shanks	9.0	10.5
Thighs	21.0	23.0
Trunk (including head and neck)	55.4	54.0

Directions for locating the center of gravity using the segmental method follow.

Apparatus

1. Line drawing on graph paper taken from photographic image of subject (Figure 14.21).

2. Worksheet with Plagenhoef et al. proportions listed (Figure 14.22).

Directions

1. The locations of the extremities of the individual segments must be marked according to the link boundaries shown in Figure 14.20. This will result in marks at the end of the second toe, ankle, knee, hip, knuckle III of the hand, wrist, shoulders, seventh cervical vertebra, and top of the head. Where these points are obscured by other body parts, an estimate must be made. The upper trunk mark is the seventh cervical vertebra, located slightly above the midpoint of the transverse line joining the shoulders. The lower trunk mark is the midpoint of the transverse line joining the hips.

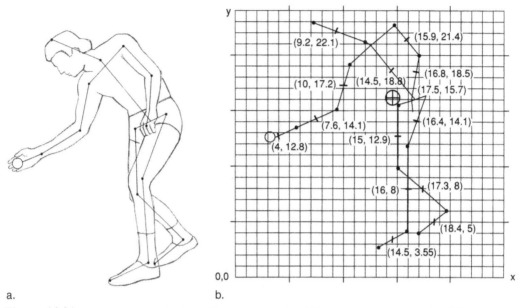

Figure 14.21   Segmental determination of the center of gravity. (a) Location of body segments. (b) The center of mass of each body segment is marked, and *x*-, *y*-coordinates are found using an arbitrarily placed *x*-, *y*-axis. With information on the proportionate mass of each body segment and the location of the center of mass of each segment, the center of gravity of the whole body may be determined using the principle of moments.

2. The extremity limits are joined to form a stick figure consisting of fourteen segments (see Figure 14.19a).

3. The mass center location for each segment length is found using the data provided in Table 14.1, where centers of gravity are located as a percentage of the distance between segment end points. The amount of the percentage distance from one segment end point is multiplied by the picture length of the segment. The resulting product is the distance from the selected end point to the center of gravity of the segment. The distance is measured from the end point, and the center of gravity is marked by a short slash mark intersecting the segment line.

4. The *x*- and *y*-axes are drawn on the paper.

5. The *x*-, *y*-coordinates for each of the fourteen segment mass centers are determined and

recorded on the diagram of the figure at the respective mass centers.

6. A worksheet such as that shown in Figure 14.20 is used to record the *x*-, *y*-coordinate values and the torques of those segments about the *x*- and *y*-axes. The individual torques are the products (col. 3) of the coordinate values (col. 2) and their related body segment proportions (col. 1).

7. The algebraic sum of the *x* products represents the *x*-coordinate of the total body's mass center, and the algebraic sum of the *y* products is the *y*-coordinate. These values are located and marked on the tracing (see Figure 14.19b).

This procedure has made it possible to locate the center of gravity of the handball player at the moment of contact with the ball. It must

Body Segment	Proportion of Body Wt.	x Value	x Products	y Value	y Products
1. Trunk	.486	14.5	7.05	18.8	9.14
2. Head & Neck	.079	9.2	0.73	22.1	1.75
3. R. Thigh	.097	15.0	1.46	12.9	1.25
4. R. Lower Leg	.045	17.3	0.79	8.0	0.36
5. R. Foot	.014	18.4	0.26	5.0	0.70
6. L. Thigh	.097	16.4	1.59	14.1	1.37
7. L. Lower Leg	.045	16.0	0.72	8.0	0.36
8. L. Foot	.014	14.5	0.20	3.5	0.05
9. R. Upper Arm	.027	10.0	0.27	17.2	0.46
10. R. Lower Arm	.014	7.6	0.11	14.1	0.20
11. R. Hand	.006	4.0	0.02	12.8	0.08
12. L. Upper Arm	.027	15.9	0.43	21.4	0.58
13. L. Lower Arm	.014	16.8	0.24	18.5	0.26
14. L. Hand	.006	17.5	0.10	15.7	0.09
x - y Resultants (product total)			13.97		16.65

x Coordinate = <u>13.97</u>

y Coordinate = <u>16.65</u>

Figure 14.22   Worksheet for locating the center of gravity using the segmental method.

be remembered that this location is for one brief moment during the performance of the skill, and the position of the center of gravity will shift with body segment shifts.

While this may seem like a cumbersome process, the basic concept is still in use in many motion-capture systems. Through the use of the principles spelled out here, motion-capture systems can perform the calculations required to pinpoint the location of the center of gravity throughout the entire motion.

Students who desire to trace the path of the center of gravity during the execution of a dynamic skill, but who do not need the accuracy of the segmental method, may find the placement of a dot on the iliac crest to be a useful estimate for the location of the body's center of gravity (Figure 14.23). This technique should be used with caution, however. It is important to remember that the center of gravity will deviate appreciably from this location in some body positions (see Figures 14.1 through 14.4).

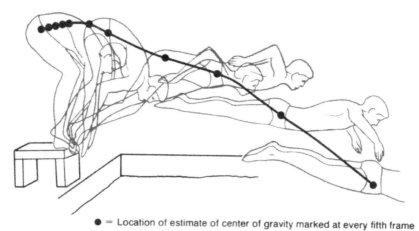

● = Location of estimate of center of gravity marked at every fifth frame

Figure 14.23   The iliac crest is used as an estimate of the location of the center of gravity of a swimmer during the execution of a racing dive. The tracking of the center of gravity of a dynamic skill is done through the use of tracings of individual video frames.

REFERENCES AND SELECTED READINGS

Bardy, B. G., Oullier, O., Bootsma, R., and Stoffregen, T.A. (2002). Dynamics of human postural transitions. *Journal of Experimental Psychology:Human Perception and Performance*, 28, 499–514.

Basmajian, J. V., & Deluca, C. J. (1985). *Muscles alive* (5th ed.). Baltimore: Williams & Wilkins.

Blackburn, J. T., Riemann, B. L., Myers, J. B., & Lehart, S. M. (2003). Kinematic analysis of the hip and trunk during bilateral stand of firm, foam, and multiaxial support surfaces. *Clinical Biomechanics*, 18, 655–661.

Bouisset, S., & Do, M. C. (2008). Posture, dynamic stability, and voluntary movement. *Clinical Neurophysiology*, 38, 345–362.

Dempster, W. T. (1955). *Space requirements of the seated operator*. Dayton, OH: Wright-Patterson Air Force Base (WADC TR 55–199).

Durkin, J. L., Dowling, J. J., & Andrews, D. M. (2002). The measurement of body segment inertial parameters using dual energy X-ray absorptiometry. *Journal of Biomechanics*, 35(12), 1575–1580.

Fiolkowski, P., Brunt, D., Bishop, M., & Woo, R. (2002). Does postural instability affect the initiation of human gait? *Neuroscience Letters*, 323(3), 167–170.

Forth, K. E., Metter, E.J., and Paloski, W.H. (2007). Age-associated differences in postural equilibrium contol: A comparison between Eqscore and minimum time to contact (TtC). *Gait and Posture* 25(1), 56–62.

Granata, K. P., & Lockhart, T. E. (2008). Dynamic stability differences in fall-prone and healthy adults. *Journal of Electromyography and Kinesiology*, 18, 172–178.

Haddad, J. M., Gagnon, J. L., Hasson, C. J., Van Emmerik, R. E. A., & Hammill, J. (2006). Evaluation of time-to-contact measures for assessing postural stability. *Journal of Applied Biomechanics*, 22, 155–161.

Henry, S. M., Fung, J., & Horak, F. B. (2001). Effect of stance width on multidirectional postural responses. *Journal of Neurophysiology*, 85(2), 559–570.

Hinrichs, R. N. (1990). Adjustments to the center of mass proportions of Clauser et al. (1969). *Journal of Biomechanics*, 23, 949–951.

Horak, F. B. (2006). Postural orientation and equilibrium: What do we need to know about neural control of balance to prevent falls? *Age and Ageing*, 35-S2, ii7–ii11.

Lovejoy, C. O. (2005a). The natural history of human gait and posture. Part 1. Spine and pelvis. *Gait and Posture, 21*(1), 95–112.

Lovejoy, C. O. (2005b). The natural history of human gait and posture. Part 2. Hip and thigh. *Gait and Posture, 21*(1), 113–124.

Plagenhoef, S., Evans, F., & Abdelnour, T. (1983). Anatomical data for analyzing human motion. *Research Quarterly, 54*, 169–178.

Pope, M. H., Goh, K. L., & Magnusson, M. L. (2002). Spine ergonomics. *Annual Review of Biomedical Engineering, 4*, 49–68.

Raymakers, J. A., Samson, M. M., & Verhaar, H. J. (2005). The assessment of body sway and the choice of the stability parameter(s). *Gait and Posture, 21*(1), 48–58.

Rougier, P.-R. (2008). What insights can be gained when analysing the resultant centre of pressure trajectory? *Clinical Neurophysiology, 38*, 363–373.

Visser, J. E., Carpenter, M. G., van der Kooij, H., & Bloem, B. R. (2008). The clinical utility of posturography. *Clinical Neurophysiology, 119*, 2424–2436.

Vuillerme, N., & Rougier, P. (2005). Effects of head extension on undisturbed upright stance control in humans. *Gait & Posture, 21*(3), 318–325.

Waterland, J. D., & Shambes, G. M. (1970). Biplane center of gravity procedure. *Perceptual Motor Skills, 30*, 511–514.

Winter, D. A., Patla, A. E., Riedtyk, S., & Ishac, M. (2001). Ankle muscle stiffness in the control of balance during quiet standing. *Journal of Neurophysiology, 85*, 2630–2633.

Wu, G., & MacLeod, M. (2001). The control of body orientation and center of mass location under asymmetrical loading. *Gait and Posture, 13*(2), 95–101.

LABORATORY EXPERIENCES

1. Define the following key terms and give an example of each that is not used in the text:
   Center of gravity
   Stability
   Base of support

2. a. Working with a partner, determine the position of your line of gravity using the reaction board method. Locate the point where this line intersects your base of support by marking it on a tracing of your feet.

   b. Determine the position of your line of gravity, leaning as far forward as possible with the body in a straight line from the top of the head to the ankles. Repeat, leaning as far backward as possible.

   c. Locate the line of gravity in the sagittal plane while leaning as far as possible to one side.

   d. Determine the height of your center of gravity with your arms at your side and then with them stretched over your head. What percentage of your total height is your center of gravity? How does this compare with averages for your sex?

   e. Choose an original position with a small or unstable base of support. Locate the point where the line of gravity intersects the base of support.

3. Make a tracing on graph paper of a picture of a person engaged in a motor skill. Locate the center of gravity using the segmental method.

4. Walk on a low balance beam and do the following:

   a. Look ahead at the wall.

   b. Look at a person who is in front of the balance beam doing a vigorous exercise such as a jumping jack.

   c. Walk with your eyes blindfolded.

   d. Walk along with a partner walking beside you. Without warning, the partner is to give you a slight but sudden sideward push. What measures do you take to maintain your balance? If you fail, explain why.

5. Build two columns of blocks, one with the blocks carefully centered one over the other, the second column with the blocks staggered but balanced. Grasping the lowest block of each column, slide the columns back and forth, changing the speed frequently and suddenly until the blocks tumble. Which column is the first to topple? Why?

11

THE DESCRIPTION OF HUMAN MOTION

OUTLINE

OBJECTIVES

At the conclusion of this chapter, the student should be able to:

1. Name the kinds of motion experienced by the human body, and describe the factors that cause and modify motion.
2. Name and properly use the terms that describe linear and rotary motion: *position, displacement, distance, speed, velocity,* and *acceleration.*
3. Explain the interrelationships that exist among displacement, velocity, and acceleration, and use the knowledge of these interrelationships to describe and analyze human motion.
4. Describe the behavior of projectiles, and explain how angle, speed, and height of projection affect that behavior.
5. Describe the relationship between linear and rotary movement, and explain the significance of this relationship to human motion.
6. Identify the critical kinematic components that would be used to fully describe the skillful performance of a selected motor task.

MOTION

If we are to understand the movements of the human musculoskeletal system and the objects put into motion by this system, we need first to turn our thoughts to the concepts of motion itself. What is motion? What determines the kind of motion that will result when an object or a part of the human body is made to move? How is motion described in mechanical terms? How do these generalities about motion apply to movements of the musculoskeletal system? Indeed, how does one know that motion is occurring?

Relative Motion

Motion is the act or process of changing place or position with respect to some reference object. Whether a body is at rest or in motion depends totally on the reference, global or local. When a person is walking down the street or riding a bicycle or serving a tennis ball, it seems obvious that movement is involved. Less obvious is the motion status of the sleeping passenger in a smoothly flying plane or of an automobile parked at a curb. If the earth is the reference point, all but the parked car are in motion relative to the earth, and even the parked car is in motion if the reference point is the sun. On the other hand, if the bicycle is the reference point, the person riding it is at rest relative to the bicycle, and the sleeping passenger is at rest with respect to anything in the plane. The relative motion of each is defined in relation to the specific reference object or point. It is possible, therefore, to be at rest and in motion at the same time relative to different reference points. The sleeping passenger is at rest relative to the plane and in motion relative to the earth. The relative motion of two bodies depends entirely on their relative velocities through space. Two joggers running at 8 km/hr in the same direction are at rest with respect to each other. However, if one jogs at 8 km/hr and the other at 10 km/hr, the faster jogger would appear to be traveling at 2 km/hr to the slower jogger and at 10 km/hr to the earth.

Cause of Motion

It is difficult to think of motion without visualizing a specific object in the act of moving. If we did not actually see how it changed from a stationary condition to a moving one, we might wonder what caused it to be set in motion. Did someone pull on it, or push against it, or perhaps blow on it or even attract it with a magnet? What are these assumed causes of motion? Without exception, each cause of motion is a form of force. Force is the instigator of movement. If we see an object in motion, we know that it is moving because a force has acted on it. We know, too, that the force must have been sufficiently great to overcome the object's inertia, or resistance to motion, for unless a force is greater than the resistance offered by the object, it cannot produce motion. We can push against a stone wall all day without moving it so much as 1 millimeter, but a bulldozer can knock down the wall at the first impact. The magnitude of the force relative to the *magnitude of the resistance* is the determining factor in causing an object to move.

Kinds of Motion

What are the ways in which an object may move? The hand moves in an arc when the forearm turns at the elbow joint and the neighboring joints are held motionless. A hockey puck may slide across the ice without turning. On the other hand, it may revolve as it slides. A figure skater spins in place. Arrows, balls, and jumpers move through the air in an arc known as a parabola. As we note the different ways in which objects move, we are impressed with the almost limitless variety in the patterns of movement. Objects move in straight paths and in curved paths; they roll, slide, and fall; they bounce; they swing back and forth like a pendulum; they rotate about a center, either partially or completely; and they frequently rotate at the same time that they move as a whole from one place to another. Although the variety of ways in which objects move appears to be almost limitless, careful consideration of these ways reveals that there are, in actuality, only two major classifications of movement patterns. These are linear or translatory and angular or rotary. Either an object moves in its entirety from one place to another, or it turns about a center of motion. Sometimes it does both simultaneously.

Linear (Translatory) Movement

This kind of movement is termed translatory because the object is translated as a whole from one location to another. Translatory movement is commonly called linear motion and is further classified as rectilinear or curvilinear. *Rectilinear motion* is the straight-line progression of an object as a whole with all its parts moving the same distance in the same direction at a uniform rate of speed. The child on the sled in Figure 11.1, a water skier pulled by a boat, or a bowling ball moving in a straight path are examples of rectilinear motion.

Curvilinear motion refers to all curved translatory movement; that is, the object moves in a curved pathway. The paths of a ball or any other projectile in flight, the wrist during the force phase in bowling (Figure 11.2), or a skier in a sweeping turn are all examples of curvilinear motion.

A special form of curvilinear motion, which on the surface does not appear to be translatory, is that called *circular motion*. This type of motion occurs when an object moves along the circumference

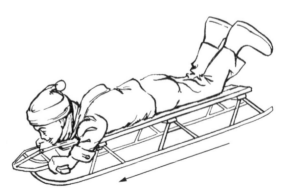

Figure 11.1 An example of rectilinear motion.

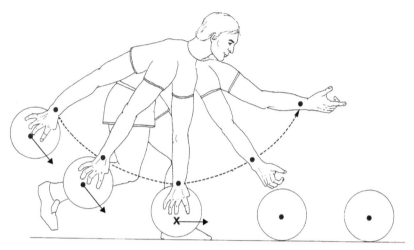

Figure 11.2   The wrist follows a curvilinear path during the delivery of a bowling ball. The arrows indicate the direction the ball would travel if it was released at that moment.

of a circle, that is, a curved path of constant radius. The logic for calling this type of motion linear relates to the fact that it occurs when an unbalanced force acts on a moving body to keep it in a circle. If that unbalanced force stops acting on the object and the object is free to move, it will move in a linear path tangent to the direction in which it is moving at the moment of release. A classic example is an object tied to the end of a string and swung in circles around the head. When the object is released, it will fly off in a straight line. The hammer in the hammer throw follows a circular path until it is released, at which time it flies along a curvilinear path until it lands. The path of a ball held in the hand as the arm moves around in windmill fashion is another example of circular motion. If the ball is released during the motion, it will fly off at a tangent and continue in a straight line until gravity forces it into a curved path (Figure 11.2). Other examples of bodies in circular motion are the gondola on a moving Ferris wheel or the knot on the ring of a spinning lariat.

Angular (Rotary) Motion

This kind of motion is typical of levers and of wheels and axles. Angular, or rotary, motion occurs when any object acting as a radius moves about a fixed point. The distance traveled may be a small arc or a complete circle and is measured as an angle, in degrees. Most human body segment motions are angular movements in which the body part moves in an arc about a fixed point. The axial joints of the skeleton act as fixed points for angular motion in the segments. The arm engages in angular motion when it moves in windmill fashion about a fixed point or axis in the shoulder. The head's motion in the act of indicating "no," the lower leg in kicking a ball, or the hand and forearm in turning a doorknob are all examples of angular motion. In each instance the moving body segment may be likened to the radius of a circle. The arm moving in windmill fashion and the lower leg and foot in kicking are the radii (Figure 11.3). In the "no" action of the head and in the doorknob being turned by the forearm and hand, the radius is perpendicular to the long axis running vertically through the middle of the head and lengthwise through the middle of the forearm and hand, respectively. These movements are not to be confused with circular motion. Circular motion describes the motion of any point on the radius, whereas angular motion is descriptive of the motion of the entire radius. When a ball is held in the hand as the arm moves in a windmill fashion,

Figure 11.3   Example of angular motion. The lower leg rotates about an axis in the knee joint. Similarly, the thigh engages in rotary motion moving about an axis in the hip joint.

the ball is moving with circular motion, while the arm acts as a radius moving with angular motion about the fixed point of the shoulder.

Other Movement Patterns

Reciprocating motion denotes repetitive movement. The use of the term is ordinarily limited to repetitive translatory movements, as illustrated by a bouncing ball or the repeated blows of a hammer, but technically it includes all kinds. The term *oscillation* refers specifically to repetitive movements in an arc. Familiar examples of this type of movement are seen in the pendulum, metronome, and playground swing.

Often an object displays a combination of rotary and translatory movement. This is sometimes referred to as general motion. The bicycle, automobile, and train move linearly as the result of the rotary movements of their wheels. Likewise, people, as they walk or run down the street, experience translatory motion because of the angular movement of their body segments. The angular motions of several segments of the body are frequently coordinated in such a way that a single related segment will move linearly. This is true in throwing darts, in shot putting, and in a lunge in fencing (Figure 11.4). Because of the angular motions of the forearm and upper arm, the hand travels linearly and thus is able to impart linear force to the dart, to the shot prior to the release, and to the foil.

Kinds of Motion Experienced by the Body

The human body experiences all kinds of motion. Because most of the joints are axial, the body segments must undergo primarily angular motion (Figure 11.5). A slight amount of translatory motion is seen in the gliding movements of the plane or irregular joints, but these movements are negligible in themselves. They occur chiefly in the carpal and tarsal joint and in the joints of the vertebral arches in conjunction with angular movements in neighboring axial joints.

The body as a whole experiences rectilinear movement when it is acted on by the force of gravity, as in coasting down a hill (Figure 11.1) or in a free fall (Figure 11.6), and likewise when acted on by an external force, as in water skiing (Figure 11.7). It experiences general motion in forward and backward rolls on the ground and in somersaults in the air, and rotary motion in twirling on ice skates. It experiences curvilinear translatory motion in diving and jumping, and it experiences reciprocating motion when swinging back and forth on a swing or a bar.

Factors That Determine the Kind of Motion

Thus far we have considered the cause of motion and the various kinds of motion on the basis of movement patterns or paths. Now we must turn to another question. What determines the kind of motion that will result when an object is made to move? The best way for the student to discover the answer is to produce each kind of motion and then analyze what was done to obtain the desired motion.

To make an object move linearly, we discover that it must be free to move and that either we must apply force uniformly against one entire side of the object or we must apply it directly in line

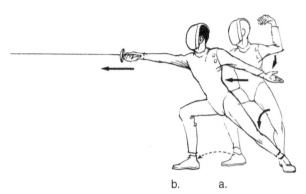

b.   a.

Figure 11.4   General motion: linear motion of one part of the body (the hand) resulting from angular motion of several segments of the body. (a) Just before lunge (thrust). (b) At completion of lunge.

Figure 11.5   An example of movement of the body caused by the body's own muscular activity. Movements of individual body segments are primarily angular.

with the object's center of gravity. The object will move in a straight line, provided it does not meet an obstacle or resistance of some sort. If its edge hits against another object or encounters a rough spot, the moving object will turn about its point of contact with the interfering obstacle. If we attempt to push a tall cabinet across a supporting surface that provides excessive friction, such as a cement floor, the cabinet will tip, even though we place our hands exactly in line with the cabinet's center of gravity and push in a horizontal direction. To move it linearly, it is necessary to apply the push

Figure 11.7 An example of movement of the body caused by an external force.

Figure 11.6 Descent from a vertical jump. An example of linear movement of the body caused by the force of gravity.

lower than the cabinet's center of gravity to compensate for the friction.

If one part of an object is "fixed," rotary motion will occur when sufficient force is applied on any portion of the object that is free to move. A lever undergoes rotary motion because, by definition, some portion of it remains in place. To move an object in the manner of a lever, it is necessary to provide a "fulcrum" or an axis and to apply force to the object at some point other than at the fulcrum. Thus, if rotary motion of a freely movable object is desired, it is necessary to apply force to it "off center" or to provide an "off center" resistance that will interfere with the motion of part of the object.

Reciprocating motion is caused by a uniform repetition of opposing force applications, and the oscillation of a pendulum is produced by repeated applications of gravitational force to a suspended object that is free to move back and forth and that is in any position other than its resting position.

In summary, the kind of motion that will be displayed by a moving object depends primarily on the kind of motion permitted in that particular kind of object. If it is a lever, it is permitted only angular motion; if it is a pendulum, oscillatory motion; and so on. If it is a freely movable object, it is permitted either translatory or rotary motion, depending on the circumstances. These circumstances include the point at which force is applied with reference to the object's center of gravity, the environmental pathways of movement available to the object, and the presence or absence of additional external factors that modify the motion.

Factors Modifying Motion

Motion is usually modified by a number of external factors, such as friction, air resistance, and water resistance. Whether these factors are a help or a hindrance depends on the circumstances and the nature of the motion. The same factor may facilitate one form of motion, yet hinder another. For instance, friction is a great help to the runner because maximum effort may be exerted without danger of slipping; on the other hand, friction hinders the rolling of a ball, as in field hockey, golf, and croquet. Again, wind or air resistance is indispensable to the sailboat's motion, but unless it is a tailwind, it impedes the runner. Likewise, water resistance is essential for propulsion of the body by means of swimming strokes and of boats through the use of oars and paddles, yet at the same time it hinders the progress of both the swimmer and the boat, especially if these present a broad surface to the water. For this reason, swimmers keep the body level, and designers plan streamlined boats. One of the major problems in movement is to learn how to take advantage of these modifying factors when they contribute to the movement in question and how to minimize them when they are detrimental to the movement. A more detailed discussion of forces influencing motion is presented in Chapters 12 and 13.

The motion of the segments of the body is also modified by anatomical factors. These include friction in the joints (minimized by synovial fluid), tension of antagonistic muscles, tension of ligaments and fasciae, anomalies of bone and joint structure, atmospheric pressure within the joint capsule, and the presence of interfering soft tissues. Except for the limitations because of fat or muscle bulk, these modifying factors are classified as internal resistance.

KINEMATIC DESCRIPTION OF MOTION

Motion has been defined as the act or process of changing place or position with respect to some reference point. Thus, to talk about motion, a starting point must be identified. Once this is done, the resultant motion, regardless of whether it is translatory or rotary, may be characterized according to the distance and direction away from the starting point, the speed of the movement, and any change in speed that may occur. This kind of motion study is called kinematics. Motion is described in terms of displacement, velocity, and acceleration with no consideration of or reference to the forces that cause or modify the motion. Linear kinematics is concerned with translatory motion and angular kinematics with rotary motion.

Linear Kinematics

Distance and Displacement

The distance an object is removed from a reference point is called its displacement. Displacement does not indicate how far the object travels in going from point A to point C. It only indicates the final change of position. A person who walks north for 3 kilometers to point B and then east for 4 kilometers to point C has walked a distance of 7 kilometers, but the displacement with respect to the starting point is only 5 kilometers (Figure 11.8). Similarly, a basketball player who

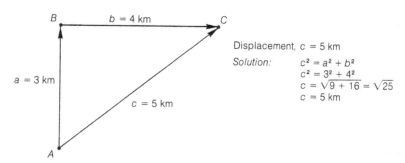

Figure 11.8   Displacement is the resultant distance an object is removed from its starting point.

runs up and down the court several times has traveled a considerable distance, but the displacement with respect to one of the end lines may be zero. Or consider the poor golfer who, blinded by the late afternoon sun, hits the ball so erratically and frequently that the route to the green, 450 yards away, crosses and recrosses the fairway many times. Regardless of the zigzag path to the green and the many changes of direction needed to get there, the ball's displacement is the straight-line distance from the tee to the green.

Displacement is a vector quantity having both magnitude and direction. It is not enough to indicate only the amount of positional change. That alone would be *distance,* a scalar quantity. The direction of the vector must also be defined. When the golfer finally reaches the green, the displacement from the hole to the green is 450 yards west. And the walker's displacement in Figure 11.8 is 5 km, in a northeast direction.

Speed and Velocity

Speed and *velocity* are frequently used to describe how fast an object is moving. These terms are often used interchangeably, but in fact there is a significant difference. Speed is related to distance and velocity to displacement. Speed tells how fast an object is moving—that is, the distance an object will travel in a given time—but it tells nothing about the direction of movement.

$$\text{Average speed} = \frac{\text{distance traveled}}{\text{time}} \text{ or } = \frac{d}{t}$$

Examples of speed measurements are a car traveling at 7 km/hr, the wind blowing at 60 mph, a ball thrown with a speed of 30 m/sec, or a sprinter running at 10 m/sec.

Velocity, on the other hand, involves direction as well as speed. Speed is a scalar quantity, whereas velocity is a vector quantity. In many activities this difference is of no concern, but in others it is of extreme importance. The speed of a football player carrying the ball may be impressive, but if the speed is not directed toward the opponent's goal, it is not providing yardage for a first down. Although the speed may be great, the velocity in the desired direction may indeed be

zero. Velocity is speed in a given direction. It is the amount of displacement per given unit of time. This is the same as saying that velocity is the rate of displacement, or

$$\text{Average velocity} = \frac{\text{displacement}}{\text{time}} \text{ or } = \frac{s}{t}$$

In the diagrams in Figure 11.9, displacement values (*s*) are represented on the *y*-axis and the time values (*t*) are on the *x*-axis. If displacement values are plotted to correspond with their time values, the line formed by connecting these plotted values represents the rate of displacement or velocity (*v*). When the rate of displacement does not change— that is, when the distance and direction traveled is the same for each equal time period—the velocity is constant, and the velocity line on the diagram is a straight line. In Figures 11.9a, b, and c, the velocity is constant; but in Figure 11.9d the curved line indicates that the rate of displacement changes, and therefore the velocity is not constant. When there is greater displacement per unit of time, the velocity increases, as does the slope of the velocity line in the diagram. Figure 11.9b shows the fastest velocity and c the slowest. In d, the displacement starts at a slow rate and then increases. If a, b, c, and d represent runners on a straight track, a, b, and c would each be running at a constant but different velocity, with b's velocity the fastest and c's the slowest. Runner d starts out at a slow velocity but increases the rate of displacement until the resultant velocity is the fastest of all four.

Where velocity is constant, as in Figure 11.9a, b, and c, the motion is said to be uniform. When the amount of displacement per unit of time varies, nonuniform motion occurs. Uniform motion is not a common characteristic of human motion, because most human movements are likely to have many variations in the rate of displacement. When the velocity of human motion is given, it is usually an average velocity that tells only the total displacement occurring in a stated period of time. Although a long-distance runner who ran the Boston Marathon (a distance of 26 miles, 385 yards), in 2.5 hours had an average velocity of 10.4 mph, it is doubtful that the velocity was uniformly 10.4 mph throughout the run. If one

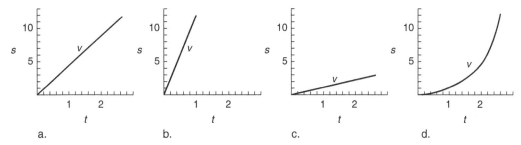

Figure 11.9 Examples of displacement–time graphs for uniform and nonuniform motion. The velocity in (a), (b), and (c) is constant.

were to record the time at which the runner passed frequent and equally spaced distance points along the route, a displacement–time graph could be prepared to show the variations in the runner's speed at various points in the course of the race. This kind of information can be quite useful in helping a coach or participant analyze the performance and strategy of the race and plan changes where needed. The narrower the distance intervals used, the greater is the possibility that critical variations in speed will become apparent. The use of motion analysis systems permits a similar analysis of brief and fast events. The distance and time data necessary for graphing and analyzing the motion patterns are obtained indirectly from the video or digital record.

In equation form, average velocity is

$$\bar{v} = \frac{s}{t}$$

The symbol s represents displacement, and t represents time. The average velocity of a tennis ball served 19 meters in 0.35 second is 19 divided by 0.35, or 54.3 m/sec in the direction of the service court.

Acceleration

When velocity changes, its rate of change is called *acceleration*. A sprint runner has an initial velocity of 0 m/sec. When the gun signals the beginning of a race, the sprinter's velocity begins to change by increasing. The rate of change in velocity is acceleration. Acceleration may be positive or negative. An increase is considered positive,

and a decrease such as slowing down at the end of the race is negative. Negative acceleration is also called deceleration.

In equation form, acceleration is expressed as

$$\bar{a} = \frac{v_f - v_i}{t}$$

where $\bar{a}$ represents average acceleration, v_f is the final velocity and v_i is the initial velocity. In other words, acceleration is any change in velocity divided by the time interval over which that change occurred.

In the example of the sprint runner, a graph of the sprinter's velocity throughout the race can be used to illustrate acceleration (Figure 11.10). As the sprinter is waiting in the starting blocks, the velocity is zero. In section a of the race, the sprinter changes from a velocity of 0 to a velocity of 9 m/sec after the first 5.6 seconds. Because this is an increase in velocity, this is positive acceleration. The acceleration for this phase of the race, the rate of change in velocity, equals the difference between the final velocity (9 m/sec) and the initial velocity (0 m/sec) divided by the time interval (5.6 sec), or 1.8 m/sec². In section b of the race, the velocity does not change but remains at a constant 9 m/sec. Because there is no change in velocity, the acceleration for this phase would be zero. To prove this, we use the equation

$$\bar{a} = \frac{v_f - v_i}{t} = \frac{9^m/_s - 9^m/_s}{9 - 5s} = \frac{0^m/_s}{4s} = 0^m/_{s^2}$$

In section c, the sprinter increases velocity again just before the finish. In this phase the acceleration

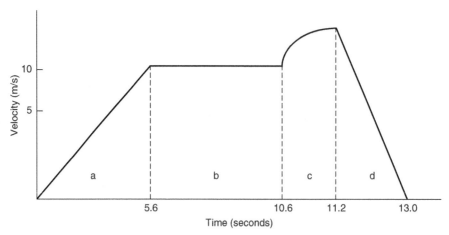

Figure 11.10 An acceleration curve showing a constant acceleration (uniform change in velocity) in (a), zero acceleration (no change in velocity) in (b), varying acceleration in (c), and constant deceleration (uniform slowing) in (d).

is not constant, so calculating an average velocity would not produce a true representation of the changes in velocity that are occurring. It is more accurate to calculate several instantaneous accelerations to plot a curve. By visually examining the curve, it can be seen that the acceleration at the beginning of this short phase is greater than the acceleration at the end of the phase. Section d of the race starts as the sprinter crosses the finish line. At this point the velocity is 10 m/sec. The sprinter now decreases velocity to come to a stop (0 m/sec) after the race. This slowing down represents negative acceleration, or deceleration.

Because velocity is always displacement divided by time and acceleration is velocity divided by time, acceleration is really displacement divided by time divided by time, and the units for measurement must reflect this. The time unit must appear twice in acceleration units. The logic for this is apparent when the units of m/sec are used for velocity in the equation for average acceleration:

$$\bar{a} = \frac{\left(\dfrac{\text{final m}}{\text{sec}} - \dfrac{\text{initial m}}{\text{sec}} \right)}{\text{sec}}$$

After the subtraction is completed, this equation becomes

$$\bar{a} = \frac{\dfrac{\text{m}}{\text{sec}}}{\text{sec}}$$

or, as commonly written, m/sec/sec or m/sec². Thus, the average acceleration of the runner in the example is 1.6 m/sec².

One usually thinks of acceleration in terms of a change in the amount of distance covered in equal units of time. Acceleration also occurs when, although the speed remains constant, there is a change in direction. The example given for Figure 11.10b is that of a runner keeping a steady pace on a straight track with no acceleration. If the runner, still running at the same speed, shifts to a circular track, acceleration occurs because of the change in direction, and the velocity–time graph would look more like Figure 11.10c.

Uniformly Accelerated Motion

When the acceleration rate is constant, the velocity change is the same during equal time periods. Under these conditions, motion is said to be uniformly accelerated. This type of acceleration does not occur with great frequency, because the change in velocity of bodies in motion is usually irregular and complicated. However, one common type of uniform acceleration is important in sport and physical education—the acceleration of freely falling bodies.

Neglecting air resistance, objects allowed to fall freely will speed up or accelerate at a uniform rate owing to the acceleration of gravity. Conversely, objects projected upward will be slowed at a uniform rate that is also due to the acceleration of gravity. The value for the acceleration of gravity changes with different locations on the earth's surface, but for most of the United States this value can be considered to be 32 ft/sec^2 or 9.80 m/sec^2. Regardless of its size or density, a falling object will be acted on by gravity so that its velocity will increase 9.8 m/sec each second it is in the air. A dropped ball starting out with a velocity of 0 m/sec will have a velocity of 9.8 m/sec at the end of 1 second, 19.6 m/sec at the end of 2 seconds, 29.4 m/sec at the end of 3 seconds, and so on. A second ball weighing twice as much will fall with exactly the same acceleration. It too will have a velocity of 29.4 m/sec at the end of 3 seconds. Of course, this example does not consider the resistance or friction of air, which can be appreciable. The lighter the object, the more it is affected. After an initial acceleration, light objects such as feathers or snowflakes may stop accelerating entirely and fall at a constant rate. Consider, for instance, the difference between the behavior of a badminton shuttle and a golf ball when dropped from a height.

The denser and heavier the free-falling object, the less air friction affects it, especially if the distance of the fall is not too great. Even heavy objects, such as sky divers falling from great distances, eventually reach a downward speed large enough to create an opposing air resistance equal to the accelerating force of gravity. When this happens, the diver no longer speeds up but continues to fall at a steady speed. This speed is called terminal velocity and amounts to approximately 120 mph (53 m/sec) for a falling sky diver. With the parachute open, the diver's velocity decreases to 12 mph steady velocity.

Laws of uniformly accelerated motion In spite of the reality of air resistance, much can be learned about the nature of free-falling bodies and uniform acceleration through a knowledge of the laws of uniformly accelerated motion. Because the acceleration of gravity is constant, the distance traveled by a freely falling body, as well as its downward velocity, can be determined for any point in time by application of these laws. Expressed in equation form, they are

$$v_f = v_i + at$$
$$s = v_i t + \tfrac{1}{2} at^2$$
$$v_f^2 = v_i^2 + 2as$$

Galileo's experiments with inclined planes enabled him to work out these equations. They apply to any type of linear motion in which acceleration is uniform. Their specific application to the effect of gravity on freely falling objects is presented in Table 11.1. If the initial velocity (v_i) is zero, as it is when an object is allowed to fall freely from a stationary position, the equations may be simplified:

$$v_f = at$$
$$s = \tfrac{1}{2} at^2$$
$$v_f^2 = 2as$$

The student may also discover that some authors, when applying these equations specifically to gravity, replace a, the symbol for acceleration, with g, the symbol for gravity.

The time an object takes to rise to the highest point of its trajectory is equal to the time an object takes to fall to its starting point. Similarly, the release speed and landing speed are the same. Other than the fact that the directions are reversed, the upward flight is a mirror image of the downward flight. Proof that the release velocity and landing velocity are equal in amount but opposite in direction can be shown mathematically by substitution of values in the motion equations. Following vector conventions, velocities upward are positive and those downward are negative. Thus the acceleration of gravity is treated as a negative value.

TABLE 11.1	Effect of Gravity on a Freely Falling Object		
	Time	**Distance Traveled** $s = v_i t + \frac{1}{2} a t^2$	**Final Velocity** $v_f = v_i + at$	**Average Velocity** $\bar{v} = \dfrac{v_i - v_f}{2}$
U.S. $a = 32$ ft/sec^2	1 sec	16 ft	32 ft/sec	16 ft/sec
	2 sec	64 ft	64 ft/sec	32 ft/sec
	3 sec	144 ft	96 ft/sec	48 ft/sec
	4 sec	256 ft	128 ft/sec	64 ft/sec
	5 sec	400 ft	160 ft/sec	80 ft/sec
Metric $a = 9.81$ m/sec^2	1 sec	4.9 m	9.8 m/sec	4.9 m/sec
	2 sec	19.6 m	19.6 m/sec	9.8 m/sec
	3 sec	44.1 m	29.4 m/sec	14.7 m/sec
	4 sec	78.4 m	39.2 m/sec	19.6 m/sec
	5 sec	122.5 m	49 m/sec	24.5 m/sec

Example Assuming that a ball is thrown upward so that it reaches a height of 5 meters before starting to fall, what is its initial velocity as it leaves the hand? What is its final velocity as it lands in the hand?

Upward Thrown Velocity
Given: $v = 0$
$\qquad a = -9.80$ m/s^2
$\qquad s = 5$ m
Find: $v_i = ?$

Solution: Using eq. (11.3) $v_f^2 = v_i^2 + 2as$
$v_f^2 = v_i^2 + 2as$
$v_f^2 = v_i^2 - 2as$
$v_i^2 = 0 + (2 \times 9.81^m/_{s^2} \times 5 \text{ m})$
$v_i^2 = 98^{m^2}/_{s^2}$
$v_i = \sqrt{98^{m^2}/_{s^2}}$
$v_i = -9.90^m/_s$

Downward Landing Velocity
Given: $v_i = 0$
$\qquad a = -9.80$ m/s^2
$\qquad s = 5$ m
Find: $v_f = ?$

$v_f^2 = v_i^2 + 2as$
$v_i^2 = 0 - (2 \times 9.81^m/_{s^2} \times 5 \text{ m})$
$v_i^2 = -98^{m^2}/_{s^2}$
$v_i = -\sqrt{98^{m^2}/_{s^2}}$
$v_i = -9.90^m/_s$

Projectiles

An object that has been given an initial velocity and then allowed to move in free fall under the influence of gravity is a projectile. Balls that are thrown, kicked, or hit; javelins; bullets or missiles; and jumpers, divers, and gymnasts while in the air are all examples of projectiles.

An object or a body is projected into the air for any of several reasons. In the case of the diver or the gymnast, the purpose of the projection is to gain maximum time in the air, or time of flight. The longer the *time of flight* the athlete can produce, the greater the number of acrobatic moves that can be performed. In other activities, a decreased time of flight may serve to deceive or avoid an opponent, as in the volleyball spike, or a smash in tennis, or an onside kick in football. Projectiles may also be released for the purpose of producing *maximum horizontal displacement.* The long jumper, the discus thrower, the shot-putter, and the batter in baseball are all examples of projection of an object for distance. Maximum displacement may also be in the vertical direction. Projections for maximum vertical displacement include such activities as the high jump and the pole vault. Projection of a body or an object for *maximum accuracy* is the purpose of actions such as shooting in basketball or soccer, passing, archery, or golf. When accuracy is the primary concern, a compromise often must be made between horizontal displacement and time in the air.

Once released, projectiles follow a predictable path. If air resistance is ignored because it is considered negligible, this path will be a parabola. The characteristic parabolic path of a projectile is the result of the constant downward force of gravity. This means that gravity will decelerate any upward motion at a rate of 9.8 m/sec^2 or will accelerate any downward motion at the same rate (Figure 11.11). All objects in free fall have the same downward acceleration whether they start from a resting position with a drop or fall or have been given some initial velocity.

Two forces, then, are acting on a projectile: the projecting force and gravity. The projecting force is a vector quantity that may act at any desired angle, depending on the purpose of the projection. The application of the projecting force produces an initial velocity in the object at some angle of projection. Because this initial release velocity is a vector quantity, it can be resolved into two component velocities, one vertical and one horizontal. The vertical component of velocity, being a vector parallel to gravity, will be directly affected by gravity. The horizontal component will not. Gravity is also a vector force that always acts in a vertical, downward direction. This downward force of gravity acts completely independently of any horizontal component of the projecting force (Figure 11.12).

If an object or a body is projected with only a horizontal velocity, then gravity, as the second force, will still act to cause that object to fall. If one object falls freely from rest at the same time

that another is projected horizontally from the same height, both objects will hit the ground at the same time. However, they will hit in different places. The dropped object will land immediately below the point of release, whereas the projected object will land some distance away. Gravity has acted on both objects equally, giving them equal vertical velocities in the downward direction, so they will fall at the same rate and land at the same time. The difference in landing points is the result of the horizontal velocity possessed by the projected object. In the time it took both objects to fall, the horizontal velocity of the projected object carried that object some distance from the point of release. This distance can be calculated using the velocity equation

$$v = s/t \qquad \text{or} \qquad s = v \times t$$

If, for instance, these two objects were balls released at a height of 2 meters, they would take 0.64 second to fall to the ground. If one was projected horizontally with a velocity of 20 m/sec, it would strike the ground at a distance of 12.8 meters from the release point ($s = 20$ m/sec $\times$ 0.64 sec; Figure 11.13).

To change the time an object is in the air, the velocity produced by projection must have some vertical component. This may be an upward component, opposing gravity, or a downward component being added to gravity. The time an object is in the air may also be varied by altering the height of release. If the balls in the previous examples were released from a height of 3 meters, both balls would be in the air for 0.78 seconds. Using the velocity equation again, it can be determined that the horizontally projected ball would now travel 15.6 meters from the point of release ($s = 20$ m/sec $\times$ 0.78 sec = 15.6 meters).

An object that is projected with only upward velocity will be decelerated by gravity until it reaches a velocity of zero. At this point, it will start to drop back toward the release point, accelerating as it falls. When the object reaches the release point, it will possess the same velocity it was given at release. The time required to reach the

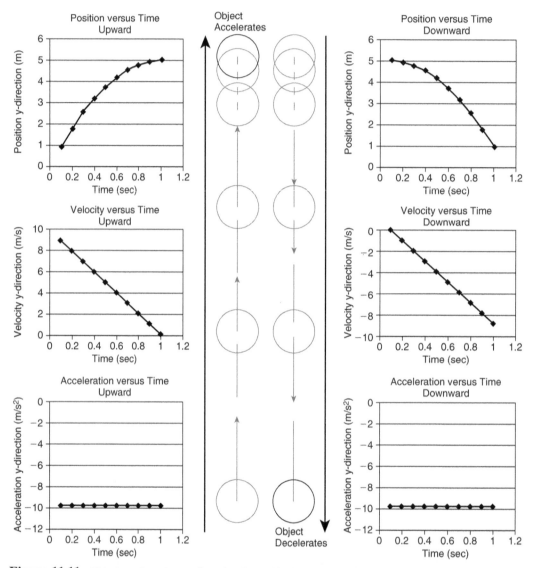

Figure 11.11   Objects projected upward are decelerated by the downward force of gravity at the same rate as those allowed to fall downward are accelerated. Both objects will cover the same distance in the same time.

highest point will be equal to the time it takes to fall back to the height from which it was released.

More often than not, objects put into flight will be projected in some direction other than exactly vertical or horizontal. A projectile of this type has both horizontal and vertical com-

ponents of the initial velocity vector. Again, these two component velocities are considered independently. The horizontal component of velocity remains constant following release (if air resistance is neglected), as no force is available to change this velocity. The vertical component

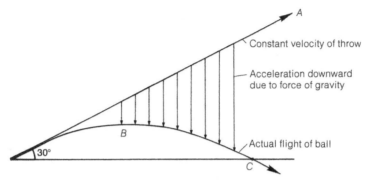

Figure 11.12 Effect of gravity on the flight of a projectile.

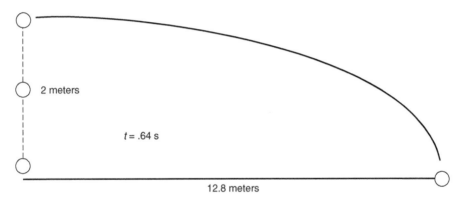

Figure 11.13 A horizontally projected object and a free-falling object released from the same height will land at the same time but in different places.

of velocity will be subject to the uniform acceleration of gravity. When the object is projected with some upward angle, gravity will act to decelerate the object to zero vertical velocity and then accelerate the object again as it falls downward. During this period of vertical deceleration and acceleration, the object is also undergoing constant horizontal motion. This combination of these two independent factors produces the parabolic flight path of the projectile as portrayed in Figure 11.14.

The horizontal distance an object will travel in space depends on both its horizontal velocity and the length of time the object is in the air, or time of flight. The time of flight depends on the maximum height reached by the object, and that, in turn, is governed by the vertical velocity imparted to the object at release. Thus the horizontal distance an object will travel depends on both the horizontal and vertical components of velocity. As will be remembered from the earlier discussion of vectors, the magnitudes of these two components will be determined by the magnitude of the initial projection velocity vector and by the angle that indicates the direction of this vector, referred to as the angle of projection. With this in mind, it can be seen that a projectile with a low angle of projection will have a relatively high horizontal velocity in relation to the vertical velocity. The low vertical velocity does little to resist the pull of

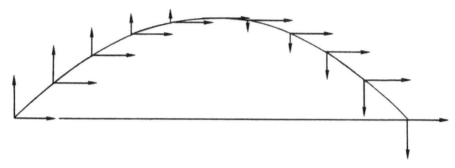

Figure 11.14   Magnitude of horizontal and vertical velocities during projectile flight.

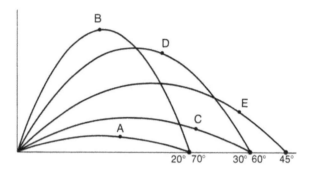

Figure 11.15   The angle of projection influences the horizontal and vertical distance covered by a projectile. Complementary angles of projection produce the same horizontal displacement.

gravity, which therefore requires very little time to decelerate the object to a vertical velocity of zero and start the drop back down. In this instance, vertical distance is low, and therefore time of flight is short, allowing little time for horizontal travel. On the other hand, if the angle of projection is large, it takes longer for the object to decelerate to zero velocity, allowing a much longer time of flight. In this instance, however, there is little horizontal velocity, so little distance can be covered in the time available. Thus it would seem that the optimum angle of projection would be a 45-degree angle, with equal magnitudes for the horizontal and vertical components. In fact, the actual optimal angle of projection depends on several factors, including purpose of the projection. A 45-degree angle of projection will maximize horizontal distance only

if release height and landing height are the same. In this case, the object will approach the landing at approximately the same angle as that at which it was projected (Figure 11.15).

If an object is projected from above the ground, as in many throwing events, a lower angle of projection may produce optimum results. This is because the object thrown will have a somewhat increased time of flight as it covers the extra distance between the height of release and the ground as it falls. With this increased time of flight, a slightly reduced vertical velocity and a slightly increased horizontal velocity will usually be optimal. The greater the difference between release height and landing height, the lower the angle of projection needs to be. If initial velocity can be increased, the optimum angle can also be increased back toward a 45-degree angle. From this discussion, then, it can be concluded that *speed of release, angle of projection,* and *height of release* are the three factors that control the range of a projectile.

Angular Kinematics

Angular kinematics is very similar to linear kinematics because it is also concerned with displacement, velocity, and acceleration. The important difference is that the displacement, velocity, and acceleration are related to rotary rather than to linear motion, and although the equations used to show the relationships among these quantities are quite similar to those used in linear motion, the units used to describe them are different (Table 11.2).

Angular Displacement

The human skeleton is made up of a system of levers that by definition are rigid bars that rotate about fixed points when force is applied. When any object acting as a rigid bar moves in an arc about an axis, the movement is called rotary, or angular, motion. An attempt to describe angular motion in linear units presents real problems. As an object moves in an arc, the linear displacement of particles spaced along that lever varies. Particles near the axis have a displacement in inches, meters, feet, or centimeters that is less than those farther away. For example, in the underarm throw pattern, the hand moves through a greater distance than the wrist and the wrist a greater distance than the elbow. Rotary motion needs rotary units to describe it. As might be expected, these units relate to the units of a circle and the fact that the circumference of a circle C is equal to $2\pi r$, where r is the radius and π is a constant value of 3.1416.

There are three interchangeable rotary, or angular, units of displacement: degrees, revolutions, and radians. One radian is the same as 57.3 degrees, and one full revolution is the same as 360 degrees or 2π radians of displacement. The word *revolution* is not stated, but it is understood when we say that a diver executed a 1 1/2

TABLE 11.2	**Quantities in Linear and Angular Motion**	
	Linear	**Angular**
SYMBOLS		
Displacement	s	θ
Velocity	v_f, v_i, v	$\omega_f, \omega_i, \omega$
Acceleration	a, a	α, α
Time	t	t
EQUATIONS		
Velocity	$v = s/t$	$\omega = \theta/t$
Acceleration	$a = \dfrac{v_f - v_i}{t}$	$\alpha = \dfrac{\omega_f - \omega_i}{t}$
LINEAR AND ANGULAR CONVERSIONS		
Displacement	$s = \theta r$	$\theta = s/r$
Velocity	$v = \omega r$	$\omega = v/r$
Acceleration	$a = \alpha r$	$\alpha = a/r$

somersault tuck. The dive could also be described as a tuck somersault of 540 (360 + 180) degrees or 3π radians. Degrees are used most frequently in the measurement of angles; but radians, the term favored by engineers and physicists, are the units most often required in equations of angular motion. The advantage of using radians is that they have no units and, therefore, may be used in equations with linear kinematic terms, as we will see. A radian is the angle at which the subtended arc of a circle is equal to the radius. The result of having 2π radians in a circle is that there are 6.28 radians in 360 degrees. If the circle is divided by the 6.28 radians it contains, it can be seen that each radian is 57.3 degrees. The symbol for angular displacement is the Greek letter θ (theta).*

Angular Velocity

The rate of rotary displacement is called angular velocity, symbolized as ω (omega). Angular velocity is equal to the angle through which the radius turns divided by the time it takes for the displacement:

$$\overline{\omega} = \frac{\theta}{t}$$

It is expressed as degrees/second, radians/second, or revolutions/second. A softball pitcher who moves the arm through an arc of 140 degrees in 0.1 second has an average angular velocity of 1,400 degrees per second. This could also be expressed as 3.88 revolutions per second or 24.43 radians per second. This velocity is called average velocity because film studies of pitchers show that the angular displacement during the execution of the skill is not uniform, and a velocity such as this represents the average velocity over the time span through which the displacement is measured. As with linear movements, most angular human movements are likely to be variable and not uniform. The longer the time span through which the displacement is measured, the more variability is

averaged. Thus, if one is interested in the velocity at a specific instant in a skill, the displacement must be measured over an extremely small time span.

Figure 11.16 shows the variations in displacement during the execution of a golf drive. Each displacement between images occurs over the same time period (approximately 0.0067 seconds), so greater spacing between images indicates greater angular displacement over the same time or greater velocity. When the total angular displacement of the golf club was measured from the beginning of the downswing to the point of contact with the ball and divided by the time it took for the swing, the average velocity of the club was 2,148 degrees/second (37.5 rad/sec). The "instant" velocity at a, however, was 1,432 degrees/sec, and at b it was 2,864 degrees/sec. Illustrations such as this, which show a motion as it occurs over very small spans of time, are produced with high-speed film or video. This golfer was filmed at a rate of approximately 150 frames per second, or 0.0067 seconds per picture.

Angular Acceleration

In the discussion of linear velocity, a change in velocity was called acceleration. The same is true for changes in angular velocity. Angular acceleration α (alpha) is the rate of change of angular velocity and is expressed in equation form as

$$\alpha = \frac{\omega_f - \omega_i}{t}$$

where ω_f is final angular velocity, ω_i is initial velocity, and t is time. If, in Figure 11.16, the angular velocity is 25 rad/sec at a and 50 rad/sec at b and the time lapse between a and b is 0.11 seconds, the angular acceleration between a and b is 241 rad/sec/sec. This value for α, indicating that the velocity increased 241 radians per second each second, would be true, of course, only if the velocity increased at a uniform rate. Otherwise this value has to be considered as an average of accelerations that may have been higher or lower during the time period studied.

*For a review of the geometry of circles and an additional explanation of degrees, radians, and revolution, see Appendix D, Part 5.

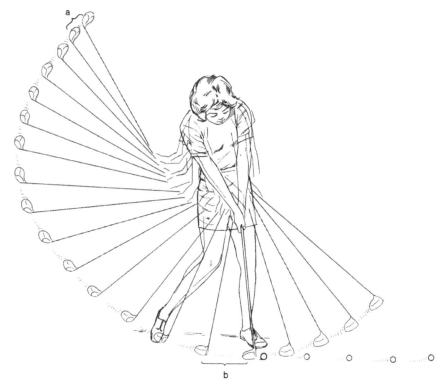

Figure 11.16   Variations in the angular displacement of a golf club over equal time intervals during the execution of a golf drive.

Relationship Between Linear and Angular Motion

The description of angular motion in terms of displacement, velocity, and acceleration can tell us a great deal about human movements, but nothing in such a description accounts for or shows the effect of the length of the radius on the outcomes of the movements. We know that, all other things being equal, a baseball hit in the middle of a bat will not go as far as one hit at the end, that a ball hit by a tennis racket will travel farther than a ball hit with the hand, and that a golf driver will cause a struck ball to travel farther than a nine iron. In each instance, greater force is imparted to the struck object because the radius of the striking implement (distance between axis and point

of contact) is longer, and greater linear velocity is generated at its end.

As can be seen in Figure 11.17, lever *PA* is shorter than lever *PB*, and lever *PB* is shorter than lever *PC*. If all three levers move through the same angular distance in the same amount of time, it is apparent that point *C* traveled farther in a curvilinear manner than either point *A* or point *B*. This curvilinear distance is difficult to measure but may be easily calculated if the angular displacement (θ) and the length of the radius (r) are known. The equation that expresses the relationship between angular and linear displacement is $s = \theta r$. Because the linear displacement of point *C* took the same amount of time as the displacements of points *A* and *B*, point *C* moved with a

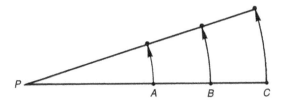

Figure 11.17   Lever *PA* < *PB* < *PC*. Although the angular displacement for all three levers is the same, the linear displacement at the end of the longer levers is greater than that at the end of the shorter levers.

greater linear velocity than either of the other two points. Point *B* had a smaller linear velocity than point *C* but a larger linear velocity than point *A*. All three levers have the same *angular velocity,* but linear velocity of the circular motion at the end of each lever is proportional to the length of the lever. An object moved at the end of a long radius will have a greater linear velocity than one moved at the end of a short radius, *if the angular velocity is kept constant. The longer the radius, the greater is the linear velocity of a point at the end of that radius.* Thus it is to the advantage of a performer to use as long a lever as possible to impart linear velocity to an object if the long lever length does not cause too great a sacrifice in angular velocity. The longer the lever, the more effort it takes to swing it. Therefore, the optimum length of the lever for a person depends on the individual's ability to maintain angular velocity. A child who cannot handle the weight of a long radius is better off with a shortened implement that can be controlled and swung rapidly, whereas a strong adult profits by using a longer radius.

If the reverse occurs—that is, if the linear velocity is kept constant—an increase in radius will result in a decrease in angular velocity. Once an object is engaged in rotary motion, the linear velocity at the end of the radius stays the same because of the conservation of momentum. The radius of rotation for a pike somersault dive is longer than that for a tuck somersault, and the radius for a layout somersault is longer than that for a pike somersault. If one starts a dive in an open position and then tucks tightly, the radius of rotation decreases but, because the linear velocity does not change, the angular velocity increases. The

same situation occurs when a figure skater rotates slowly about a vertical axis with arms and one leg out to the side and brings the arms and leg close to the axis. The radius decreases and the angular velocity increases. To slow down, the skater again reaches out with arms and leg. Figure 11.18 shows the effect of shortening the radius while maintaining a constant linear velocity at the end of the radius. *Shortening the radius will increase the angular velocity, and lengthening it will decrease the angular velocity.* Points *a* and *b* on radii *A* and *B* have moved through the same linear distance, but the angular displacement for *A* is greater than that for *B*. If the displacements of *a* and *b* each take place in the same amount of time, the linear velocities will be equal, but the angular velocity for *A* will be greater than that for *B*.

The relationship that exists between the angular velocity of an object moving in a rotary fashion and the linear velocity at the end of its radius is expressed by the equation

$$\bar{v} = \omega r$$

To use any of the equations relating linear and angular motion, the angular measures must be

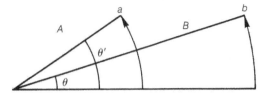

Figure 11.18   Increasing the length of the radius decreases the angular velocity when the linear velocity remains constant.

expressed in radians. If the angle is expressed in degrees, it can be converted to radians simply by dividing by 57.3.

Either form of the equation shows the direct proportionality that exists between linear velocity and the radius. For any given angular velocity, the linear velocity is proportional to the radius. If the radius doubles, the linear velocity does likewise. And for any given linear velocity, the angular velocity is inversely proportional to the radius. If the radius doubles, the angular velocity decreases by half. To achieve higher linear velocities at the end of levers, the motions must be done with longer levers or higher angular velocities (Figure 11.19).

Figure 11.19   Long levers and high angular velocities result in high linear velocities at the ends of the levers. Thus the tennis racket, an extension of a long body lever, is able to impart high linear velocity to the ball.

REFERENCES AND SELECTED READINGS

Bartlett, A. A. (2005). Television, football, and physics: Experiments in kinematics. *The Physics Teacher,* 43, 393.

Dapena J., Gutierrez-Davila, M., Soto, V. M., & Rojas, F. J. (2003). Prediction of distance in hammer throwing. *Journal of Sports Sciences,* 21(1), 21–28.

Ozkaya, N., Nordin, M., & Frankel, V. H. (1999). *Fundamentals of biomechanics: Equilibrium,* *motion, and deformation* (2nd ed.). New York: Springer.

Trizeren, A. (2000). *Human body dynamics: Classical mechanics and human movement.* New York: Springer.

Zatsiorsky, V. M. (1998). *Kinematics of human motion.* Champaign, IL.: Human Kinetics.

LABORATORY EXPERIENCES

1. Define the following key terms:

Linear motion	Velocity
Angular or rotary motion	Acceleration
Distance	Gravity
Speed	Projectile
Displacement	

2. Choose one of the following activities:
   Running long jump
   Basketball jump shot
   Softball pitching
   Identify the critical linear and angular kinematic elements of the selected skill. Explain how each of these elements contributes to successful performance.

3. An Olympic skater who participated in the men's speed-skating events had the following times: 1,500 m in 2 min 2.96 sec; 5,000 m in 7 min 23.61 sec; and 10,000 m in 15 min 1.35 sec. What was his average speed for each of these events?

4. Using the concept of acceleration, explain how a swimmer can have a better time for a 100-m race in a 25-m pool than in a 100-m pool.

5. How much time will a batter have to decide to swing at a pitch and still hit it under these circumstances?
   a. The pitcher throws the ball at 80 mph.
   b. The distance from the ball release to the plate is 56 ft.
   c. It takes the batter 0.30 sec to get the bat to the desired contact point.

6. With the help of several classmates, prepare a displacement–time graph and a velocity–time graph for your performance on two 50-m dash efforts: one in which you run through the end, and one in which you stop right at 50 m. Class members should be spaced at 5-m intervals along your running path, each with a stopwatch. On the signal for you to go, each timer will start the watch and stop it when you pass that timer's position. Prepare a table with the following data for each run:
   a. Distance intervals
   b. Times recorded at each interval
   c. Times over each 5-m interval (subtract adjacent times)
   d. Average velocity over each 5-m interval
   For each set of data, prepare a displacement–time graph and a velocity–time graph for the whole run. Describe your run in terms of displacement, velocity, and acceleration. Compare your graphs to those of other groups and note any differences.

7. An arrow shot straight up into the air reached a height of 75 m. With what velocity did it leave the bow? How long was the arrow in the air?

8. Place one coin near the edge of a table and another on the end of a ruler (as shown in Figure 11.20). While pressing the center of the ruler to the table with an index finger, strike one end of it in the direction indicated so that both coins land on the ground. Diagram the path of each. Which hits the floor first? Explain.

9. Throw a ball so that it is projected vertically upward. Catch it at the same height it was released. Have a partner measure the time the ball is in the air—that is, from the time of release to the time the ball lands in your hand.

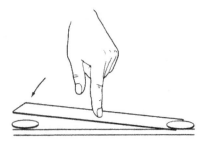

Figure 11.20

Determine the velocity of the ball at the moment of release and the distance the ball traveled before it started its descent. Graph the flight of the ball on a piece of graph paper. Break the flight of the ball into five sections: (1) from initiation of upward motion of the hand to just prior to release, (2) from moment of release to just before maximum height, (3) at maximum height, (4) from maximum height to just before you catch the ball, (5) from the ball contact to the ball being brought to rest. For each section, describe the displacement, velocity, and acceleration.

10. While walking along at a constant speed, project a ball vertically into the air. If you continue to walk without changing your speed or direction, where will the ball land? Explain. Draw a diagram of the ball's flight, indicating the forces acting on it.

11. Assume that you are able to throw a ball with a velocity of 24 m/sec and at an angle of 45 degrees with the horizontal. If it is caught at the same height from the ground at which it was released, neglecting air resistance, how far will it go? How long will it be in flight? Repeat with a 30-degree angle of release. How would these values change if the landing height were lowered?

12. Using Figure 11.3, determine the angular velocity of the lower leg at the knee joint at the beginning of the force phase and at the moment of foot contact with the ball. The time between each stick-figure tracing is 0.0156 sec. What is the linear velocity at the ankle at the moment of contact if the lower leg is 35 cm (knee joint to ankle joint)?

CHAPTER

12

Linear Kinetics
of Human Movement

After completing this chapter, you will be able to:

Identify Newton's laws of motion and gravitation and describe practical illustrations of the laws.

Explain what factors affect friction and discuss the role of friction in daily activities and sports.

Define impulse and momentum and explain the relationship between them.

Explain what factors govern the outcome of a collision between two bodies.

Discuss the relationships among mechanical work, power, and energy.

Solve quantitative problems related to kinetic concepts.

ONLINE LEARNING CENTER RESOURCES

www.mhhe.com/hall6e

Log on to our Online Learning Center (OLC) for access to these additional resources:

- Online Lab Manual
- Flashcards with definitions of chapter key terms
- Chapter objectives
- Chapter lecture PowerPoint presentation
- Self-scoring chapter quiz
- Additional chapter resources
- Web links for study and exploration of chapter-related topics

What can people do to improve traction when walking on icy streets? Why do some balls bounce higher on one surface than on another? How can football linemen push larger opponents backward? In this chapter, we introduce the topic of kinetics with a discussion of some important basic concepts and principles relating to linear kinetics.

NEWTON'S LAWS

Sir Isaac Newton (1642–1727) discovered many of the fundamental relationships that form the foundation for the field of modern mechanics. These principles highlight the interrelationships among the basic kinetic quantities introduced in Chapter 3.

Law of Inertia

Newton's first law of motion is known as the *law of inertia*. This law states the following:

> A body will maintain a state of rest or constant velocity unless acted on by an external force that changes the state.

In other words, a motionless object will remain motionless unless there is a net force (a force not counteracted by another force) acting on it. Similarly, a body traveling with a constant speed along a straight path will continue its motion unless acted on by a net force that alters either the speed or the direction of the motion.

It seems intuitively obvious that an object in a static (motionless) situation will remain motionless barring the action of some external force. We assume that a piece of furniture such as a chair will maintain a fixed position unless pushed or pulled by a person exerting a net force to cause its motion. When a body is traveling with a constant velocity, however, the enactment of the law of inertia is not so obvious, because, in most situations, external forces do act to reduce velocity. For example, the law of inertia implies that a skater gliding on ice will continue gliding with the same speed and in the same direction, barring the action of an external force. But in reality, friction and air resistance are two forces normally present that act to slow skaters and other moving bodies.

A skater has a tendency to continue gliding with constant speed and direction because of inertia. Photo courtesy of Karl Weatherly/Getty Images.

Law of Acceleration

Newton's second law of motion is an expression of the interrelationships among force, mass, and acceleration. This law, known as the *law of acceleration,* may be stated as follows for a body with constant mass:

> A force applied to a body causes an acceleration of that body of a magnitude proportional to the force, in the direction of the force, and inversely proportional to the body's mass.

When a ball is thrown, kicked, or struck with an implement, it tends to travel in the direction of the line of action of the applied force. Similarly, the greater the amount of force applied, the greater the speed the ball has. The algebraic expression of the law is a well-known formula that expresses the quantitative relationships among an applied force, a body's mass, and the resulting acceleration of the body:

$$F = ma$$

Thus, if a 1 kg ball is struck with a force of 10 N, the resulting acceleration of the ball is 10 m/s^2. If the ball has a mass of 2 kg, the application of the same 10 N force results in an acceleration of only 5 m/s^2.

Newton's second law also applies to a moving body. When a defensive football player running down the field is blocked by an opposing player, the velocity of the defensive player following contact is a function of the player's original direction and speed and the direction and magnitude of the force exerted by the offensive player.

Law of Reaction

The third of Newton's laws of motion states that every applied force is accompanied by a reaction force:

> For every action, there is an equal and opposite reaction.

In terms of forces, the law may be stated as follows:

> When one body exerts a force on a second, the second body exerts a reaction force that is equal in magnitude and opposite in direction on the first body.

When a person leans with a hand against a rigid wall, the wall pushes back on the hand with a force that is equal and opposite to that exerted by the hand on the wall. The harder the hand pushes against the wall, the greater is the amount of pressure felt across the surface of the hand where it contacts the wall. Another illustration of Newton's third law of motion is found in Sample Problem 12.1.

During gait, every contact of a foot with the floor or ground generates an upward reaction force. Researchers and clinicians measure and study these ground reaction forces (GRFs) in analyzing differences in gait patterns across the life span and among individuals with handicapping conditions. Researchers have studied the GRFs that are sustained with every footfall during running to investigate factors related to both performance and running-related injuries. The magnitude of the vertical component of the GRF during running on a level

In accordance with Newton's third law of motion, ground reaction forces are sustained with every footfall during running. Photo courtesy of Digital Vision/Getty Images.

SAMPLE PROBLEM 12.1

A 90 kg ice hockey player collides head-on with an 80 kg player. If the first player exerts a force of 450 N on the second player, how much force is exerted by the second player on the first?

Known

$$m_1 = 90 \text{ kg}$$
$$m_2 = 80 \text{ kg}$$
$$F_1 = 450 \text{ N}$$

Solution

This problem does not require computation. According to Newton's third law of motion, for every action, there is an equal and opposite reaction. If the force exerted by the first player on the second has a magnitude of 450 N and a positive direction, then the force exerted by the second player on the first has a magnitude of 450 N and a negative direction.

$$-450 \text{ N}$$

386   BASIC BIOMECHANICS

FIGURE 12-1

Typical ground reaction force patterns for rearfoot strikers and others. Runners may be classified as rearfoot, midfoot, or forefoot strikers according to the portion of the shoe that usually contacts the ground first.

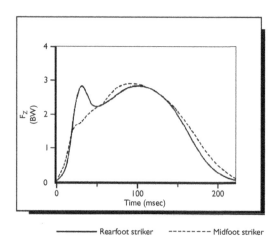

Rearfoot striker ——————   Midfoot striker --------

surface is generally two to three times the runner's body weight, with the pattern of force sustained during ground contact varying with running style. Runners are classified as rearfoot, midfoot, or forefoot strikers, according to the portion of the shoe first making contact with the ground. Typical vertical GRF patterns for rearfoot strikers and others are shown in Figure 12-1.

Other factors influencing GRF patterns include running speed, running duration, knee flexion angle at contact, stride length, fatigue, footwear, surface stiffness, surface smoothness, light intensity, and grade (8). During treadmill running at 3 m/s at a grade of −9°, impacts perpendicular to the surface increase on the order of 54% compared to level running, significantly increasing the potential for stress-related injury (12). The presence of fatigue, on the other hand, slightly reduces peak impact forces, secondary to reduced step length and increased knee flexion at contact (11).

Although it may seem logical that harder running surfaces would generate larger ground reaction forces, this has not been documented. When encountering surfaces of different stiffness, runners typically make individual adjustments in running kinematics that tend to maintain GRFs at a constant level (9). This may be explained to some extent by runners' sensitivity to the shock waves resulting from every heel strike that propagate upward, dynamically loading the musculoskeletal system. There is evidence that when the magnitude of the GRF increases, dynamic loading of the musculoskeletal system increases at five times the rate of the increase in the GRF (29). Research has shown that muscle activity is elicited to minimize soft-tissue vibrations arising from impact forces during running, another sign of runners' sensitivity to dynamic loading (21, 22).

As discussed in Chapter 10, runners generally increase stride length as running speed increases over the slow-to-moderate speed range. Longer strides tend to generate GRFs with larger retarding horizontal components (Figure 12-2). This is one reason that overstriding can be counterproductive. With longer stride lengths and more extended knee angles at contact, muscles crossing the knee also absorb more of the shock that is transmitted upward through the musculoskeletal system, which may translate to additional stress being placed on the knees (7).

•*Since the ground reaction force is an external force acting on the human body, its magnitude and direction affect the body's velocity.*

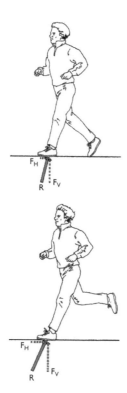

FIGURE 12-2

Use of a longer stride length
during running increases
the retarding horizontal
component (F_H) of the ground
reaction force (R).

Since the GRF is an external force acting on the human body, its magnitude and direction have implications for performance in many sporting events. In the high jump, for example, skilled performers are moving with a large horizontal velocity and a slight downwardly directed vertical velocity at the beginning of the stride before takeoff. The GRF reduces the jumper's horizontal velocity and creates an upwardly directed vertical velocity (Figure 12-3). Better jumpers not only enter the takeoff phase of the jump with high horizontal velocities but also effectively use the GRF to convert horizontal velocity to upward vertical velocity (5). Although baseball and softball pitching are often thought of as being primarily upper extremity motions, with GRFs approaching 139% body weight (BW) vertically, 24% BW anteriorly, and 42% BW medially, windmill softball pitchers are commonly seen for lower extremity injuries (14). Maximizing the distance of drives in golf requires generation of large GRFs, with a greater proportion of the GRF on the back foot during the backswing and transfer of this proportion to the front foot during the downswing (17).

Law of Gravitation

Newton's discovery of the law of universal gravitation was one of the most significant contributions to the scientific revolution and is considered by many to mark the beginning of modern science (4). According to legend, Newton's thoughts on gravitation were provoked either by his observation of a falling apple or by his actually being struck on the head by a falling apple. In his writings on the subject, Newton used the example of

388   BASIC BIOMECHANICS

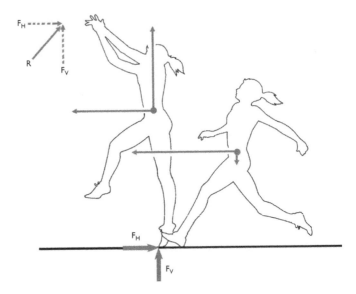

FIGURE 12-3

During the high jump takeoff, the horizontal component (F_H) of the ground reaction force (R) decreases the performer's horizontal velocity, and the vertical component (F_V) can contribute to upward vertical velocity.

the falling apple to illustrate the principle that every body attracts every other body. Newton's law of gravitation states the following:

All bodies are attracted to one another with a force proportional to the product of their masses and inversely proportional to the square of the distance between them.

Stated algebraically, the law is the following:

$$F_g = G\frac{m_1 m_2}{d^2}$$

The force of gravitational attraction is F_g, G is a numerical constant, m_1 and m_2 are the masses of the bodies, and d is the distance between the mass centers of the bodies.

For the example of the falling apple, Newton's law of gravitation indicates that just as the earth attracts the apple, the apple attracts the earth, although to a much smaller extent. As the formula for gravitational force shows, the greater the mass of either body, the greater the attractive force between the two. Similarly, the greater the distance between the bodies, the smaller the attractive force between them.

For biomechanical applications, the only gravitational attraction of consequence is that generated by the earth because of its extremely large mass. The rate of gravitational acceleration at which bodies are attracted toward the surface of the earth (9.81 m/s^2) is based on the earth's mass and the distance to the center of the earth.

MECHANICAL BEHAVIOR OF BODIES IN CONTACT

According to Newton's third law of motion, for every action there is an equal and opposite reaction. However, consider the case of a horse hitched to a cart. According to Newton's third law, when the horse exerts a force on the cart to cause forward motion, the cart exerts a backward force of

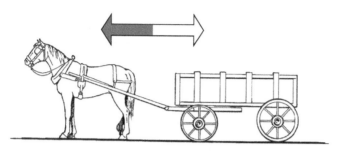

equal magnitude on the horse (Figure 12-4). Considering the horse and
the cart as a single mechanical system, if the two forces are equal in magnitude and opposite in direction, their vector sum is zero. How does the
horse-and-cart system achieve forward motion? The answer relates to the
presence of another force that acts with a different magnitude on the cart
than on the horse: the force of friction.

Friction

Friction is a force that acts at the interface of surfaces in contact in the
direction opposite the direction of motion or impending motion. Because
friction is a force, it is quantified in units of force (N). The magnitude of
the generated friction force determines the relative ease or difficulty of
motion for two objects in contact.

    Consider the example of a box sitting on a level tabletop (Figure 12-5).
The two forces acting on the undisturbed box are its own weight and a
reaction force (R) applied by the table. In this situation, the reaction force
is equal in magnitude and opposite in direction to the box's weight.

    When an extremely small horizontal force is applied to this box, it
remains motionless. The box can maintain its static position because the
applied force causes the generation of a friction force at the box/table
interface that is equal in magnitude and opposite in direction to the small
applied force. As the magnitude of the applied force becomes greater and
greater, the magnitude of the opposing friction force also increases to a
certain critical point. At that point, the friction force present is termed
maximum static friction (F_m). If the magnitude of the applied force is
increased beyond this value, motion will occur (the box will slide).

    Once the box is in motion, an opposing friction force continues to act.
The friction force present during motion is referred to as kinetic friction
(F_k). Unlike static friction, the magnitude of kinetic friction remains at a
constant value that is *less than* the magnitude of maximum static friction. Regardless of the amount of the applied force or the speed of the
occurring motion, the kinetic friction force remains the same. Figure 12-6
illustrates the relationship between friction and an applied external force.

    What factors determine the amount of applied force needed to move an
object? More force is required to move a refrigerator than to move the
empty box in which the refrigerator was delivered. More force is also
needed to slide the refrigerator across a carpeted floor than to do so across
a smooth linoleum floor. Two factors govern the magnitude of the force of
maximum static friction or kinetic friction in any situation: the coefficient
of friction, represented by the lowercase Greek letter mu (μ), and the normal (perpendicular) reaction force (R):

$$F = \mu R$$

friction
*force acting over the area of contact
between two surfaces in the direction
opposite that of motion or motion
tendency*

maximum static friction
*maximum amount of friction that
can be generated between two static
surfaces*

kinetic friction
*constant-magnitude friction
generated between two surfaces in
contact during motion*

coefficient of friction
*number that serves as an index of
the interaction between two surfaces
in contact*

normal reaction force
*force acting perpendicular to two
surfaces in contact*

390   BASIC BIOMECHANICS

The magnitude of the friction force changes with increasing amounts of applied force.

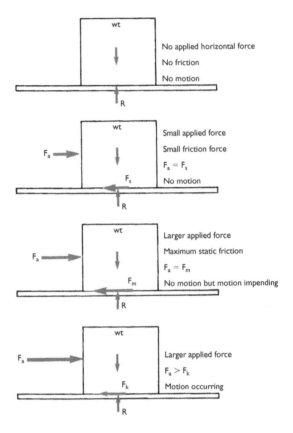

No applied horizontal force

No friction

No motion

Small applied force

Small friction force

$F_a = F_s$

No motion

Larger applied force

Maximum static friction

$F_a = F_m$

No motion but motion impending

Larger applied force

$F_a > F_k$

Motion occurring

The coefficient of friction is a unitless number indicating the relative ease of sliding, or the amount of mechanical and molecular interaction between two surfaces in contact. Factors influencing the value of μ are the relative roughness and hardness of the surfaces in contact and the type of molecular interaction between the surfaces. The greater the mechanical and molecular interaction, the greater the value of μ. For example, the coefficient of friction between two blocks covered with rough sandpaper is larger than the coefficient of friction between a skate and a smooth surface

As long as a body is static (unmoving), the magnitude of the friction force developed is equal to that of an applied external force. Once motion is initiated, the magnitude of the friction force remains at a constant level below that of maximum static friction.

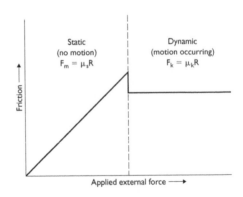

Static
(no motion)
$F_m = \mu_s R$

Dynamic
(motion occurring)
$F_k = \mu_k R$

Friction

Applied external force

of ice. The coefficient of friction describes the interaction between two surfaces in contact and is not descriptive of either surface alone. The coefficient of friction for the blade of an ice skate in contact with ice is different from that for the blade of the same skate in contact with concrete or wood.

The coefficient of friction between two surfaces assumes one or two different values, depending on whether the bodies in contact are motionless (static) or in motion (kinetic). The two coefficients are known as the *coefficient of static friction* (μ_s) and the *coefficient of kinetic friction* (μ_k). The magnitude of maximum static friction is based on the coefficient of static friction:

$$F_m = \mu_s R$$

The magnitude of the kinetic friction force is based on the coefficient of kinetic friction:

$$F_k = \mu_k R$$

For any two bodies in contact, μ_k is always smaller than μ_s. Kinetic friction coefficients of 0.0071 have been reported for standard ice hockey skates on ice, with new blade designs involving flaring of the blade near the bottom edge lowering the coefficient of friction even further (10). Use of the coefficients of static and kinetic friction is illustrated in Sample Problem 12.2.

•*Because μ_k is always smaller than μ_s, the magnitude of kinetic friction is always less than the magnitude of maximum static friction.*

SAMPLE PROBLEM 12.2

The coefficient of static friction between a sled and the snow is 0.18, with a coefficient of kinetic friction of 0.15. A 250 N boy sits on the 200 N sled. How much force directed parallel to the horizontal surface is required to start the sled in motion? How much force is required to keep the sled in motion?

Known

$$\mu_s = 0.18$$
$$\mu_k = 0.15$$
$$wt = 250 \text{ N} + 200 \text{ N}$$

Solution

To start the sled in motion, the applied force must exceed the force of maximum static friction:

$$F_m = \mu_s R$$
$$= (0.18)(250 \text{ N} + 200 \text{ N})$$
$$= 81 \text{ N}$$

The applied force must be greater than 81 N.

To maintain motion, the applied force must equal the force of kinetic friction:

$$F_k = \mu_k R$$
$$= (0.15)(250 \text{ N} + 200 \text{ N})$$
$$= 67.5 \text{ N}$$

The applied force must be at least 67.5 N.

392   BASIC BIOMECHANICS

FIGURE 12-7

As weight increases, the normal reaction force increases.

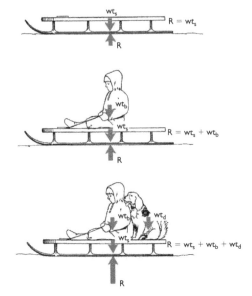

The other factor affecting the magnitude of the friction force generated is the normal reaction force. If weight is the only vertical force acting on a body sitting on a horizontal surface, R is equal in magnitude to the weight. If the object is a football blocking sled with a 100 kg coach standing on it, R is equal to the weight of the sled plus the weight of the coach. Other vertically directed forces such as pushes or pulls can also affect the magnitude of R, which is always equal to the vector sum of all forces or force components acting normal to the surfaces in contact (Figure 12-7).

The magnitude of R can be intentionally altered to increase or decrease the amount of friction present in a particular situation. When a football coach stands on the back of a blocking sled, the normal reaction force exerted by the ground on the sled is increased, with a concurrent increase in the amount of friction generated, making it more difficult for a player to move the sled. Alternatively, if the magnitude of R is decreased, friction is decreased and it is easier to initiate motion.

How can the normal reaction force be decreased? Suppose you need to rearrange the furniture in a room. Is it easier to push or pull an object such as a desk to move it? When a desk is pushed, the force exerted is typically directed diagonally downward. In contrast, force is usually directed diagonally upward when a desk is pulled. The vertical component of the push or pull either adds to or subtracts from the magnitude of the normal reaction force, thus influencing the magnitude of the friction force generated and the relative ease of moving the desk (Figure 12-8).

● *It is advantageous to pull with a line of force that is directed slightly upward when moving a heavy object.*

The amount of friction present between two surfaces can also be changed by altering the coefficient of friction between the surfaces. For example, the use of gloves in sports such as golf and racquetball increases the coefficient of friction between the hand and the grip of the club or racquet. Similarly, lumps of wax applied to a surfboard increase the roughness of the board's surface, thereby increasing the coefficient of friction between the board and the surfer's feet. The application of a thin, smooth coat of wax to the bottom of cross-country skis is designed to decrease the coefficient of friction between the skis and the snow, with different waxes used for various snow conditions.

● *Racquetball and golf gloves are designed to increase the friction between the hand and the racquet or club, as are the grips on the handles of the rackets and clubs themselves.*

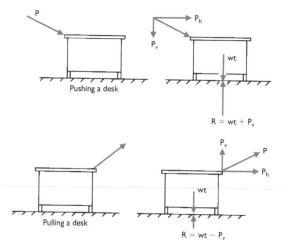

FIGURE 12-8

From a mechanical perspective, it is easier to pull than to push an object such as a desk, since pulling tends to decrease the magnitude of R and F, whereas pushing tends to increase R and F.

A widespread misconception about friction is that greater contact surface area generates more friction. Advertisements often imply that wide-track automobile tires provide better traction (friction) against the road than tires of normal width. However, the only factors known to affect friction are the coefficient of friction and the normal reaction force. Because wide-track tires typically weigh more than normal tires, they do increase friction to the extent that they increase R. However, the same effect can be achieved by carrying bricks or cinder blocks in the trunk of the car, a practice often followed by people who regularly drive on icy roads. Wide-track tires do tend to provide the advantages of increased lateral stability and increased wear, since larger surface area reduces the stress on a properly inflated tire.

Friction exerts an important influence during many daily activities. Walking depends on a proper coefficient of friction between a person's shoes and the supporting surface. If the coefficient of friction is too low, as when a person with smooth-soled shoes walks on a patch of ice, slippage will occur. The bottom of a wet bathtub or shower stall should provide a coefficient of friction with the soles of bare feet that is sufficiently large to prevent slippage.

The amount of friction present between ballet shoes and the dance studio floor must be controlled so that movements involving some amount of sliding or pivoting—such as *glissades*, *assembles*, and *pirouettes*—can be executed smoothly but without slippage. Rosin is often applied to dance floors because it provides a large coefficient of static friction but a significantly smaller coefficient of dynamic friction. This helps to prevent slippage in static situations and allows desired movements to occur freely.

A controversial disagreement occurred between Glenn Allison, a retired professional bowler and member of the American Bowling Congress Hall of Fame, and the American Bowling Congress. The dispute arose over the amount of friction present between Allison's ball and the lanes on which he bowled a perfect score of 300 in three consecutive games. According to the congress, his scores could not be recognized because the lanes he used did not conform to Congress standards for the amount of conditioning oil present (18), which gave Allison the unfair advantage of added ball traction.

The coefficient of friction between a dancer's shoes and the floor must be small enough to allow freedom of motion but large enough to prevent slippage.

●*Rolling friction is influenced by the weight, radius, and deformability of the rolling object, as well as by the coefficient of friction between the two surfaces.*

The magnitude of the rolling friction present between a rolling object, such as a bowling ball or an automobile tire, and a flat surface is approximately one-hundredth to one-thousandth of that present between sliding surfaces. Rolling friction occurs because both the curved and the flat surfaces are slightly deformed during contact. The coefficient of friction between the surfaces in contact, the normal reaction force, and the size of the radius of curvature of the rolling body all influence the magnitude of rolling friction.

●*The synovial fluid present at many of the joints of the human body greatly reduces the friction between the articulating bones.*

The amount of friction present in a sliding or rolling situation is dramatically reduced when a layer of fluid, such as oil or water, intervenes between two surfaces in contact. The presence of synovial fluid serves to reduce the friction, and subsequently the mechanical wear, on the diarthrodial joints of the human body. The coefficient of friction in a total hip prosthesis is approximately 0.01 (23).

Revisiting the question presented earlier about the horse and cart, the force of friction is the determining factor for movement. The system moves forward if the magnitude of the friction force generated by the horse's hooves against the ground exceeds that produced by the wheels of the cart against the ground (Figure 12-9). Because most horses are shod to increase the amount of friction between their hooves and the ground, and most cart wheels are round and smooth to minimize the amount of friction they generate, the horse is usually at an advantage. However, if the horse stands on a slippery surface or if the cart rests in deep sand or is heavily loaded, motion may not be possible.

Momentum

Another factor that affects the outcome of interactions between two bodies is momentum, a mechanical quantity that is particularly important in situations involving collisions. Momentum may be defined generally as the quantity of motion that an object possesses. More specifically, linear momentum is the product of an object's mass and its velocity:

linear momentum
quantity of motion, measured as the product of a body's mass and its velocity

$$M = mv$$

A static object (with zero velocity) has no momentum; that is, its momentum equals zero. A change in a body's momentum may be caused by either a change in the body's mass or a change in its velocity. In most human movement situations, changes in momentum result from changes in velocity. Units of momentum are units of mass multiplied by units of velocity, expressed in terms of kg · m/s. Because velocity is a vector quantity, momentum is also a vector quantity and is subject to the rules of vector composition and resolution.

●*Momentum is a vector quantity.*

When a head-on collision between two objects occurs, there is a tendency for both objects to continue moving in the direction of motion originally possessed by the object with the greatest momentum. If a 90 kg hockey player traveling at 6 m/s to the right collides head-on with an 80 kg player traveling at 7 m/s to the left, the momentum of the first player is the following:

$$M = mv$$
$$= (90 \text{ kg}) (6 \text{ m/s})$$
$$= 540 \text{ kg} \cdot \text{m/s}$$

The momentum of the second player is expressed as follows:

$$M = mv$$
$$= (80 \text{ kg}) (7 \text{ m/s})$$
$$= 560 \text{ kg} \cdot \text{m/s}$$

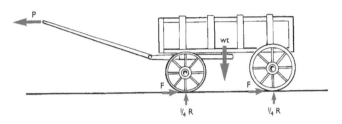

FIGURE 12-9

A horse can pull a cart if the horse's hooves generate more friction than the wheels of the cart.

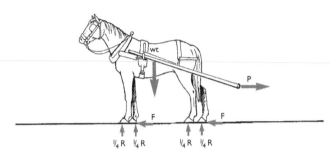

Since the second player's momentum is greater, both players would tend to continue moving in the direction of the second player's original velocity after the collision. Actual collisions are also affected by the extent to which the players become entangled, by whether one or both players remain on their feet, and by the elasticity of the collision.

Neglecting these other factors that may influence the outcome of the collision, it is possible to calculate the magnitude of the combined velocity of the two hockey players after the collision using a modified statement of Newton's first law of motion (see Sample Problem 12.3). Newton's first law may be restated as the *principle of conservation of momentum:*

> In the absence of external forces, the total momentum of a given system remains constant.

The principle is expressed in equation format as the following:

$$M_1 = M_2$$
$$(mv)_1 = (mv)_2$$

Subscript 1 designates an initial point in time and subscript 2 represents a later time.

Applying this principle to the hypothetical example of the colliding hockey players, the vector sum of the two players' momenta before the collision is equal to their single, combined momentum following the collision (see Sample Problem 12.3). In reality, friction and air resistance are external forces that typically act to reduce the total amount of momentum present.

●*In the absence of external forces, momentum is conserved. However, friction and air resistance are forces that normally act to reduce momentum.*

Impulse

When external forces do act, they change the momentum present in a system predictably. Changes in momentum depend not only on the magnitude of the acting external forces but also on the length of time

SAMPLE PROBLEM 12.3

A 90 kg hockey player traveling with a velocity of 6 m/s collides head-on with an 80 kg player traveling at 7 m/s. If the two players entangle and continue traveling together as a unit following the collision, what is their combined velocity?

Known

$m_1 = 90$ kg
$v_1 = 6$ m/s
$m_2 = 80$ kg
$v_2 = -7$ m/s

m = 90 kg
v = 6 m/s

m = 80 kg
v = 7 m/s

Collision

m = (90 + 80) kg
v = ?

Solution
The law of conservation of momentum may be used to solve the problem, with the two players considered as the total system.

$$\textit{Before collision} \quad \textit{After collision}$$
$$m_1v_1 + m_2v_2 = (m_1 + m_2)\,(v)$$
$$(90\text{ kg})\,(6\text{ m/s}) + (80\text{ kg})\,(-7\text{ m/s}) = (90\text{ kg} + 80\text{ kg})\,(v)$$
$$540\text{ kg}\cdot\text{m/s} - 560\text{ kg}\cdot\text{m/s} = (170\text{ kg})\,(v)$$
$$-20\text{ kg}\cdot\text{m/s} = (170\text{ kg})\,(v)$$

$v = 0.12$ m/s in the 80 kg player's original direction of travel.

impulse
product of a force and the time interval over which the force acts

over which each force acts. The product of force and time is known as impulse:

$$\text{impulse} = Ft$$

When an impulse acts on a system, the result is a change in the system's total momentum. The relationship between impulse and momentum is derived from Newton's second law:

$$F = ma$$
$$F = m\frac{(v_2 - v_1)}{t}$$

$$Ft = (mv)_2 - (mv)_1$$
$$Ft = \Delta M$$

SAMPLE PROBLEM 12.4

A toboggan race begins with the two crew members pushing the toboggan to get it moving as quickly as possible before they climb in. If crew members apply an average force of 100 N in the direction of motion of the 90 kg toboggan for a period of 7 s before jumping in, what is the toboggan's speed (neglecting friction) at that point?

Known

$$F = 100 \text{ N}$$
$$t = 7 \text{ s}$$
$$m = 90 \text{ kg}$$

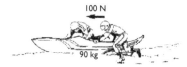

100 N

90 kg

Solution

The crew members are applying an impulse to the toboggan to change the toboggan's momentum from zero to a maximum amount. The impulse–momentum relationship may be used to solve the problem.

$$Ft = (mv)_2 - (mv)_1$$
$$(100 \text{ N}) (7 \text{ s}) = (90 \text{ kg}) (v) - (90 \text{ kg}) (0)$$

$$v = 7.78 \text{ m/s in the direction of force application}$$

Subscript 1 designates an initial time and subscript 2 represents a later time. An application of this relationship is presented in Sample Problem 12.4.

Significant changes in an object's momentum may result from a small force acting over a large time interval or from a large force acting over a small time interval. A golf ball rolling across a green gradually loses momentum because its motion is constantly opposed by the force of rolling friction. The momentum of a baseball struck vigorously by a bat also changes because of the large force exerted by the bat during the fraction of a second it is in contact with the ball. It is little surprise that elite sprinters have been shown to develop significantly greater impulse against the starting blocks as compared to well-trained but subelite sprinters (25).

The amount of impulse generated by the human body is often intentionally manipulated. When a vertical jump is performed on a force platform, a graphical display of the vertical GRF across time can be generated (Figure 12-10). Since impulse is the product of force and time, the impulse is the area under the force–time curve. The larger the impulse generated against the floor, the greater the change in the performer's momentum, and the higher the resulting jump. Theoretically, impulse can be increased by increasing either the magnitude of applied force or the time interval over which the force acts. Practically, however, when time of force application against the ground is prolonged during vertical jump execution, the magnitude of the force that can be generated is dramatically reduced, with the ultimate result being a smaller impulse. For performing a maximal vertical jump, the performer must maximize impulse by optimizing the trade-off between applied force magnitude and force duration.

398   BASIC BIOMECHANICS

Force–time histories for **A**
high, and **B** low vertical
jumps by the same performer.
The shaded area represents
the impulse generated against
the floor during the jump.

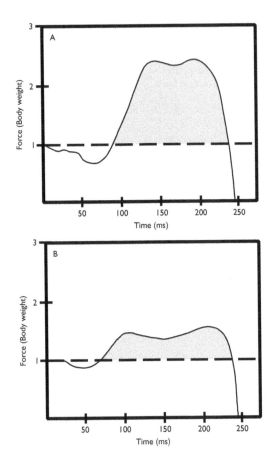

Impulse can also be intentionally manipulated during a landing from a jump (Figure 12-11). A performer who lands rigidly will experience a relatively large GRF sustained over a relatively short time interval. Alternatively, allowing the hip, knee, and ankle joints to undergo flexion during the landing increases the time interval over which the landing force is absorbed, thereby reducing the magnitude of the force sustained. Research has shown that females tend to land in a more erect posture than males, with greater shock absorption occurring in the knees and ankles, and a concomitant greater likelihood of lower-extremity injury (6). One-foot landings also tend to generate higher impact forces and faster loading rates than two-foot landings (27).

It is also useful to manipulate impulse when catching a hard-thrown ball. "Giving" with the ball after it initially contacts the hands or the glove before bringing the ball to a complete stop will prevent the force of the ball from causing the hands to sting. The greater the period is between making initial hand contact with the ball and bringing the ball to a complete stop, the smaller is the magnitude of the force exerted by the ball against the hand, and the smaller is the likelihood of experiencing a sting.

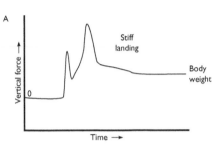

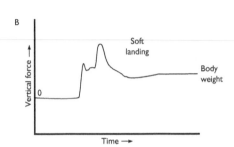

FIGURE 12-11

Representations of ground reaction forces during vertical jump performances: **A**. a rigid landing, **B**. a landing with hip, knee, and ankle flexion occurring. Note the differences in the magnitudes and times of the landing impulses.

Impact

The type of collision that occurs between a struck baseball and a bat is known as an impact. An impact involves the collision of two bodies over an extremely small time interval during which the two bodies exert relatively large forces on each other. The behavior of two objects following an impact depends not only on their collective momentum but also on the nature of the impact.

For the hypothetical case of a perfectly elastic impact, the relative velocities of the two bodies after impact are the same as their relative velocities before impact. The impact of a superball with a hard surface approaches perfect elasticity, because the ball's speed diminishes little during its collision with the surface. At the other end of the range is the perfectly plastic impact, during which at least one of the bodies in contact deforms and does not regain its original shape, and the bodies do not separate. This occurs when modeling clay is dropped on a surface.

Most impacts are neither perfectly elastic nor perfectly plastic, but somewhere between the two. The coefficient of restitution describes the relative elasticity of an impact. It is a unitless number between 0 and 1. The closer the coefficient of restitution is to 1, the more elastic is the impact; and the closer the coefficient is to 0, the more plastic is the impact.

The coefficient of restitution governs the relationship between the relative velocities of two bodies before and after an impact. This relationship, which was originally formulated by Newton, may be stated as follows:

> When two bodies undergo a direct collision, the difference in their velocities immediately after impact is proportional to the difference in their velocities immediately before impact.

impact
collision characterized by the exchange of a large force during a small time interval

perfectly elastic impact
impact during which the velocity of the system is conserved

perfectly plastic impact
impact resulting in the total loss of system velocity

coefficient of restitution
number that serves as an index of elasticity for colliding bodies

400   BASIC BIOMECHANICS

"Giving" with the ball during a catch serves to lessen the magnitude of the impact force sustained by the catcher.

This relationship can also be expressed algebraically as the following:

$$-e = \frac{\text{relative velocity after impact}}{\text{relative velocity before impact}}$$

$$-e = \frac{v_1 - v_2}{u_1 - u_2}$$

In this formula, e is the coefficient of restitution, u_1 and u_2 are the velocities of the bodies just before impact, and v_1 and v_2 are the velocities of the bodies immediately after impact (Figure 12-12).

In tennis, the nature of the game depends on the type of impacts between ball and racket and between ball and court. All other conditions being equal, a tighter grip on the racket increases the apparent coefficient of restitution between ball and racket (16). When a pressurized tennis ball is punctured, there is a reduction in the coefficient of restitution between ball and surface of 20% (15). Other factors of influence are racket size, shape, balance, flexibility, string type and tension, and swing kinematics (30).

FIGURE 12-12

The differences in two balls' velocities before impact is proportional to the difference in their velocities after impact. The factor of proportionality is the coefficient of restitution.

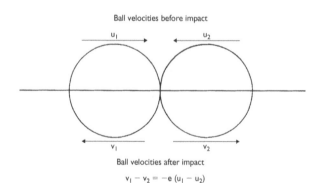

Ball velocities before impact

Ball velocities after impact

$$v_1 - v_2 = -e\,(u_1 - u_2)$$

SAMPLE PROBLEM 12.5

A basketball is dropped from a height of 2 m onto a gymnasium floor. If the coefficient of restitution between ball and floor is 0.9, how high will the ball bounce?

Known

$$h_d = 2 \text{ m}$$
$$e = 0.9$$

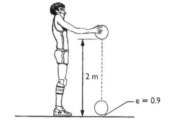

Solution

$$e = \sqrt{\frac{h_b}{h_d}}$$

$$0.9 = \sqrt{\frac{h_b}{2 \text{ m}}}$$

$$0.81 = \frac{h_b}{2 \text{ m}}$$

$$\boxed{h_b = 1.6 \text{ m}}$$

The nature of impact between the bat and the ball is also an important factor in the sports of baseball and softball. The hitting surface of the bat is convex, in contrast to the surface of the tennis racquet, which deforms to a concave shape during ball contact. Consequently, hitting a baseball or softball in a direct, rather than a glancing, fashion is of paramount concern. Research has shown that aluminum baseball bats produce significantly higher batted ball speeds than do wood bats, which suggests that the coefficient of restitution between an aluminum bat and baseball is higher than that between a wood bat and baseball (13).

In the case of an impact between a moving body and a stationary one, Newton's law of impact can be simplified because the velocity of the stationary body remains zero. The coefficient of restitution between a ball and a flat, stationary surface onto which the ball is dropped may be approximated using the following formula:

$$e = \sqrt{\frac{h_b}{h_d}}$$

In this equation, e is the coefficient of restitution, h_d is the height from which the ball is dropped, and h_b is the height to which the ball bounces (see Sample Problem 12.5). The coefficient of restitution describes the interaction between two bodies during an impact; it is *not* descriptive of any single object or surface. Dropping a basketball, a golf ball, a racquetball, and a baseball onto several different surfaces demonstrates that some balls bounce higher on certain types of surfaces (Figure 12-13).

The coefficient of restitution is increased by increases in both impact velocity and temperature. In sports such as baseball and tennis, increases in both incoming ball velocity and bat or racket velocity increase the coefficient

402   BASIC BIOMECHANICS

Bounce heights of a
basketball, golf ball,
racquetball, and baseball
all dropped onto the same
surface from a height of 1 m.

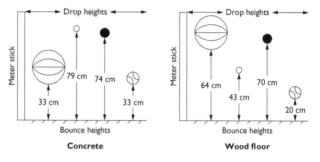

•*Increases in impact velocity
and temperature increase the
coefficient of restitution.*

of restitution between bat or racket and ball, and contribute to a livelier ball
rebound from the striking instrument. In racquetball and squash, where the
ball is constantly being deformed against the wall, the ball's thermal energy
(temperature) is increased over the course of play. As ball temperature
increases, its rebound from both racquet and wall becomes more lively.

WORK, POWER, AND ENERGY RELATIONSHIPS

Work

The word *work* is commonly used in a variety of contexts. A person can
speak of "working out" in the weight room, doing "yard work," or "working
hard" to prepare for an exam. However, from a mechanical standpoint,
work is defined as force applied against a resistance, multiplied by the
displacement of the resistance in the direction of the force:

work
*in a mechanical context, force
multiplied by the displacement of the
resistance in the direction of the force*

$$W = Fd$$

When a body is moved a given distance as the result of the action of an
applied external force, the body has had work performed on it, with the
quantity of work equal to the product of the magnitude of the applied
force and the distance through which the body was moved. When a force
is applied to a body but no net force results because of opposing forces
such as friction or the body's own weight, no mechanical work has been
done, since there has been no movement of the body.

When the muscles of the human body produce tension resulting in the
motion of a body segment, the muscles perform work on the body segment, and the mechanical work performed may be characterized as either
positive or negative work, according to the type of muscle action that predominates. When both the net muscle torque and the direction of angular
motion at a joint are in the same direction, the work done by the muscles
is said to be *positive*. Alternatively, when the net muscle torque and the
direction of angular motion at a joint are in opposite directions, the work
done by the muscles is considered to be *negative*. Although many movements of the human body involve co-contraction of agonist and antagonist
muscle groups, when concentric contraction prevails the work is positive,
and when eccentric contraction prevails the work is negative. During an
activity such as running on a level surface, the net negative work done by
the muscles is equal to the net positive work done by the muscles.

•*Mechanical work should not be
confused with caloric expenditure.*

Performing positive mechanical work typically requires greater caloric
expenditure than performing the same amount of negative mechanical
work. However, no simple relationship between the caloric energy required

for performing equal amounts of positive and negative mechanical work has been discovered, and the picture is complicated by the fact that agonist and other muscle groups often co-contract (1, 19).

Units of work are units of force multiplied by units of distance. In the metric system, the common unit of force (N) multiplied by a common unit of distance (m) is termed the *joule* (J).

$$1 \text{ J} = 1 \text{ Nm}$$

Power

Another term used in different contexts is power. In mechanics, power refers to the amount of mechanical work performed in a given time:

$$\text{power} = \frac{\text{work}}{\text{change in time}}$$

$$P = \frac{W}{\Delta t}$$

Using the relationships previously described, power can also be defined as the following:

$$\text{power} = \frac{\text{force} \times \text{distance}}{\text{change in time}}$$

$$P = \frac{Fd}{\Delta t}$$

Because velocity equals the directed distance divided by the change in time, the equation can also be expressed as the following:

$$P = Fv$$

Units of power are units of work divided by units of time. In the metric system, joules divided by seconds are termed *watts* (W):

$$1 \text{ W} = 1 \text{ J/s}$$

In activities such as throwing, jumping, and sprinting and in Olympic weight lifting, the athlete's ability to exert mechanical power or the combination of force and velocity is critical to successful performance. Peak power is strongly associated with maximum isometric strength (26). A problem involving mechanical work and power is shown in Sample Problem 12.6.

Energy

Energy is defined generally as the capacity to do work. Mechanical energy is therefore the capacity to do mechanical work. Units of mechanical energy are the same as units of mechanical work (joules, in the metric system). There are two forms of mechanical energy: kinetic energy and potential energy.

Kinetic energy (KE) is the energy of motion. A body possesses kinetic energy only when in motion. Formally, the kinetic energy of linear motion is defined as one-half of a body's mass multiplied by the square of its velocity:

$$KE = \tfrac{1}{2} mv^2$$

If a body is motionless (v = 0), its kinetic energy is also zero. Because velocity is squared in the expression for kinetic energy, increases in a

power
rate of work production, calculated as work divided by the time during which the work was done

● *The ability to produce mechanical power is critical for athletes competing in explosive track-and-field events.*

kinetic energy
energy of motion, calculated as $\tfrac{1}{2} mv^2$

potential energy
energy by virtue of a body's position or configuration, calculated as the product of weight and height

SAMPLE PROBLEM 12.6

A 580 N person runs up a flight of 30 stairs of riser (height) of 25 cm during a 15 s period. How much mechanical work is done? How much mechanical power is generated?

Known

$$\text{wt (F)} = 580 \text{ N}$$
$$h = 30 \times 25 \text{ cm}$$
$$t = 15 \text{ s}$$

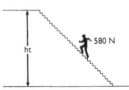

Solution

For mechanical work:

$$W = Fd$$
$$= (580 \text{ N}) (30 \times 0.25 \text{ m})$$

$$\boxed{W = 4350 \text{ J}}$$

For mechanical power:

$$P = \frac{W}{t}$$
$$= \frac{4350 \text{ J}}{15 \text{ s}}$$

$$\boxed{P = 290 \text{ watts}}$$

---

body's velocity create dramatic increases in its kinetic energy. For example, a 2 kg ball rolling with a velocity of 1 m/s has a kinetic energy of 1 J:

$$KE = \tfrac{1}{2} mv^2$$
$$= (0.5) (2 \text{ kg}) (1 \text{ m/s})^2$$
$$= (1 \text{ kg}) (1 \text{ m}^2/\text{s}^2)$$
$$= 1 \text{ J}$$

If the velocity of the ball is increased to 3 m/s, kinetic energy is significantly increased:

$$KE = \tfrac{1}{2} mv^2$$
$$= (0.5) (2 \text{ kg}) (3 \text{ m/s})^2$$
$$= (1 \text{ kg}) (9 \text{ m}^2/\text{s}^2)$$
$$= 9 \text{ J}$$

The other major category of mechanical energy is potential energy (PE), which is the energy of position. More specifically, potential energy is a body's weight multiplied by its height above a reference surface:

$$PE = wt \cdot h$$
$$PE = ma_g h$$

In the second formula, m represents mass, a_g is the acceleration of gravity, and h is the body's height. The reference surface is usually the floor or the ground, but in special circumstances, it may be defined as another surface.

Because in biomechanical applications the weight of a body is typically fixed, changes in potential energy are usually based on changes in the body's height. For example, when a 50 kg bar is elevated to a height of 1 m, its potential energy at that point is 490.5 J:

$$PE = ma_gh$$
$$= (50 \text{ kg}) (9.81 \text{ m/s}^2) (1 \text{ m})$$
$$= 490.5 \text{ J}$$

Potential energy may also be thought of as stored energy. The term *potential* implies potential for conversion to kinetic energy. A special form of potential energy is called strain energy (SE), or elastic energy. Strain energy may be defined as follows:

$$SE = \tfrac{1}{2} kx^2$$

strain energy
capacity to do work by virtue of a deformed body's return to its original shape

In this formula, k is a spring constant, representing a material's relative stiffness or ability to store energy on deformation, and x is the distance over which the material is deformed. When an object is stretched, bent, or otherwise deformed, it stores this particular form of potential energy for later use. For example, when the muscles and tendons of the human body are stretched, they store strain energy that is released to increase the force of subsequent contraction, as discussed in Chapter 6. During an activity such as a maximal-effort throw, stored energy in stretched musculotendinous units can contribute significantly to the force and power generated and to the resulting velocity of the throw (20). Because they are more extensible than muscle, it is primarily the tendons that store and return elastic energy, with longer tendons performing this function more effectively than shorter ones (3). The Achilles tendon, in particular, stores and returns large amounts of mechanical energy, providing a large component of the mechanical work required for walking (24). Likewise, when the end of a diving board or a trampoline surface is depressed, strain energy is created. Subsequent conversion of the stored energy to kinetic energy enables the surface to return to its original shape and position. The poles used by vaulters store strain energy as they bend, and then release kinetic energy and increase the potential energy of the athlete as they straighten during the performance of the vault (2).

During the pole vault, the bent pole stores strain energy for subsequent release as kinetic energy and heat. Photo courtesy of Chu's Marters, University of Delaware.

Conservation of Mechanical Energy

Consider the changes that occur in the mechanical energy of a ball tossed vertically into the air (Figure 12-14). As the ball gains height, it also gains potential energy (ma_gh). However, since the ball is losing velocity with increasing height because of gravitational acceleration, it is also losing kinetic energy ($\tfrac{1}{2} mv^2$) At the apex of the ball's trajectory (the instant between rising and falling), its height and potential energy are at a maximum value, and its velocity and kinetic energy are zero. As the ball starts to fall, it progressively gains kinetic energy while losing potential energy.

The correlation between the kinetic and potential energies of the vertically tossed ball illustrates a concept that applies to all bodies when the only external force acting is gravity. The concept is known as the *law of conservation of mechanical energy,* which may be stated as follows:

> When gravity is the only acting external force, a body's mechanical energy remains constant.

Since the mechanical energy a body possesses is the sum of its potential and kinetic energies, the relationship may also be expressed as the following:

$$(PE + KE) = C$$

406   BASIC BIOMECHANICS

Height, velocity, potential energy, and kinetic energy change for a 1 kg ball tossed upward from a height of 1 m. Note that PE + KE = C (a constant) throughout the trajectory.

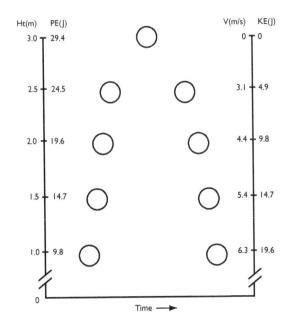

In this formula, C is a constant; that is, it is a number that remains constant throughout the period of time during which gravity is the only external force acting. Sample Problem 12.7 quantitatively illustrates this principle.

Principle of Work and Energy

● *When gravity is the only acting external force, any change in a body's potential energy necessitates a compensatory change in its kinetic energy.*

There is a special relationship between the quantities of mechanical work and mechanical energy. This relationship is described as the *principle of work and energy,* which may be stated as follows:

The work of a force is equal to the change in energy that it produces in the object acted on.

Algebraically, the principle may be represented thus:

$$W = \Delta KE + \Delta PE + \Delta TE$$

In this formula, KE is kinetic energy, PE is potential energy, and TE is thermal energy (heat). The algebraic statement of the principle of work and energy indicates that the change in the sum of the forms of energy produced by a force is quantitatively equal to the mechanical work done by that force. When a tennis ball is projected into the air by a ball-throwing machine, the mechanical work performed on the ball by the machine results in an increase in the ball's mechanical energy. Prior to projection, the ball's potential energy is based on its weight and height, and its kinetic energy is zero. The ball-throwing machine increases the ball's total mechanical energy by imparting kinetic energy to it. In this situation, the change in the ball's thermal energy is negligible. Sample Problem 12.8 provides a quantitative illustration of the principle of work and energy.

The work–energy relationship is also evident during movements of the human body. For example, the arches in runners' feet act as a mechanical spring to store, and subsequently return, strain energy as they cyclically deform and then regain their resting shapes. The ability of the arches to

SAMPLE PROBLEM 12.7

A 2 kg ball is dropped from a height of 1.5 m. What is its velocity immediately before impact with the floor?

Known

$$m = 2kg$$
$$h = 1.5 \text{ m}$$

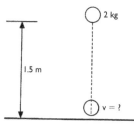

Solution

The principle of the conservation of mechanical energy may be used to solve the problem. The total energy possessed by the ball when it is held at a height of 1.5 m is its potential energy. Immediately before impact, the ball's height (and potential energy) may be assumed to be zero, and 100% of its energy at that point is kinetic.

Total (constant) mechanical energy possessed by the ball:

$$PE + KE = C$$
$$(wt)\,(h) + \tfrac{1}{2}\,mv^2 = C$$
$$(2 \text{ kg})\,(9.81 \text{ m/s}^2)\,(1.5 \text{ m}) + 0 = C$$
$$29.43 \text{ J} = C$$

Velocity of the ball before impact:

$$PE + KE = 29.43 \text{ J}$$

$$(wt)\,(h) + \tfrac{1}{2}\,mv^2 = 29.43 \text{ J}$$

$$(2 \text{ kg})\,(9.81 \text{ m/s}^2)\,(0) + \tfrac{1}{2}\,(2 \text{ kg})\,v^2 = 29.43 \text{ J}$$

$$v^2 = 29.43 \text{ J/kg}$$

$$\boxed{v = 5.42 \text{ m/s}}$$

---

function as a spring reduces the amount of mechanical work that would otherwise be required during running.

Two-joint muscles in the human body also serve to transfer mechanical energy from one joint to another, thereby reducing the mechanical work required of the muscles crossing the second joint during a given movement. For example, during takeoff for a vertical jump, when the hip extensors work concentrically to produce hip extension, if the rectus femoris remains isometrically contracted, a secondary effect is an extensor torque exerted at the knee. In this case, it is the hip extensors that produce the knee extensor torque, since the length of the rectus femoris does not change.

It is important not to confuse the production of mechanical energy or mechanical work by the muscles of the human body with the consumption of chemical energy or caloric expenditure. Factors such as concentric versus eccentric muscular contractions, the transfer of energy between body segments, elastic storage and reuse of energy, and limitations in joint ranges of motion complicate direct quantitative calculation of the

408   BASIC BIOMECHANICS

How much mechanical work is required to catch a 1.3 kg ball traveling at a velocity of 40 m/s?

Known

$$m = 1.3 \text{ kg}$$
$$v = 40 \text{ m/s}$$

v = 40 m/s

1.3 kg

Solution

The principle of work and energy may be used to calculate the mechanical work required to change the ball's kinetic energy to zero. Assume that the potential energy and thermal energy of the ball do not change:

$$W = \Delta Ke$$
$$= (\tfrac{1}{2} mv^2)_2 - (\tfrac{1}{2} mv^2)_1$$
$$= 0 - (\tfrac{1}{2}) (1.3 \text{ kg}) (40 \text{ m/s})^2$$

$$\boxed{W = 1040 \text{ J}}$$

relationship between mechanical and physiological energy estimates (28). Approximately 25% of the energy consumed by the muscles is converted into work, with the remainder changed to heat or used in the body's chemical processes.

Table 12-1 summarizes the formulas used in this chapter.

TABLE 12-1

Formula Summary

DESCRIPTION	FORMULA
Force = (mass)(acceleration)	$F = ma$
Friction = (coefficient of friction)(normal reaction force)	$F = \mu R$
Linear momentum = (mass)(velocity)	$M = mv$
Coefficient of restitution = $\dfrac{\text{relative velocity after impact}}{\text{relative velocity before impact}}$	$-e = \dfrac{v_1 - v_2}{u_1 - u_2}$
Work = (force) (displacement of resistance)	$W = Fd$
Power = $\dfrac{\text{work}}{\text{time}}$	$P = \dfrac{W}{t}$
Power = (force)(velocity)	$P = Fv$
Kinetic energy = $\tfrac{1}{2}$ (mass)(velocity squared)	$KE = \tfrac{1}{2} mv^2$
Potential energy = (weight)(height)	$PE = ma_g h$
Strain energy = $\tfrac{1}{2}$ (spring constant)(deformation squared)	$SE = \tfrac{1}{2} kx^2$
Potential energy + kinetic energy = constant	$PE + KE = C$
Work = change in energy	$W = \Delta KE + \Delta PE + \Delta TE$

SUMMARY

Linear kinetics is the study of the forces associated with linear motion. The interrelationships among many basic kinetic quantities are identi-fied in the physical laws formulated by Sir Isaac Newton.

Friction is a force generated at the interface of two surfaces in contact when there is motion or a tendency for motion of one surface with respect to the other. The magnitudes of maximum static friction and kinetic friction are determined by the coefficient of friction between the two surfaces and by the normal reaction force pressing the two surfaces together. The direction of friction force always opposes the direction of motion or motion tendency.

Other factors that affect the behavior of two bodies in contact when a collision is involved are momentum and elasticity. Linear momentum is the product of an object's mass and its velocity. The total momentum present in a given system remains constant barring the action of external forces. Changes in momentum result from impulses, external forces acting over a time interval. The elasticity of an impact governs the amount of velocity present in the system following the impact. The relative elasticity of two impacting bodies is represented by the coefficient of restitution.

Mechanical work is the product of force and the distance through which the force acts. Mechanical power is the mechanical work done over a time interval. Mechanical energy has two major forms: kinetic and potential. When gravity is the only acting external force, the sum of the kinetic and potential energies possessed by a given body remains constant. Changes in a body's energy are equal to the mechanical work done by an external force.

INTRODUCTORY PROBLEMS

1. How much force must be applied by a kicker to give a stationary 2.5 kg ball an acceleration of 40 m/s^2? (Answer: 100 N)
2. A high jumper with a body weight of 712 N exerts a force of 3 kN against the ground during takeoff. How much force does the ground exert on the high jumper? (Answer: 3 kN)
3. What factors affect the magnitude of friction?
4. If μ_s between a basketball shoe and a court is 0.56, and the normal reaction force acting on the shoe is 350 N, how much horizontal force is required to cause the shoe to slide? (Answer: >196 N)
5. A football player pushes a 670 N blocking sled. The coefficient of static friction between sled and grass is 0.73, and the coefficient of kinetic friction between sled and grass is 0.68.
   a. How much force must the player exert to start the sled in motion?
   b. How much force is required to keep the sled in motion?
   c. Answer the same two questions with a 100 kg coach standing on the back of the sled.
      (Answers: a. >489.1 N; b. 455.6 N; c. >1205.2 N, 1122.7 N)
6. Lineman A has a mass of 100 kg and is traveling with a velocity of 4 m/s when he collides head-on with lineman B, who has a mass of 90 kg and is traveling at 4.5 m/s. If both players remain on their feet, what will hap-pen? (Answer: lineman B will push lineman A backward with a velocity of 0.03 m/s)
7. Two skaters gliding on ice run into each other head-on. If the two skaters hold onto each other and continue to move as a unit after the collision, what will be their resultant velocity? Skater A has a velocity of 5 m/s and a mass of 65 kg. Skater B has a velocity of 6 m/s and a mass of 60 kg. (Answer: v = 0.28 m/s in the direction originally taken by skater B)

8. A ball dropped on a surface from a 2 m height bounces to a height of 0.98 m. What is the coefficient of restitution between ball and surface? (Answer: 0.7)

9. A set of 20 stairs, each of 20 cm height, is ascended by a 700 N man in a period of 1.25 s. Calculate the mechanical work, power, and change in potential energy during the ascent. (Answer: W = 2800 J, P = 2240 W, PE = 2800 J)

10. A pitched ball with a mass of 1 kg reaches a catcher's glove traveling at a velocity of 28 m/s.
    a. How much momentum does the ball have?
    b. How much impulse is required to stop the ball?
    c. If the ball is in contact with the catcher's glove for 0.5 s during the catch, how much average force is applied by the glove?
    (Answers: a. 28 kg · m/s; b. 28 N s; c. 56 N)

ADDITIONAL PROBLEMS

1. Identify three practical examples of each of Newton's laws of motion, and clearly explain how each example illustrates the law.

2. Select one sport or daily activity, and identify the ways in which the amount of friction present between surfaces in contact affects performance outcome.

3. A 2 kg block sitting on a horizontal surface is subjected to a horizontal force of 7.5 N. If the resulting acceleration of the block is 3 m/s^2, what is the magnitude of the friction force opposing the motion of the block? (Answer: 1.5 N)

4. Explain the interrelationships among mechanical work, power, and energy within the context of a specific human motor skill.

5. Explain in what ways mechanical work is and is not related to caloric expenditure. Include in your answer the distinction between positive and negative work and the influence of anthropometric factors.

6. A 108 cm, 0.73 kg golf club is swung for 0.5 s with a constant acceleration of 10 rad/s^2. What is the linear momentum of the club head when it impacts the ball? (Answer: 3.9 kg · m/s)

7. A 6.5 N ball is thrown with an initial velocity of 20 m/s at a 35° angle from a height of 1.5 m.
    a. What is the velocity of the ball if it is caught at a height of 1.5 m?
    b. If the ball is caught at a height of 1.5 m, how much mechanical work is required?
    (Answers: a. 20 m/s; b. 132.5 J)

8. A 50 kg person performs a maximum vertical jump with an initial velocity of 2 m/s.
    a. What is the performer's maximum kinetic energy during the jump?
    b. What is the performer's maximum potential energy during the jump?
    c. What is the performer's minimum kinetic energy during the jump?
    d. How much is the performer's center of mass elevated during the jump?
    (Answers: a. 100 J; b. 100 J; c. 0; d. 20 cm)

9. Using the principle of conservation of mechanical energy, calculate the maximum height achieved by a 7 N ball tossed vertically upward with an initial velocity of 10 m/s. (Answer: 5.1 m)

10. Select one of the following sport activities and speculate about the changes that take place between kinetic and potential forms of mechanical energy.
    a. A single leg support during running
    b. A tennis serve
    c. A pole vault performance
    d. A springboard dive

NAME _____

DATE _____

LABORATORY EXPERIENCES

1. At the *Basic Biomechanics* Online Learning Center (www.mhhe.com/hall6e), go to Student Resources, Chapter 12, Lab Manual, Lab 1, then view Newton's Laws Animation 1 and Animation 2 and Energy Animation 1. Identify the principles that are illustrated, and write explanations of what is demonstrated.

Principle in Newton's Laws Animation 1: _____

Explanation: _____

_____

Principle in Newton's Laws Animation 2: _____

Explanation: _____

_____

Principle in Energy Animation 1: _____

Explanation: _____

_____

2. Following the instructions above, go to the online lab manual and click on Collisions in One Dimension. Play this simulation with all different possible combinations of variable settings. Identify the principle that is illustrated, and write an explanation of what is demonstrated.

Principle: _____

Explanation: _____

_____

_____

_____

3. Have each member of your lab group remove one shoe. Use a spring scale to determine the magnitude of maximum static friction for each shoe on two different surfaces. (Depending on the sensitivity of the spring scale, you may need to load the shoe with weight.) Present your results in a table, and write a paragraph explaining the results.

Shoe	Shoe Weight	Applied Force	μ_s
_____	_____	_____	_____
_____	_____	_____	_____
_____	_____	_____	_____
_____	_____	_____	_____
_____	_____	_____	_____

Explanation: _____

_____

_____

_____

412   BASIC BIOMECHANICS

4. Drop five different balls from a height of 2 m on two different surfaces, and carefully observe and record the bounce heights. Calculate the coefficient of restitution for each ball on each surface, and write a paragraph explaining your results.

Ball	Drop Height	Bounce Height	e

5. Using a stopwatch, time each member of your lab group running up a flight of stairs. Use a ruler to measure the height of one stair, then multiply by the number of stairs to calculate the total change in height. Calculate work, power, and change in potential energy for each group member.

Group Member	Wt (N)	Mass (kg)	Time (s)	Av. Vel. (m/s)	Ht Δ (m)	Work (J)	Power (W)	ΔPE (J)

REFERENCES

1. Arampatzis A, Knicker A, Metzler V, and Brüggeman G: Mechanical power in running: a comparison of different approaches, *J Biomech* 33:457, 2000.
2. Arampatzis A, Schade F, and Brüggemann G-P: Effect of the pole-human body interaction on pole vaulting performance, *J Biomech* 37:1353, 2004.
3. Biewener AA and Roberts TJ: Muscle and tendon contributions to force, work, and elastic energy savings: a comparative perspective, *Exerc Sport Sci Rev* 28:99, 2000.
4. Chang YH and Kram R: Metabolic cost of generating horizontal forces during human running, *J Appl Physiol* 86:1657, 1999.
5. Dapena J: Biomechanics of elite high jumpers. In Terauds J et al, eds: *Sports biomechanics,* Del Mar, CA, 1984, Academic Publishers.
6. Decker MJ, Torry MR, Wyland DJ, Sterett WI, and Steadman J: Gender differences in lower extremity kinematics, kinetics and energy absorption during landing, *Clin Biomech* 18:662, 2003.
7. Derrick TR: The effects of knee contact angle on impact forces and accelerations, *Med Sci Sports Exerc* 36:832, 2004.
8. Derrick TR and Mercer JA: Ground/foot impacts: measurement, attenuation, and consequences, *Med Sci Sports Exerc* 36:830, 2004.
9. Dixon SJ, Collop AC, and Batt ME: Surface effects on ground reaction forces and lower extremity kinematics in running, *Med Sci Sports Exerc* 32:1919, 2000.
10. Federolf PA, Mills R, Nigg B: Ice friction of flared ice hockey skate blades, *J Sports Sci* 26:1201, 2008.
11. Gerlach KE, White SC, Burton HW, Dorn JM, Leddy JJ, and Horvath PJ: Kinetic changes with fatigue and relationship to injury in female runners, *Med Sci Sports Exerc* 37:657, 2005.
12. Gottschall JS and Kram R: Ground reaction forces during downhill and uphill running, *J Biomech* 38:445, 2005.
13. Greenwald RM, Penna LH, and Crisco JJ: Differences in batted ball speed with wood and aluminum baseball bats: a batting cage study, *J Appl Biomech* 17:241, 2001.
14. Guido JA Jr, Werner SL, and Meister K: Lower-extremity ground reaction forces in youth windmill softball pitchers, *J Strength Cond Res* 23:1873, 2009.
15. Haake SJ, Carre MJ, and Goodwill SR: The dynamic impact characteristics of tennis balls with tennis rackets, *J Sports Sci* 21:839, 2003.
16. Hatze H: The relationship between the coefficient of restitution and energy losses in tennis rackets, *J Appl Biomech* 9:124, 1993.
17. Hume PA, Keogh J, and Redi D: The role of biomechanics in maximizing distance and accuracy of golf shots, *Sports Med* 35:429, 2005.
18. Kiefer J: Bowling: the great oil debate. In Schrier EW and Allman WF, eds: *Newton at the bat,* New York, 1984, Charles Scribner's Sons.
19. Neptune RR and van den Bogert AJ: Standard mechanical energy analyses do not correlate with muscle work in cycling, *J Biomech* 31:239, 1998.
20. Nigg BM: The role of impact forces and foot pronation: a new paradigm, *Clin J Sport Med* 11:2, 2001.
21. Nigg BM and Wakeling JM: Impact forces and muscle tuning: a new paradigm, *Exerc Sport Sci Rev* 29:37, 2001.
22. Newton RU et al: Influence of load and stretch shortening cycle on the kinematics, kinetics and muscle activation that occurs during explosive upper-body movements, *Eur J Appl Physiol* 75:333, 1997.
23. Saikko VO: A three-axis hip joint simulator for wear and friction studies on total hip prostheses, *Proc Inst Mech Eng* [H] 210:175, 1996.
24. Sawicki GS, Lewis CL, Ferris DP: It pays to have a spring in your step, *Exerc Sport Sci Rev* 37:130, 2009.
25. Slawinski J, Bonnefoy A, Levêque JM, Ontanon G, Riquet A, Dumas R, and Chèze L: Kinematic and kinetic comparisons of elite and well-trained sprinters during sprint start, *J Strength Cond Res* 24:896, 2010.
26. Stone MH, Sanborn K, O'Bryant HS, Hartman M, Stone ME, Proulx C, Ward B, and Hruby J: Maximum strength-power-oerformance relationships in collegiate throwers, *J Strength Cond Res* 17:739, 2003.

27. Tillman MD, Criss RM, Brunt D, and Hass CJ: Landing constraints influence ground reaction forces and lower extremity EMG in female volleyball players, *J Appl Biomech* 20:38, 2004.
28. Van de Walle P, Desloovere K, Truijen S, Gosselink R, Aerts P, and Hallemans A: Age-related changes in mechanical and metabolic energy during typical gait, *Gait Posture* 31:495, 2010.
29. Voloshin A: The influence of walking speed on dynamic loading on the human musculoskeletal system, *Med Sci Sports Exerc* 32:1156, 2000.
30. Wu SK, Gross MT, Prentice WE, and Yu B: Comparison of ball-and-racquet impact force between two tennis backhand stroke techniques, *J Orthop Sports Phys Ther* 31:247, 2001.

ANNOTATED READINGS

Brughelli M and Cronin J: A review of research on the mechanical stiffness in running and jumping: methodology and implications, *Scand J Med Sci Sports* 18:417, 2008.
Discusses the scientific literature related to rate of force development, elastic energy storage and utilization, and athletic performance.

Marín PJ and Rhea MR: Effects of vibration training on muscle power: a meta-analysis, *J Strength Cond Res* 24:871, 2010.
Reviews the scientific literature on fostering increases in muscular power through vibration training.

Moxnes JF and Hausken K: A dynamic model of Nordic diagonal stride skiing, with a literature review of cross country skiing, *Comput Methods Biomech Biomed Engin* 12:531, 2009.
Reviews the scientific literature on Nordic diagonal stride skiing, including the relationships of static and dynamic friction to skier weight, velocity, kicking force angle, and terrain.

Stefani RT: The relative power output and relative lean body mass of World and Olympic male and female champions with implications for gender equity, *J Sports Sci* 24:1329, 2006.
Discusses gender-related differential performance of female and male Olympic and World champions relative to power output applied to the environment.

RELATED WEBSITES

Advanced Medical Technology, Inc.
http://www.amti.com/
Provides information on the AMTI force platforms with reference to ground reaction forces in gait analysis, balance and posture, and other topics.

Answers.com: Mechanical Work
http://www.answers.com/topic/mechanical-work
Lists definitions and examples of mechanical work.

Fear of Physics: What Is Friction?
http://www.fearofphysics.com/Friction/frintro.html
Includes text and illustrations, plus a link to a simulation.

Kistler
http://www.kistler.com
Describes a series of force platforms for measuring ground reaction forces.

Scienceworld: Friction
http://scienceworld.wolfram.com/physics/Friction.html
Includes definitions and examples of friction coefficients.

The Exploratorium's Science of Hockey
http://www.exploratorium.edu/hockey/
Explains scientific concepts related to hockey, including the friction between ice and skate and the mechanics of skating.

The Physics Classroom: Mechanical Energy
http://www.physicsclassroom.com/Class/energy/U5L1d.html
Includes definitions, illustrations, and questions with answers related to work and energy.

KEY TERMS

coefficient of friction	number that serves as an index of the interaction between two surfaces in contact
coefficient of restitution	number that serves as an index of elasticity for colliding bodies
friction	force acting at the area of contact between two surfaces in the direction opposite that of motion or motion tendency
impact	collision characterized by the exchange of a large force during a small time interval
impulse	product of a force and the time interval over which the force acts
kinetic energy	energy of motion calculated as $\frac{1}{2}mv^2$
kinetic friction	constant magnitude friction generated between two surfaces in contact during motion
linear momentum	quantity of motion, measured as the product of a body's mass and its velocity
maximum static friction	maximum amount of friction that can be generated between two static surfaces
normal reaction force	force acting perpendicular to two surfaces in contact
perfectly elastic impact	impact during which the velocity of the system is conserved
perfectly plastic impact	impact resulting in the total loss of system velocity
potential energy	energy by virtue of a body's position or configuration, calculated as the product of weight and height
power	rate of work production, calculated as work divided by the time during which the work was done
strain energy	capacity to do work by virtue of a deformed body's return to its original shape
work	in a mechanical context, force multiplied by the displacement of the resistance in the direction of the force

C H A P T E R

15

Human Movement in a Fluid Medium

After completing this chapter, you will be able to:

Explain the ways in which the composition and flow characteristics of a fluid affect fluid forces.

Define *buoyancy* and explain the variables that determine whether a human body will float.

Define *drag*, identify the components of drag, and identify the factors that affect the magnitude of each component.

Define *lift* and explain the ways in which it can be generated.

Discuss the theories regarding propulsion of the human body in swimming.

ONLINE LEARNING CENTER RESOURCES

www.mhhe.com/hall6e

Log on to our Online Learning Center (OLC) for access to these additional resources:

- Online Lab Manual
- Flashcards with definitions of chapter key terms
- Chapter objectives
- Chapter lecture PowerPoint presentation
- Self-scoring chapter quiz
- Additional chapter resources
- Web links for study and exploration of chapter-related topics

The ability to control the action of fluid forces differentiates elite from average swimmers.

W hy are there dimples in a golf ball? Why are some people able to float while others cannot? Why are cyclists, swimmers, downhill skiers, and speed skaters concerned with streamlining their bodies during competition?

Both air and water are fluid mediums that exert forces on bodies moving through them. Some of these forces slow the progress of a moving body; others provide support or propulsion. A general understanding of the actions of fluid forces on human movement activities is an important component of the study of the biomechanics of human movement. This chapter introduces the effects of fluid forces on both human and projectile motion.

THE NATURE OF FLUIDS

fluid
substance that flows when subjected to a shear stress

●*Air and water are fluids that exert forces on the human body.*

●*The velocity of a body relative to a fluid influences the magnitude of the forces exerted by the fluid on the body.*

Although in general conversation the term *fluid* is often used interchangeably with the term *liquid*, from a mechanical perspective, a fluid is any substance that tends to flow or continuously deform when acted on by a shear force. Both gases and liquids are fluids with similar mechanical behaviors.

Relative Motion

Because a fluid is a medium capable of flow, the influence of the fluid on a body moving through it depends not only on the body's velocity but also on the velocity of the fluid. Consider the case of waders standing in the shallow portion of a river with a moderately strong current. If they stand still,

FIGURE 15-1

The relative velocity of a moving body with respect to a fluid is equal to the vector subtraction of the velocity of the wind from the velocity of the body.

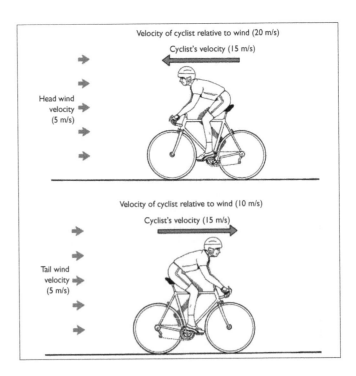

Velocity of cyclist relative to wind (20 m/s)

Cyclist's velocity (15 m/s)

Head wind velocity (5 m/s)

Velocity of cyclist relative to wind (10 m/s)

Cyclist's velocity (15 m/s)

Tail wind velocity (5 m/s)

they feel the force of the current against their legs. If they walk upstream against the current, the current's force against their legs is even stronger. If they walk downstream, the current's force is reduced and perhaps even imperceptible.

When a body moves through a fluid, the relative velocity of the body with respect to the fluid influences the magnitude of the acting forces. If the direction of motion is directly opposite the direction of the fluid flow, the magnitude of the velocity of the moving body relative to the fluid is the algebraic sum of the speeds of the moving body and the fluid (Figure 15-1). If the body moves in the same direction as the surrounding fluid, the magnitude of the body's velocity relative to the fluid is the difference in the speeds of the object and the fluid. In other words, the relative velocity of a body with respect to a fluid is the vector subtraction of the absolute velocity of the fluid from the absolute velocity of the body (see Sample Problem 15.1). Likewise, the relative velocity of a fluid with respect to a

relative velocity
velocity of a body with respect to the velocity of something else, such as the surrounding fluid

SAMPLE PROBLEM 15.1

A sailboat is traveling at an absolute speed of 3 m/s against a 0.5 m/s current and with a 6 m/s tailwind. What is the velocity of the current with respect to the boat? What is the velocity of the wind with respect to the boat?

Known

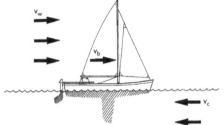

$$v_b = 3 \text{ m/s} \rightarrow$$
$$v_c = 0.5 \text{ m/s} \leftarrow$$
$$v_w = 6 \text{ m/s} \rightarrow$$

Solution

The velocity of the current with respect to the boat is equal to the vector subtraction of the absolute velocity of the boat from the absolute velocity of the current.

$$v_{c/b} = v_c - v_b$$
$$= (0.5 \text{ m/s} \leftarrow) - (3 \text{ m/s} \rightarrow)$$
$$= (3.5 \text{ m/s} \leftarrow)$$

The velocity of the current with respect to the boat is 3.5 m/s in the direction opposite that of the boat.

The velocity of the wind with respect to the boat is equal to the vector subtraction of the absolute velocity of the boat from the absolute velocity of the wind.

$$v_{w/b} = v_w - v_b$$
$$= (6 \text{ m/s} \rightarrow) - (3 \text{ m/s} \rightarrow)$$
$$= (3 \text{ m/s} \rightarrow)$$

The velocity of the wind with respect to the boat is 3 m/s in the direction in which the boat is sailing.

478   BASIC BIOMECHANICS

FIGURE 15-2

Laminar flow is characterized by smooth, parallel layers of fluid.

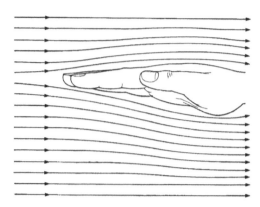

body moving through it is the vector subtraction of the velocity of the body from the velocity of the fluid.

Laminar versus Turbulent Flow

When an object such as a human hand or a canoe paddle moves through water, there is little apparent disturbance of the immediately surrounding water if the relative velocity of the object with respect to the water is low. However, if the relative velocity of motion through the water is sufficiently high, waves and eddies appear.

laminar flow
flow characterized by smooth, parallel layers of fluid

When an object moves with sufficiently low velocity relative to any fluid medium, the flow of the adjacent fluid is termed laminar flow. Laminar flow is characterized by smooth layers of fluid molecules flowing parallel to one another (Figure 15-2).

turbulent flow
flow characterized by mixing of adjacent fluid layers

When an object moves with sufficiently high velocity relative to a surrounding fluid, the layers of fluid near the surface of the object mix, and the flow is termed *turbulent.* The rougher the surface of the body, the lower the relative velocity at which turbulence is caused. Laminar flow and turbulent flow are distinct categories. If any turbulence is present, the flow is nonlaminar. The nature of the fluid flow surrounding an object can dramatically affect the fluid forces exerted on the object. In the case of the human body during swimming, flow is neither completely laminar nor completely turbulent, but transitional between the two (30).

Fluid Properties

Other factors that influence the magnitude of the forces a fluid generates are the fluid's density, specific weight, and viscosity. As discussed in Chapter 3, density (ρ) is defined as mass/volume, and the ratio of weight to volume is known as specific weight (γ). The denser and heavier the fluid medium surrounding a body, the greater the magnitude of the forces the fluid exerts on the body. The property of fluid viscosity involves the internal resistance of a fluid to flow. The greater the extent to which a fluid resists flow under an applied force, the more viscous the fluid is. A thick molasses, for example, is more viscous than a liquid honey, which is more viscous than water. Increased fluid viscosity results in increased forces exerted on bodies exposed to the fluid.

•*Atmospheric pressure and temperature influence a fluid's density, specific weight, and viscosity.*

Atmospheric pressure and temperature influence a fluid's density, specific weight, and viscosity, with more mass concentrated in a given unit of fluid volume at higher atmospheric pressures and lower temperatures.

FLUID*	DENSITY (kg/m^3)	SPECIFIC WEIGHT (n/m^3)	VISCOSITY (ns/m^2)
Air	1.20	11.8	.000018
Water	998	9,790	.0010
Seawater⁺	1,026	10,070	.0014
Ethyl alcohol	799	7,850	.0012
Mercury	13,550.20	133,000.0	.0015

TABLE 15-1

Approximate Physical Properties of Common Fluids

*Fluids are measured at 20°C and standard atmospheric pressure.
⁺10°C, 3.3% salinity.

Because molecular motion in gases increases with temperature, the viscosity of gases also increases. The viscosity of liquids decreases with increased temperature because of a reduction in the cohesive forces among the molecules. The densities, specific weights, and viscosities of common fluids are shown in Table 15-1.

BUOYANCY

Characteristics of the Buoyant Force

Buoyancy is a fluid force that always acts vertically upward. The factors that determine the magnitude of the buoyant force were originally explained by the ancient Greek mathematician Archimedes. Archimedes' principle states that the magnitude of the buoyant force acting on a given body is equal to the weight of the fluid displaced by the body. The latter factor is calculated by multiplying the specific weight of the fluid by the volume of the portion of the body that is surrounded by the fluid. Buoyancy (F_b) is calculated as the product of the displaced volume (V_d) and the fluid's specific weight γ:

$$F_b = V_d\gamma$$

For example, if a water polo ball with a volume of 0.2 m^3 is completely submerged in water at 20°C, the buoyant force acting on the ball is equal to the ball's volume multiplied by the specific weight of water at 20°C:

$$F_b = V_d\gamma$$
$$= (0.2 \text{ m}^3)(9790 \text{ N/m}^3)$$
$$= 1958 \text{ N}$$

The more dense the surrounding fluid, the greater the magnitude of the buoyant force. Since seawater is more dense than freshwater, a given object's buoyancy is greater in seawater than in freshwater. Because the magnitude of the buoyant force is directly related to the volume of the submerged object, the point at which the buoyant force acts is the object's center of volume, which is also known as the *center of buoyancy*. The center of volume is the point around which a body's volume is equally distributed.

Flotation

The ability of a body to float in a fluid medium depends on the relationship between the body's buoyancy and its weight. When weight and the buoyant force are the only two forces acting on a body and their magnitudes are

Archimedes' principle
physical law stating that the buoyant force acting on a body is equal to the weight of the fluid displaced by the body

center of volume
point around which a body's volume is equally distributed and at which the buoyant force acts

equal, the body floats in a motionless state, in accordance with the principles of static equilibrium. If the magnitude of the weight is greater than that of the buoyant force, the body sinks, moving downward in the direction of the net force.

Most objects float statically in a partially submerged position. The volume of a freely floating object needed to generate a buoyant force equal to the object's weight is the volume that is submerged.

Flotation of the Human Body

In the study of biomechanics, buoyancy is most commonly of interest relative to the flotation of the human body in water. Some individuals cannot float in a motionless position, and others float with little effort. This difference in floatability is a function of body density. Since the density of bone and muscle is greater than the density of fat, individuals who are extremely muscular and have little body fat have higher average body densities than individuals with less muscle, less dense bones, or more body fat. If two individuals have an identical body volume, the one with the higher body density weighs more. Alternatively, if two people have the same body weight, the person with the higher body density has a smaller body volume. For flotation to occur, the body volume must be large enough to create a buoyant force greater than or equal to body weight (see Sample Problem 15.2). Many individuals can float only when holding a large volume of inspired air in the lungs, a tactic that increases body volume without altering body weight.

> •*In order for a body to float, the buoyant force it generates must equal or exceed its weight.*

The orientation of the human body as it floats in water is determined by the relative position of the total-body center of gravity relative to the total-body center of volume. The exact locations of the center of gravity and center of volume vary with anthropometric dimensions and body composition. Typically, the center of gravity is inferior to the center of volume due to the relatively large volume and relatively small weight of the lungs. Because weight acts at the center of gravity and buoyancy acts at the center of volume, a torque is created that rotates the body until it is positioned so that these two acting forces are vertically aligned and the torque ceases to exist (Figure 15-3).

> •*People who cannot float in swimming pools may float in Utah's Great Salt Lake, in which the density of the water surpasses even that of seawater.*

When beginning swimmers try to float on their back, they typically assume a horizontal body position. Once the swimmer relaxes, the lower end of the body sinks, because of the acting torque. An experienced teacher instructs beginning swimmers to assume a more diagonal position in the water before relaxing into the back float. This position minimizes torque and the concomitant sinking of the lower extremity. Other strategies that a swimmer can use to reduce torque on the body when entering a back float position include extending the arms backward in the water above the head and flexing the knees. Both tactics elevate the location of the center of gravity, positioning it closer to the center of volume.

During swimming with the front crawl stroke, the center of buoyancy is shifted toward the feet when the recovery arm and part of the head are above the surface of the water. At this point in the stroke cycle, the buoyant torque tends to elevate the feet, rather than the reverse (49).

DRAG

Drag is a force caused by the dynamic action of a fluid that acts in the direction of the free-stream fluid flow. Generally, a drag is a *resistance* force: a force that slows the motion of a body moving through a fluid. The

SAMPLE PROBLEM 15.2

When holding a large quantity of inspired air in her lungs, a 22 kg girl has a body volume of 0.025 m^3. Can she float in fresh water if γ equals 9810 N/m^3? Given her body volume, how much could she weigh and still be able to float?

Known

$$m = 22 \text{ kg}$$
$$V = 0.025 \text{ m}^3$$
$$\gamma = 9810 \text{ N/m}^3$$

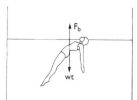

Solution

Two forces are acting on the girl: her weight and the buoyant force. According to the conditions of static equilibrium, the sum of the vertical forces must be equal to zero for the girl to float in a motionless position. If the buoyant force is less than her weight, she will sink, and if the buoyant force is equal to her weight, she will float completely submerged. If the buoyant force is greater than her weight, she will float partly submerged. The magnitude of the buoyant force acting on her total body volume is the product of the volume of displaced fluid (her body volume) and the specific weight of the fluid:

$$F_b = V_\gamma$$
$$= (0.025 \text{ m}^3) (9810 \text{ N/m}^3)$$
$$= 245.52 \text{ N}$$

Her body weight is equal to her body mass multiplied by the acceleration of gravity:

$$wt = (22 \text{ kg}) (9.81 \text{ m/s}^2)$$
$$= 215.82 \text{ N}$$

Since the buoyant force is greater than her body weight, the girl will float partly submerged in freshwater.

> Yes, she will float.

To calculate the maximum weight that the girl's body volume can support in freshwater, multiply the body volume by the specific weight of water.

$$wt_{max} = (0.025 \text{ m}^3) (9810 \text{ N/m}^3)$$
> $$wt_{max} = 245.25 \text{ N}$$

---

drag force acting on a body in relative motion with respect to a fluid is defined by the following formula:

$$F_D = \tfrac{1}{2} C_D \rho A_p v^2$$

In this formula, F_D is drag force, C_D is the coefficient of drag, ρ is the fluid density, A_p is the projected area of the body or the surface area of the body oriented perpendicular to the fluid flow, and v is the relative velocity

coefficient of drag
unitless number that is an index of a body's ability to generate fluid resistance

482   BASIC BIOMECHANICS

FIGURE 15-3

A. A torque is created on a swimmer by body weight (acting at the center of gravity) and the buoyant force (acting at the center of volume). **B.** When the center of gravity and the center of volume are vertically aligned, this torque is eliminated.

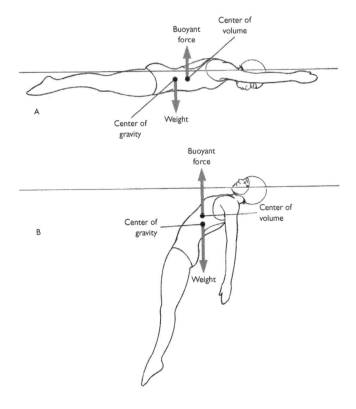

of the body with respect to the fluid. The coefficient of drag is a unitless number that serves as an index of the amount of drag an object can generate. Its size depends on the shape and orientation of a body relative to the fluid flow, with long, streamlined bodies generally having lower coefficients of drag than blunt or irregularly shaped objects. Approximate coefficients of drag for the human body in positions commonly assumed during participation in several sports are shown in Figure 15-4.

The formula for the total drag force demonstrates the exact way in which each of the identified factors affects drag. If the coefficient of drag, the fluid density, and the projected area of the body remain constant, drag increases with the square of the relative velocity of motion. This relationship is referred to as the theoretical square law. According to this law, if cyclists double their speed and other factors remain constant, the drag force opposing them increases fourfold. The effect of drag is more consequential when a body is moving with a high velocity, which occurs in sports such as cycling, speed skating, downhill skiing, the bobsled, and the luge.

In swimming, the drag on a moving body is 500–600 times higher than it would be in the air, with the magnitude of drag varying with the anthropometric characteristics of the individual swimmer, as well as with the stroke used (41). Researchers distinguish between passive drag, which is generated by the swimmer's body size, shape, and position in the water, and active drag, which is associated with the swimming motion. Passive drag is inversely related to a swimmer's buoyancy, which has been found to have a small but important influence on sprint swimming perfor-

theoretical square law
drag increases approximately with the square of velocity when relative velocity is low

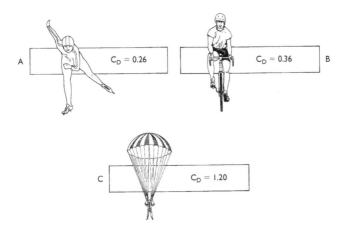

FIGURE 15-4

Approximate coefficients of drag for the human body. **A.** Frontal drag on a speed skater. **B.** Frontal drag on a cyclist in touring position. **C.** Vertical drag on a parachutist falling with the parachute fully opened. Modified from Roberson JA and Crowe CT: *Engineering fluid mechanics* (2nd ed), Boston, 1980, Houghton Mifflin.

mance (28). Passive drag on male swimmers is also significantly reduced with shoulder-to-knee and shoulder-to-ankle swimsuits as compared to briefs (30).

Three forms of resistance contribute to the total drag force. The component of resistance that predominates depends on the nature of the fluid flow immediately adjacent to the body.

Skin Friction

One component of the total drag is known as skin friction, surface drag, or viscous drag. This drag is similar to the friction force described in Chapter 12. Skin friction is derived from the sliding contacts between successive layers of fluid close to the surface of a moving body (Figure 15-5). The layer of fluid particles immediately adjacent to the moving body is slowed because of the shear stress the body exerts on the fluid. The next adjacent layer of fluid particles moves with slightly less speed because of friction between the adjacent molecules, and the next layer is affected in turn. The number of layers of affected fluid becomes progressively larger as the flow moves in the downstream direction along the body. The entire region within which fluid velocity is diminished because of the shearing resistance caused by the boundary of the moving body is the boundary layer. The force the body exerts on the fluid in creating the boundary layer

skin friction
surface drag
viscous drag
resistance derived from friction between adjacent layers of fluid near a body moving through the fluid

boundary layer
layer of fluid immediately adjacent to a body

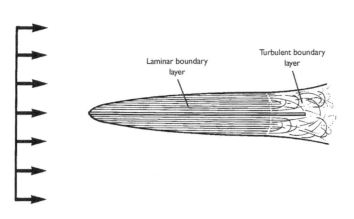

Laminar boundary layer

Turbulent boundary layer

FIGURE 15-5

The fluid boundary layer for a thin, flat plate, shown from the side view. The laminar boundary layer gradually becomes thicker as flow progresses along the plate.

484   BASIC BIOMECHANICS

results in an oppositely directed reaction force exerted by the fluid on the body. This reaction force is known as *skin friction.*

Several factors affect the magnitude of skin friction drag. It increases proportionally with increases in the relative velocity of fluid flow, the surface area of the body over which the flow occurs, the roughness of the body surface, and the viscosity of the fluid. Skin friction is always one component of the total drag force acting on a body moving relative to a fluid, and it is the major form of drag present when the flow is primarily laminar. For front crawl swimming, kayaking, and rowing, skin friction drag predominates at velocities between 1 and 3 m/s (35).

Among these factors, the one that a competitive athlete can readily alter is the relative roughness of the body surface. Athletes can wear tight-fitting clothing composed of a smooth fabric rather than loose-fitting clothing or clothing made of a rough fabric. A 10% reduction of drag occurs when a speed skater wears a smooth spandex suit as opposed to the traditional wool outfit (46). A 6% decrease in air resistance results from cyclists' use of appropriate clothing, including sleeves, tights, and smooth covers over the laces of the shoes (21). Competitive male swimmers and cyclists often shave body hair to reduce skin friction.

The other factor affecting skin friction that athletes can alter in some circumstances is the amount of surface area in contact with the fluid. Carrying an extra passenger such as a coxswain in a rowing event results in a larger wetted surface area of the hull because of the added weight; as a result, skin friction drag is increased.

Form Drag

form drag
profile drag
pressure drag
resistance created by a pressure differential between the lead and rear sides of a body moving through a fluid

A second component of the total drag acting on a body moving through a fluid is form drag, which is also known as profile drag or pressure drag. Form drag is always one component of the drag on a body moving relative to a fluid. When the boundary layer of fluid molecules next to the surface of the moving body is primarily turbulent, form drag predominates. Form drag is the major contributor to overall drag during most human and projectile motion. It is the predominant type of drag for front crawl swimming, kayaking, and rowing at velocities of less than 1 m/s (35).

When a body moves through a fluid medium with sufficient velocity to create a pocket of turbulence behind the body, an imbalance in the pressure surrounding the body—a *pressure differential*—is created (Figure 15-6). At the upstream end of the body where fluid particles meet the body head-on, a zone of relative high pressure is formed. At the downstream end of the body where turbulence is present, a zone of relative low pressure is created. Whenever a pressure differential exists, a force is directed from the region of high pressure to the region of low pressure. For example, a vacuum cleaner creates a suction force because a region of relative low pressure (the relative vacuum) exists inside the machine housing. This force, directed from front to rear of the body in relative motion through a fluid, constitutes form drag.

FIGURE 15-6

Form drag results from the suctionlike force created between the positive pressure zone on a body's leading edge and the negative pressure zone on the trailing edge when turbulence is present.

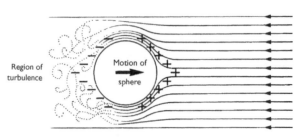

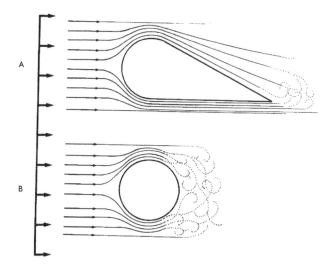

The effect of streamlining is a reduction in the turbulence created at the trailing edge of a body in a fluid.
A. A streamlined shape.
B. A sphere.

Several factors affect the magnitude of form drag, including the relative velocity of the body with respect to the fluid, the magnitude of the pressure gradient between the front and rear ends of the body, and the size of the surface area that is aligned perpendicular to the flow. Both the size of the pressure gradient and the amount of surface area perpendicular to the fluid flow can be reduced to minimize the effect of form drag on the human body. For example, streamlining the overall shape of the body reduces the magnitude of the pressure gradient. Streamlining minimizes the amount of turbulence created and hence minimizes the negative pressure that is created at the object's rear (Figure 15-7). Assuming a more crouched body position also reduces the body's projected surface area oriented perpendicular to the fluid flow.

Competitive cyclists, skaters, and skiers assume a streamlined body position with the smallest possible area of the body oriented perpendicular to the oncoming airstream. Even though the low-crouched aeroposition assumed by competitive cyclists increases the cyclist's metabolic cost as compared to an upright position, the aerodynamic benefit is an over tenfold reduction in drag (16). Similarly, race cars, yacht hulls, and some cycling helmets are designed with streamlined shapes. The aerodynamic frame and handlebar designs for racing cycles also reduce drag (5, 37).

Streamlining is also an effective way to reduce form drag in the water. The ability to streamline body position during freestyle swimming is a characteristic that distinguishes elite from subelite performers (6). Using a triathlon wet suit can reduce the drag on a competitor swimming at a typical triathlon race pace of 1.25 m/s by as much as 14%, because the buoyant effect of the wet suit results in reduced form drag on the swimmer (11, 43).

The nature of the boundary layer at the surface of a body moving through a fluid can also influence form drag by affecting the pressure gradient between the front and rear ends of the body. When the boundary layer is primarily laminar, the fluid separates from the boundary close to the front end of the body, creating a large turbulent pocket with a large negative pressure and thereby a large form drag (Figure 15-8). In contrast, when the boundary layer is turbulent, the point of flow separation is closer to the rear end of the body, the turbulent pocket created is smaller, and the resulting form drag is smaller.

• *Streamlining helps to minimize form drag.*

486   BASIC BIOMECHANICS

A. Laminar flow results in an early separation of flow from the boundary and a larger drag producing wake as compared to **B**, turbulent boundary flow.

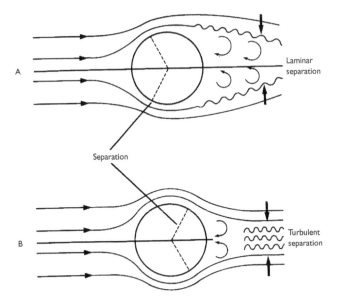

A streamlined cycling helmet.

The nature of the boundary layer depends on the roughness of the body's surface and the body's velocity relative to the flow. As the relative velocity of motion for an object such as a golf ball increases, changes in the acting drag occur (Figure 15-9). As relative velocity increases up to a certain critical point, the theoretical square law is in effect, with drag increasing with the square of velocity. After this critical velocity is reached, the boundary layer becomes more turbulent than laminar, and form drag diminishes because the pocket of reduced pressure on the trailing edge of the ball becomes smaller. As velocity increases further, the effects of skin friction and form drag grow, increasing the total drag. The dimples in a golf ball are carefully engineered to produce a turbulent boundary layer at the ball's surface that reduces form drag on the ball over the range of velocities at which a golf ball travels.

FIGURE 15-9

Drag increases approximately with the square of velocity until there is sufficient relative velocity (v_1) to generate a turbulent boundary layer. As velocity increases beyond this point, form drag decreases. After a second critical relative velocity (v_2) is reached, the drag again increases.

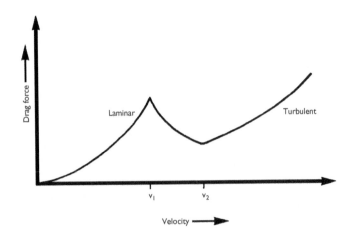

Cyclists drafting to minimize form drag.

Another way in which form drag can be manipulated is through drafting, the process of following closely behind another participant in speed-based sports such as cycling and automobile racing. Drafting provides the advantage of reducing form drag on the follower, since the leader partially shelters the follower's leading edge from increased pressure against the fluid. Depending on the size of the pocket of reduced pressure behind the leader, a suctionlike force may also help to propel the follower forward. In swimming, the optimal drafting distance behind another swimmer in a swimming pool is 0–50 cm from the toes of the lead swimmer (7). Drafting has even been found to improve performance during a long-distance swim, particularly for faster and leaner swimmers (8).

Wave Drag

The third type of drag acts at the interface of two different fluids, for example, at the interface between water and air. Although bodies that are completely submerged in a fluid are not affected by wave drag, this form of drag can be a major contributor to the overall drag acting on a human swimmer, particularly when the swim is done in open water. When a swimmer moves a body segment along, near, or across the air and water interface, a wave is created in the more dense fluid (the water). The reaction force the water exerts on the swimmer constitutes wave drag.

wave drag
resistance created by the generation of waves at the interface between two different fluids, such as air and water

The magnitude of wave drag increases with greater up-and-down motion of the body and increased swimming speed. The height of the bow wave generated in front of a swimmer increases proportionally with swimming velocity, although at a given velocity, skilled swimmers produce smaller waves than less-skilled swimmers, presumably due to better technique (less up-and-down motion) (42). At fast swimming speeds (over 3 m/s), wave drag is generally the largest component of the total drag acting on the swimmer (35). For this reason, competitive swimmers typically propel themselves underwater to eliminate wave drag for a small portion of the race in events in which the rules permit it. One underwater stroke is allowed following the dive or a turn in the breaststroke, and a distance of up to 15 m is allowed underwater after a turn in the backstroke. In most swimming pools, the lane lines are designed to minimize wave action by dissipating moving surface water.

488   BASIC BIOMECHANICS

The bow wave generated by a competitive swimmer.

LIFT FORCE

lift
force acting on a body in a fluid in a direction perpendicular to the fluid flow

While drag forces act in the direction of the free-stream fluid flow, another force, known as lift, is generated perpendicular to the fluid flow. Although the name *lift* suggests that this force is directed vertically upward, it may assume any direction, as determined by the direction of the fluid flow and the orientation of the body. The factors affecting the magnitude of lift are basically the same factors that affect the magnitude of drag:

$$F_L = \tfrac{1}{2}\, C_L \rho A_p v^2$$

coefficient of lift
unitless number that is an index of a body's ability to generate lift

In this equation, F_L represents lift force, C_L is the coefficient of lift, ρ is the fluid density, A_p is the surface area against which lift is generated, and v is the relative velocity of a body with respect to a fluid. The factors

The lane lines in modern swimming pools are designed to minimize wave action, enabling faster racing times.

FORCE	FACTORS
Buoyant force	Specific weight of the fluid Volume of fluid displaced
Skin friction	Density of the fluid Relative velocity of the fluid Amount of body surface area exposed to the flow Roughness of the body surface Viscosity of the fluid
Form drag	Density of the fluid Relative velocity of the fluid Pressure differential between leading and rear edges of the body Amount of body surface area perpendicular to the flow
Wave drag	Relative velocity of the wave Amount of surface area perpendicular to the wave Viscosity of the fluid
Lift force	Relative velocity of the fluid Density of the fluid Size, shape, and orientation of the body

TABLE 15-2

Factors Affecting the Magnitudes of Fluid Forces

affecting the magnitudes of the fluid forces discussed are summarized in Table 15-2.

Foil Shape

One way in which lift force may be created is for the shape of the moving body to resemble that of a foil (Figure 15-10). When the fluid stream encounters a foil, the fluid separates, with some flowing over the curved surface and some flowing straight back along the flat surface on the opposite side. The fluid that flows over the curved surface is positively accelerated relative to the fluid flow, creating a region of relative high-velocity flow. The difference in the velocity of flow on the curved side of the foil as opposed to the flat side of the foil creates a pressure difference in the fluid, in accordance with a relationship derived by the Italian scientist Bernoulli. According to the Bernoulli principle, regions of relative high-velocity fluid flow are associated with regions of relative low pressure, and regions of relative low-velocity flow are associated with regions of relative high pressure. When these regions of relative low and high pressure are created on opposite sides of the foil, the result is a lift force directed perpendicular to the foil from the zone of high pressure toward the low-pressure zone.

foil
shape capable of generating lift in the presence of a fluid flow

Bernoulli principle
an expression of the inverse relationship between relative velocity and relative pressure in a fluid flow

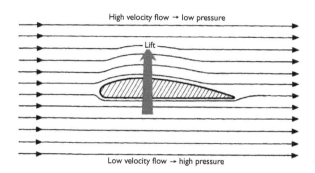

FIGURE 15-10

Lift force generated by a foil shape is directed from the region of relative high pressure on the flat side of the foil toward the region of relative low pressure on the curved side of the foil.

Different factors affect the magnitude of the lift force acting on a foil. The greater the velocity of the foil relative to the fluid, the greater the pressure differential and the lift force generated. Other contributing factors are the fluid density and the surface area of the flat side of the foil. As both of these variables increase, lift increases. An additional factor of influence is the *coefficient of lift,* which indicates a body's ability to generate lift based on its shape.

The human hand resembles a foil shape when viewed from a lateral perspective. When a swimmer slices a hand through the water, it generates lift force directed perpendicular to the palm. Synchronized swimmers use a sculling motion, rapidly slicing their hands back and forth, to maneuver their bodies through various positions in the water. The lift force generated by rapid sculling motions enables elite synchronized swimmers to support their bodies in an inverted position with both legs extended completely out of the water.

The semifoil shapes of projectiles such as the discus, javelin, football, boomerang, and frisbee generate some lift force when oriented at appropriate angles with respect to the direction of the fluid flow. Spherical projectiles such as a shot or a ball, however, do not sufficiently resemble a foil and cannot generate lift by virtue of their shape.

angle of attack
angle between the longitudinal axis of a body and the direction of the fluid flow

The angle of orientation of the projectile with respect to the fluid flow—the angle of attack—is an important factor in launching a lift-producing projectile for maximum range (horizontal displacement). A positive angle of attack is necessary to generate a lift force (Figure 15-11). As the angle of attack increases, the amount of surface area exposed perpendicularly to the fluid flow also increases, thereby increasing the amount of form drag acting. With too steep an attack angle, the fluid cannot flow along the curved side of the foil to create lift. Airplanes that assume too steep an ascent can stall and lose altitude until pilots reduce the attack angle of the wings to enable lift (25).

To maximize the flight distance of a projectile such as the discus or javelin, it is advantageous to maximize lift and minimize drag. Form drag, however, is minimum at an angle of attack of 0°, which is a poor angle for generating lift. The optimum angle of attack for maximizing range is the angle at which the lift/drag ratio is maximum. The largest lift/drag ratio for a discus traveling at a relative velocity of 24 m/s is generated at an angle of attack of 10° (14). For both the discus and the javelin, however, the single most important factor related to distance achieved is release speed (1, 17).

lift/drag ratio
the magnitude of the lift force divided by the magnitude of the total drag force acting on a body at a given time

When the projectile is the human body during the performance of a jump, maximizing the effects of lift while minimizing the effects of drag is more complicated. In the ski jump, because of the relatively long period during which the body is airborne, the lift/drag ratio for the human body is particularly important. Research on ski jumping indicates that for optimal performance, ski jumpers should have a flattened body with a large frontal area (for generating lift) and a small body weight (for enabling greater acceleration) during takeoff. The effect of lift is immediate at takeoff, resulting in a higher initial vertical velocity than the jumper generates through impulse against the ramp surface (47). During the first part of the flight, jumpers should assume a small angle of attack to minimize drag (Figure 15-12). During the latter part of the flight, they should increase attack angle up to that of maximum lift. Jumping into a headwind dramatically increases jump length because of the increase in lift acting on the jumper (31).

Magnus Effect

Spinning objects also generate lift. When an object in a fluid medium spins, the boundary layer of fluid molecules adjacent to the object spins

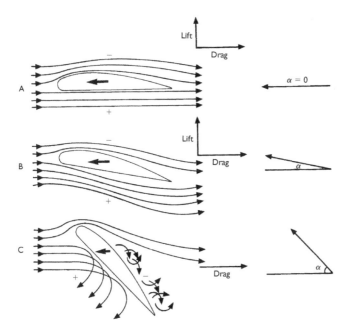

FIGURE 15-11

A. Drag and lift are small because the angle of attack (α) does not create a sufficiently high pressure differential across the top and bottom surfaces of the foil. **B.** An angle of attack that promotes lift. **C.** When the angle of attack is too large, the fluid cannot flow over the curved surface of the foil, and no lift is generated. **D.** When the angle of attack is below the horizontal, lift is created in a downward direction. Modified from Maglischo E: *Swimming faster: A comprehensive guide to the science of swimming,* Palo Alto, CA, 1982, Mayfield.

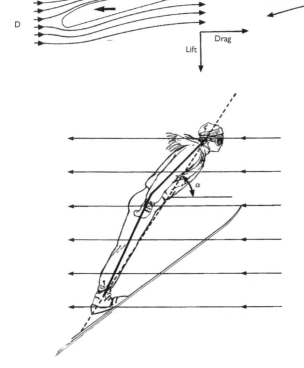

FIGURE 15-12

The angle of attack is the angle formed between the primary axis of a body and the direction of the fluid flow.

492   BASIC BIOMECHANICS

FIGURE 15-13

FIGURE 15-13

The relationship between ski jump length and the performer's angle of attack. Modified from Denoth J, Luethi SM, and Gasser HH: Methodological problems in optimization of the flight phase in ski jumping, Int J Sport Biomech 3:404, 1987.

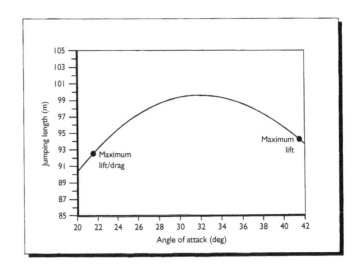

FIGURE 15-14

Magnus force results from the pressure differential created by a spinning body.

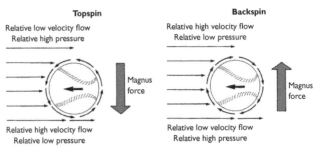

Magnus force
lift force created by spin

Magnus effect
deviation in the trajectory of a spinning object toward the direction of spin, resulting from the Magnus force

• *A ball projected with spin follows a trajectory that curves in the direction of the spin.*

with it. When this happens, the fluid molecules on one side of the spinning body collide head-on with the molecules in the fluid free-stream (Figure 15-14). This creates a region of relative low velocity and high pressure. On the opposite side of the spinning object, the boundary layer moves in the same direction as the fluid flow, thereby creating a zone of relative high velocity and low pressure. The pressure differential creates what is called the Magnus force, a lift force directed from the high-pressure region to the low-pressure region.

Magnus force affects the flight path of a spinning projectile as it travels through the air, causing the path to deviate progressively in the direction of the spin, a deviation known as the Magnus effect. When a tennis ball or table tennis ball is hit with topspin, the ball drops more rapidly than it would without spin, and the ball tends to rebound low and fast, often making it more difficult for the opponent to return the shot. The nap on a tennis ball traps a relatively large boundary layer of air with it as it spins, thereby accentuating the Magnus effect. The Magnus effect can also result from sidespin, as when a pitcher throws a curveball (Figure 15-15). The modern-day version of the curveball is a ball that is intentionally pitched with spin, causing it to follow a curved path in the direction of the spin throughout its flight path.

The extent to which a ball curves, or "breaks," in the horizontal and vertical planes is dependent on the orientation of the spinning ball's axis

FIGURE 15-15

The trajectory of a ball thrown with sidespin follows a regular curve due to the Magnus effect. The dashed line shows the illusion seen by the players on the field.

of rotation. If the axis of rotation is perfectly vertical, all of the Magnus effect occurs in the horizontal plane. Alternatively, if the axis of rotation is oriented horizontally, the Magnus effect is restricted to the vertical plane. Curveballs thrown by major league pitchers spin as quickly as 27 revolutions per second and deviate horizontally as much as 40 cm over the pitcher-to-batter distance (44).

Soccer players also use the Magnus effect when it is advantageous for a kicked ball to follow a curved path, as may be the case when a player executing a free kick attempts to score. The "banana shot" consists of a kick executed so that the kicker places a lateral spin on the ball, curving it around the wall of defensive players in front of the goal (Figure 15-16).

The Magnus effect is maximal when the axis of spin is perpendicular to the direction of relative fluid velocity. Golf clubs are designed to impart some backspin to the struck ball, thereby creating an upwardly directed Magnus force that increases flight time and flight distance (Figure 15-17).

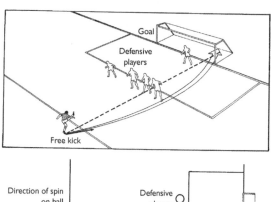

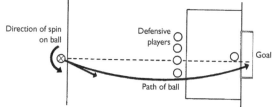

FIGURE 15-16

A banana shot in soccer results from imparting sidespin to the ball.

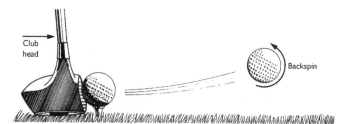

FIGURE 15-17

The loft on a golf club is designed to produce backspin on the ball. A properly hit ball rises because of the Magnus effect.

When a golf ball is hit laterally off-center, a spin about a vertical axis is also produced, causing a laterally deviated Magnus force that causes the ball to deviate from a straight path. When backspin and sidespin have been imparted to the ball, the resultant effect of the Magnus force on the path of the ball depends on the orientation of the ball's resultant axis of rotation to the airstream and on the velocity with which the ball was struck. When a golf ball is struck laterally off-center by a right-handed golfer, the ball unfortunately follows a curved path to one side—commonly known as a hook (to the left) or a slice (to the right).

PROPULSION IN A FLUID MEDIUM

Whereas a headwind slows a runner or cyclist by increasing the acting drag force, a tailwind can actually contribute to forward propulsion. Theoretical calculations indicate that a tailwind of 2 m/s improves running time during a 100 m sprint by approximately 0.18 s (48). A tailwind affects the relative velocity of a body with respect to the air, thereby modifying the resistive drag acting on the body. Thus, a tailwind of a velocity greater than the velocity of the moving body produces a drag force in the direction of motion (Figure 15-18). This force has been termed propulsive drag.

Analyzing the fluid forces acting on a swimmer is more complicated. Resistive drag acts on a swimmer, yet the propulsive forces exerted by the water in reaction to the swimmer's movements are responsible for the swimmer's forward motion through the water. The motions of the body segments during swimming produce a complex combination of drag and lift forces throughout each stroke cycle, and even among elite swimmers, a wide range of kinetic patterns during stroking have been observed. As a result, researchers have proposed several theories regarding the ways in which swimmers propel themselves through the water.

propulsive drag
force acting in the direction of a body's motion

propulsive drag theory
theory attributing propulsion in swimming to propulsive drag on the swimmer

Propulsive Drag Theory

The oldest theory of swimming propulsion is the propulsive drag theory, which was proposed by Counsilman and Silvia (9) and is based on Newton's third law of motion. According to this theory, as a swimmer's hands and arms move backward through the water, the forwardly directed reaction force generated by the water produces propulsion. The theory also suggests that the horizontal components of the downward and backward motion of the foot and the upward and backward motion of the opposite foot generate a forwardly directed reaction force from the water.

FIGURE 15-18

Drag force acting in the same direction as the body's motion may be thought of as propulsive drag because it contributes to the forward velocity of the body.

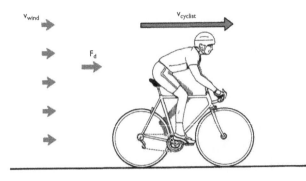

When high-speed movie films of skilled swimmers revealed that swimmers' hands and feet followed a zigzag rather than a straight-back path through the water, the theory was modified. It was suggested that this type of movement pattern enabled the body segments to push against still or slowly moving water instead of water already accelerated backward, thereby creating more propulsive drag. Research shows that holding the hands with the fingers comfortably spread with approximately 12 degrees between them, or a resting hand posture, is optimal for increasing drag against the palm during swimming (26, 29). However, propulsive drag may not be the major contributor to propulsion in swimming.

Propulsive Lift Theory

The propulsive lift theory was proposed by Counsilman in 1971 (4). According to this theory, swimmers use the foillike shape of the hand by employing rapid lateral movements through the water to generate lift. The lift is resisted by downward movement of the hand and by stabilization of the shoulder joint, which translates the forward-directed force to the body, propelling it past the hand. The theory was modified by Firby (13) in 1975, with the suggestion that swimmers use their hands and feet as propellers, constantly changing the pitches of the body segments to use the most effective angle of attack.

A number of investigators have since studied the forces generated by the body segments during swimming. It has been shown that lift does contribute to propulsion and that a combination of lift and drag forces acts throughout a stroke cycle. The relative contributions of lift and drag vary with the stroke performed, the phase within the stroke, and the individual swimmer. For example, lift is the primary force acting during the breaststroke, whereas lift and drag contribute differently to various phases of the front crawl stroke (38). Drag generated by the swimmer's hand is maximal when hand orientation is nearly perpendicular to the flow, and lift is maximal when the hand moves in the direction of either the thumb or the little finger (2).

propulsive lift theory
theory attributing propulsion in swimming at least partially to lift acting on the swimmer

Vortex Generation

Researchers have found a poor correlation between physiological and mechanical approaches to calculating propelling efficiency in swimming (3). This has led to the speculation that some unknown processes may play a role in swimming propulsion, with one possibility being the generation of vortices in the water by the swimmer. Vortex shedding has been found to play a role in the propulsion of both flying and swimming vertebrates and insects (12, 36). The generation of thrust in racing canoe and kayak paddling has also been described in terms of the mechanics of vortex–ring wakes (18). The observation that a swimmer performing the dolphin kick leaves behind a series of bound vortices, or columns of rotating water, has also been made (45). More research is needed to clarify the role of vortex generation in swimming propulsion.

Stroke Technique

Just as running speed is the product of stride length and stride rate, swimming speed is the product of stroke length (SL) and stroke rate (SR). Of the two, SL is more directly related to swimming speed among competitive freestyle swimmers (10, 40). Comparison of male and female swimmers performing at the same competitive distances reveals nearly identical SRs, but longer SLs resulting in higher velocities for the males (34). At slower speeds, skilled freestyle swimmers are able to maintain constant, high levels of SL, with a progressive reduction in SL as exercise intensity increases due to local muscle fatigue (19). The same phenomenon has been observed over the course of distance events, with a general decrease in SL and swimming speed after the first 100 m (22). Research suggests that recreational freestyle swimmers seeking to improve swimming performance should concentrate on applying more force to the water during each stroke to increase SL, as opposed to stroking faster. (50). Interestingly, the contribution of the flutter kick in the front crawl is more related to superior ankle flexibility than to vertical jump power or body size (27). Among backstrokers, although the ability to achieve a high swimming speed is related to SL at submaximal levels, increased speed is achieved through increased SR and decreased SL (20). Better performance in the breaststroke is achieved through highly effective work per stroke, optimal stroke rate, and a glide phase, with less skilled performers tending to use faster stroke rates and less gliding (15, 23, 39).

Another technique variable of importance during freestyle swimming is body roll. In one study, competitive swimmers were found to roll an average of approximately 60° to the nonbreathing side (24). Research shows that body roll in swimming is caused by the turning effect of the fluid forces acting on the swimmer's body. The contribution of body roll is important, since it enables the swimmer to employ the large, powerful muscles of the trunk rather than relying solely on the muscles of the shoulder and arm. It also facilitates the breathing action without any interruption of stroke mechanics (32). Body roll can influence the path of the hand through the water almost as much as the mediolateral motions of the hand relative to the trunk (24). In particular, an increase in body roll has been shown to increase the swimmer's hand speed in the plane perpendicular to the swimming direction, thereby increasing the potential for the hand to develop propulsive lift forces (33). With increasing swimming speed, general body roll decreases, although trunk twist increases, allowing swimmers to benefit from the rolling of the upper trunk, while limiting the increase in the drag of the lower extremity (51).

SUMMARY

The relative velocity of a body with respect to a fluid and the density, specific weight, and viscosity of the fluid affect the magnitudes of fluid forces. The fluid force that enables flotation is buoyancy. The buoyant force acts vertically upward; its point of application is the body's center of volume; and its magnitude is equal to the product of the volume of the displaced fluid and the specific gravity of the fluid. A body floats in a static position only when the magnitude of the buoyant force and body weight are equal and when the center of volume and the center of gravity are vertically aligned.

Drag is a fluid force that acts in the direction of the free-stream fluid flow. Skin friction is a component of drag that is derived from the sliding contacts between successive layers of fluid close to the surface of a moving body. Form drag, another component of the total drag, is caused by a pressure differential between the lead and trailing edges of a body moving with respect to a fluid. Wave drag is created by the formation of waves at the interface between two different fluids, such as water and air.

Lift is a force that can be generated perpendicular to the free-stream fluid flow by a foil-shaped object. Lift is created by a pressure differential in the fluid on opposite sides of a body that results from differences in the velocity of the fluid flow. The lift generated by spin is known as the Magnus force. Propulsion in swimming appears to result from a complex interplay of propulsive drag and lift.

INTRODUCTORY PROBLEMS

For all problems, assume that the specific weight of freshwater equals 9810 N/m^3 and the specific weight of seawater (saltwater) equals $10,070 \text{ N/m}^3$.

1. A boy is swimming with an absolute speed of 1.5 m/s in a river where the speed of the current is 0.5 m/s. What is the velocity of the swimmer with respect to the current when the boy swims directly upstream? Directly downstream? (Answer: 2 m/s in the upstream direction; 1 m/s in the downstream direction)

2. A cyclist is riding at a speed of 14 km/hr into a 16 km/hr headwind. What is the wind velocity relative to the cyclist? What is the cyclist's velocity with respect to the wind? (Answer: 30 km/hr in the direction of the wind; 30 km/hr in the direction of the cyclist)

3. A skier traveling at 5 m/s has a speed of 5.7 m/s relative to a headwind. What is the absolute wind speed? (Answer 0.7 m/s)

4. A 700 N man has a body volume of 0.08 m^3. If submerged in freshwater, will he float? Given his body volume, how much could he weigh and still float? (Answer: Yes; 784.8 N)

5. A racing shell has a volume of 0.38 m^3. When floating in freshwater, how many 700 N people can it support? (Answer: 5)

6. How much body volume must a 60 kg person have to float in freshwater? (Answer: 0.06 m^3)

7. Explain the implications for flotation due to the difference between the specific weight of freshwater and the specific weight of seawater.

8. What strategy can people use to improve their chances of floating in water? Explain your answer.

9. What types of individuals may have a difficult time floating in water? Explain your answer.

10. A beach ball weighing 1 N and with a volume of 0.03 m^3 is held submerged in seawater. How much force must be exerted vertically downward to hold the ball completely submerged? To hold the ball one-half submerged? (Answer: 301.1 N; 150.05 N)

ADDITIONAL PROBLEMS

1. A cyclist riding against a 12 km/hr headwind has a velocity of 28 km/hr with respect to the wind. What is the cyclist's absolute velocity? (Answer: 16 km/hr)

2. A swimmer crossing a river proceeds at an absolute speed of 2.5 m/s on a course oriented at a 45° angle to the 1 m/s current. Given that the absolute velocity of the swimmer is equal to the vector sum of the velocity of the current and the velocity of the swimmer with respect to the current, what is the magnitude and direction of the velocity of the swimmer with respect to the current? (Answer: 3.3 m/s at an angle of 32.6° to the current)

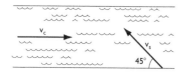

3. What maximum average density can a body possess if it is to float in freshwater? Seawater?

4. A scuba diver carries camera equipment in a cylindrical container that is 45 cm long, 20 cm in diameter, and 22 N in weight. For optimal maneuverability of the container under water, how much should its contents weigh? (Answer 120.36 N)

5. A 50 kg person with a body volume of 0.055 m^3 floats in a motionless position. How much body volume is above the surface in freshwater? In saltwater? (Answer: 0.005 m^3; 0.0063 m^3)

6. A 670 N swimmer oriented horizontally in freshwater has a body volume of 0.07 m^3 and a center of volume located 3 cm superior to the center of gravity.
   a. How much torque does the swimmer's weight generate?
   b. How much torque does the buoyant force acting on the swimmer generate?
   c. What can the swimmer do to counteract the torque and maintain a horizontal position?
   (Answer: 0; 20.6 N-m)

7. Based on your knowledge of the action of fluid forces, speculate as to why a properly thrown boomerang returns to the thrower.

8. Explain the aerodynamic benefits of drafting on a bicycle or in an automobile.

9. What is the practical effect of streamlining? How does streamlining alter the fluid forces acting on a moving body?

10. Explain why a curveball curves. Include a discussion of the aerodynamic role of the seams on the ball.

NAME _____

DATE _____

LABORATORY EXPERIENCES

1. At the *Basic Biomechanics* Online Learning Center (www.mhhe.com/hall6e), go to Student Center, Chapter 15, Lab Manual, Lab 1, then view Fluids Animation 1. Identify the principle illustrated, and write an explanation of what is demonstrated.

Principle: _____

Explanation: _____

_____

_____

_____

_____

2. Slice a hollow ball such as a table tennis ball or a racquet ball in half and float one-half of the ball (concave side up) in a container of water. Gradually add lead shot to the half ball until it floats with the cut edge at the surface of the water. Remove the half ball from the water, then measure its diameter and calculate its volume. Weigh the ball along with the lead shot that was placed in the ball. Using your measurements, calculate the specific weight of the water in the container. Repeat the experiment using water at different temperatures or using different liquids.

Ball diameter: _____ ball volume: _____ weight of shot: _____

Specific weight of water: _____ specific weight of second fluid: _____

Calculations:

3. Position a container of water on a scale and record its weight. Insert your hand, fingers first, into the water until the water line is at the wrist joint. Record the weight registered on the scale. Subtract the original weight of the container from the new weight, divide the difference in half, and add the result to the original weight of the container to arrive at the target weight. Slowly elevate your hand from the water until the target weight is reached. Mark the water line on your hand. What does this line represent? _____

4. Using a stopwatch, time yourself while riding an escalator. Either measure or estimate the length of the escalator and calculate the escalator's speed. Again using a stopwatch, time yourself while carefully running up the escalator and calculate your speed. Calculate your speed relative to the speed of the escalator.

Time riding escalator: _____ time running up escalator: _____

Your speed relative to the elevator's speed: _____

Calculation:

500   BASIC BIOMECHANICS

5. Use a variable-speed fan and a spring scale to construct a mock wind tunnel. Position the fan so that it blows vertically upward, and suspend the spring scale from a rigid arm above the fan. This apparatus can be used to test the relative drag on different objects suspended from the scale. Notice that relative drag among different objects may change with fan speed.

Object	Drag

REFERENCES

1. Bartlett R, Müller E, Lindinger S, Brunner F, and Morriss C: Three-dimensional evaluation of the kinematic release parameters for javelin throwers of different skill levels, *J Appl Biomech* 12:58, 1996.

2. Berger MA, deGroot G, and Hollander AP: Hydrodynamic drag and lift forces on human hand/arm models, *J Biomech* 28:125, 1995.

3. Berger MA, Hollander AP, and deGroot G: Technique and energy losses in front crawl swimming, *Med Sci Sports Exerc* 29:1491, 1997.

4. Brown RM and Counsilman JE: The role of lift in propelling swimmers. In Cooper JM, ed: *Biomechanics,* Chicago, 1971, Athletic Institute.

5. Capelli C et al.: Energy cost and efficiency of riding aerodynamic bicycles, *Eur J Appl Physiol* 67:144, 1993.

6. Cappaert JM, Pease DL, and Troup JP: Three-dimensional analysis of the men's 100-m freestyle during the 1992 Olympic games, *J Appl Biomech* 11:103, 1995.

7. Chatard J-C and Wilson B: Drafting distance in swimming, *Med Sci Sports Exerc* 35:1176, 2003.

8. Chollet D, Hue O, Auclair F, Millet G, and Chatard JC: The effects of drafting on stroking variations during swimming in elite male triathletes, *Eur J Appl Physiol* 82:413, 2000.

9. Counsilman JE: *Science of swimming,* Englewood Cliffs, NJ, 1968, Prentice Hall.

10. Craig AB, Jr. et al.: Velocity, stroke rate and distance per stroke during elite swimming competition, *Med Sci Sports Exerc* 17:625, 1985.

11. De Lucas RD, Balikian P, Neiva CM, Greco CC, and Denadai BS: The effects of wet suits on physiological and biomechanical indices during swimming, *J Sci Med Sport* 3:1, 2000.

12. Ellington CP: Unsteady aerodynamics of insect flight, *Symp Soc Exp Biol* 49:109, 1995.

13. Firby H: *Howard Firby on swimming,* London, 1975, Pelham Books.

14. Ganslen RV: *Aerodynamic factors which influence discus flight.* Research report, University of Arkansas.

15. Garland Fritzdorf S, Hibbs A, and Kleshnev V: Analysis of speed, stroke rate, and stroke distance for world-class breaststroke swimming, *J Sports Sci* 27(4):373, 2009.

16. Gnehm P, Reichenback S, Altpeter E, Widmer H, and Hoppeler H: Influence of different racing positions on metabolic cost in elite cyclists, *Med Sci Sports Exerc* 29:818, 1997.

17. Hay JG and Yu B: Critical characteristics of technique in throwing the discus, *J Sports Sci* 13:125, 1995.

18. Jackson PS: Performance prediction for Olympic kayaks, *J Sports Sci* 13:239, 1995.

19. Keskinen KL and Komi PV: Stroking characteristics of front crawl swimming during exercise, *J Appl Biomech* 9:219, 1993.

20. Klentrou PP and Montpetit RR: Energetics of backstroke swimming in males and females, *Med Sci Sports Exerc* 24:371, 1992.

21. Kyle CR and Burke E: Improving the racing bicycle, *Mechanical Engineering* 106:34, 1984.

22. Laffite LP, Vilas-Boas JP, Demarle A, Silva J, Fernandes R, and Billat VL: Changes in physiological and stroke parameters during a maximal 400-m free swimming test in elite swimmers, *Can J Appl Physiol* 29 Suppl:S17, 2004.

23. Leblanc H, Seifert L, and Chollet D: Arm-leg coordination in recreational and competitive breaststroke swimmers, *J Sci Med Sport* 12:352, 2009.

24. Liu Q, Hay JG, and Andrews JG: Body roll and handpath in freestyle swimming: an experimental study, *J Appl Biomech* 9:238, 1993.

25. Maglischo E: *Swimming faster: a comprehensive guide to the science of swimming,* Palo Alto, CA, 1982, Mayfield Publishing.

26. Marinho DA, Barbosa TM, Reis VM, Kjendlie PL, Alves FB, Vilas-Boas JP, Machado L, Silva AJ, and Rouboa AI: Swimming propulsion forces are enhanced by a small finger spread, *J Appl Biomech* 26:87, 2010.

502 BASIC BIOMECHANICS

27. McCullough AS, Kraemer WJ, Volek JS, Solomon-Hill GF Jr, Hatfield DL, Vingren JL, Ho JY, Fragala MS, Thomas GA, Häkkinen K, and Maresh CM: Factors affecting flutter kicking speed in women who are competitive and recreational swimmers, *J Strength Cond Res* 23:2130, 2009.

28. McLean SP and Hinrichs RN: Buoyancy, gender, and swimming performance, *J Appl Biomech* 16:248, 2000.

29. Minetti AE, Machtsiras G, and Masters JC: The optimum finger spacing in human swimming, *J Biomech* 42:2188, 2009.

30. Mollendorf JC, Termin AC, Oppenheim E, and Pendergast DR: Effect of swim suit design on passive drag, *Med Sci Sports Exerc* 36:1029, 2004.

31. Müller W: Determinants of ski-jump performance and implications for health, safety and fairness, *Sports Med* 39:85, 2009.

32. Payton CJ, Bartlett RM, Baltzopoulos V, and Coombs R: Upper extremity kinematics and body roll during preferred-side breathing and breath-holding front crawl swimming, *J Sports Sci* 17:689, 1999.

33. Payton CJ, Hay JG, and Mullineaux DR: The effect of body roll on hand speed and hand path in front crawl swimming—a simulation study, *J Appl Biomech* 13:300, 1997.

34. Pelayo P, Sidney M, Kherif T, Chollet D, and Tourny C: Stroking characteristics in freestyle swimming and relationships with anthropometric characteristics, *J Appl Biomech* 12:197, 1996.

35. Pendergast D, Mollendorf J, Zamparo P, Termin A 2nd, Bushnell D, and Paschke D: The influence of drag on human locomotion in water, *Undersea Hyperb Med* 32:45, 2005.

36. Rayner JM: Dynamics of the vortex wakes of flying and swimming vertebrates, *Symp Soc Exp Biol* 49:131, 1995.

37. Richardson RS and Johnson SC: The effect of aerodynamic handlebars on oxygen consumption while cycling at a constant speed, *Ergonomics* 37:859, 1994.

38. Schleihauf RE: A hydrodynamic analysis of swimming propulsion. In Terauds J and Bedingfield E, eds: *Swimming III,* Baltimore, 1979, University Park Press.

39. Seifert L, Leblanc H, Chollet D, and Delignières D: Inter-limb coordination in swimming: effect of speed and skill level, *Hum Mov Sci* 29:103, 2010.

40. Seifert L, Toussaint HM, Alberty M, Schnitzler C, and Chollet D: Arm coordination, power, and swim efficiency in national and regional front crawl swimmers, *Hum Mov Sci* 29:426, 2010.

41. Taïar R, Sagnes P, Henry C, Dufour AB, and Rouard AH: Hydrodynamics optimization in butterfly swimming: position, drag coefficient and performance, *J Biomech* 32:803, 1999.

42. Takamoto M, Ohmichi H, and Miyashita M: Wave height in relation to swimming velocity and proficiency in front crawl stroke. In Winter D et al, eds: *Biomechanics IX-B,* Champaign, IL, 1985, Human Kinetics Publishers.

43. Tomikawa M and Nomura T: Relationships between swim performance, maximal oxygen uptake and peak power output when wearing a wetsuit, *J Sci Med Sport* 12:317, 2009.

44. Townend MS: *Mathematics in sport,* New York, 1984, John Wiley & Sons.

45. Ungerechts BE: On the relevance of rotating water flow for the propulsion in swimming. In Jonsson B, ed: *Biomechanics X-B,* Champaign, IL, 1987, Human Kinetics Publishers.

46. van Ingen Schenau GJ: The influence of air friction in speed skating, *J Biomech* 15:449, 1982.

47. Virmavirta M, Kivekas J, and Komi PV: Take-off aerodynamics in ski jumping, *J Biomech* 34:465, 2001.

48. Ward-Smith AJ: A mathematical analysis of the influence of adverse and favourable winds on sprinting, *J Biomech* 18:351, 1985.

49. Yanai T: Rotational effect of buoyancy in frontcrawl: does it really cause the legs to sink? *J Biomech* 34:235, 2001.

50. Yanai T: Stroke frequency in front crawl: Its mechanical link to the fluid forces required in non-propulsive directions, *J Biomech* 36:53, 2003.

51. Yanai T: Buoyancy is the primary source of generating bodyroll in front-crawl swimming, *J Biomech* 37: 605, 2004.

ANNOTATED READINGS

Barbosa TM, Bragada JA, Reis VM, Marinho DA, Carvalho C, and Silva AJ: Energetics and biomechanics as determining factors of swimming performance: updating the state of the art, J Sci Med Sport 13:262, 2010.
Reviews the scientific literature on the interplay between performance, energetic, and biomechanics in competitive swimming.

Haake SJ: The impact of technology on sporting performance in Olympic sports, 27:1421, 2009.
Discusses the dramatic effects of technological advances in apparel and equipment on sport, comparing the performance statistics for the 100-m sprint, pole vault, javelin, and cycling.

Psycharakis SG and Sanders RH: Body roll in swimming: a review, J Sports Sci 28:229, 2010.
Reviews the scientific literature on effective utilization of body roll in swimming.

Toussaint HM, de Hollander AP, van den Berg C, and Vorontsov AR: Biomechanics of swimming. In Garrett WE and Kirkendall DT: *Exercise and sport science,* Philadelphia, 2000, Lippincott Williams & Wilkins.
Comprehensive review of literature on the effects of drag in swimming and on swimming propulsion techniques and theories.

RELATED WEBSITES

Circulation and the Magnus Effect
http://www.phys.virginia.edu/classes/311/notes/aero/node2.html
Shows a diagram and includes discussion of the Magnus force with practical examples.

NASA: Lift from Pressure
http://www.grc.nasa.gov/WWW/K-12/airplane/right1.html
Provides narrative, definitions of related terms, and slides illustrating lift concepts.

NASA: Lift to Drag Ratio
http://www.grc.nasa.gov/WWW/K-12/airplane/ldrat.html
Provides narrative, definitions of related terms, and slides illustrating lift / drag ratio concepts.

NASA: Relative Velocities
http://www.grc.nasa.gov/WWW/K-12/airplane/move2.html
Provides narrative, definitions of related terms, and slides illustrating relative velocity concepts.

NASA: What Is Drag?
http://www.grc.nasa.gov/WWW/K-12/airplane/drag1.html
Provides narrative, definitions of related terms, and slides illustrating drag concepts.

Tennis: The Magnus Effect
http://wings.avkids.com/Tennis/Book/magnus-01.html
Description and animated drawing of the Magnus effect on a spinning tennis ball.

The Drag Force on a Sphere http://www.ma.iup.edu/MathDept/Projects/CalcDEMma/drag/drag0.html
Provides links to pages on the graph of the drag coefficient versus Reynolds number and two models for drag force.

The Open Door Website: Relativity
http://www.saburchill.com/physics/chapters/0083.html
Provides description of a quantitative relative velocity problem with entertaining graphics.

The Physics Classroom: Relative Velocity
http://www.physicsclassroom.com/Class/vectors/U3L1f.html
Includes explanation, graphics, and animations demonstrating relative velocity.

Relative Velocity Applet http://www.math.gatech.edu/~carlen/2507/notes/classFiles/partOne/RelVel.html
Interactive application that enables control of two moving points and provides the ability to graph the absolute and relative motions of the points.

U.S. Centennial of Flight Commission
http://www.centennialofflight.gov/essay/Dictionary/four_forces/DI24.htm
Provides illustrated discussion about the forces acting on an airplane.

504   BASIC BIOMECHANICS

KEY TERMS

angle of attack	angle between the longitudinal axis of a body and the direction of the fluid flow
Archimedes' principle	physical law stating that the buoyant force acting on a body is equal to the weight of the fluid displaced by the body
Bernoulli principle	an expression of the inverse relationship between relative velocity and relative pressure in a fluid flow
boundary layer	layer of fluid immediately adjacent to a body
center of volume	point around which a body's volume is equally balanced and at which the buoyant force acts
coefficient of drag	unitless number that is an index of a body's ability to generate fluid resistance
coefficient of lift	unitless number that is an index of a body's ability to generate lift
fluid	substance that flows when subjected to a shear stress
foil	shape capable of generating lift in the presence of a fluid flow
form drag pressure drag profile drag	resistance created by a pressure differential between the lead and rear sides of a body moving through a fluid
laminar flow	flow characterized by smooth, parallel layers of fluid
lift	force acting on a body in a fluid in a direction perpendicular to the fluid flow
lift/drag ratio	the magnitude of the lift force divided by the magnitude of the total drag force acting on a body at a given time
Magnus effect	deviation in the trajectory of a spinning object toward the direction of spin, resulting from the Magnus force
Magnus force	lift force created by spin
propulsive drag	force acting in the direction of a body's motion
propulsive drag theory	theory attributing propulsion in swimming to propulsive drag on the swimmer
propulsive lift theory	theory attributing propulsion in swimming at least partially to lift acting on the swimmer
relative velocity	velocity of a body with respect to the velocity of something else, such as the surrounding fluid
skin friction surface drag viscous drag	resistance derived from friction between adjacent layers of fluid near a body moving through the fluid
theoretical square law	drag increases approximately with the square of velocity when relative velocity is low
turbulent flow	flow characterized by mixing of adjacent fluid layers
wave drag	resistance created by the generation of waves at the interface between two different fluids, such as air and water

Basic Mathematics and Related Skills

NEGATIVE NUMBERS

Negative numbers are preceded by a minus sign. Although the physical quantities used in biomechanics do not have values that are less than zero in magnitude, the minus sign is often used to indicate the direction opposite the direction regarded as positive. Therefore, it is important to recall the following rules regarding arithmetic operations involving negative numbers:

1. Addition of a negative number yields the same results as subtraction of a positive number of the same magnitude:

$$6 + (-4) = 2$$
$$10 + (-3) = 7$$
$$6 + (-8) = -2$$
$$10 + (-23) = -13$$
$$(-6) + (-3) = -9$$
$$(-10) + (-7) = -17$$

2. Subtraction of a negative number yields the same result as addition of a positive number of the same magnitude:

$$5 - (-7) = 12$$
$$8 - (-6) = 14$$
$$-5 - (-3) = -2$$
$$-8 - (-4) = -4$$
$$-5 - (-12) = 7$$
$$-8 - (-10) = 2$$

3. Multiplication or division of a number by a number of the opposite sign yields a negative result:

$$2 \times (-3) = -6$$
$$(-4) \times 5 = -20$$
$$9 \div (-3) = -3$$
$$(-10) \div 2 = -5$$

4. Multiplication or division of a number by a number of the same sign (positive or negative) yields a positive result:

$$3 \times 4 = 12$$
$$(-3) \times (-2) = 6$$
$$10 \div 5 = 2$$
$$(-15) \div (-3) = 5$$

EXPONENTS

Exponents are superscript numbers that immediately follow a base number, indicating how many times that number is to be self-multiplied to yield the result:

$$
\begin{aligned}
5^2 &= 5 \times 5 \\
&= 25 \\
3^2 &= 3 \times 3 \\
&= 9 \\
5^3 &= 5 \times 5 \times 5 \\
&= 125 \\
3^3 &= 3 \times 3 \times 3 \\
&= 27
\end{aligned}
$$

SQUARE ROOTS

Taking the square root of a number is the inverse operation of squaring a number (multiplying a number by itself). The square root of a number is the number that yields the original number when multiplied by itself. The square root of 25 is 5, and the square root of 9 is 3. Using mathematics notation, these relationships are expressed as the following:

$$
\begin{aligned}
\sqrt{25} &= 5 \\
\sqrt{9} &= 3
\end{aligned}
$$

Because -5 multiplied by itself also equals 25, -5 is also a square root of 25. The following notation is sometimes used to indicate that square roots may be either positive or negative:

$$
\begin{aligned}
\sqrt{25} &= +5 \\
\sqrt{9} &= +3
\end{aligned}
$$

ORDER OF OPERATIONS

When a computation involves more than a single operation, a set of rules must be used to arrive at the correct result. These rules may be summarized as follows:

1. Addition and subtraction are of equal precedence; these operations are carried out from left to right as they occur in an equation:

$$
\begin{aligned}
7 - 3 + 5 &= 4 + 5 \\
&= 9 \\
5 + 2 - 1 + 10 &= 7 - 1 + 10 \\
&= 6 + 10 \\
&= 16
\end{aligned}
$$

2. Multiplication and division are of equal precedence; these operations are carried out from left to right as they occur in an equation:

$$
\begin{aligned}
10 \div 5 \times 4 &= 2 \times 4 \\
&= 8 \\
20 \div 4 \times 3 \div 5 &= 5 \times 3 \div 5 \\
&= 15 \div 5 \\
&= 3
\end{aligned}
$$

3. Multiplication and division take precedence over addition and subtraction. In computations involving some combination of operations not of the same level of precedence, multiplication and division are carried out before addition and subtraction are carried out:

$$3 + 18 \div 6 = 3 + 3$$
$$= 6$$
$$9 - 2 \times 3 + 7 = 9 - 6 + 7$$
$$= 3 + 7$$
$$= 10$$
$$8 \div 4 + 5 - 2 \times 2 = 2 + 5 - 2 \times 2$$
$$= 2 + 5 - 4$$
$$= 7 - 4$$
$$= 3$$

4. When parentheses ( ), brackets [ ], or braces { } are used, the operations enclosed are performed first, before the other rules of precedence are applied:

$$2 \times 7 + (10 - 5) = 2 \times 7 + 5$$
$$= 14 + 5$$
$$= 19$$
$$20 \div (2 + 2) - 3 \times 4 = 20 \div 4 - 3 \times 4$$
$$= 5 - 3 \times 4$$
$$= 5 - 12$$
$$= -7$$

USE OF A CALCULATOR

Simple computations in biomechanics problems are often performed quickly and easily with a handheld calculator. However, the correct result can be obtained on a calculator only when the computation is set up properly and the rules for ordering of operations are followed. Most calculators come with an instruction manual that contains sample calculations. It is worthwhile to completely familiarize yourself with your calculator's capabilities, particularly use of the memory, before using it to solve problems.

PERCENTAGES

A percentage is a part of 100. Thus, 37% represents 37 parts of 100. To find 37% of 80, multiply the number 80 by 0.37:

$$80 \times 0.37 = 29.6$$

The number 29.6 is 37% of 80. If you want to determine the percentage of the number 55 that equals 42, multiply the fraction by 100%:

$$\frac{42}{55} \times 100\% = 76.4\%$$

The number 42 is 76.4% of 55.

SIMPLE ALGEBRA

The solution of many problems involves setting up an equation containing one or more unknown quantities represented as variables such as x. An equation is a statement of equality implying that the quantities expressed on the left side of the equals sign are equal to the quantities expressed on the right side of the equals sign. Solving a problem typically requires calculation of the unknown quantity or quantities contained in the equation.

The general procedure for calculating the value of a variable in an equation is to isolate the variable on one side of the equals sign and then to carry out the operations among the numbers expressed on the other side of the equals sign. The process of isolating a variable usually involves performing a series of operations on both sides of the equals sign. As long as the same operation is carried out on both sides of the equals sign, equality is preserved and the equation remains valid:

$$x + 7 = 10$$

Subtract 7 from both sides of the equation:

$$x + 7 - 7 = 10 - 7$$
$$x + 0 = 10 - 7$$
$$x = 3$$
$$y - 3 = 12$$

Add 3 to both sides of the equation:

$$y - 3 + 3 = 12 + 3$$
$$y - 0 = 12 + 3$$
$$y = 15$$
$$z \times 3 = 18$$

Divide both sides of the equation by 3:

$$z \times 3 \div 3 = \frac{18}{3}$$
$$z \times 1 = \frac{18}{3}$$
$$z = 6$$
$$q \div 4 = 2$$

Multiply both sides of the equation by 4:

$$q \div 4 \times 4 = 2 \times 4$$
$$q = 2 \times 4$$
$$q = 8$$
$$x \div 3 + 5 = 8$$

Subtract 5 from both sides of the equation:

$$x \div 3 + 5 - 5 = 8 - 5$$
$$x \div 3 = 3$$

Multiply both sides of the equation by 3:

$$x \div 3 \times 3 = 3 \times 3$$
$$x = 9$$
$$y \div 4 - 7 = -2$$

Add 7 to both sides of the equation:

$$y \div 4 - 7 + 7 = -2 + 7$$
$$y \div 4 = 5$$

Multiply both sides of the equation by 4:

$$y \div 4 \times 4 = 5 \times 4$$
$$y = 20$$
$$z^2 = 36$$

Take the square root of both sides of the equation:

$$z = 6$$

MEASURING ANGLES

The following procedure is used for measuring an angle with a protractor:

1. Place the center of the protractor on the vertex of the angle.
2. Align the zero line on the protractor with one of the sides of the angle.
3. The size of the angle is indicated on the protractor scale where the other side of the angle intersects the scale. (Be sure to read from the correct scale on the protractor. Is the angle greater or less than 90°?)

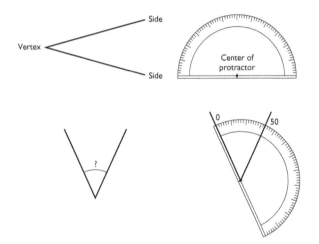

If you are unfamiliar with the use of a protractor, check yourself by verifying the sizes of the following three angles:

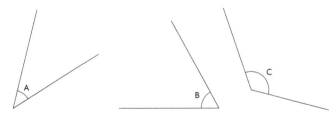

(Answer: A = 45°, B = 60°, C = 123°)

B

Trigonometric Functions

Trigonometric functions are based on relationships present between the sides and angles of triangles. Many functions are derived from a right triangle—a triangle containing a right (90°) angle. Consider the right triangle below with sides A, B, and C, and angles α, β, and γ.

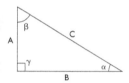

Side C, which is the longest side and the side opposite the right angle, is known as the *hypotenuse of the triangle*.

A commonly used trigonometric relationship for right triangles is the *Pythagorean theorem*. The Pythagorean theorem is an expression of the relationship between the hypotenuse and the other two sides of a right triangle:

> The sum of the squares of the lengths of the two sides of a right triangle is equal to the square of the length of the hypotenuse.

Using the sides of the labeled triangle yields the following:

$$A^2 + B^2 = C^2$$

Suppose that sides A and B are 3 and 4 units long, respectively. The Pythagorean theorem can be used to solve for the length of side C:

$$\begin{aligned} C^2 &= A^2 + B^2 \\ &= 3^2 + 4^2 \\ &= 9 + 16 \\ &= 25 \\ C &= 5 \end{aligned}$$

Three trigonometric relationships are based on the ratios of the lengths of the sides of a right triangle. The sine (abbreviated *sin*) of an angle is defined as the ratio of the length of the side of the triangle opposite the angle to the length of the hypotenuse. Using the labeled triangle yields the following:

$$\sin \alpha = \frac{\text{opposite}}{\text{hypotenuse}} = \frac{A}{C}$$

$$\sin \beta = \frac{\text{opposite}}{\text{hypotenuse}} = \frac{B}{C}$$

With $A = 3$, $B = 4$, and $C = 5$:

$$\sin \alpha = \frac{A}{C} = \frac{3}{5} = 0.6$$

$$\text{sig } \beta = \frac{B}{C} = \frac{4}{5} = 0.8$$

The cosine (abbreviated *cos*) of an angle is defined as the ratio of the length of the side of the triangle adjacent to the angle to the length of the hypotenuse. Using the labeled triangle yields the following:

$$\cos \alpha = \frac{\text{adjacent}}{\text{hypotenuse}} = \frac{B}{C}$$

$$\cos \beta = \frac{\text{adjacent}}{\text{hypotenuse}} = \frac{A}{C}$$

With $A = 3$, $B = 4$, and $C = 5$:

$$\cos \alpha = \frac{B}{C} = \frac{4}{5} = 0.8$$

$$\cos \beta = \frac{A}{C} = \frac{3}{5} = 0.6$$

The third function, the tangent (abbreviated *tan*) of an angle, is defined as the ratio of the length of the side of the triangle opposite the angle to that of the side adjacent to the angle. Using the labeled triangle yields the following:

$$\tan \alpha = \frac{\text{opposite}}{\text{adjacent}} = \frac{A}{B}$$

$$\tan \beta = \frac{\text{opposite}}{\text{adjacent}} = \frac{B}{A}$$

With $A = 3$, $B = 4$, and $C = 5$:

$$\tan \alpha = \frac{A}{B} = \frac{3}{4} = 0.75$$

$$\tan \beta = \frac{B}{A} = \frac{4}{3} = 1.33$$

Two useful trigonometric relationships are applicable to *all* triangles. The first is known as the law of sines:

The ratio between the length of any side of a triangle and the angle opposite that side is equal to the ratio between the length of any other side of the triangle and the angle opposite that side.

With respect to the labeled triangle, this may be stated as the following:

$$\frac{A}{\sin \alpha} = \frac{B}{\sin \beta} = \frac{C}{\sin \gamma}$$

A second trigonometric relationship applicable to *all* triangles is the law of cosines:

> The square of the length of any side of a triangle is equal to the sum of the squares of the lengths of the other two sides of the triangle minus two times the product of the lengths of the other two sides and the cosine of the angle opposite the original side.

This relationship yields the following for each of the sides of the labeled triangle:

$$A^2 = B^2 + C^2 - 2BC \cos \alpha$$
$$B^2 = A^2 + C^2 - 2AC \cos \beta$$
$$C^2 = A^2 + B^2 - 2AB \cos \gamma$$

A table of the values of the basic trigonometric functions follows.

Table of Basic Trigonometric Function Values

DEG	SIN	COS	TAN	DEG	SIN	COS	TAN
00	.0000	1.0000	.0000	—	—	—	—
01	.0175	.9998	.0175	46	.7193	.6947	1.0355
02	.0349	.9994	.0349	47	.7314	.6820	1.0723
03	.0523	.9986	.0524	48	.7431	.6691	1.1106
04	.0698	.9976	.0699	49	.7547	.6561	1.1504
05	.0872	.9962	.0875	50	.7660	.6428	1.1918
06	.1045	.9945	.1051	51	.7771	.6293	1.2349
07	.1219	.9925	.1228	52	.7880	.6157	1.2799
08	.1392	.9903	.1405	53	.7986	.6018	1.3270
09	.1564	.9877	.1584	54	.8090	.5878	1.3764
10	.1736	.9848	.1763	55	.8192	.5736	1.4281
11	.1908	.9816	.1944	56	.8290	.5592	1.4826
12	.2079	.9781	.2126	57	.8387	.5446	1.5399
13	.2250	.9744	.2309	58	.8480	.5299	1.6003
14	.2419	.9703	.2493	59	.8572	.5150	1.6643
15	.2588	.9659	.2679	60	.8660	.5000	1.7321
16	.2756	.9613	.2867	61	.8746	.4848	1.8040
17	.2924	.9563	.3057	62	.8829	.4695	1.8807
18	.3090	.9511	.3249	63	.8910	.4540	1.9626
19	.3256	.9455	.3443	64	.8988	.4384	2.0503
20	.3420	.9397	.3640	65	.9063	.4226	2.1445
21	.3584	.9336	.3839	66	.9135	.4067	2.2460
22	.3746	.9272	.4040	67	.9205	.3907	2.3559
23	.3907	.9205	.4245	68	.9279	.3746	2.4751
24	.4067	.9135	.4452	69	.9336	.3584	2.6051
25	.4226	.9063	.4663	70	.9397	.3420	2.7475
26	.4384	.8988	.4877	71	.9456	.3256	2.9042
27	.4540	.8910	.5095	72	.9511	.3090	3.0779
28	.4695	.8829	.5317	73	.9563	.2924	3.2709
29	.4848	.8746	.5543	74	.9613	.2756	3.4874
30	.5000	.8660	.5774	75	.96593	.2588	3.7321
31	.5150	.8572	.6009	76	.9703	.2419	4.0108
32	.5299	.8480	.6249	77	.9744	.2250	4.3315
33	.5446	.8387	.6494	78	.9781	.2079	4.7046
34	.5592	.8290	.6745	79	.9816	.1908	5.1446
35	.5736	.8192	.7002	80	.9848	.1736	5.6713
36	.5878	.8090	.7265	81	.9877	.1564	6.3138
37	.6018	.7986	.7536	82	.9903	.1391	7.1154
38	.6157	.7880	.7813	83	.9925	.1219	8.1443
39	.6293	.7771	.8098	84	.9945	.1045	9.5144
40	.6428	.7660	.8391	85	.99625	.0872	11.4301
41	.6561	.7547	.8693	86	.9976	.0698	14.3007
42	.6691	.7431	.9004	87	.99866	.05239	19.0811
43	.6820	.7314	.9325	88	.9994	.0349	28.6363
44	.6947	.7193	.9657	89	.9998	.0175	57.2900
45	.7071	.7071	1.0000	90	1.0000	.0000	Infinity

Common Units
of Measurement

This appendix contains factors for converting between metric units commonly used in biomechanics and their English system equivalents. In each case, a value expressed in a metric unit can be divided by the conversion factor given to yield the approximate equivalent in an English unit, or a value expressed in an English unit can be multiplied by the conversion factor to find the metric unit equivalent. For example, to convert 100 Newtons to pounds, do the following:

$$\frac{100 \text{ N}}{4.45 \text{ N/lb}} = 22.5 \text{ lb}$$

To convert 100 pounds to Newtons, do the following:

$$(100 \text{ lb}) (4.45 \text{ N/lb}) = 445 \text{ N}$$

VARIABLE	METRIC UNIT	← MULTIPLY BY DIVIDE BY →	ENGLISH UNIT
Distance	Centimeters	2.54	Inches
	Meters	0.3048	Feet
	Kilometers	1.609	Miles
Speed	Meters/second	0.447	Miles/hour
Mass	Kilograms	14.59	Slugs
Force	Newtons	4.448	Pounds
Work	Joules	1.355	Foot-pounds
Power	Watts	745.63	Horsepower
Energy	Joules	1.355	Foot-pounds
Linear momentum	Kilogram-meters/second	4.448	Slug-feet/second
Impulse	Newton-seconds	4.448	Pound-seconds
Angular momentum	Kilogram-meters^2/second	1.355	Slug-feet^2/second
Moment of inertia	Kilogram-meters^2	1.355	Slug-feet^2
Torque	Newton-meters	1.355	Foot-pounds

APPENDIX

D

Anthropometric Parameters for the Human Body*

Segment Lengths

SEGMENT	MALES	FEMALES
Head and neck	10.75	10.75
Trunk	30.00	29.00
Upper arm	17.20	17.30
Forearm	15.70	16.00
Hand	5.75	5.75
Thigh	23.20	24.90
Lower leg	24.70	25.70
Foot	4.25	4.25
Segment lengths expressed in percentages of total body height.		

Segment Weights

SEGMENT	MALES	FEMALES
Head	8.26	8.20
Trunk	46.84	45.00
Upper arm	3.25	2.90
Forearm	1.87	1.57
Hand	0.65	0.50
Thigh	10.50	11.75
Lower leg	4.75	5.35
Foot	1.43	1.33
Segment weights expressed in percentages of total body weight		

From Plagenhoef S, Evans FG, and Abdelnour T: Anatomical data for analyzing human motion, Res Q Exerc Sport 54:169, 1983.

*The values reported in these tables represent mean values for limited numbers of individuals as reported in the scientific literature.

SEGMENT	MALES	FEMALES
Head and neck	55.0	55.0
Trunk	63.0	56.9
Upper arm	43.6	45.8
Forearm	43.0	43.4
Hand	46.8	46.8
Thigh	43.3	42.8
Lower leg	43.4	41.9
Foot	50.0	50.0

Segmental center of gravity locations expressed in percentages of segment lengths; measured from the proximal ends of segments.

Segmental Center of Gravity Locations

SEGMENT	MALES		FEMALES	
	PROXIMAL	DISTAL	PROXIMAL	DISTAL
Upper arm	54.2	64.5	56.4	62.3
Forearm	52.6	54.7	53.0	64.3
Hand	54.9	54.9	54.9	54.9
Thigh	54.0	65.3	53.5	65.8
Lower leg	52.9	64.2	51.4	65.7
Foot	69.0	69.0	69.0	69.0

Segmental radii of gyration expressed in percentages of segment lengths

Segmental Radii of Gyration Measured from Proximal and Distal Segment Ends

C H A P T E R 9

SPORT AND EXERCISE PSYCHOLOGY

O B J E C T I V E S

After reading this chapter the student should be able to—

- Describe the psychological benefits of participation in sport and physical activities.
- Understand the different theories of behavior and their potential application to exercise adherence.
- Discuss the roles of anxiety and arousal in the performance of motor skills and the application of intervention strategies to enhance performance.
- Understand motivation, goal setting, self-talk, and imagery and how they can be effectively used in physical education, exercise, and sport.

Sport and exercise psychology has its legacy in psychology. In the 1970s, as the academic scope of physical education grew, sport psychology emerged as a subdiscipline. Initially, sport psychologists focused on competitive sport and the elite athlete. As the subdiscipline grew, sport psychologists became interested in studying participation in exercise and other facets of physical activity. Additionally, their focus broadened from working with elite competitors to include people of all ages and abilities. The name of the subdiscipline today, sport and exercise psychology, reflects this expanded focus.

This chapter provides a short introduction to sport and exercise psychology. It includes a brief overview of the development of the subdiscipline. Selected topics within sport and exercise psychology are briefly discussed; space limitations preclude the inclusion of more topics and limit the depth of discussion. Given that caveat, this chapter presents information on motivation, the psychological benefits of physical activity, exercise adherence, personality, anxiety and arousal, imagery, goal setting, self-talk, and various intervention strategies. It is hoped that this brief glimpse will stimulate your interest in this area and encourage further study.

SPORT AND EXERCISE PSYCHOLOGY

Sport and exercise psychology is a rapidly growing subdiscipline of physical education, exercise science, and sport. Initially, this subdiscipline was closely aligned with motor learning; however, during the last two decades it has evolved as a distinct field of study. The definition and scope, historical development, and areas of study within sport and exercise psychology are described briefly in this section.

Definition and Scope

Sport and exercise psychology is defined by Vealey as "the systematic scholarly study of the behavior, feelings, and thoughts of people engaged in sport, exercise, and physical activity."[1] According to the Association for the Advancement of Applied Sport Psychology, sport and exercise psychology focuses on the psychological and mental aspects of participation in sport and exercise, seeking to understand how psychological processes influence and are influenced by participation.[2] The International Society of Sport Psychology states that "this dynamic field can enhance the experience of men, women, and children of all ages who participate in physical activity, ranking from those who do so for personal enjoyment to those who pursue a specific activity at the elite level."[3]

The scope of sport and exercise psychology is quite broad, encompassing both theoretical and applied approaches and reflecting close ties to the discipline of psychology. The initial work in the subdisicpline focused on sport and elite athletes. Today, the focus has expanded and includes the psychological dimensions of competitive sport participation and engagement in fitness, exercise, and physical activity. Sport and exercise psychology seeks to understand, influence, and improve the experiences of people of all ages and abilities, ranging from the youth sport participant to the elite Olympic performer and from the elderly individual engaging in an exercise rehabilitation program following a heart attack to the healthy adult who enjoys lifting weights on a regular basis.

Historical Development

The early history of sport and exercise psychology is closely related to motor learning. As these areas of study grew in the 1970s in the United States,

Paralympians mentally rehearse their performances before the competition begins.

they began to emerge as separate subdisciplines of the academic discipline of physical education; however, in Europe today, these areas remain closely aligned under the umbrella of sport psychology.

In the late 1890s and early 1900s, physical educators and psychologists began to write about the psychological aspects of physical education and sport. The most notable of these early researchers was Norman Triplett, who, in 1898, studied the effects of the presence of other people on the performance of motor skills.[1] The influence of the presence of other people—that is, an audience—on motor performance later developed into an area of research known as social facilitation.[1]

In 1918, Coleman Griffith, commonly recognized as the father of sport psychology, began his groundbreaking work in sport psychology as a doctoral student at the University of Illinois.[4] Later,

as director of the Athletic Research Laboratory at Illinois, Griffith engaged in research on motor learning and on the psychological aspects of sport. Additionally, he taught sport psychology classes, published numerous research articles, and authored two books considered classics in the field—*Psychology of Coaching* (1926) and *Psychology of Athletics* (1928). Like the applied sport psychologists of today, Griffith's research extended outside of the laboratory setting; he observed and interviewed outstanding athletes and coaches of the time, such as Red Grange and Knute Rockne, regarding motivation and the psychology of coaching.[4] In 1938, Griffith was hired by Philip Wrigley as the Chicago Cubs baseball team's sport psychologist. In this capacity, Griffith worked with players and researched ways to enhance motivation and develop self-confidence.

From 1940 to 1965, Gill characterizes the research in sport psychology as sporadic.[4] Following World War II, colleges and universities established motor behavior research programs. As previously mentioned in the chapter on motor learning and control, Henry, Slater-Hammel, Hubbard, and Lawther were instrumental in developing research programs focusing on motor learning and performance. These research programs included some work on topics currently within the realm of sport psychology today. Another important contribution of this time was Warren Johnson's study, in 1949, of pregame emotion in football, which served as the basis for later research on emotions associated with competition.[4] Lawther's publication, in 1951, of *The Psychology of Coaching* reflected an applied sport psychology orientation to coaching athletes.

In the 1960s, several texts were published that included information about the psychological aspects of sport and learning. These books introduced both undergraduate and graduate physical education students to both motor learning and sport psychology.[4] Bryant Cratty, who became one of the most prolific authors in the field, published *Movement Behavior and Motor Learning* in 1964 and *Psychology and Physical Activity* in 1967.[4] In 1968, Robert Singer's textbook *Motor Learning*

LIFESPAN AND CULTURAL PERSPECTIVES: Sport and Exercise Psychology

- How do sociocultural factors influence participants' adherence to an exercise program?
- Does age influence the psychological benefits derived from participation in physical activity?
- Do personality traits and psychological dispositions of elite athletes vary by ethnicity or gender?
- How can self-efficacy be developed in children with low skill ability?
- What interventions are most effective in mediating the effects of anxiety in Senior Games competitors?

and Human Performance was published.[4] Another book published during this era caused considerable controversy—Bruce Ogilvie and Thomas Tutko's book *Problem Athletes and How to Handle Them* (1966). Gill notes that this book was criticized by scholars intent on advancing the scientific nature of sport psychology for its clinical approach and lack of a scientific framework.[4] However, the book was popular among coaches and helped set the stage for applied sport psychology in the 1980s.[4]

The late 1960s and the 1970s marked the emergence of sport psychology as a subdiscipline of physical education. Courses were developed for inclusion within the graduate and undergraduate physical education curriculums, graduate programs were inaugurated and research programs established, professional societies were organized, and specialized sport psychology journals were created. Scholars such as Rainer Martens, Dorothy Harris, Daniel Landers, and William Morgan helped shape the direction of the field.[1,4]

As the amount of research grew and interest in sport psychology developed, outlets for dissemination of research and forums for the exchange of ideas were needed. In 1965, the International Society of Sport Psychology was founded. Two years later, in 1967, professionals interested in motor learning and sport psychology formed the North American Society for the Psychology of Sport and Physical Activity (NASPSPA). In 1975, the Sport Psychology Academy was organized as part of NASPE, a substructure of AAHPERD. *Research Quarterly* and journals in the parent field of psychology served as the major outlets for publication of research until the *Journal of Sport Psychology* began publication in 1979.

However, during this time sport psychology was still aligned with motor learning and drew heavily on the parent discipline of psychology for theories. Much of the work was conducted in laboratory settings, rather than within sport, and offered little help to teachers, coaches, and participants.[4] In 1979, Martens called for a greater emphasis on applied issues within sport psychology, including a focus on more relevant issues, a greater emphasis on field-based rather than laboratory-based research, and the development of sport-specific conceptual models.[4] This shift in focus was reflected in the work of sport psychologists in the 1980s.

The 1980s marked a period of tremendous expansion for sport psychology. Many scholars embraced a more applied approach to sport psychology. More field-based research with sport participants was conducted, and a greater emphasis was placed on the application of research to real-world sports events. In 1986, the Association for the Advancement of Applied Sport Psychology (AAASP) was organized; it comprises three interrelated focus areas: intervention and performance enhancement, health psychology, and social psychology. In 1987, the inaugural volume of *The Sport Psychologist* was published, providing another outlet for scholarly work with an applied focus.

Another factor that helped shape the field was the growing interest of more clinically trained psychologists in sport psychology.[4] One noteworthy contribution during this time frame was that of Richard Suinn, a clinical psychologist whose work with the US Olympic ski team did much to bring sport psychology to public attention.[4] Another significant step in the growth of sport psychology occurred in 1986, when Division 47, Exercise and Sport Psychology, became a formal division within the American Psychological Association.

It was during the 1980s that exercise psychology evolved as a specialized area of study. Researchers became interested in understanding the psychological aspects of fitness, exercise, health, and wellness, including psychological factors that influence participation and the influence of participation on those involved. Attention was also directed toward enhancing the experience for those participants involved in health-related physical activity. This growth of interest occurred at a time when more and more research and public attention was being directed toward the significant contribution of physical activity to health. To reflect the expanding scope of the subdiscipline, in 1988, the *Journal of Sport Psychology* was renamed the *Journal of Sport and Exercise Psychology.*

Sport and exercise psychology during the 1990s and today reflects the rich diversity of this subdiscipline, both in research and practice. As Gill writes,

> Some researchers emphasize theory-based basic research with tight controls, and search for underlying physiological mechanisms; others shun traditional research, using interpretive approaches and searching for experiential knowledge. Some are not concerned with research at all, but seek information on strategies and techniques to educate, consult, or clinically treat sport and exercise participants.[4]

Some researchers seek to focus exclusively on sport psychology; others on exercise psychology. As sport and exercise psychology continues to grow and evolve in the twenty-first century, Gill suggests that it is likely that more sport- and exercise-specific approaches will develop and that

there will be a greater appreciation "of the richer understanding that can be gained through collaborative research across specializations, such as exercise physiology and motor learning."[4]

Areas of Study

Sport and exercise psychology includes many different areas of study. Sport and exercise psychologists are interested in understanding factors that influence participation in sport and exercise. For example, why do some athletes "choke" under pressure? Why do some postcardiac patients fail to complete their rehabilitation program? Sport and exercise psychology also studies the psychological outcomes derived from participation. For instance, does participation in an exercise program reduce stress and alleviate depression? Does participation in youth sport build character?

Sport and exercise psychology can also help physical educators, exercise scientists, and sport leaders make modifications to sport and exercise programs to enrich the experience for the participants involved. This could include helping athletes learn techniques to regulate their level of arousal to achieve optimal performance, teaching coaches how to promote self-confidence or to motivate their athletes, or building more social support into exercise programs to promote adherence and provide greater enjoyment for the participants.

Areas of study within sport and exercise psychology include attentional focus, personality, aggression and violence, self-confidence and self-efficacy, self-talk, arousal, social reinforcement, adherence, team building, commitment, and level of aspiration. Researchers design and assess the effectiveness of various interventions to enhance performance and participation, such as cognitive restructuring, mental rehearsal, and social support. Researchers are also interested in factors that cause people to become involved in sport and exercise and those factors that lead to peoples dropping out or discontinuing participation.

The amount of research produced by scholars in sport and exercise psychology has grown tremendously over the past decade. Examples of questions that may be investigated by researchers include:

- Is the personality profile of the outstanding or elite athlete different from that of the average athlete or nonathlete?
- How does participation in an exercise program influence one's body image? Or one's feelings of self-efficacy and control?
- What are the psychological benefits derived from participation in physical activity? What is the dose-response relationship between physical activity and psychological effects?
- Does one's personality change as a result of participation in sport or an exercise program? If so, what is the nature of the change?
- In what way does anxiety influence performance in various types of sports?
- How can an athlete deal most effectively with the stress of competition? What strategy would be most helpful for an athlete to use to deal with the pressure of competition?
- What factors influence an individual's adherence to an exercise or rehabilitation program?
- Does participation in sport empower athletes with disabilities?
- How does an individual's self-confidence affect his or her performance? How can self-confidence be developed most effectively and then used to maximize performance?
- How can self-efficacy in adolescents be increased to promote the establishment of beneficial physical activity patterns?

These are only a sample of the type of questions that may be addressed by researchers in sport and exercise psychology.

Sport psychologists today work with both male and female athletes to help them perform at their optimal level. Sport psychologists work with professional sport teams, national sport teams (US Olympic teams in various sports), and intercollegiate teams. Some professional athletes or athletes that compete at an elite level, such as in figure skating, may engage the services of a sport psychologist to help them achieve their goals.

Knowledge of sport psychology is important to coaches at all levels. It can help coaches more fully understand the psychological impact of their coaching behaviors and decisions on the athletes. Coaches can incorporate information from sport psychology into their preparation of athletes for competition and use information during competition to help their teams perform at their highest possible level. Additionally, coaches may find it beneficial to understand the factors that contribute to athletes' continuing commitment to a sport and the factors that predispose athletes to discontinue sport participation.

Specialists in exercise psychology focus their efforts on individuals participating in exercise and rehabilitation programs. Researchers have sought to identify the psychological determinants of participation in physical activity and the factors that influence the completion of rehabilitation regimens. Given the documented evidence supporting the contribution of regular physical activity to health, understanding the psychological dimensions of participation is of critical importance to physical education, exercise science, and sport professionals working in these areas. Such an understanding can help practitioners design programs and structure experiences to enhance the probability that program participants will engage in physical activity to the extent necessary to realize health benefits and incorporate physical activity into their lifestyle.

Sport and exercise psychologists can provide educational or clinical services, depending on their credentials. Clinical sport psychologists have extensive training in psychology and are licensed by state boards to treat people with psychopathology. Clinical sports psychologists may treat participants with personality disorders, eating disorders, or chemical dependency. They supplement their training in psychology with additional training in sport and exercise psychology.

Educational sport and exercise psychologists often have a background in physical education, exercise science, and sport, with extensive training in sport and exercise psychology. They are not licensed psychologists. The AAASP offers a certification program for applied sport psychology that recognizes attainment of professional knowledge in sport psychology, including health and exercise psychology, intervention and performance enhancement, and social psychology. Upon meeting the requirements for certification, an individual is conferred the title of Certified Consultant, Association for the Advancement of Applied Sport Psychology.

Certified consultants engage in educational activities focused on the "development and understanding of cognitive, behavioral, and affective skills in participants of all ages and at all skill levels."[2] Examples of educational activities include informing individuals and groups about the role of psychological factors in exercise, physical activity, and sport and teaching participants specific psychological skills such as imagery or coping skills that they can use to enhance their participation.[2] Another activity is the education of organizations and groups in areas such as development of team cohesion, strategies to promote exercise adherence, and modification of youth sport programs to enhance the experience for the young athletes. As the AAASP notes, "Although some individuals may possess coaching expertise and/or knowledge of the analysis and treatment of psychopathology, these two areas are excluded from the role definition association with AAASP certification."[2]

Sport and exercise psychology encompasses many areas of study. The next section will provide a brief overview of some topics within this subdiscipline. First, the psychological benefits of physical activity are presented, followed by information on motivation and exercise adherence. Personality, anxiety and arousal, goal setting, self-talk, and mental imagery are addressed. A short discussion of various psychological intervention techniques concludes the chapter.

PSYCHOLOGICAL BENEFITS OF PHYSICAL ACTIVITY

The role of physical activity in enhancing well-being is receiving increased professional and public recognition. The physiological effects of engaging in physical activity on a regular basis are well documented. There is also a growing body of evidence supporting the psychological benefits of physical activity.[5,6] Psychological benefits have been noted for both aerobic and resistance exercise. It appears that moderate-intensity exercise has the best psychological benefits.

Benefits

The psychological benefits of participating in physical activity include

- Improved health-related quality of life, by enhancing both psychological and physical well-being.
- Improved mood. Mood states influence our outlook on life, emotions, thought processes, and behaviors.
- Apparently allieviated symptoms associated with mild depression. Physical activity may be a valuable adjunct to therapy in cases of chronic, severe depression.
- Reduced state anxiety—that is, feelings of tension, apprehension, and fear associated with various situations.
- Effective stress management. Physical activity can serve as a buffer against stress as well as provide a healthful means of stress reduction.
- Contribution to the development of the self. Physical activity enhances self-concept and improves self-esteem or feelings of worth. It also promotes greater self-efficacy and self-confidence.
- Affiliation with other human beings, an important psychological need.
- Opportunities to experience peak moments. Peak moments are characterized by feelings of being lost or absorbed in the activity, feelings of "flow," or feelings of powerfulness or being able to do no wrong. Participants have reported feelings of euphoria, such as the runner's high.
- Recreation and a change of pace from long hours of work or study. Individuals return to their daily routine feeling refreshed, both mentally and physically.
- Challenges that, when successfully met, provide a sense of achievement. Some physical activities include certain elements of risk, such as mountain climbing, that provide excitement and opportunities for mastery.

PSYCHOLOGICAL BENEFITS OF PHYSICAL ACTIVITY

- Improves health-related quality of life
- Enhances mood
- Alleviates symptoms of mild depression
- Reduces state and trait anxiety
- Serves as a buffer against stress and means of stress reduction
- Enhances self-efficacy, self-confidence, self-esteem
- Offers a means of affiliation with others
- Improves cognitive functioning
- Provides opportunities to refresh and reenergize
- Presents challenges that can lead to sense of achievement
- Gives means for nonverbal expression of emotion
- Provides opportunities for creative and aesthetic expression

- Aesthetic and creative experiences. Activities such as dance allow individuals to express their emotions in a nonverbal manner and provide opportunities for individual interpretation.

The psychological benefits of physical activity are being increasingly understood and offer exciting possibilities for research.

Mechanism of Effect

Researchers have advanced several hypotheses to explain the effects of exercise on mental health. Hypotheses have been developed that explain the mechanism of effect from a psychological or a physiological perspective. Among the psychological hypotheses offered are the cognitive behavioral hypothesis and the distraction hypothesis. One physiological hypothesis that has received considerable attention is the endorphin hypothesis.

According to the *cognitive behavior hypothesis*, participation in exercise promotes positive thoughts and feelings.[7] These serve to counteract negative thoughts and feelings as well as mood states associated with depression and anxiety.[7] Nonexercisers who begin and adhere to an exercise program, a task many nonexercisers perceive as difficult, experience enhanced feelings of competence and an increase in self-efficacy.[7] Increased

self-efficacy is also associated with effort and persistence, factors that will help individuals continue to participate in exercise and reap the psychological benefits.[7]

The *distraction hypothesis* proposes that the psychological benefits of exercise accrue because engaging in exercise distracts individuals from their cares, worries, and frustrations.[8] Exercise provides individuals with a "time out" from events and issues in their life that are associated with feelings of anxiety or depression.

The *endorphin hypothesis* explains that psychological benefits associated with exercise are due to the increased secretion of endorphins. Endorphins are chemicals produced in the brain in response to a stimuli, including stressors. As a stressor, exercise elicits the production of endorphins. Elevated levels of endorphins are associated with improved mood and enhanced sense of well-being. Endorphins are also associated with a reduction in pain. The general well-being produced by endorphins reduces levels of depression, anxiety, and other negative mood states.[8] The popular press often refers to the improved mood associated with prolonged exercise as the "runner's high." Although there is agreement that the body does produce endorphins in response to prolonged exercise, the research on the mechanism of positive effects has been equivocal.

Although many hypotheses have been advanced, the mechanism by which exercise promotes psychological benefits is not clear at this point in time. Research investigating these and other hypotheses yields conflicting results. What is known, however, is that there is a positive relationship between exercise and various psychological states. Before starting an exercise program, individuals should consult with their physician.

The value of physical activity as a therapeutic modality is increasing, and new avenues are being explored. However, Fontaine points out that several important questions need to be addressed about the therapeutic value of physical activity (PA). These questions include:

1. How and under what circumstances should PA be incorporated into therapy for patients with mental health disorders?
2. What are the long-term effects of PA on mental health disorders?
3. Does regular PA protect against developing mental health disorders?
4. What is the optimal PA prescription for various mental health disorders?[9]

Fontaine notes that despite these questions, it appears that physical activity can play an important role in the treatment of mental health disorders.[9]

Dance therapy and recreation therapy (see Chapter 13) utilize physical activity as part of therapeutic and rehabilitation processes. The role of physical activity in improving mental health and psychological well-being offers exciting possibilities in treatment and prevention.

MOTIVATION

Motivation is a critical factor in learning, performance, and participation in sport and physical activity. It influences the initiation, maintenance, and intensity of behavior. Motivation directs and energizes us; it determines whether or not we will practice with a high level of intensity or get up at 6 A.M. to workout before work. Motivation influences whether we will continue an activity or choose to discontinue participation. As previously discussed in Chapter 5, motivation can be influenced by internal and external factors.

Individuals are intrinsically motivated when the motive for starting or engaging in a behavior is derived from the individual's own desires, enjoyment, needs, and aspirations. For example, a soccer player who engages in the sport because she loves the "beautiful game" and has a passion for it that drives her to participate and an adult who desires to be healthy and joins a water aerobics program are intrinsically motivated. Intrinsic motives drive a person who is quadriplegic and seeks to challenge himself by playing quad rugby; he relishes the competition associated with the sport as well as the camaraderie gained from being part of a team.

On the other hand, individuals are extrinsically motivated when they engage in an activity in hopes of gaining external rewards. An employee who signs up for a worksite fitness program to gain the $1,000 bonus promised by the employer for participation is extrinsically motivated. A young gymnast who competes to gain trophies and the approval of her parents is participating for the external rewards.

Intrinsic motivation is more conductive to long-term commitment and engagement in sport and physical activity. As professionals, it is important for us to realize the importance of intrinsic motivation in sustaining involvement by participants in our programs. There are many theories explaining motivation. However, as Vealey points out, "the key to understanding motivation is realizing that all humans, regardless of their individual goals, are motivated to feel competent, worthy, and self-determining."[1] The question, then, for us as professionals is, what can we do to help individuals develop or increase their intrinsic motivation?[1] This answer is complex and reflects an intersection of a multitude of factors, but simply stated, we can create opportunities to help individuals develop competence and promote feelings of self-efficacy. We can promote feelings of personal accomplishment, recognize hard work, engender self-confidence, and offer support as individuals pursue their goals. It is important that we recognize that participants' motives for participation in our programs vary, and we need to respect their motives. However, if we want to sustain participation, we must focus on promoting intrinsic motivation.

Motivation is critical to achievement. Whether it is achievement in the athletic arena or as a participant in lifelong physical activity, motivation plays an important role in determining whether or not an individual will persist until a goal is achieved. Goal setting is a critical facet of motivation. Having both short- and long-term goals helps individuals focus their behavior and mobilize their energies in the right direction. Physical education, exercise science, and sport professionals can help individuals achieve their goals by assisting them in developing realistic goals, creating positive expectations for success, providing encouragement, offering appropriate feedback, assisting them to redefine their goals when necessary, and developing new goals as

desired goals are achieved. Goal setting is discussed more later in the chapter.

Motivation is critical to the initiation, persistence, or maintenance of the desired behavior, whether it is related to participation in competitive sport or engagement in physical activity for health, enjoyment, or recreation. What motivates an individual to begin a new sport or to start a fitness routine? Equally important, once the new behavior is initiated, what contributes to an individual's continuing the behavior? And what motivates an individual to work hard to achieve desired goals? Sustaining engagement in physical activity is important to the realization of the physiological and psychological benefits associated with participation in regular physical activity. Research on exercise adherence has helped us determine factors that contribute to individuals' continuing to work-out and incorporating physical activity into their lives. This is discussed later in the chapter.

As professionals, we must develop effective behavioral strategies to help sedentary individuals adopt a healthy, active lifestyle.

EXERCISE ADHERENCE

An expanding area of research is investigation of exercise adherence. Researchers have found that patients' adherence to prescribed medical regimens is a great concern. Although figures vary, authorities estimate that half of all patients fail to comply with their medical treatment.[10] The past decade has brought greater recognition of the value of exercise as a therapeutic modality. Exercise is increasingly being prescribed as part of an overall treatment approach to several diseases, including cardiovascular diseases and diabetes. Unfortunately, the compliance rates for participants in exercise programs are similar to those in other medical regimens. Adherence to supervised exercise programs ranges from about 50% to 80% in the first 6 months.[10] Other researchers report that only 30% of individuals who begin an exercise program will be exercising at the end of 3 years.[11]

Knowledge that a particular behavior has either good or harmful influences on our health does not consistently affect our behavior. Most individuals are aware of the behaviors that detract from wellness—smoking, high-fat diet, sedentary lifestyle, and so on—yet continue to engage in these behaviors despite the health consequences. Why aren't more people active? Despite the known benefits, why are there so few participants? And what can be done about it?

Understanding Behavior Change

How do you get people to begin to lead a more active lifestyle? How do you promote behavior change? Many theories and models of human behavior have been used to guide interventions to promote a more physically active lifestyle and encourage health-promoting behaviors. Among the models are the classic learning theories, the health belief model, social cognitive theory, the transtheoretical model, and the ecological perspective.

The *classic learning theories* emphasizes that learning a new complex pattern of behavior, such as moving from a sedentary to an active lifestyle, is achieved by altering many of the small behaviors that compose the overall behavior. This suggests that a targeted behavior, such as walking continuously for 30 minutes a day, is best learned by breaking down the behavior into smaller goals to be achieved, such as walking for 10 minutes daily. Incremental increases, such as adding 5 minutes to daily walking a week, are then made as the behavior is gradually shaped toward the targeted goal. Rewards and incentives, both immediate and long-range, serve as reinforcement and motivation for the individual to achieve and maintain the targeted behavior. Looking better, receiving a T-shirt for participation, and experiencing a feeling of accomplishment all strengthen and sustain the behavior change.

The *health belief model* emphasizes that the adoption of a health behavior depends on the person's perception of four factors: the severity of the potential illness, the person's susceptibility to that illness, the benefits of taking action, and the barriers to action. Incorporation of cues to action, such as listing walking on your daily to-do list, is important in eliciting and sustaining the desired behavior. *Self-efficacy*, a person's confidence in his or her capability to perform the desired behavior, is included as an important component of this model.

Social cognitive theory states that behavior change is influenced by environmental factors, personal factors, and attributes of the behavior itself. Self-efficacy is central to this model. A person must believe in his or her ability to perform the behavior (self-efficacy) and must perceive an incentive for changing his or her behavior. The outcomes derived from the behavior must be valued by the person. These benefits can be immediate in nature, such as feelings of satisfaction or enjoyment from engaging in the behavior, or long-term, such as improved health from being physically active on a regular basis.

The *theory of reasoned action* is based on the idea that the most important determinant of an individual's behavior is the intention to perform that behavior. The intention to perform a behavior is influenced by two factors: the individual's attitude

SELECTED THEORIES AND MODELS OF HEALTH BEHAVIOR CHANGE

Classic learning theory	New behaviors are learned.
	• Achievement of smaller goals leads to attainment of overall goals • Reinforcement and motivation are critical
Health belief model	Adoption of a health behavior depends on the person's perception of four factors:
	• Severity of the potential illness • Susceptibility to that illness • Benefits of taking action • Barriers to action
	Self-efficacy plays an important role.
Social cognitive theory	Behavior change is influenced by environmental and personal factors and attributes of the behavior itself.
	• Self-efficacy is a critical component • Requires a perceived incentive for changing behavior • Outcomes must be valued by the person.
Theory of reasoned action and theory of planned behavior	Behavior change is strongly influenced by intention to change, which depends on:
	• Individual's attitude toward the behavior • Opinions of relevant others regarding the change • Perceived control over behavior
Transtheoretical model	Behavior change proceeds through stages:
	• Precontemplation • Contemplation • Preparation • Action • Maintenance • Termination
	Decisional balance and self-efficacy play an important role in the adoption of new behaviors.
Ecological approach	Health behavior change is affected by:
	• Individual factors • Sociocultural context • Environmental influences

TRANSTHEORETICAL MODEL AND ITS APPLICATION TO PROMOTION OF PHYSICAL ACTIVITY

Stage of Change	Behaviors	Suggested Approaches by Professional
Precontemplation	No intention to change behavior in next 6 months	Educate the individual and deliver a clear message about the importance of physical activity to health
Contemplation	Awareness of the problem, the pros and cons of change; intention to take action within next 6 months	Highlight the benefits of change and try to shift the decisional balance
Preparation	Taking small steps or developing a specific plan of action to begin physical activity program (e.g., checking out walking routes or joining a fitness club)	Help the individual identify the best time to walk and safe walking route; teach the individual warm-up and cooldown stretches; assist the individual in developing a progressive walking plan (20 minutes at a moderate pace three times a week progressing to 30 minutes of brisk walking most days of the week)
Action	Making modifications in lifestyle and engaging in physical activity (e.g., getting up an hour earlier to fit walking into day); commitment to exercise	Encourage and support the individual in becoming active; help the individual monitor physical activity; discuss modifications in program as situation changes
Maintenance	Sustaining the change in behavior for at least 6 months; becoming increasingly confident in ability to sustain change (e.g., continuing to walk on daily basis); exercise becomes routine	Support the individual in remaining active; explore ideas with the individual for continuing to be active even when the schedule changes and the individual can't walk at the usual time, etc.
Termination	Behavior is fully integrated into lifestyle (e.g., walking is planned for as part of the day's activities); exercise patterns are integral part of life	The individual walks as part of the daily routine; offer to be available as a resource
Relapse	Move to previous stage	Remind the individual that relapse gives the opportunity to rethink physical activity strategy—what worked and what should be changed; encourage the individual to recommence physical activity at an appropriate level

Source: Adapted from Duffy FD and Schnirring L. "How to Counsel Patients about Exercise: An Office-Friendly Approach." *The Physician and Sportsmedicine*, 28(10), 53–54, 2000.

toward the behavior and the influence of relevant others in the environment. The individual's attitude reflects beliefs about the outcomes of the behavior and the values gained from changing the behavior. If the individual sees the outcome of changing a behavior as positive, this increases the likelihood of change. If relevant others support changing behavior, and the individual is strongly motivated by the opinions of others, this also supports behavior change. *The theory of planned action* incorporates the tenets of the theory of reasoned action and adds another concept—perceived control. *Perceived control* is similar to the concept of self-efficacy and reflects the individual's beliefs about his or her ability to perform the behavior. Individuals who intend to become more active are more likely to do so if they see being active as having a positive benefit, receive support from others for being active, and perceive themselves as being successful in being physically active.

The *transtheoretical model* of health behavior uses the concept of stages of change to integrate the processes and principles of change relating to health behavior.[12] (See the Transtheoretical Model and Its Application to Promotion of Physical Activity box.) The transtheoretical model views behavioral change as a spiraling continuum that begins at a "firm conviction to maintain the status quo by never changing, and proceeds through the conditions of someday, soon, now, and forever."[13] The stages of change are:

- Precontemplation is the stage at which people have no intention to change behavior within the foreseeable future, usually the next 6 months.
- Contemplation is the stage at which people are intending to take action sometime in the next 6 months.
- Preparation is the stage at which people take small or inconsistent steps toward change.
- Action is the point at which individuals have made modifications in their lifestyle. They are engaging in the health-promoting behavior.
- Maintenance is sustaining the change in behavior for at least 6 months. During this time, people become increasingly confident that they can maintain their changes.
- Termination is the stage in which the behavior is fully integrated into the lifestyle. People in this stage have a high degree of self-confidence that, despite temptations to relapse, they will continue the behavior.[12,13]

In this approach, a relapse or discontinuation of the behavior, such as ceasing to exercise, is seen as a return from the action or maintenance stage to an earlier stage. Relapse should be dealt with in a positive way so that the person does not see it as a failure and become demoralized, but rather perceives it as part of the process of change. Relapse presents individuals with an opportunity to learn which behavior strategies worked and which ones did not.[14]

Decisional balance and self-efficacy are important aspects of the transtheoretical model. *Decisional balance* involves weighing the relative pros and cons of the behavioral change, that is, perceived benefits, drawbacks, and barriers to change.[15] Self-efficacy is a person's confidence about his or her competence or abilities in a specific situation. In the context of behavioral change, self-efficacy is a person's belief that he or she can maintain a healthy behavior, such as exercising, or abstain from an unhealthy behavior, such as smoking.

The transtheoretical model has most frequently been applied to the cessation of unhealthy, addictive behaviors and more recently to the acquisition of healthy behaviors such as exercise. This model has been used to predict the use of sport psychology consultations by collegiate athletes.[16] It offers physical education, exercise science, and sport professionals great insight into the process of change and guidelines for developing intervention programs.

Another model that has increased in popularity in the last decade is the ecological approach. One criticism of many theories and models for changing health behavior is that they emphasize individual behavior change while paying little attention to the sociocultural and environmental influences on behavior. The *ecological approach* emphasizes a comprehensive approach to health, including developing individual skills and creating supportive, health-promoting environments. Creating longer-lasting changes and maintaining health-promoting habits can be enhanced by addressing environmental and societal barriers to change, such as limitations imposed by poverty on access to services or the difficulty in jogging or walking if one lives in an unsafe neighborhood. These interventions can take place in the family,

---

PROMOTING EXERCISE ADHERENCE

- Structure program to optimize social support to participants
- Offer programs at convenient times and locations
- Utilize goal setting, on both a short- and long-term basis
- Provide frequent assessment of progress
- Use qualified and enthusiastic leaders
- Foster communication between leader and participants
- Develop rapport among leader and participants
- Involve a variety of enjoyable activities
- Give participants a choice of activities
- Tailor frequency, intensity, and duration of activities to individuals' needs
- Incorporate reinforcement and rewards

---

school, worksite, community, and health institutions. Societal and environmental influences on health behavior must be considered by physical education, exercise science, and sport professionals.

Promoting Adherence

What are factors that promote adherence, encourage persistence, and prevent dropping out? Researchers have identified several factors that predispose individuals to drop out of exercise programs. In general, the researchers found that low self-motivation, depression, and low self-efficacy were related to decisions to quit the program, as was denial of the seriousness of one's cardiac condition.[10,17,18] Higher dropout rates were found among smokers, blue-collar workers, and individuals who either are obese, exhibit the type A behavior pattern, perceive that exercise has few health benefits, lead physically inactive lifestyles, or work in sedentary occupations. Lack of social support from significant others, family problems, and job-related responsibilities that interfered with the exercise program were also identified as factors associated with quitting. Social support from other participants was important to individuals who continued in the program. Group exercise programs usually had lower dropout rates than individually designed programs. Programs that were inconvenient to attend and that

involved high-intensity exercise were associated with higher dropout rates than programs that were conveniently located and offered exercise of a less-intense nature.

Knowing the factors associated with exercise program dropout enables practitioners to target intervention strategies to those individuals at greatest risk of discontinuing their participation. Intervention strategies to improve adherence include educational approaches and behavioral approaches. Educational approaches provide participants with information to increase their knowledge and understanding. Behavioral approaches focus on increasing individual involvement in the program and creating more healthful behavior patterns. These methods use such strategies as reinforcement, contracting, self-monitoring, goal setting, tailoring programs to meet individuals' lifestyles, and enhancement of self-efficacy. Behavioral approaches have been found to be more effective than educational approaches in promoting adherence.

Exercise adherence also can be enhanced through careful program design. One approach is structuring the program to increase the social support available to participants. Successful strategies include forming exercise groups rather than having the individual exercise alone and involving significant others, such as family members or friends, in encouraging the participant to exercise. Offering programs at times and locations convenient to the participant is important in maintaining involvement. The use of goal setting combined with periodic assessment of progress, use of qualified and enthusiastic leaders, establishment of ongoing leader and participant communication and rapport, and inclusion of a variety of enjoyable activities to meet individual needs are some techniques that can promote exercise adherence and reduce dropout rates.

The issue of adherence to treatment is also beginning to be addressed in the realm of sports medicine. Many of the psychosocial factors that contribute to exercise adherence are also critical to the success of rehabilitation programs. There is increased recognition that sports medicine specialists' and athletic trainers' knowledge of injury mechanisms and treatment protocols is not enough to ensure successful completion of the rehabilitation program. Researchers have found that rehabilitation adherence can be enhanced through the use of such strategies as goal setting, establishing effective communication, tailoring the program to individual needs, monitoring progress, and building a collaborative relationship to achieve the goals of therapy.[19] Social support has also been linked to rehabilitation adherence.

Social support is a complex, multidimensional construct and has been found to be related in many ways to health outcomes. With respect to rehabilitation, social support has been found to relieve distress, enhance coping, and help an injured athlete remain motivated throughout the recovery.[20] It has also been found to strengthen relationships between the injured athlete and team members, coaches, and providers of health care.[20] Understanding the significant role social support plays in exercise and rehabilitation adherence can assist physical education, exercise science, and sport professionals in developing psychosocial rehabilitation interventions.

Young professionals aspiring to work in fitness and rehabilitation fields, such as corporate fitness, athletic training, and cardiac rehabilitation, will find knowledge from the subdiscipline of sport and exercise psychology very valuable in their work.

PERSONALITY

Researchers have long been interested in personality types in sport. Some researchers sought to address the question of whether sport influences personality; other researchers have investigated whether there were personality differences between athletes and nonathletes. Still other researchers undertook the task of identifying the psychological differences between elite athletes and their less successful counterparts. One of the questions was whether it would be possible to predict the success of an athlete based on his or her personality characteristics.

Nature of Personality

Vealey describes *personality* as "the unique blend of the psychological characteristics and behavioral tendencies that make individuals different from and similar to each other."[1] Anshel describes personality as traits possessed by an individual that are enduring and stable.[21] Because traits are enduring and stable, they predispose an individual to consistently act in certain ways in most, but not all, situations; thus, there is a degree of predictability to an individual's actions. Anshel suggests that psychological dispositions (i.e., broad, pervasive ways of relating to people and situations) may be more helpful in studying athletes' psychological characteristics.[21] Personality traits are linked to predispositions. The personality traits of dominance, trait anxiety, and internal locus of control are linked to the type A disposition.

Personality and Sport

The early research focused on the relationship between personality traits and sport performance. Researchers addressed questions such as:

- Do athletes differ from nonathletes?
- Can athletes in certain sports be distinguished from athletes in other sports on the basis of their personality?
- Do individuals participate in certain sports because of their personality characteristics?

- Do highly skilled athletes have different personality profiles than less skilled athletes in the same sport?
- Are there certain personality traits that can predict an athlete's success in a sport?[22]

Researchers' findings have revealed contradictory answers to each of these questions. In many instances, problems in research design have contributed to these contradictory results. Cox, after an extensive review of the research on personality and sport, offers the following generalizations about men and women athletes relative to the questions posed above:

- Athletes and nonathletes differ with respect to personality characteristics. Various researchers have reported that athletes are more independent, objective, self-confident, competitive, and outgoing or extroverted, and less anxious than nonathletes.
- Sport participation has an effect on the personality development of young athletes during their formative years. Thus, youth sport experience can positively or negatively affect the development of personality.
- Athletes in one sport can be differentiated from athletes in another sport based on their personality characteristics. Perhaps the clearest example occurs between individual sport athletes and team sport athletes. It has been shown that individual sport athletes are less extroverted, more independent, and less anxious than team sport participants.
- World-class athletes can be correctly differentiated from less-skilled athletes by their psychological profile 70% of the time. Personality profiles that include situational measures of psychological states have been shown to be the most accurate in predicting level of athletic performance.[22]

While Cox has advanced some generalizations based on an overview of research in the area, much of the research is still inconclusive.[22]

Despite the controversies and the limitations of personality trait research, there is some agreement about the psychological characteristics of highly skilled athletes. Anshel reports:

> Highly skilled athletes score relatively low in neuroticism, tension, depression, anger, fatigue, and confusion. They tend to score very high in self-confidence, self-concept, self-esteem, vigor, need achievement, dominance, aggression, intelligence, self-sufficiency, mental toughness, independence (autonomy), sociability, creativity, stability, and extroversion. A composite of the psychological profiles of elite athletes reveals a person who is mentally healthy, physically and psychological mature, and committed to excellence.[21]

Anshel points out that these characteristics serve as a model of the elite athlete, but the value of applying these characteristics as the basis for athletic selection, promotion, or elimination is questionable.[21]

As interest in personality in sport grew, different approaches began to be utilized to study personality and psychological characteristics of athletes. The interactionist approach views behavior as being influenced by both the traits of the individual and situational and environmental factors. The study of personality states is another approach that has been undertaken by researchers to study athletes. Unlike traits, which are relatively stable, states fluctuate and are a manifestation of the individual's behaviors and feelings at a particular moment, reflecting the interaction of traits and situational factors. For example, anxiety has both a trait dimension (how you typically respond to situations) and a state dimension (how you feel at this moment or at particular point in time, such as before the start of the competition).

The emergence of cognitive psychology offers another perspective to understand the behaviors, feelings, and thoughts of athletes. According to this theory, individuals continuously process information from the environment, interpret the information, and then behave based on their appraisal of the situation. Cognitive psychology recognizes that individuals' thoughts about themselves and the situation influence their actions. Vealey reports that researchers using the cognitive approach were able to distinguish between successful and less-successful athletes.[1] Compared to less-successful athletes, successful athletes:

- possess more self-confidence,
- employ more effective coping strategies to maintain their optimal competitive focus despite obstacles and distractions,
- more efficiently regulate their level of activation to be appropriate for the task at hand,
- tend to be more positively preoccupied with their sport, and
- have a high level of determination and commitment to excellence.[21]

Anshel discusses psychological predispositions of highly successful athletes.[21] These athletes are characterized by risk taking. Risk taking involves engaging in actions that can lead to bodily harm and psychological harm, such as failure. Elite athletes take greater and more frequent performance risks than their less-successful competitors and enjoy that challenge of competitive sport. Highly competitive, they strive for success and measure their success by performing at their personal best rather than by just winning alone. Elite athletes are highly self-confident and possess a high degree of self-efficacy, a conviction that they can successfully perform the skills to yield the desired outcome. High expectations for success contribute to their achievement. However, they also have the ability to cope with failure and learn from their mistakes. They are able to shift

their attention to the critical cues in the environment as the situation demands. Additionally, elite athletes can effectively manage their stress through the use of appropriate coping techniques and intervention strategies (e.g., self-talk, relaxation).

The research on personality and psychological characteristics of athletes, while at times presenting conflicting results, does offer us some insights into the psychological characteristics and thoughts of athletes. Differences in traits, predispositions, and cognitions influence athletes' behaviors and experiences in sport. What can be said with some degree of assurance is that each athlete must be treated as an individual.

ANXIETY AND AROUSAL

The goal of coaches, teachers, and sport psychologists is to optimize an individual's performance. To achieve this goal they must consider the effect of anxiety and arousal on performance.

Nature of Anxiety and Arousal

Anxiety, as defined by Levitt, is a subjective feeling of apprehension accompanied by a heightened level of physiological arousal.[23] *Physiological arousal* is an autonomic response that results in the excitation of various organs of the body. Examples of this phenomenon seen in athletes are

Optimal arousal is important for superior performance. The level of optimal arousal varies according to the individual and the sport.

SIGNS OF ELEVATED AROUSAL AND HEIGHTENED ANXIETY

- Sweaty hands
- Frequent urge to urinate
- Increased respiration rate
- Elevated heart rate
- Deterioration in coordination
- Inappropriate narrowing of attention
- Distractibility
- Negative self-talk

sweaty hands, frequent urge to urinate, increased respiration rate, increased muscle tension, and elevated heart rate.

Anxiety is commonly classified in two ways. Trait anxiety is an integral part of an individual's personality. It refers to the individual's tendency to classify environmental events as either threatening or nonthreatening. State anxiety is an emotional response to a specific situation that results in feelings of fear, tension, or apprehension (e.g., apprehension about an upcoming competition). The effects of both state and trait anxiety on motor performance have been studied by sport psychologists.

Anxiety, Arousal, and Performance

Coaches and teachers continually attempt to find the optimal level of arousal that allows individuals to perform their best. An arousal level that is too low or too high can have a negative impact on performance. A low level of arousal in an individual is associated with such behaviors as low motivation, inattention, and inappropriate and slow movement choices. A high level of arousal in an individual can cause deterioration in coordination, inappropriate narrowing of attention, distractibility, and a lack of flexibility in movement responses. It is important for each individual to find his or her optimal level of arousal for a given activity. However, no one knows for sure exactly how to consistently reach this ideal state. A variety of approaches have been employed by physical education, exercise science, and sport professionals in pursuit of this goal. These techniques include pep talks, motivational slogans and bulletin boards, relaxation training, imagery, and in some cases the professional services of a sport psychologist.

Sport psychologists and researchers have studied the relationships among anxiety, arousal, and sport performance. Cox, after a review of the research in this area, offered the following ideas:

- Athletes who feel threatened by fear of failure experience a high level of anxiety. Fear of failure can be reduced by defining success in individual terms and keeping winning in perspective.

- Athletes who possess high levels of trait anxiety tend to experience high levels of state anxiety when confronted with competition. Coaches who are aware of their athletes' levels of trait anxiety can better understand how they are likely to respond in a competitive situation. This knowledge will help coaches select appropriate strategies to adjust athletes' levels of state anxiety and arousal to an optimal level.

- Athletes' perceptions of a given situation influence their level of state anxiety. Not all athletes react to the competitive situation in the same manner. Each athlete perceives the same situation in a different way. Coaches must be aware that when placed in the same competitive situation, athletes experience different levels of anxiety. That is why "psych" talks may be an effective means of regulating the arousal level of some athletes and ineffective with other athletes. Techniques must be tailored to the individual athlete and the situation.

- An optimal level of arousal is essential for peak performance. The individual characteristics of the athlete, the nature of the skill to be performed, and the competitive situation influence the level of arousal needed.

- As the arousal level increases, athletes tend to exhibit the dominant or habitual response. Under the stress of competition, they tend to revert to skills they are most comfortable performing. Thus, if a volleyball player has been recently trained to pass the ball in a low trajectory to the setter, under the stress of competition, the player may revert to the safer, easier-to-perform high-trajectory pass.[22]

Research in sport psychology suggests several ways that coaches can help their athletes achieve their optimal performance, whether that means decreasing their level of arousal and anxiety or increasing it. One way to determine whether an athlete is "feeling up" as opposed to "uptight" is to help athletes accurately identify their feelings, encourage them to monitor their feelings and arousal levels before, during, and after competition, and help them learn and use appropriate strategies to enable them to reach their optimal state.

Anshel identifies several different approaches that can serve to reduce anxiety and arousal. These approaches include:

- Use physical activity to release stress and anxiety. A warm-up can provide an effective means to reduce stress; however, be careful that it is not so emotionally or physically intense that it leads to the depletion of the athletes' energy.
- To reduce the anxiety associated with the performance of new tasks and activities, develop, teach, and practice a precompetition routine so that it is comfortable and familiar to the athletes.
- Simulate games in practice to allow athletes to rehearse skills and strategies until they are mastered.
- Tailor preparation for the competition to the individual athlete. Athletes prepare for competition in different ways. Some athletes prefer to sit quietly before the competition, relax in their own way, and reflect on what they need to do in the upcoming events. Other athletes thrive on an exciting, noisy locker-room atmosphere and a high-emotion pep talk from the coach. Whenever possible, individualize athletes' preparation.
- Focus on building self-confidence and high but realistic expectations. Personal insecurities, self-doubts, low self-esteem, and fears about the competition heighten anxiety. Highlighting the athletes' strengths, reviewing game strategies, and expressing confidence in the athletes' abilities and efforts help promote positive thoughts, alleviate doubt, and decrease negative thinking.
- Assist athletes in coping with errors by keeping errors in perspective. Help the athletes to stay focused on present and future events when an error occurs, rather than dwelling on past events. Emphasize the opportunity to learn from mistakes, and help athletes avoid negative self-statements, which tend to exacerbate anxiety and disrupt performance.[21]

There are a host of additional strategies that coaches can use to help athletes manage their anxiety and arousal. Once again, coaches must be prepared to work with athletes as individuals and determine which approach best suits each athlete.

What can coaches do to "psych up" a team? Increasing the team's and athletes' levels of arousal is sometimes necessary. Anshel suggests that coaches take into account each athlete's ability level, age, psychological needs, and skills to be performed.[21] Remember that athletes respond differently to various techniques and need different levels of arousal to perform different tasks.[21] Coaches can also use a multitude of different strategies to increase arousal, including increasing the intensity of their voice, using loud and fast-paced music, setting specific performance goals, and using the warm-up to help athletes adjust their level of arousal.[21] Some coaches show video of the opponents, whereas other coaches may show highlights of the athletes' successful performances.[21]

Managing anxiety and arousal is a challenging task. Coaches must recognize that athletes' perceptions of a situation influence their anxiety and arousal. Individual differences in athletes' physical and psychological states require that techniques to help athletes achieve their optimal performance must be individualized. Anxiety can affect other factors that influence an athlete's performance, such as attention.

REDUCING ANXIETY AND AROUSAL TO ENHANCE PERFORMANCE

- Use appropriate physical activity, such as warm-ups
- Develop and use a precompetition routine
- Design practice situations to simulate competition
- Tailor preparation to the individual
- Build self-confidence and high, realistic expectations
- Help athletes keep errors in perspective
- Keep athletes' focus on the present event, not on past events
- Promote the use of positive self-talk
- Incorporate relaxation training as necessary

Psychological skills help athletes perform at their maximum level.

GOAL SETTING

Goal setting is important in many of the different environments in which physical education, exercise scientists, and sport leaders work. Goal setting can be used to help students in school physical education, athletes on sports teams, clients rehabilitating an injury, or adults involved in fitness programs. Goal setting is important both as a motivational strategy and as a strategy to change behavior or enhance performance. It is also used as an intervention strategy to rectify problems or to redirect efforts.

Types of Goals

According to Weinberg, a *goal* can be defined as "that which an individual is trying to accomplish; it is the object or aim of an action."[24] Goal setting focuses on specifying a specific level of proficiency to be attained within a certain period of time.[25] Goals can be categorized as outcome goals, performance goals, and process goals.

Outcome goals typically focus on interpersonal comparisons and the end result of an event. An example of an outcome goal is winning first place at the Senior Games regional track meet at the end of the season. Whether an outcome goal is achieved or not is influenced in part by the ability and play of the opponent.

Performance goals refer to the individual's actual performance in relation to personal levels of achievement. Striving to increase ground balls won in lacrosse from five to ten, decreasing the time to walk a mile from 20 minutes to 15 minutes, increasing the amount of weight that can be lifted following knee reconstruction, and improving one's free-throw percentage from 35% to 50% are examples of performance goals.

Lastly, *process goals* focus on how a particular skill is performed. For example, increasing axial rotation in swimming the backstroke and following through on the tennis backhand are two examples of process goals that focus on the improvement of technique. As technique improves, improvements in performance are likely to follow.

How Goal Setting Works

Goal setting leads to improved performance. Locke, Shaw, Saari, and Latham identify four distinct ways in which goal setting influences performance. It focuses attention, mobilizes effort, nurtures persistence, and leads to the development of new learning strategies.[26]

Goal setting leads to the focusing of attention on the task at hand and on the achievement of the goal related to that task. When there are no specific goals, attention has a tendency to wander, drifting from one item to the next without any particular attention or intent. When specific goals are set, individuals can direct their attention to that task and its accomplishments. For example, a volleyball player who has a goal of getting 15 kills in a match can then focus his efforts on the specific elements of the skill that will help accomplish this goal.

Once a goal is determined, to achieve the goal, individuals must direct their efforts toward its attainment. This mobilization of effort, in and of itself, can lead to improved performance. Knowing what you want to accomplish and having specific strategies to achieve it influence motivation and increase effort.

Not only does goal setting focus one's attention and mobilize one's efforts, but it encourages persistence. Persistence is critical. Often the attainment of goals involves a concentrated effort over an extended period of time. There may be periods of frustration and failure as individuals learn new strategies or challenge themselves to higher levels of achievement. Individuals need to persist in pursuit of their goals.

Development of relevant learning strategies is an essential aspect of goal setting. Strategies can include learning new techniques and changing the manner in which a skill is practiced. Strategies can also include developing a plan by which incremental changes in performance or behavior can be attained. For example, an individual desiring to lose 30 pounds through a combination of healthy dieting and increased physical activity may need to learn strategies to select healthier foods, to develop and modify a walking program, and to learn how to continue to maintain the weight loss once it is accomplished.

Properly implemented, goal setting can lead to improvements in performance and changes in behavior. Goals can be outcome, process, or performance oriented. Goal setting improves performance by directing attention, mobilizing effort, encouraging persistence, and introducing new strategies. Goal setting requires careful planning if it is to be effective as a motivational strategy or intervention strategy.

Principles of Effective Goal Setting

Several principles provide guidance for physical educators, exercise scientists, and sport leaders involved in goal setting. It is important that the goal setting program be structured and implemented correctly, because a decrement in performance can actually occur from improper goal setting. To help you get started with goal setting, think "SMART." SMART is an acronym suggested by Weinberg and Gould to help professionals remember the critical characteristics of effective goals.[27] Goals should be specific, measurable, action oriented, realistic, and timely.

Specific goals have been linked to higher levels of performance than no goals or general do-your-best-type goals. While do-your-best goals may be motivating and encouraging, they do not have as powerful an impact on performance as having specific goals. Furthermore, general goals such as "I want to be a better swimmer" or "I want to be healthier" are not as effective as specific goals. It is hard to monitor general goals or to know what types of changes need to be made to achieve them. A specific goal, such as a swimmer stating, "I want to reduce my time in the 200 freestyle to 1 minute 56 seconds from 2 minutes 5 seconds by the championships," is more likely to result in improvements in performance.

Additionally, measurable goals allow progress to be more easily monitored. Measurable goals provide individuals with feedback, which helps motivate them and sustain involvement. An individual who sets a goal of walking 30 minutes a day for 5 days a week at a brisk pace of 12 minutes a mile or less can easily monitor whether progress is being made toward goal attainment. Action goals, also referred to as observable goals, are goals that can be assessed through observation

---

SMART GOAL SETTING

- Specific—set specific versus general goals
- Measurable—design measurable goals to facilitate monitoring of progress
- Action-oriented—assess goal attainment by viewing person's actions
- Realistic—make goals challenging but achievable with effort, persistence, and hard work
- Timely—establish time frame for achievement

---

of a person's actions. By viewing the person's actions, you can determine whether or not the individual is exhibiting the desired goal or behavior.

Identification of the time frame for achievement is a critical part of goal setting. Will the goal be accomplished by the end of the season? Or within 1 month? The time frame should be long enough so that it gives a reasonable time to accomplish the goal. If the time frame is too short, it appears unrealistic, which may cause the individual to give up prematurely. If the time frame is too long, there is a tendency to procrastinate.

Goals that individuals establish should be moderately difficult so that the individuals feel challenged and have to extend themselves to achieve the goals. Goals must be perceived by individuals to be realistic and achievable with effort, persistence, and hard work.

Both Weinberg[24] and Cox,[7] noted sport psychologists, suggest several other principles that should be incorporated into goal setting in addition to the SMART goal characteristics. These include writing goals down, incorporating different types of goals into the program, setting short-term and long-term goals, providing individual goals within the group context, determining goals for both practice and competition, ensuring that goals are internalized by the individuals, regularly evaluating progress, and providing for individual differences.

Goals should be written down and monitored regularly to determine if progress is being made.

Some swimmers religiously chart each practice, writing down times for each set of repeats in a swim diary. Other swimmers may only chart their meet performances. What's important is that the individual knows his or her goal, writes it down, and tracks its progress consistently.

A variety of goals should be integrated into the goal setting plan. A combination of outcome, performance, and process goals is recommended. When individuals set goals based on their own performance, they feel more in control. Goals based on outcome measures, such as winning and losing, can lead to a loss of motivation and higher levels of anxiety.[7] The reason is that there are many aspects of an outcome goal that individuals cannot control, such as their opponents' ability. Furthermore, using a combination of different types of goals presents individuals with additional opportunities for success. For example, a swimmer can finish third and fail to achieve an outcome goal of finishing first in the event, but feel successful by posting a personal best time for the event, a performance goal.

Setting a long-term goal provides a direction for individuals' efforts. In addition to long-term goals, short-term goals should be established. Short-term goals play an important role in goal achievement. They serve as stepping stones to the long-term goal. Short-term goals provide individuals with benchmarks by which to judge their progress. This form of feedback serves to keep motivation and performance high. It allows individuals to focus on improvement in smaller increments and helps make the long-term goal task seem less overwhelming.

Goals should be set for different circumstances. Goals are important for both practice and competition. What happens in practice is reflected during performance in competition. Daily practices are a critical component of competitive success. If a tennis player wants to improve his first-serve percentage during competition, this goal should be given attention during practice. Practices also provide the opportunity to work on other goals that contribute to team success, such as working hard or communicating more with teammates.

Setting goals is the first step toward achievement. Participants in the Tenneco Health and Fitness program record their progress.

Goals can also be set for teams. Team goals provide a focus for practice goals. For example, if the lacrosse team's goal is to be ranked number one in the conference on winning ground balls, practice time should be allocated to the achievement of that goal. Additionally, individual performance goals that contribute to the achievement of the team goal, such as working on skills to increase the percentage of ground balls won, should receive attention.

Social support is acknowledged as an important factor in goal achievement. Social support has been found to be critical in achieving rehabilitation goals as well as health goals. For example, in cardiac rehabilitation programs, where individuals set goals related to fitness and nutrition, eliciting the support of a spouse or significant other increases the likelihood that individuals will achieve their goals. Expressions of social support, such as genuine concern and encouragement, also help individuals remain motivated and committed when they are discouraged or frustrated or hit a performance plateau.

Acceptance and internalization of goals by the individual is one of the most critical aspects of goal setting. Individuals must commit to the goals and invest themselves in their attainment. Allowing individuals to set their own goals increases their commitment to their achievement. Goals set by others, such as a personal trainer or a coach, may cause individuals not to feel ownership of the goals. Ownership can be enhanced by using a collaborative approach to goal setting. If goals are not determined by the individual, but are assigned by others, professionals should make sure that the individual commits to the assigned goal.

Provision for frequent evaluation needs to be incorporated into the goal setting plan. Evaluative feedback helps individuals assess the effectiveness of their goals and whether or not their goal achievement strategies are working. Additionally, goal setting is a dynamic process. Frequent evaluation allows both short- and long-term goals to be adjusted to reflect progress, the changing circumstances of the individuals, or the effectiveness of learning strategies.

Individual differences need to be taken into account when setting goals. Some individuals thrive on challenges and welcome goals whose achievement, although attainable, will be difficult. Other individuals require a boost in self-confidence and may benefit from a goal setting approach that uses many short-term goals, the achievement of which enhances their feelings of competence. Individual circumstances should be reflected in goal setting.

Physical education, exercise science, and sport professionals may find goal setting to be an integral part of their work. Goal setting can be used effectively in many different ways to help individuals improve their performance or change their behaviors relative to physical activity.

ENHANCING PERFORMANCE THROUGH SELF-TALK

What thoughts run through your head before an athletic performance? As you sit and wait to give a 10-minute speech in front of a class, what are you thinking? As you set out on your daily 3-mile jog, what conversations do you have with yourself in your head? What did you say to yourself as you took a test for this course? Cognitive approaches in sport and exercise psychology focus on understanding the relationship between individuals' thoughts, feelings, and behavior or performance.

Nature of Self-Talk

What individuals say to themselves during performance can be positive or negative. These thoughts and associated feelings can influence self-confidence, which, in turn, impacts performance. Who would you rather have take a penalty kick in soccer—a soccer player who steps up to take the shot and thinks, "I consistently make this shot in practice; I can do it" or a player who steps up to take the shot and thinks, "What if I miss?" Which player's self-talk is more conducive to successful performance? Understanding and modifying individuals' self-talk is one focus of cognitive sport and exercise psychology.

According to Williams and Leffingwell, "Self-talk occurs whenever an individual thinks, whether making statements internally or externally."[28] *Self-talk* is thoughts that occupy individuals' mind or spoken words, and they can be positive or negative in nature. Positive self-talk

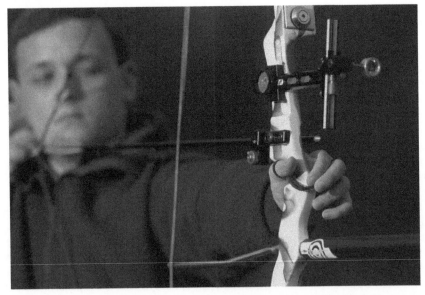

Self-talk can help individuals focus their attention and concentrate on relevant cues.

does not guarantee an outstanding performance, but it does enhance factors associated with better performance, such as self-confidence and a task-relevant focus of attention.[28] Sport and exercise psychologists use a variety of strategies to promote positive self-talk and to counteract the effects of negative self-talk.

Types of Self-Talk

There are several different types of self-talk. Task-relevant statements reinforce technique. For example, a volleyball setter may use the cue "diamond" to remind himself of the correct hand position. Positive self-statements refer to talk that encourages effort or persistence or reinforces feelings of confidence. A cross-country runner, facing an uphill stretch during the last kilometer, may say to herself, "I can do it" as a way of encouraging herself to push through to the finish. A third form of self-talk is mood words—words designed to elicit an increase in intensity or arousal. "Turn it on," a swimmer says to himself as he completes the last 50 yards of a 1,500-yard freestyle race.

Application of Self-Talk

There are several uses of self-talk. Self-talk can be effective in enhancing skill acquisition, focusing attention, modifying activation, and promoting self-confidence.[28] Self-talk is not only for athletes, but is also useful for individuals engaging in a variety of physical activities.

Self-talk can be useful when learning a new skill or modifying a previously learned skill or habit. Self-talk can range from rehearsing key words of the steps involved in a skill to the use of a cue word such as "step" to serve as a reminder of what to do. It is important that the self-talk focus on the desirable movement, versus what not to do. For example, if a tennis player wants to toss the ball higher in preparation for the serve, appropriate self-talk would be "High toss," not "Don't toss the ball so low."

Focusing attention is another effective use for self-talk. During practices or competition, athletes' attention may wander or be directed inappropriately. Cue words such as "focus" help athletes regain their

concentration. Self-statements can also be used to help athletes focus on relevant task cues such as "mark up" or "adjust position relative to the ball."

The right intensity at the right time is critical in performance. Self-talk can be used by athletes to modify their intensity or arousal so that it is at an optimal level. Self-statements may be helpful in decreasing activation ("relax") or increasing it ("get psyched").

Promoting self-confidence is an effective use of self-talk. Self-confidence is influenced by a variety of factors, such as performance outcomes and skill ability. Self-confidence is also influenced by self-talk. Individuals' self-talk affects their self-confidence, either positively or negatively. Self-confidence is undermined with negative self-talk and feelings of doubt. Although self-criticism can provide an important source of feedback to improve later performances, it is important that it not be overgeneralized ("My shot went wide because of the direction of my follow-through" versus "I'm a terrible player"). Positive self-talk enhances feelings of competence. Self-statements prior to and during competition should be positive in nature and engender high levels of motivation and effort.

Modifying Self-Talk

Some individuals may not even be aware of their self-talk or its potential to impact performance. Sport and exercise psychologists work with individuals to help them use self-talk effectively. For individuals who have negative self-talk, steps can be taken to help them make changes. Williams and Leffingwell identify several approaches to modifying self-talk: thought stopping, changing negative thoughts to positive thoughts, countering, and reframing.[28]

Thought stopping uses a trigger or cue to immediately interrupt unwanted thoughts when they occur. An athlete who hears herself begin to say "I can't…" can interrupt this negative thought by saying to herself or out loud the word "Stop," or by visualizing a red traffic stop sign. Interrupting the negative thought before it leads to negative feelings and adversely influences behavior can have a beneficial effect on performance. With consistent use of thought-stopping, the frequency of unwanted negative self talk can be decreased.

Replacing negative thoughts with positive thoughts is another approach. With this approach, negative self-statements are immediately followed by positive self-statements. For example, a basketball player who misses a foul shot may make the negative statement "I never am good from the foul line." The player can replace that negative statement with "I made five of my eight shots tonight. With more practice, I can increase that percentage." Compared to thought stopping, this approach encourages individuals to replace a negative thought with a positive one, rather than simply stopping the negative thought.

Countering focuses on challenging individuals' beliefs that lead them to accept negative statements as being the truth. Countering uses facts, reason, and rational thinking to refute negative thoughts. Once these negative thoughts are refuted, individuals are more accepting of positive self-statements. For example, an athlete may perceive herself as someone who chokes under pressure can counter that belief by examining her past performances in pressure situations. When the evidence is reviewed, it shows that the athlete actually performs well under pressure, especially in critical games. Now she is helped to replace the negative thought with "I know I can come through under pressure."

The technique of *reframing* focuses on altering individuals' view of the world or changing their perspective. Through this approach, negative statements are changed to positive statements by interpreting the situation differently. An athlete who is nervous and perceives his pounding heart as reflecting his anxiety can reinterpret this as "I'm geared up and ready to go." Athletes fearful of competition and the associated stress of winning and losing can be helped to reinterpret competition as a challenge and an opportunity to test themselves while providing the additional benefit of identifying areas of improvement.

Changing the self-talk of individuals presents a challenge to sport and exercise psychologists.

First, individuals may not be aware of their negative self talk. Before modifying self-talk, sport and exercise psychologists need to help individuals realize that self-talk can be self-defeating and adversely influence performance. Exploring the underlying beliefs that perpetuate negative self-talk, such as low self-esteem, is also an important part of the process. In some cases, dealing with the underlying cause of the negative self-talk will require additional interventions. Another challenge is that thought patterns are deeply ingrained and changing them, just like changing any other habit, requires motivation, new skills, practice, and patience.

For greatest effectiveness in modifying negative self-talk, Williams and Leffingwell suggest using a combination of thought stoppage, changing negative thoughts to positive thoughts, reframing and countering.[28] Self-talk is only one cognitive approach that can be used to enhance the performance of individuals as well as their personal development.

The use of self-talk is not limited to the realm of athletics. Students in physical education classes can be taught to use cognitive strategies, such as self-talk, to enhance their feelings of competence as movers. When starting a new activity unit, some students might engage in self-talk such as "I'm no good at this." This negative statement and others like them result in loss of motivation and lack of effort. Instead, students can be helped to reframe their self-talk and to see that the new unit presents them with an opportunity to improve their skills or learn new ones.

Self-talk can play a critical role in the adoption of a physically active lifestyle. Middle-aged individuals just beginning an exercise program after two decades of inactivity may experience self-defeating thoughts that ultimately may lead to their discontinuing participation. "I can't do this—I was never athletic anyway" may precipitate participant dropout. Self-talk may also affect participation in rehabilitation programs. For example, a gymnast rehabilitating a shoulder after rotator cuff surgery may be beset with self-doubts about whether he will be able to return to competition. Negative self-talk such as "This is a waste of time" may lead to less than full effort being expended during the performance of the rehabilitation exercises. As a professional, you need to recognize that such negative self-talk can have an adverse impact on achievements by participants in your programs. With training, physical educators, exercise scientists, and sport professionals can learn how to effectively modify self-talk to enhance the experiences of participants in their programs.

MENTAL IMAGERY TO ENHANCE PERFORMANCE

Imagery is an important mental training tool found to be effective in improving the performance of athletes. Recreational marathoners, Olympic platform divers, and professional golfers are among the thousands of athletes that use imagery to improve their performance. Imagery develops a blueprint for performance, enabling athletes to improve their physical skills and psychological functioning during competition. Imagery can assist athletes in attaining their goals.

Vealey and Greenleaf define *imagery* as the "process of using all the senses to re-create or create an experience in the mind."[28] Anderson explains that "mental imagery occurs when a person images an experience. The person 'sees' the image, 'feels' the movements and/or the environment in which it takes place, and 'hears' the sounds of the movement—the crowd, the water, the starting gun."[29] In contrast to daydreaming, imagery is a systematic process that is consciously controlled by the person, who takes an active role in creating and manipulating the images and structuring the experience. Imagery does not involve overt physical movements. Imagery in conjunction with physical practice can improve performance.

Nature of Imagery

There are two types of imagery: external imagery and internal imagery. Athletes who engage in *external imagery* see themselves performing as if they were watching a video of their performance. For instance, when a golfer observes herself completing a putt for par on a sunny day or a quarterback watches himself successfully throw a pass through the hands of a defender to the outstretched hands of his receiver, they are using external imagery.

Internal imagery is when athletes construct the image of the performance from the perspective of their own eyes, as if they were inside their body when executing the skill. From this perspective, athletes' images are formed from what they would actually see, feel, and hear in the situation if they were actually there. Using internal imagery, a surfer would feel her muscles tense and relax as she balances and moves up and down the board, adjusting her body position to ride the wave; she would see the sun beating down on the ocean, the waves forming, and her feet's position on the board. She would notice the sparkling water droplets from the ocean on her body, and hear the sound of the surf. Athletes using internal imagery see the experience from within themselves.

Athletes who are skilled at the use of imagery can use both the internal and external perspectives effectively. Some sport psychologists suggest that internal imagery is most effective for rehearsing skills and refining performance, and external imagery may be most helpful in assisting athletes to correct critical aspects of their performance.[28]

Vividness is a critical feature of imagery. *Vividness* refers to the clarity and detail of the mental image constructed by the athletes. Vividness is enhanced through the use of color, incorporation of multiple senses, and integration of emotion within the imagery.[28] Imagery goes beyond just the visualization or seeing of an event. The incorporation of other senses, such as kinesthetic (sensations of the body as it moves into different positions), gustatory (taste), olfactory (smell), auditory (hearing), and tactile (touch) senses, adds much to the vividness of the image.

The use of multiple senses enriches the detail of the image. If you compare the two descriptions of the images that follow, it is easy to see how the use of multiple senses enhances the image. One swimmer uses only vision in constructing a visualization of his event—the 400-yard individual medley. The swimmer images swimming and seeing the wall coming closer and closer with each stroke as he approaches the turn. Another swimmer also visualizes the wall coming closer and closer with each stroke. But he adds information from his other senses to increase the richness of the image. The swimmer images feeling the undulations of his body in the butterfly stroke, smelling the familiar odor of the chlorine in the pool, maintaining the pressure on the palms of his hands and soles of his feet with each stroke, and hearing the roar of the crowd as he sprints home with his freestyle, closing in on a record time.

Adding emotions to imagery further enhances its vividness. The swimmer can enhance his image by adding the feelings associated with the anxiety he experiences as he walks out on deck to the event, waiting behind the starting block to be introduced. As he hears himself being introduced and the roar of the crowd, he can feel the excitement of the race and the challenge it presents, and replace anxiety with the confidence he has gained from months of hard work. As he completes the race and looks up to the scoreboard to see his time, he can image feeling jubilant and excited at achieving a personal best. In experiencing these emotions, athletes should tune into the associated physiological responses, such as their heart rate or sweaty palms, and recognize the positive and negative thoughts associated with the various emotions. Emotions coupled with multisensory input enhance the effectiveness of imagery.

Controllability is an essential feature of effective imagery. Vealey and Greenleaf define *controllability* as "the ability of athletes to imagine exactly what they intend to imagine, and also the ability to manipulate aspects of the images that they wish to change."[25] Athletes must be able to control their images so that they can manipulate the image in certain ways to focus on critical aspects of performance. The ability to control images allows athletes to re-create experiences and view them from different perspectives. It also allows athletes to place themselves in situations that have not

occurred previously and rehearse different ways to effectively deal with these situations. If the situation occurs, athletes can respond to it competently and confidently because they have imagined their response. Being able to control the content and perspective of the image is critical to its effectiveness.

Uses of Imagery

Imagery is a versatile mental training technique and can be used in many different ways by athletes to enhance their performance. Vealey and Greenleaf identify seven uses for imagery: developing sport skills, correcting errors, rehearsing performance strategies, creating an optimal mental focus for competition, developing preperformance routines, learning and enhancing mental skills, and facilitating recovery from injuries and return to competition.[25]

Learning and practicing sport skills is one way that imagery can enhance athletes' performances. Athletes should select one or two skills to rehearse in their mind. They should rehearse these skills, focusing their imagery on executing the skill perfectly; this practice will help create a mental blueprint of the response. Athletes should incorporate as much relevant sensory information as they can. Athletes who are just beginning to learn a skill may benefit from viewing video of correctly performed skills. Coaches can also demonstrate the correct performance as well as provide verbal cues that will assist the athlete in correctly sequencing the skill's components or

---

IMAGERY USES

- Learn and practice sport skills
- Correct errors
- Rehearse performance strategies
- Optimize mental focus
- Enhance preperformance routines
- Strengthen mental skills
- Facilitate recovery from injury

mastering its timing. Athletes can perform the imagery on their own or the coach can incorporate imagery into the regular practice.

Error correction is another use for imagery. Athletes frequently receive feedback from their coaches suggesting corrections in skill execution or adjustments in execution of strategies. To enhance the effectiveness of this feedback, athletes can use imagery. After receiving feedback from the coach, athletes should image their performance with the corrections integrated into the image. Imagery allows athletes to experience how the skill or play looks and feels when performed correctly.

Learning and practicing performance strategies is another way that imagery can be used effectively by athletes. This allows athletes to rehearse what they would do in specific situations. For example, after a coach reviews set plays on a corner kick, soccer players can image themselves moving through the plays. This approach can also be used after the coach reviews a scouting report on an opponent. Using imagery, players can rehearse the strategies they will use against the opponent. For example, basketball players can rehearse the strategies they will use to counter the opponents' full-court press.

Imagery is also a useful tool for athletes seeking to optimize their mental focus. They can rehearse creating and maintaining a strong mental focus during competition. Vealey and Greenleaf suggest that coaches can assist athletes with this aspect of imagery by posing and helping answer two questions: "What will it be like?" and "How will I respond?"[28] Helping athletes understand the distractions, crowd noise and booing, and challenges in the competitive environment, such as poor officiating, allows them to imagine themselves effectively dealing with these situations. This advance preparation helps athletes to respond with greater confidence and composure, not react. Imagery allows athletes to gain experience in responding to a diversity of competitive challenges, whether expected or not.

Imagery is often incorporated into preperformance routines. Many athletes have a set routine they use prior to the performance of a skill, and imagery is a part of this routine. For example, a basketball player taking a free throw carefully positions her feet a certain way at the line, bounces the ball a set number of times, spins the ball in her hands, places her hands for the shot, and then takes a deep breath and exhales before shooting. Before releasing the ball, the player visualizes it leaving her hand, spinning, and entering the basket without touching a rim. Preperformance routines have beneficial effects on athletes' performance. These routines are practiced until they are automatic, essentially becoming part of the skill sequence.

Imagery can be used to strengthen a variety of mental skills critical to athletes' performance. It can enhance self-confidence and engender feelings of competence. This can be done by having athletes mentally re-create past successful performances, focusing on their accomplishments and the feelings associated with them. They can also rehearse via imagery coping confidently with performance errors, effectively managing their emotions in the heat of competition, and assertively meeting unexpected challenges during performance. The regulation of arousal is another way imagery can be used by athletes. Athletes can use imagery to psych up for a competition or to decrease their arousal if too high.

Facilitating recovery from injury and return to competition is another way that athletes can use imagery. When athletes cannot participate in practices because they are injured, they can attend practices and mentally image rehearsing skills and strategies. They can imagine themselves engaging in practices, performing drills, and scrimmaging, just as if they were participating. Imagery can also be used by athletes to enhance their recovery by setting rehabilitation goals and imaging their attainment.

Imagery can be used in many different ways to enhance athletes' performance. It can facilitate the learning of skills and correction of mistakes, and provide opportunities to rehearse and experiment with different performance strategies and tactics. Imagery can be used to strengthen athletes' mental skills and to aid in returning to

---

⚡ ⚡ FOCUS ON CAREER: Exercise and Sport Psychology ⚡ ⚡

PROFESSIONAL ORGANIZATIONS	• American Psychological Association—Division 47: Exercise and Sport Psychology (www.apa47.org) • Association for the Advancement of Applied Sport Psychology (www.aaasponline.org) • North American Society for the Psychology of Sport and Physical Activity (www.naspspa.org)
PROFESSIONAL JOURNALS	• *Journal of Applied Sport Psychology* • *Journal of Sport and Exercise Psychology* • *Research Quarterly for Exercise and Sport* • *The Sport Psychologist*

---

competition following injury. Athletes use imagery during their training, immediately prior to and during a competitive event, and following competition. When using imagery, it is important that the skill or situation be visualized correctly. If the skill is imaged incorrectly, performance decrement could occur. As imagery is learned and practiced, users should be encouraged to be accurate and precise in their imagery in order to gain maximum benefit.

Imagery is an important mental skill. Even though imagery was discussed in relation to athletes, it can be used in a variety of performance situations, such as public speaking or taking the National Athletic Trainers' Association certification exam. Imagery, goal setting, and self-talk are important mental skills that can enhance the learning and performance of people in a variety of situations.

INTERVENTION STRATEGIES

In recent years, coaches, teachers, and sport psychologists have turned to a variety of intervention strategies to help athletes achieve their optimal performance. As discussed earlier, anxiety and arousal can have harmful effects on athletes'

performance. Athletes' performance can also suffer due to lack of motivation, poor level of self-confidence, and, because of the intimate relationship between the mind and the body, negative thoughts and feelings about themselves and their capabilities. With the help of appropriate intervention techniques, athletes learn skills and strategies to regulate their physiological and psychological state to achieve optimum performance.

Sometimes athletes experience excessive anxiety and arousal, which causes a deterioration in their performance. Intervention strategies focusing on reducing this level would benefit these athletes. One way to deal with elevated levels of arousal is through the use of a variety of relaxation techniques. These techniques teach the individual to scan the body for tension (arousal is manifested in increased muscular tension) and, after identifying a higher-than-optimal level of tension, to reduce the tension to the appropriate level by relaxing. Once specific relaxation techniques are learned, this process should take only a few minutes. Types of relaxation training include progressive relaxation, autogenic training, transcendental meditation, and biofeedback. A note of caution is in order here, however. Athletes should be careful not to relax or reduce their level of arousal too much, because this will have a harmful influence on their performance.

In recent years, the use of cognitive strategies to facilitate optimum performance has gained increased acceptance. Cognitive strategies teach athletes psychological skills that they can employ in their mental preparation for competition. In addition to focusing on alleviating the harmful effects of anxiety and arousal, these cognitive strategies can also be used to enhance motivation and self-confidence and to improve performance consistency. These approaches include cognitive restructuring, thought stopping, self-talk, hypnosis and self-hypnosis, goal setting, and mental imagery.

Some cognitive intervention techniques focus on changing athletes' thoughts and perceptions. Self-talk, previously discussed, is an example of a cognitive intervention technique. Cognitive strategies can also be used to alter athletes' perceptions of events, thus reducing anxiety. Affirmation of athletes' ability to succeed in an upcoming competition is another cognitive strategy frequently used to promote optimal performance.

Imagery is the visualization of a situation. This technique has been used in a variety of ways to enhance performance. It can be used to mentally practice skills or to review outstanding previous performances. By remembering the kinesthetic sensations associated with the ideal performance, the athlete hopes to replicate or improve performance. Imagery has also been used as an anxiety reduction technique. The athlete visualizes anxiety-producing situations and then sees himself or herself successfully coping with the experience, thus increasing confidence to perform successfully in similar situations.

Intervention strategies have proved useful in helping athletes maximize their performance. These strategies are not only for athletes but also have implications for all participants in physical activities and sport. For example, the beginning jogger may derive as much benefit from goal setting as the high-level performer. The practitioner using these strategies must be cognizant of individual differences; otherwise, performance may be affected adversely.

The growth of sport and exercise psychology has provided physical education, exercise science, and sport professionals with a clearer understanding of various psychological factors that may affect an individual's performance. Sport and exercise psychologists have been able to enhance individual performance through the use of a diversity of intervention strategies. Although much of the work done in the area of sport psychology has been with athletes, many of the findings and techniques are applicable to participants in a variety of physical activity settings such as school, community, and corporate fitness programs. As the field of sport and exercise psychology continues to expand, practitioners will gain further insight into how to enhance the performance of all individuals.

SUMMARY

Sport and exercise psychology is concerned with the application of psychological theories and concepts to sport and physical activity. Although the physiological benefits of physical activity are well documented, physical education, exercise science, and sport professionals also need to be familiar with the psychological benefits of engaging in physical activity on a regular basis. Unfortunately, too many adults are inactive, and many adults who start a physical activity program drop out. Motivation influences the initiation, maintenance, and intensity of behavior. Exercise adherence focuses on understanding the factors that influence initiation and continuation of physical activity programs. Several theories have been used in research on physical activity participation and health behavior change, including classic learning theories, the belief model, the transtheoretical model, social cognitive theory, and the ecological perspective.

Sport psychologists have studied many different areas relative to athletic performance, including personality, anxiety, and arousal. Goal setting, imagery, and self-talk are three approaches used to help individuals improve their performance. To help athletes perform at their best, sport psychologists assist athletes in learning and using a variety of intervention strategies. Some of the findings, methodology, and intervention strategies of sport psychologists can also be used in other physical activity settings to help us better understand and enhance the experiences of participants in our physical activity programs.

DISCUSSION QUESTIONS

1. Motivation affects our initiation, persistence, and intensity of behavior. Reflect back on your participation in athletics or consider your commitment to being physically active on a daily basis. What motivated you to begin participating in your sport or to start working out? If you ended your participation, what were the reasons for discontinuing? Were you more intrinsically or extrinsically motivated?

2. Many different models have been developed to provide a framework to understand and promote behavior change. Which model do you believe has the greatest potential to encourage adults to change from a sedentary lifestyle to a more active one? Explain your choice. What commonalities do you find between the models and how can you use this information to help participants engaged in physical activity programs?

3. Think carefully about your experiences in organized sport. What strategies did coaches use to motivate the team and psych them up for competition? Which strategies were the most effective and which were least effective? Why? How did coaches account for individual differences among athletes in their motivational strategies?

4. Self-talk can have an impact on performance, either facilitating or hindering achievement. Think back to a recent performance situation, in either sport or another aspect of your life, perhaps like giving a speech. What was your self-talk before, during, and after the event? Did it help, hurt, or not impact your performance?

SELF-ASSESSMENT ACTIVITIES

These activities are designed to help you determine if you have mastered the materials and competencies presented in this chapter.

1. Justify the claim that participation in physical activity can have positive psychological benefits. Develop a 500-word essay to substantiate your claim.

2. Using the information provided in the Get Connected box, access the MindTools or Athletic Insight site and read about one of the topics in sport and exercise psychology. Choose a topic that interests you. Then write one to two pages summarizing what you have learned and discussing how you can apply that information in your professional career.

3. Too many people are inactive on a regular basis. Furthermore, many people who begin an exercise program drop out. Using the information on exercise adherence, create a brochure that highlights both the physiological and psychological benefits of regular physical activity. Then include in your brochure information that would encourage people to begin and stay involved in a program (e.g., small groups with individually designed exercise programs). Be sure to include images and pictures highlighting physical activity and a catchy title.

4. In recent years, the field of sport psychology has expanded tremendously. As a practitioner, whether a teacher, coach, adapted physical educator, athletic trainer, or exercise physiologist, you are concerned with optimizing individuals' performance. Discuss the roles of anxiety, arousal, attention, self-talk, and goal setting in the performance of motor skills and the use of intervention strategies to enhance performance.

REFERENCES

1. Vealey RS: Psychology of sport and exercise. In SJ Hoffman and JC Harris, editors, Introduction to kinesiology: studying physical activity, Champaign, Ill., 2000, Human Kinetics.

2. Association for Applied Sport Psychology (www.appliedpsychonline.org).

3. International Society of Sport Psychology (www.issponline.org).

4. Gill D: Sport and exercise psychology. In JD Massengale and RA Swanson, editors, The history of exercise and sport science, Champaign, Ill., 1997, Human Kinetics.

5. US Department of Health and Human Services: Physical activity and health: a report of the surgeon general, Atlanta, Ga., 1996, US Department of Health and Human Services, Centers for Disease Control and Prevention, National Center for Chronic Disease Prevention and Health Promotion.

6. Berger BG: Psychological benefits of an active lifestyle: what we know and what we need to know, Quest 48:330–353, 1996.

7. Cox RH: Sport psychology: concepts and applications, ed 5, New York, 2002, McGraw-Hill.

8. Petruzzello SJ: Exercise and sports psychology. In SB Brown, Introduction to exercise science, Philadelphia, 2001, Lippincott Williams & Wilkins.

9. Fontaine KR: Physical activity improves mental health, The Physician and Sportsmedicine 28(10):83–84, 2000.

10. Brannon L and Feist J: Health psychology: an introduction to behavior and health, ed 2, Belmont, Calif., 1992, Wadsworth.

11. Dishman RK and Sallis JF: Determinants and interventions for physical activity and exercise. In C Brochard, RJ Shephard, and T Stephens, editors, Physical activity and health, fitness, and health: international proceedings and consensus statement, Champaign, Ill., 1994, Human Kinetics.

12. Prochaska JO and Velicer WF: The transtheoretical model of health behavior change, American Journal of Health Promotion 12:38–48, 1997.

13. Samuelson M: Commentary: changing unhealthy lifestyle: who's ready . . . who's not?: an argument in support of the stages of change component of the transtheoretical model, American Journal of Health Promotion 12:13–14, 1997.

14. Duffy FD, with Schnirring L: How to counsel patients about exercise—An office-friendly approach, The Physician and Sportsmedicine 28(10):53–54, 2000.

15. Herrick AB, Stone WJ, and Mettler MM: Stages of change, decisional balance, and self-efficacy across four health behaviors in a worksite environment, Journal of Health Promotion 12:49–56, 1997.

16. Leffingwell TR, Rider SP, and Williams JM: Application of the transtheoretical model to psychological skills training, The Sport Psychologist, 15:168–187, 2001.

17. King AC, Blair SN, Bild DE, Dishman RK, Dubbert PK, Marcus BH, Oldridge NB, Paffenbarge RS, Jr., Powell KE, and Yaeger KK: Determinants of physical activity and intervention in adults, Medicine and Science in Sports and Exercise Supplement 24(6):S221–S236, 1992.

18. Nieman, DC: Fitness and sports medicine: an introduction, Palo Alto, Calif., 1990, Bull.

19. Fisher AC, Scriber KC, Matheny ML, Alderman MH, and Bitting LA: Enhancing athletic injury rehabilitation adherence, Journal of Athletic Training 28(4):312–318, 1993.

20. Bianco T and Eklund RC: Conceptual considerations for social support research and exercise settings: the case of sport injury, Journal of Sport and Exercise Psychology, 23:85–107, 2001.

21. Anshel MH: Sport psychology from theory to practice, Scottsdale, Ariz., 1997, Gorsuch Scarisbrick.

22. Cox RH: Sport psychology concepts and applications, ed 6, New York, 2007, McGraw-Hill.

23. Levitt EE: The psychology of anxiety, Hillsdale, N.J., 1980, Earlbaum.

24. Weinberg RS: Goal setting in sport and exercise: research to practice. In JL Van Raalte and BW

340   **PART II**   Foundations of Physical Education, Exercise Science, and Sport

Brewer, Exploring sport and exercise psychology, ed 2, Washington, D.C., 2002, American Psychological Association.

25. Vealey RS and Greenleaf CA: Seeing is believing: understanding and using imagery in sport. In JM Williams, Applied sport psychology: personal growth to peak performance, ed 5, New York, 2006, McGraw-Hill.

26. Locke EA, Shaw KN, Saari LM, and Latham GP: Goal-setting and task performance, Psychological Bulletin 90:125–152, 1981.

27. Weinberg RS and Gould D: Foundations of sport and exercise psychology, Champaign, Ill., 1999, Human Kinetics.

28. Williams JM and Leffingwell TR: Cognitive strategies in sport and exercise psychology. In JL Van Raalte and BW Brewer, Exploring sport and exercise psychology, ed 2, Washington, D.C., 2002, American Psychological Association.

29. Anderson A: Learning strategies in physical education: self-talk, imagery, and goal-setting, JOPERD 68(1):30–35, 1997.

CHAPTER 2

Personality as a Core Characteristic of the Individual

KEY TERMS

Athletic Motivation Inventory
Athletic pyramid
Big five personality traits
Cattell 16 PF
Cognitive-affective
  processing system
Disposition
Emotional intelligence
Global personality traits
Gravitational hypothesis
Interactional model
MMPI
Multivariate approach
Myers-Briggs Type
  Indicator
Personality
Personality paradox
Personality profile
Personality trait
Resilience

Troutwine Athletic Profile
Winning Profile Athletic
  Instrument

Sport psychologists have long been intrigued with the question of whether or not successful athletic performance can be accurately predicted on the basis of personality assessment. Personality assessment was apparently a factor in the Indianapolis Colts professional football team's decision to select Peyton Manning over Ryan Leaf to be its first-round draft pick in 1998 (Carey, 1999; Rand, 2000). History records that Manning went on to stardom with the Colts, while Ryan Leaf continued to struggle with the San Diego Chargers and later was traded. Ryan Leaf retired in the year 2002 after a lack-luster career (King, 2002). This single event is built up in the press as evidence of the

Athletes also exhibit interesting personality styles. Courtesy Kansas State University Sports Information.

effectiveness of personality testing in predicting athletic success. Apparently, a large percentage of professional teams use personality testing to assist them in making personnel decisions. Not everyone, however, agrees with this practice.

In the 1960s and 1970s, research involving the athlete and personality assessment was very popular. Ruffer (1975, 1976a, 1976b), for example, cited 572 sources of original research in a compilation of references on the relationship between personality and athletic performance. In recent years, however, interest in this kind of research has waned because of a lack of consistent correlation between personality factors and athletic prowess. However, in view of the current practice of many teams in the National Football League to include personality assessment in decision making, it behooves the sport psychology student to be knowledgeable about personality and personality assessment in sport.

Concepts to be introduced and studied in this section include (a) a definition of personality,

(b) theories of personality, (c) measurement of personality, and (d) personality and sport performance. As we shall learn, personality assessment involves measuring relatively stable personality traits, and not unstable mood and emotion.

Personality Defined

As defined by Kalat (1999, p. 477), **personality** is "all the consistent ways in which the behavior of one person differs from that of others, especially in social situations." The key words in this definition are the words "consistent" and "differs." An individual's personality defines the person in unique ways that remain stable and consistent over time. If an athlete consistently exhibits the characteristics of being assertive on and off the athletic field, we might say that he is an assertive person.

One of the difficulties scientists have in determining the personality characteristics of an individual is that the individual may purposefully or inadvertently "mask" her true personality. Hollander (1976) wrote about this problem when he said that *typical responses* and *role-related behaviors* don't always reflect a person's true personality, or *psychological core*. A typical response is indicative of how an individual usually behaves in a social setting, while a role-related behavior is indicative of how the person behaves in various specific situations. Consider the example of the athlete who is being recruited to play football at a major university. The university representative asks the high school football coach about the athlete's personality. The coach responds that he is very quiet, but hard-working. When this same question is asked of the athlete's girlfriend, she replies that he is actually very sociable and outgoing.

Theories of Personality

In this section we will consider five major theoretical approaches to the study of personality: psychodynamic theory, social learning theory, humanistic theory, trait theory, and Jung's theory of personality types. Each will be briefly discussed.

Psychodynamic Theory

Sigmund Freud's psychodynamic theory (1933) and his method of treating personality disturbances were based primarily upon self-analysis and extensive clinical observation of neurotics. Two distinguishing characteristics of the psychodynamic approach to personality have been its emphasis upon in-depth examination of the *whole* person, and its emphasis upon unconscious motives.

In Freud's view, the id, ego, and superego form the tripartite structure of personality. The id represents the unconscious instinctual core of personality; in a sense, the id is the pleasure-seeking mechanism. In contrast, the ego represents the conscious, logical, reality-oriented aspect of the personality. The superego represents the conscience of the individual. Essentially, Freud advocated a conflict theory of personality. In this respect, the three parts of the psychic structure are always in conflict. The individual's personality is the sum total of the dynamic conflicts

between the impulse to seek release and the inhibition against these impulses.

Social Learning Theory

From the viewpoint of social learning theory, behavior is not simply a function of unconscious motives (as in psychoanalytic theory) or underlying predispositions. Rather, human behavior is a function of social learning and the strength of the situation. An individual behaves according to how she has learned to behave, as this is consistent with environmental constraints. If the environmental situation is prominent, the effect of personality traits or unconscious motives upon behavior should be minimal.

The origin of social learning theory can be traced to Clark Hull's (1943) theory of learning and to B. F. Skinner's (1953) behaviorism. Hull's stimulus-response theory of learning was based on laboratory experimentation with animals. According to stimulus-response theory, an individual's behavior in any given situation is a function of his learned experiences. Other researchers, such as Miller and Dollard (Miller, 1941), Mischel (1986), and Bandura (1977, 1986), extended the Hullian notions of complex human behavior.

Humanistic Theory

The major proponents of the humanistic theory of personality are Carl Rogers and Abraham Maslow. Unlike the pessimistic Freud, Rogers and Maslow argued that human nature is inherently healthy and constructive. At the center of the humanistic theory of personality is the concept of *self-actualization*. The human organism possesses an innate drive or tendency to enhance itself, to realize capacities, and to act to become a better and more self-fulfilled person. In the developing personality, openness to experiences that then shape the individual is of critical importance. It is not necessarily the experience that shapes the individual, but the individual's perception of that experience. Self-actualization is an ongoing process of seeking congruence between one's experiences and one's self-concept. Rogers's

CONCEPT   Five basic approaches for explaining the phenomenon of personality include psychodynamic theory, social learning theory, humanistic theory, trait theory, and Jung's theory of personality.

APPLICATION   In attempting to explain behavior on the basis of personality, it is important to recognize the ramifications of adopting one theoretical approach over another. The teacher's or coach's belief system will influence athlete-coach interactions.

influence on the development of the humanistic theory of personality is largely due to his method of psychotherapy, which is nondirective and client-centered. Maslow's contribution to the humanistic theory is in the development of his hierarchical motive system based on the notion of hierarchical needs.

Trait Theory

The basic position of trait, or factor, theory is that personality can be described in terms of traits possessed by individuals. These **personality traits** are considered synonymous with **dispositions** to act in a certain way. Traits are considered to be stable, enduring, and consistent across a variety of differing situations. Those who exhibit the trait of a need to achieve success, for example, can be expected to have a disposition toward competitiveness and assertiveness in many situations. A disposition toward a certain trait means not that the individual will *always* respond in this manner, but that a certain likelihood exists.

Among the most ardent advocates of trait psychology are psychologists such as Gordon Allport, Raymond Cattell, and Hans Eysenck. Cattell (1965, 1973) identified 35 different traits that he believed describe a personality. Using a similar approach, British psychologists (Eysenck & Eysenck, 1968) concentrated on the dimensional traits of neuroticism-stability and introversion-extraversion.

Jung's Theory of Personality

Up to this point, reliance on trait theory has overshadowed Jung's theory of personality types in the sport psychology literature. As articulated by

Jacobi (1973) and more recently by Beauchamp, Maclachlan, and Lothian (2005), the foundation of Carl Jung's theory of personality is the notion that an individual's personality is based on two personality attitudes (introversion and extraversion) and four functions or mental processes (thinking, feeling, sensing, and intuition). The two functions of thinking and feeling are classified as being rational or judging, while the two functions of sensing and intuition are classified as being irrational or perceiving. The combination of the two attitudes and the four functions allows for the categorization of individuals into eight personality types. Because each of these eight personality types can be either primary (dominant) or inferior (auxillary) you have a total of 16 possible personality types. Jung, however, argued against simply classifying individuals into genetically determined personality typologies. While Jung recognized the influence of genetic factors in shaping personality, he also believed that individuals are active agents in shaping their own personalities as they interact with the environment and other people. The Myers-Briggs Type Indicator, to be discussed in the measurement section of this chapter, is based on Carl Jung's theory of personality.

The Measurement of Personality

This section will identify and briefly discuss various techniques used for assessing personality. It should be pointed out that the various methods of assessing personality correspond closely to the basic personality theories we have just discussed. For example, projective tests such as the Rorschach test are closely linked to the psychoanalytic theory of personality. Conversely, the various paper-and-pencil inventories are linked to trait theory. In this brief overview of personality measurement techniques, the reader should be aware that many issues regarding personality assessment remain unresolved. The methods outlined here are not perfect; nor do psychologists agree on the meaning of the results of any particular test.

Three basic classes of measurement techniques may be identified. These are (1) rating scales, (2) unstructured projective tests, and (3) questionnaires. Each of these three categories will now be discussed, with particular emphasis upon the questionnaire method. The questionnaire method is highlighted because it is the measurement technique most commonly used by sport psychologists today.

Rating Scales

Characteristically, *rating scales* involve the use of a judge or judges who are asked to observe an individual in some situation. The judges employ the use of a checklist or scale that has been predesigned for maximum objectivity. Usually, if the checklist is used properly and the judges are well trained, the results can be fairly reliable and objective.

Typically, two types of situations are involved in personality assessment using rating scales. These are the *interview* and the *observation of performance*. In the interview, the judge asks the subject numerous open-ended and specific questions designed to ascertain personality traits and general impressions. Observation of a participant during some type of performance situation is the second kind of rating system used for ascertaining personality. As with the interview, observations can be effective if the checklist being used is well-designed and planned, and if the observer is highly trained.

Unstructured Projective Procedures

The foregoing rating methods are generally used for ascertaining data on traits of personality, although in many instances inferences may be made concerning underlying motives. Projective procedures may also be used to identify traits, but

they are commonly used to determine information about underlying motives. Projective techniques allow subjects to reveal their inner feelings and motives through unstructured tasks. These unstructured techniques are used primarily in clinical psychology and are somewhat synonymous with the psychoanalytic and humanistic approaches to explaining personality. The underlying assumption in the unstructured test situation is that if subjects perceive that there are no right or wrong responses, they will likely be open and honest in their responses.

Several kinds of unstructured tests have been developed. Among them are the Rorschach Test (Sarason, 1954), the Thematic Apperception Test (Tompkins, 1947), the Sentence Completion Test (Holsopple & Miale, 1954), and the House-Tree-Person Test (Buck, 1948). For our purposes, only the Rorschach (also known as the "inkblot") and Thematic Apperception Tests (TAT) will be discussed. The inkblot and the TAT are by far the most commonly used projective tests.

The Rorschach Test Herman Rorschach, a Swiss psychiatrist, was the first to apply the inkblot to the study of personality (Kalat, 1999). The Rorschach test was introduced in 1921, and remains the most famous of all the projective testing devices. The test material consists of ten cards. Each card has an inkblot on it, which is symmetrical and intricate. Some of the cards are entirely in black and white, while others have a splash of color or are nearly all in color. The cards are presented to the subject one at a time and in a prescribed order. As the cards are presented, the subject is encouraged to tell what he sees. The tester keeps a verbatim record of the subject's responses to each, and notes any spontaneous remarks, emotional reactions, or other incidental behaviors. After all the cards have been viewed, the examiner questions the subject in a systematic manner regarding associations made with each card.

The Thematic Apperception Test The Thematic Apperception Test, developed by Henry Murray and his associates in 1943 at the Harvard

University Psychological Clinic, has been used almost as extensively as the Rorschach test. The TAT is composed of nineteen cards containing pictures depicting vague situations, and one blank card. The subject is encouraged to make up a story about each picture. In contrast to the vague blots in the Rorschach test, pictures in the TAT are rather clear and vivid. It is believed that subjects reveal or project important aspects of their personalities as they weave the characters and objects in the pictures into either an oral or a written story.

Structured Questionnaires

The structured questionnaire is a paper-and-pencil test in which the subject answers specific true-false or Likert scale–type statements. A typical Likert scale–type statement is illustrated in the following example:

In athletic situations, I find myself getting very uptight and anxious as the contest progresses.

DEFINITELY FALSE				*DEFINITELY TRUE*
1	2	3	4	5

There are many different kinds of questionnaire-type personality inventories. Certain specific personality types or traits are believed to be identified through the administration of these questionnaires. For our purposes we will focus our discussion on the four most commonly used personality inventories. One of these inventories was developed to be used with individuals suffering from personality disorders, while the other three were developed for normal populations. All of these inventories are of interest, because both have been used in sport-related research involving athletes. Following the discussion of these four general inventories, we will briefly discuss the personality inventories designed specifically for athletes. In addition, we will discuss inventories designed to measure emotional intelligence and resilience as they relate to sport performers.

Minnesota Multiphasic Personality Inventory

The Minnesota Multiphasic Personality Inventory (**MMPI**) is the most widely used of all personality inventories. The MMPI consists of a series of true-false questions designed to measure certain personality traits and clinical conditions such as depression. The original version of the MMPI, composed of 550 items, was developed in the 1940s and is still in use (Hathaway & McKinley, 1940). A revised version of the inventory, composed of 567 items, was developed in 1990 and named the MMPI-2 (Butcher, Graham, Williams, & Ben-Porath, 1990). These authors also developed a new form of the inventory to be used with adolescents (MMPI-A). Traits measured by the MMPI-2 include the following: hypochondria, depression, hysteria, psychopathic deviation, masculinity-feminity, paranoia, obsessive-compulsive behavior, schizophrenia, hypomania, and social introversion.

Cattell's Sixteen Factor Personality Inventory

Developed by Robert Cattell (1965), the Sixteen Factor Personality Inventory (**Cattell 16 PF**) is based upon 35 personality traits originally identified by Cattell. Through a statistical process known as factor analysis, Cattell reduced the 35 specific traits to 16 broader traits or factors. The 16 factors measured by the 16 PF are believed to be personality traits exhibited by normal individuals. The current edition of the 16 PF is titled the 16 PF Fifth Edition (Russell & Karol, 1994), and is composed of 185 items.

Cattell believed that the 16 traits measured by the 16 PF could be further condensed down to five secondary or **global personality traits.** Cattell's global traits and the big five traits are presented in table 2.1 along with Cattell's 16 primary traits. In comparing the descriptions of the Cattell global traits with those of the big five traits, it is clear that they are not exactly the same. However, extraversion appears on both lists, and neuroticism and anxiety are essentially the same.

From Cattell's perspective, it is interesting to look at table 2.1 to see what factors constitute

TABLE 2.1 | Primary and Global Personality Traits Associated with the 16 PF, as Well as Personality Traits Associated with the "Big Five"

16 PF Primary Traits	16 PF Global Traits	Big Five Traits
1. Warmth	1. Extraversion	1. Extraversion
2. Reasoning	2. Anxiety	2. Neuroticism
3. Emotional Stability	3. Tough-Mindedness	3. Conscientiousness
4. Dominance	4. Independence	4. Openness
5. Liveliness	5. Self-Control	5. Agreeableness
6. Rule-Consciousness		
7. Social Boldness		
8. Sensitivity		
9. Vigilance		
10. Abstractedness		
11. Privateness		
12. Apprehension		
13. Openness to Change		
14. Self-Reliance		
15. Perfectionism		
16. Tension		

what we call personality. Of even greater interest is the plotting of the an individual's standardized scores for each of the 16 personality traits on a line graph. Plotted standardized scores produce what sport psychologists call a **personality profile.** A hypothetical personality profile is illustrated in figure 2.1.

NEO–Five Factor Personality Inventory

The NEO–Five Factor Personality Inventory (NEO-FFI) is a 60-item personality inventory designed to measure the **big five personality traits** of extraversion, neuroticism, conscientiousness, openness, and agreeableness. The 60-item NEO-FFI is extracted from the more comprehensive NEO Personality Inventory-R (Costa & McCrae, 1992). For ease of administration and when time is important, Gosling, Rentfrow, and Swann (2009), reported on the development and testing of both a 5- and 10-item version of the NEO-FFI. Of the two brief versions, their data supported the use of the 10-item version over the 5-item.

Myers-Briggs Type Indicator The **Myers-Briggs Type Indicator** (MBTI; Myers, 1962; Myers, McCaulley, Quenk, & Hammer, 1998) is based on Jung's theory of personality types, previously introduced. While the MBTI has not been used very often with athlete populations, it has been used extensively in business and in other professions where organizational leadership and behavior are important (e.g., industry, corporations, armed forces). The MBTI is composed of 93 forced choice questions that represent word pairs that the participant must decide between. Based on the choices that are made, the participant is assigned one of 16 personality types. Scores on other types are not necessarily dismissed, as a participant may score relatively high on more than one typology. As explained by Beauchamp et al. (2005), the results of the MBTI provide the athlete and coach with a theoretical framework for interacting with each other and other members of a team. If everyone on an athletic team completes the MBTI, then the results provide a framework

FIGURE 2.1 | Personality profile showing how an athlete's scores compare to the population mean (zero).

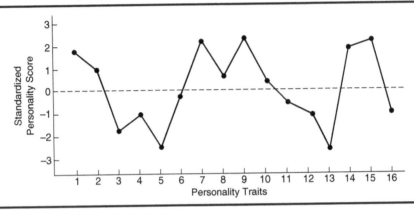

for athletes to learn more about themselves as well as about other members of the team.

Structured Questionnaires Designed for Athletes

In addition to the specific personality inventories identified in the previous paragraphs, sport psychologists have developed personality inventories designed to measure personality traits in athletes. These inventories have generally been developed for the purpose of studying the relationship between personality and athletic performance. A few of these inventories will be introduced here.

Before we begin this discussion, you should know that *no scientific study to date has shown a strong statistical relationship between personality variables and athletic ability.* We will look at the evidence on this matter later in the chapter, but for now it is important for you to understand this fact about personality testing. This statement casts doubt on the practices of professional teams that use personality testing for the purposes of team selection, especially if they give significant weight to results of the testing. Personality testing can play an important role in player development, but no evidence exists to justify its use in making personnel decisions. If a test developer believes that he has developed an inventory that can accurately predict athletic success, he has the responsibility to put it to the test and make the data available to scientists. Three personality/psychological inventories will be mentioned in this section, along with a brief discussion of two inventories designed to measure a single personality trait.

Athletic Motivation Inventory   The **Athletic Motivation Inventory** (AMI) was developed by Thomas Tutko, Bruce Ogilvie, and Leland Lyon at the Institute for the Study of Athletic Motivation at San Jose State College (Tutko & Richards, 1971, 1972). According to its authors, the AMI measures a number of personality traits related to high athletic achievement: drive, aggression, determination, responsibility, leadership, self-confidence, emotional control, mental toughness, coachability, conscience development, and trust.

The reliability and validity of the instrument have been questioned by Rushall (1973), Corbin (1977), and Martens (1975). However, Tutko and Richards (1972) say that thousands of athletes have been tested and that the AMI was originally based upon the 16 PF and the Jackson Personality Research Form (Ogilvie, Johnsgard, & Tutko, 1971).

CONCEPT & APPLICATION

CONCEPT   Many structured personality inventories are available for measuring the personality traits of athletes. Each of these inventories or tests was designed for a specific purpose and with a particular participant in mind. Tests should be selected with care.

APPLICATION   In terms of reliability and validity, the Cattell 16 PF is a good test to be used for measuring the personality of athletes. When using this test, consult your team sport psychologist, your school psychologist, or other trained professionals regarding the correct administration of the test and interpretation of results.

Perhaps the real concern of sport psychologists is not that the test is more or less reliable than other personality inventories, but that the developers implied that it could predict athletic success. No other organization, researcher, or promoter has made similar claims about other more distinguished personality inventories. The unsubstantiated claims of the developers of the AMI hurt the field of sport psychology in terms of legitimacy.

A study by Davis (1991) supports this position. Davis studied the relationship between AMI subscales and psychological strength in 649 ice hockey players who were eligible for the National Hockey League (NHL) entry draft. The criterion measure of psychological strength was based on an evaluation of on-ice play by NHL scouts. The results showed that less than 4 percent of the variance in scout ratings was accounted for by AMI scores ($r = .20$). This outcome suggests that the AMI is a poor predictor of psychological strength of ice hockey players.

Winning Profile Athletic Instrument   The **Winning Profile Athletic Instrument** (WPAI) was developed by Jesse Llobet of PsyMetrics. The WPAI is a fifty-item inventory that measures conscientiousness and mental toughness. Llobet (1999) reported internal reliability coefficients of .83 and .87 for these two factors respectively. When completing the instrument, athletes are asked to use their own sport as a frame of reference for answering questions. In one investigation, Llobet (1999) reported correlations of between .30 and .43 between WPAI scores and coaches' ratings for

conscientiousness and mental toughness. In a second study, Paa, Sime, and Llobet (1999) administered the WPAI to high school, collegiate, semiprofessional, and professional athletes. Results showed significant differences between the mean total WPAI scores for high school athletes and all other groups, and between collegiate athletes and professional athletes.

Troutwine Athletic Profile   The **Troutwine Athletic Profile** (TAP) was developed by Bob Troutwine, a professor of psychology at William Jewell College (Carey, 1999; Rand, 2000). According to news reports, the TAP was used by the Indianapolis Colts to help them make their decision to select Peyton Manning over Ryan Leaf in the 1998 professional football draft. Psychometric properties of the TAP have not been published in any of the mainline sport psychology journals; nor has anything scientific been published about the validity of the test in terms of predicting athletic success.

Emotional Intelligence   Depending on how it is measured, **emotional intelligence** may be conceptualized as either a personality trait or as a mental ability to be learned. The two approaches to conceptualize emotional intelligence are captured within the two emotional intelligence inventories described below. Regardless of which approach is used to measure emotional intelligence, it is expected that emotional intelligence is associated with the ability to regulate emotions and with increased positive mood and self-esteem (Schutte, Malouff, Simunek, McKenley, & Hollander, 2002).

Emotional Intelligence Scale The Emotional Intelligence Scale (EIS; Schutte, Malouff, Hall, et al., 1998; Schutte, Malouff, Simunek, et al., 2002) is a 32-item inventory designed to measure emotional intelligence as a relatively stable personality disposition or trait. As originally conceptualized, the EIS measured emotional intelligence as a unidimensional construct (single score). However, based on a factor analysis study, it was suggested that emotional intelligence, as measured by the EIS, was actually multidimensional in nature and composed of four relatively independent subscales (Petrides & Furnham, 2000). These four subscales were (a) perception of emotions, (b) managing emotions in the self, (c) social skills or managing others' emotions, and (d) utilizing emotions. In an applied study involving baseball players, Zizzi, Deaner, and Hirschhorn (2003) observed that emotional intelligence, as measured by the EIS, was correlated with pitching but not hitting performance.

Mayer-Salovey-Caruso Emotional Intelligence Test The Mayer-Salovey-Caruso Emotional Intelligence Test (MSCEIT; Mayer, Salovey, & Caruso, 2002) is a 141-item scale designed to measure specific emotional intelligence skills that may be learned over time. As originally conceptualized by Mayer and Salovey (1997), emotional intelligence is composed of the following four skills or branches: (a) ability to perceive and express emotion, (b) ability to assimilate emotion in thought, (c) ability to understand and analyze emotion, and (d) ability to regulate emotions. The advantage of the learned ability approach to conceptualizing emotional intelligence is that it is optimistic in nature, as it implies that one can learn to be emotionally intelligent. Meyer and Fletcher (2007) provide an excellent contrast between the trait and learned ability approach to conceptualizing emotional intelligence. In the final analysis, Meyer and Fletcher argue in favor of the learned ability approach to conceptualizing emotional intelligence.

Resilience The importance of resilience in sport is addressed by Galli and Vealey (2008). In their research, they asked athletes how they overcome their most difficult and challenging examples of adversity (e.g., injury, slump, burnout, college transition, illness). Four general themes emerged from this research, including dealing with agitation and adversity through coping strategies, positive outcomes from the agitation and coping process, identification of personal resources to support coping efforts, and sociocultural influences that also support coping efforts. Taken together these four themes formed the basis of their conceptual model of how sport resilience is developed. In addressing the notion of resilience theory, Richardson (2002) identified three levels or waves of resiliency inquiry. The first wave involves the identification of the qualities possessed by resilient individuals. The second wave involves a description of the disruptive process by which resilient qualities are integrated or learned by individuals. The Galli and Vealey investigation is an example of this kind of research. The third wave involves the process by which individual athletes discover the innate and learned forces within themselves that allow them to possess personal resilience. As explained by Richardson (2002), personal **resilience** is the force within the individual that drives a person to confront and overcome adversity. This force may be described as an innate righting mechanism and as the human capacity to confront and overcome adversity.

As conceptualized by Bartone, Ursano, Wright, and Ingraham (1989), the Dispositional Resilience Scale (DRS) is a 45-item inventory that measures dispositional resilience or hardiness. The inventory measures the three dimensions of control, commitment, and challenge. An abbreviated version of the DRS was also suggested by the developers of the DRS. The abbreviated version is composed of 30 items also rated on a 4-point Likert scale. High scores on the three dimensions indicate high resilience, while low scores indicate low resilience.

Personality and Sport Performance

Since 1960, several comprehensive literature reviews have been completed in an attempt to clarify the relationship between personality and

In the paragraphs that follow, sport personality research will be synthesized and general conclusions drawn on several topics of interest.

Athletes Versus Nonathletes

John McEnroe dominated men's professional tennis in the 1980s though superior skill and a volatile personality. Courtesy Kansas State University Sports Information.

sport performance (Cofer & Johnson, 1960; Cooper, 1969; Hardman, 1973; Ogilvie, 1968, 1976; Morgan, 1980b). Of these, the review by Morgan (1980b) provided the most comprehensive treatment of the subject. While not fully endorsing the position that personality profiles can accurately predict sport performance, Morgan argued that the literature shows a consistent relationship between personality and sport performance when (a) response distortion is removed, and (b) data are analyzed using a multivariate approach. A **multivariate approach** is used when multiple measures of personality are analyzed simultaneously, as opposed to separately. Since personality is multifaceted and complex, it is appropriate that statistics used to analyze personality measures also be complex. While it is good to remember that the relationship between sport performance and personality is far from crystal clear, it seems equally true that certain general conclusions can be drawn.

Athletes differ from nonathletes on many personality traits (Gat & McWhirter, 1998). It is often a matter of conjecture whether these differences favor the athletes or the nonathletes. Schurr, Ashley, and Joy (1977) clearly showed that athletes who participate in team and individual sports are more independent, more objective, and less anxious than nonathletes. From Hardman's (1973) review it is also clear that the athlete is often more intelligent than average. Additionally, Cooper (1969) describes the athlete as being more self-confident, competitive, and socially outgoing than the nonathlete. This is supportive of Morgan's (1980b) conclusions that the athlete is basically an extravert and low in anxiety.

In several investigations, a number of comparisons have been made between an athlete's score on various personality and psychological inventories and scores associated with norm groups. For example, compared to published normative data, the scores of professional cowboys indicate that they tend to be alert, enthusiastic, forthright, self-sufficient, reality based, and practical (McGill, Hall, Ratliff, & Moss, 1986). Compared to norm groups, elite rock climbers exhibit low anxiety, emotional detachment, low superegos, and high levels of sensation seeking (Robinson, 1985).

While the evidence favors the conclusion that the athlete differs from the nonathlete in many personality traits, the problem arises in the definition of what constitutes an athlete. In the Schurr et al. (1977) research, an athlete was defined as a person who participated in the university intercollegiate athletic program. This would seem to be a viable criterion. However, this classification system has not been universally adopted by researchers. Some studies, for example, have classified intramural and club sports participants as athletes. Other studies have required that participants earn

<table>
<tr><td>

| 2.3 | CONCEPT & APPLICATION |
</td></tr>
</table>

2.3	CONCEPT & APPLICATION

CONCEPT Generally speaking, athletes differ from nonathletes in many personality traits. For example, it can be demonstrated that athletes are generally more independent, objective, and extraverted than nonathletes, but less anxious.

APPLICATION As a coach, expect your athletes to be generally higher in such traits as independence,

extraversion, and self-confidence, and lower in anxiety, than nonathletes. One cannot, however, rank athletes on the basis of these traits or make team roster decisions based on them. A statistical relationship (often low) does not suggest a cause-and-effect relationship.

2.4	CONCEPT & APPLICATION

CONCEPT Athletes tend to be more extraverted, independent, and self-confident than nonathletes because of a process of "natural selection," and not necessarily due to learning. Individuals who exhibit certain personality traits may tend to gravitate toward athletics. An important exception to this principle occurs in the formative years before the young athlete reaches maturity. During the early maturing years, the youth sport experience is critical in forming positive personality traits such as independence and low trait anxiety.

APPLICATION Coaches and teachers who work with young boys and girls must be very careful that the athletic experience is a positive one in the lives of young people. Athletic programs designed for youth should place a premium on the development of feelings of self-worth, confidence, and independence, and relegate winning to a position of secondary importance. Winning must not be more important than the needs of the boys and girls.

awards, such as letters, in order to be considered athletes. Until some unifying system is adopted, it will always be difficult to compare results from one study with those from another.

Developmental Effects of Athletic Participation upon Personality

Given that athletes and nonathletes differ on the personality dimensions of extraversion and stability, is this due to the athletic experience (learning), or to a natural selection process in which individuals possessing certain personality traits gravitate

toward athletics? Perhaps an unequivocal answer to this question will never be known; however, the evidence typically supports the **gravitational hypothesis.** Individuals who possess stable, extraverted personalities tend to gravitate toward the athletic experience. As the competitive process weeds out all but the keenest of competitors, those who remain are those having the greatest levels of extraversion and stability. This could be described as sort of an athletic Darwinism (survival of the fittest). Some of the studies that support the gravitational model are those by Kane (1970) and Rushall (1970).

CONCEPT & APPLICATION

CONCEPT   Generally speaking, it can be demonstrated that differences exist in the personalities of athletes who engage in different types of sports. Perhaps the clearest distinction occurs between athletes involved in team sports and those involved in individual sports. For example, team sport athletes are more extraverted, dependent, and anxious than individual sport athletes. Certainly, one might expect some differences to emerge between football players and tennis players in terms of personality traits.

APPLICATION   Personality profiles may be used by trained sport psychologists to help athletes decide which sports to devote their energies to, but they should never be used to coerce the athletes into making such decisions. If a young athlete with a tennis player's personality wants to be a golfer, so be it. Occasionally, an athlete reaches a juncture in her athletic career when she must decide between two sports in order to devote adequate time to academic work. Perhaps consideration of the athlete's personality profile would be useful at this point.

The viability of the gravitational model, however, does not preclude the possibility that sport participation can enhance personality development. In this respect, Tattersfield (1971) has provided longitudinal evidence that athletic participation before maturity has a developmental effect upon personality. Specifically, Tattersfield monitored the personality profiles of boys participating in an age-group swimming program across a five-year training period. Significant changes toward greater extraversion, stability, and dependence were observed in the boys during this period. From an educational perspective, all but the factor of dependence would be considered positive in nature.

Personality Sport Type

Can personality profiles of athletes in one sport be reliably differentiated from those of athletes in another sport? Perhaps the first real attempts to answer this question were made with bodybuilders. Research by Henry (1941), Thune (1949), and Harlow (1951), for example, suggested that bodybuilders suffer from feelings of masculine inadequacy, and are overly concerned with health, body build, and manliness. A study by Thirer and Greer (1981), however, would tend to cast doubt on these earlier stereotypes. In a well-conceived and controlled study, the authors concluded that intermediate and competitive

bodybuilders were high in achievement motivation and resistance to change, but relatively normal in all other traits measured. They found no support for the previous generalities and negative stereotyping sometimes applied to bodybuilders.

Kroll and Crenshaw (1970) reported a study in which highly skilled football, wrestling, gymnastic, and karate athletes were compared on the basis of Cattell's 16 PF. The results showed that when the football players and wrestlers were contrasted with the gymnasts and karate participants, significantly different personality profiles emerged. The wrestlers and football players had similar profiles, while the gymnasts and karate athletes differed from each other, as well as from the wrestlers and football players.

Similarly, Singer (1969) observed that collegiate baseball players (a team sport) differed significantly from tennis players (an individual sport) in several personality variables. Specifically, tennis players scored higher than baseball players on the desire to do one's best, desire to lead, and ability to analyze others, but were less willing to accept blame.

Schurr et al. (1977), in their signal research, clearly demonstrated that personality profile differences exist between players of team and individual sports, and between players of direct and parallel sports. Team sport athletes were observed to be more anxious, dependent, extraverted,

| 2.6 | CONCEPT & APPLICATION |

CONCEPT   In many cases, athletes playing different positions on the same team can be differentiated as a function of personality characteristics. This is especially pronounced in sports in which athletes are required to do very different kinds of things. Point guards in basketball, setters in volleyball, quarterbacks in American football, and goalies in soccer and/or ice hockey can be expected to exhibit personality characteristics decidedly different from those of some other position players.

APPLICATION   Personality characteristics of athletes can be considered in the selection of players for certain specialized positions. Results of personality tests and the like may be helpful in identifying a self-confident, energetic, and outgoing extravert to run your multiple offense in volleyball or your motion offense in basketball. You may also ascertain that an individual has these same important characteristics by simply observing athletes in competitive situations. It may not take a pencil-and-paper test to tell you that Mary excels at taking charge of the team when she is on the court. One should not forget, however, that physical characteristics such as speed, power, and quickness are also critically important.

and alert-objective, but less sensitive-imaginative, than individual sport athletes. Direct sport athletes (basketball, football, soccer, etc.) were observed to be more independent and to have less ego strength than parallel sport athletes (volleyball, baseball, etc.).

Clingman and Hilliard (1987) examined the personality characteristics of super-adherers and found them to differ significantly from the population norm in the personality traits of achievement, aggression, autonomy, dominance, endurance, harm avoidance, and play. Super-adherers are runners, swimmers, cyclists, and triathletes who are dedicated to endurance activities. While data were not provided, the expectation is that the super-adherer would also differ from athletes in other sports in certain personality traits.

The literature shows that athletes in one sport often differ in personality type and profile from athletes in other sports (Franken, Hill, & Kierstead, 1994). It seems reasonable, for example, to expect a football player to be more aggressive, anxious, and tolerant of pain than a golfer or a tennis player. However, the point still needs to be made that the state of the art (or science) is still not so refined that one could feel justified in arbitrarily categorizing young athletes based on their personality profiles.

Player Position and Personality Profile

In the previous section, the notion of personality types among athletes of differing sports was discussed. It was concluded that in many circumstances, differences exist between the personality profiles of athletes from different sports. The same concept can be applied to whether athletes of a certain sport exhibit different personality profiles based on player position.

In recent years we have experienced an age of superspecialization in team sports. In baseball, outfielders are inserted based on whether they hit left- or right-handed. In football, the offense and defense of the same team rarely come in contact with each other. In volleyball, hitters and setters have specialized roles that dictate the sorts of defensive and offensive assignments they fulfill. Similar kinds of specializations can be observed with most other team sports.

While this area of research would seem to be of interest to coaches and athletes, very little has been reported on it. Cox (1987) asked the following question relative to the sport of volleyball. Do center blockers, strong-side hitters, and setters display different psychological profiles due to their different assignments? The participants were

157 female volleyball players who participated in an invitational volleyball tournament. The results indicated that the three groups of athletes were very similar in terms of their psychological profiles, with the exception of certain attentional focus variables. Compared to middle blockers and strong-side hitters, setters were observed to have a broad internal focus and be able to think about several things at one time. The setter on a volleyball team is like the point guard on a basketball team or the quarterback on a football team. She must be cognizant at all times of what plays to call and of the strengths and weaknesses of front-line attackers, as well as the strengths and weaknesses of the opposing team's blockers and defensive alignment.

In a similar study reported by Schurr, Ruble, Nisbet, and Wallace (1984), a comparison was made between player position in football and personality traits. Using the Myers-Briggs Type Inventory (MBTI), the authors concluded that linesmen differ significantly from backfield players in terms of judging and perceiving traits. Linesmen tend to be more organized and practical, while defensive and offensive backs are more flexible and adaptable. Interestingly, no reliable differences were noted between offensive and defensive linesmen, while offensive backs tended to be more extraverted and defensive backs more introverted.

Personality Profiles of Athletes Differing in Skill Level

The ability to distinguish between successful and unsuccessful athletes in any particular sport using personality traits has never been particularly successful (Davis & Mogk, 1994; Morgan, 1980b). For example, Kroll (1967), using collegiate wrestlers, and Kroll and Carlson (1967), using karate participants, could not successfully distinguish between the successful and unsuccessful performers. Rushall (1972), using football players, and Singer (1969), using tennis and baseball players, likewise could not distinguish between the successful and unsuccessful players. In addition,

Craighead, Privette, and Byrkit (1986) were unable to distinguish between starters and nonstarters in high school boys' basketball.

A study by Williams and Parkin (1980) provides clarity to this line of reasoning. Specifically, they compared the personality profiles (Cattell's 16 PF) of 18 international-level male hockey players with those of 34 national-level and 33 club players. Their results showed that the international players had significantly different profiles from the club players, but that the national-level players could not be distinguished from players in either of the other two groups.

Thus, one exception to the general rule that skill level cannot be differentiated as a function of personality may occur when *elite athletes* are compared with athletes of lesser ability. Notice that in the Williams and Parkin (1980) study cited above, international-level hockey players exhibited personality profiles that differed from those of club-level players, but not national-level players. Silva (1984) provided a plausible explanation for this phenomenon. As illustrated in figure 2.2, as aspiring elite athletes move up the **athletic pyramid,** they become more alike in their personality and psychological traits. At the base or entrance level of sport, athletes are very heterogeneous, or have different personalities. However, certain personality traits will enhance an athlete's likelihood of advancing to a higher level, while other traits will undermine it. Through a process of "natural selection," at each higher level of the athletic personality pyramid, the athletes become more alike, or more homogeneous, in their personality traits. When trying to differentiate between athletes of varying skill levels in the middle and lower parts of the pyramid, we meet with failure. Elite athletes, however, will exhibit similar profiles and will differ as a group from less-skilled groups.

The Female Athlete

The conclusions and generalizations that have been drawn from the previous comparison areas have come primarily through research conducted

FIGURE 2.2 | The personality-performance athletic pyramid.

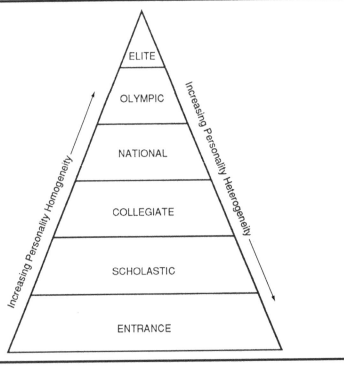

Source: From Personality and sport performance: Controversy and challenge by Silva, J. M., III. (1984). In J. M., Silva, III and R. S. Weinberg (Eds.), *Psychological foundations of sport,* Human Kinetics Publishers, Inc. Reproduced by permission of publisher.

on male rather than female participants. This is not to say that the conclusions would have been any different if female participants had been used. Indeed, we should expect the results to be essentially the same. However, after a thorough review of the available literature, Morgan (1980a) drew this conclusion: "Comparisons of college athletes and nonathletes, or athletes from different sport groups, did not appear to be consistent in the literature dealing with females" (p. 60). Morgan blames methodological and design problems for the inconsistent results. He points out that this inconsistency seems to disappear when the successful or elite female athlete is compared with the "normative" female.

After reviewing much of the available literature on the female athlete and personality, Williams (1980) cautiously concluded that the "normative" female differs in personality profile from the successful female athlete. Specifically, the female athlete is found to exhibit personality traits much like those of both the normative male and the male athlete (i.e., assertive, achievement-oriented, dominant, self-sufficient, independent, aggressive, intelligent, and reserved). For example, in comparison with available norms, female bodybuilders were observed to be more extraverted, more vigorous, less anxious, less neurotic, less depressed, less angry, and less confused (Freedson, Mihevic, Loucks, & Girandola, 1983).

CONCEPT & APPLICATION

CONCEPT   As they move up the athletic pyramid, as illustrated in figure 2.2, athletes become more alike, or homogeneous, in terms of both their personalities and their skill levels. Correlations between athletic ability and personality traits are either nonexistent or trivial for athletes within the same hierarchical level.

APPLICATION   Results of personality testing should not be used to decide who should be first- or second-string players on an athletic team. Similarly, results of personality testing should not be used to decide whether an athlete is selected for a team at any level of competition. Results of personality testing are somewhat effective in distinguishing players on an elite level from players on a lower level, but this provides little new information. Results of personality testing may provide some useful diagnostic information to help an athlete make needed personal adjustments, but they provide only a small amount of athletic ability information. Organizations that insist on using personality or psychological testing to make personnel decisions will make some good decisions, but they will also make a lot of bad decisions.

The Interactional Model

In the previous sections, we learned that personality alone is a weak predictor of athletic behavior (performance). The individual, however, does not normally function in isolation. The athlete, possessed with a distinct set of personality traits, performs alongside other individuals and in changing environmental conditions (situation). It is believed, therefore, that the sum of the two plus their interaction would be a stronger predictor of athletic behavior. The notion that the personality interacts with situation to predict performance is known as the **interactional model.** Situational factors include stressful situations and perceived intensity of the situations. Information about personality plus information about the situation plus the interaction between the two is a better predictor of athlete behavior than personality or the situation alone. This relationship is represented in the following formula:

$$\text{Behavior} = \text{Personality} + \text{Situation} + P \times S + \text{Error}$$

The error in the formula represents all of the *unmeasured* factors that may contribute to athletic behavior.

The relationship between the personality of the individual and the situation is illustrated in figure 2.3. In this figure, the total pie represents all the factors that can contribute to athletic behavior or performance. Only a small part of the total pie is due to factors associated with the athlete's personality. Another small portion is due to factors directly related to the situation and independent of or unrelated to the person. Next, a certain part of the pie is represented by the interaction between the personality and the situation. When factors associated with the athlete's personality, the environmental situation, and the interaction between these three are summed, approximately 30 percent of the athlete's behavior is accounted for. If we were to consider only the athlete's personality, then we could explain only about 10 to 15 percent of the athlete's performance or behavior.

While the interaction concept illustrated in figure 2.3 is conceptually accurate, the reality is that in many situations the strength of the environmental conditions is so strong that it essentially dwarfs the influence of personality on performance. For example, consider the situation in which a basketball player is sent to the foul line to shoot two free throws with his team trailing by one point and there is no time left on the clock. The athlete shooting the

FIGURE 2.3 | Illustration showing the contribution of personality and situation to total athlete behavior.

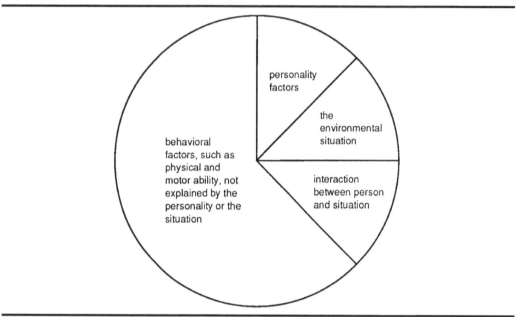

free throw may have a disposition to be low in anxiety, but it is unlikely that anyone could approach this situation without feeling anxious. In this particular situation, the athlete who normally hits 85 percent of his free throws might hit both shots or uncharacteristically miss one or both. It is also conceivable that an athlete who normally hits 65 percent of her free throws might hit both shots and win the game. In both situations, the athlete's personality remains the same because it is relatively stable, yet actual athlete behavior (performance) may be inconsistent. Smith (2006) referred to this inconsistency between behavior and personality as the **personality paradox.**

Based on earlier work by Mischel and Shoda (1995) Smith proposed the **cognitive affective processing system** (CAPS) (Figure 2.4) as a way to explain the personality paradox. According to CAPS, an individual's personality interacts with

the environment (situation) to determine a behavioral response (performance). The actual response (shooting the free throws), however, is filtered through the five elements of the CAPS system. The resultant behavioral response will be the end result of the filtering. Because every situation is different, the behavioral responses will also be different and inconsistent from one occasion to the next. This is true despite the fact that the athlete's basic personality has not changed from one situation to the next. As illustrated in figure 2.4, the five elements of the CAPS system are as follows:

1. Stimuli are *encoded* and are mentally represented in memory.

2. Predetermined *expectations* and *beliefs* confer meaning on events.

3. *Affects* and *emotions* influence behavior.

4. Personal *goals* and *values* influence behavior.

CONCEPT & APPLICATION

2.8

CONCEPT The combined and interactive effects of personality and the environment constitute a stronger predictor of athletic performance than personality alone.

APPLICATION The fact that Linda is an anxious person may not be predictive of athletic performance, but the fact that Linda is an anxious person *and* that she gets very anxious in competitive

situations might be. These two factors together, and the interaction between them, may create a situation that will not be conducive to consistent ground stroking in competitive tennis. The coach needs to know more about Linda than that she is generally an anxious person. The coach also needs to know how she responds in a specific competitive situation.

FIGURE 2.4 | The Cognative-Affective Processing System (CAPS) applied to athlete behaviour (based on Mischel & Shoda, 1995; Smith, 2006).

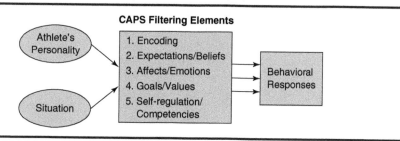

5. *Competencies* and *self-regulation skills* interact with the other four elements to determine behavior.

The fifth element of the filter interacts with the other four elements to determine how the environmental

situation interacts with personality to determine the behavioral response. Behavioral responses are inconsistent and vary from situation to situation because of the changing environmental situation and the influence of the elements of the filter.

Summary

Personality is defined as all the consistent ways in which the behavior of one person differs from that of others, especially in social situations. An individual's personality defines the person in unique ways that remain stable and consistent over time. A person's typical responses and role-related

behaviors don't always reflect that person's true personality.

Five theories or approaches to studying personality were reviewed. These were (1) the psychodynamic approach, (2) social learning theory, (3) humanistic theory, (4) the trait theory approach, and (5) Jung's theory of personality types. A number of different approaches to measuring personality were also discussed. These included rating scales, projective procedures, and pencil-and-paper inventories. A number of different personality inventories were described, including the Minnesota Multiphasic Personality Inventory, Cattell's 16 PF, the NEO–Five Factor Personality Inventory, the Myers-Briggs Type Indicator, the Athletic Motivation Inventory, the Winning Profile Athletic Instrument, and the Troutwine Athletic Profile. In addition, inventories that measure emotional intelligence and resilience were discussed.

Several factors were considered concerning whether a relationship exists between athletic performance and an athlete's personality. The following conclusions were drawn: (1) athletes differ from nonathletes on many personality traits; (2) athletes who exhibit certain personality traits gravitate toward athletic involvement; (3) athletes in one sport often differ in personality, type, and profile from athletes in other sports; (4) an association exists between personality and player position in some sports; (5) it is difficult to discriminate between players of differing skill level based purely upon personality variables; (6) elite athletes can be discriminated from athletes of low ability based on personality variables; and (7) female athletes are very similar to male athletes in the general conclusions that have been drawn.

Personality by itself is an important but relatively weak predictor of athletic performance and behavior. In conjunction with the situation or environment, however, the influence of personality on behavior is enhanced (the interaction model). The interaction model is described in mathematical terms as follows: Behavior = Personality (P) + Situation (S) + P × S + error. The application of the cognitive-affective processing system (CAPS) helps to explain the nature of the interaction model. Personality of the athlete and the environment are filtered by five elements of the CAPS to determine the athlete's response. The five elements are encoding, beliefs, affect, goal and values, and self-regulation skills. The most important of these five elements are the competencies and self-regulation skills possessed by the athlete.

Critical Thought Questions

1. Why do you think the big five personality traits do not agree exactly with Cattell's five global traits?

2. Now that you have studied the various ways that sport psychologists measure personality, which inventory would you recommend for use? Why?

3. Given that research does not support the use of personality profiles for making athlete personnel decisions, why do you think the practice persists?

4. Provide a summary statement about the existence and strength of the relationship between personality and athletic performance.

5. Why would the interactional model improve the prediction of athletic performance? Do you think it improves it enough to make the model useful for personnel decisions about athletes?

6. Discuss the cognitive-affective processing system (CAPS) as a way of understanding the interaction model.

Glossary

Athletic Motivation Inventory A personality inventory designed to predict athletic success (Institute for the Study of Athletic Motivation).

athletic pyramid A pyramid showing less-skilled players at the base and more highly skilled players at the top. Athletes at the bottom are more heterogeneous in terms of personality characteristics, while those at the top are more homogeneous.

big five personality traits Trait psychologists identified the five major personality traits to be neuroticism, extraversion, agreeableness, conscientiousness, and openness.

Cattell 16 PF Cattell's Personality Factor Questionnaire, measuring the 16 source traits of personality.

Cognitive-affective processing system (CAPS) Model of leadership and personality that explains how personality interacts with the environment to produce a behavioral response.

disposition A tendency to behave in a certain manner. Also called a personality trait.

Emotional intelligence The innate or learned ability to regulate emotions, typically associated with positive mood and self-esteem.

global personality traits Cattell's version of the big five personality traits: extraversion, anxiety, tough-mindedness, independence, and self-control.

gravitational hypothesis The notion that athletes possessing stable, extraverted personalities gravitate toward athletics.

interactional model An approach to sport personality based on the notion that both personality traits and situational states should be used in any prediction equation.

MMPI Minnesota Multiphasic Personality Inventory; a 12-scale test designed for clinical populations.

multivariate approach The practice of measuring and analyzing correlated dependent variables simultaneously, as opposed to separately, as in the univariate approach.

Myers-Briggs Type Indicator A personality inventory, based on Jung's theory of personality types, that categorizes individuals according to personality type.

personality All the consistent ways in which the behavior of one person differs from that of others, especially in social situations.

Personality paradox The seeming contradiction that although personality traits within an individual are considered to be stable and consistent, the individual's behavioral responses in varied situations are not consistent.

personality profile The plotting of an athlete's standardized personality scores on a line or bar graph.

personality trait A disposition to exhibit certain personality characteristics.

Resilience The force within the individual that drives a person to confront and overcome adversity.

Troutwine Athletic Profile A personality inventory designed to predict athletic success (Troutwine).

Winning Profile Athletic Instrument A personality inventory designed to predict athletic success (PsyMetrics).

CHAPTER

4

Motivational Processes and the Facilitation of Quality Engagement in Sport

Joan L. Duda, *The University of Birmingham*
Darren C. Treasure, *Competitive Advantage International*

I've always believed that if you put in the work, the results will come. I don't do things halfheartedly. Because I know if I do, then I can expect half-hearted results. That's why I approached practices the same way I approached games. You can't turn it on and off like a faucet. I couldn't dog it during practice and then, when I need that extra push late in the game, expect it to be there.
 —Michael Jordan, National Basketball Association MVP 1988, 1991, 1993, 1996, and 1998

The principle is competing against yourself. It's about self-improvement, about being better than you were the day before.

 —Steve Young, VP Super Bowl XXIX

Michael Jordan and Steve Young speak to the very essence of why understanding motivation is of such interest to coaches, parents, sport psychologists, and athletes alike. Motivation is the foundation of sport performance and achievement. Without it, even the most talented athlete is unlikely to reach his or her full potential. Motivation is also pertinent to how the athlete experiences and responds to sport. Whether or not sport contributes positively or negatively to athletes' welfare is linked to motivation-related factors. In spite of its significance in the athletic milieu, however, motivation is one of the most misunderstood psychological constructs among sport participants and practitioners.

What is motivation, and how does an athlete or his or her coach optimize it? Some think that whether an athlete is high or low in motivation is somehow inherent in the athlete's personality—a relatively unchangeable characteristic of the person. Others believe coaches "motivate" athletes, perhaps in their pre-game "pep talks" or in the techniques they use in practice to foster their athletes' focus and intensity. There is, perhaps, some truth in each of these perspectives. However, sport motivation is more complex and multifaceted than either.

Contemporary research shows motivation to be dependent both on some malleable, psychological tendencies of the athletes themselves *and* on aspects of the social environments in which they develop, train, and compete. In particular, variations in motivation are held to be a function of the diverse ways in which athletes *interpret* their sport-related experiences. These different ways of interpreting sport stem from individual dispositional differences between athletes and situational dynamics.

How do we decide if an athlete is motivated? Is good or poor performance the best or only indicator? In general, researchers suggest that motivation is inferred from variability in **behavioral patterns.** For example, John, a club tennis player, seeks out opponents who really challenge his game. Whether practicing or competing, John tries his hardest to get to every shot and to hit it well, even when down love–40 in a game or behind 1–5 in a set. John maximizes the tennis talent that he has. When an athlete such as John tries hard, seeks out challenge, persists in the face of adversity, and performs up to his ability level on a reasonably consistent basis, we typically conclude that this person is highly motivated. In contrast, if John were to hold back in training or a match and not give his best effort, prefer to play opponents or work on drills that are too easy or way beyond his capabilities, regularly experience performance impairment or fail to live up to his potential, and contemplate dropping out or actually quitting tennis, we infer that motivational problems abound.

A number of factors need to be considered before we can determine the degree to and way in which the participant is motivated. It is important to take into account how much motivation the individual has (i.e., the *quantity* of motivation) as well as the *quality* of that motivation (Duda, 2001, 2005). Typically, the quantity of motivation is reflected in how "into" her or his sport the athlete is at the present time and how well she or he is currently performing. The quality of motivation is inferred by the athlete's

sustained and positive engagement in the sport. This includes both the athlete's accomplishments and the degree of enjoyment and psychological and physical benefits associated with sport involvement. Variability in the quantity and quality of sport motivation are intricately linked with how athletes *think* before, during, and after their engagement in sport.

What thoughts appear critical to variations in motivation? Researchers (e.g., Ryan & Deci, 2002) have shown that individuals feel and act more motivated when they think they have the competence to meet the demands of the task at hand and believe they have some control, or autonomy, in regard to their participation. The assumption that perceptions of ability and autonomy are critical to motivational patterns is fundamental to a number of popular contemporary theories of motivated behavior. Three of those theoretical frameworks, which have provided a foundation for research and practice on sport motivation, will be reviewed here. These are (1) self-efficacy or social cognitive theory, (2) the achievement goal frameworks, and (3) self-determination theory.

Believing That One Can: The Construct of Self-Efficacy

I don't even think about the prospect of not winning—it never occurs to me. I really am that confident.

—Daley Thompson, 1984 and 1988
Olympic decathlon champion

Negative thoughts lead to a negative performance; the connection is as straightforward as that.

—Sally Gunnell, Olympic gold medalist,
world record holder, and world champion
400 meter hurdler

Although not exactly synonymous with the concept of self-efficacy, the words of Daley Thompson, one of the world's greatest ever athletes, are a clear testament to the "power of positive thinking." The words of Sally Gunnell also provide insight into the effect of negative thinking—namely, that if you don't think you can do it you won't.

Positive thinking is thought to be a very important antecedent of positive behavioral patterns, especially in challenging, achievement-oriented contexts such as competitive sport. Athletes think positively when they believe they can do something effectively, that is, when they think in a self-efficacious manner. (See Chapter 17 for a more complete discussion of positive versus negative thinking.) **Self-efficacy** is defined as a person's judgment about her or his capability to successfully perform a particular task (Bandura, 1986). Such judgments relate to the *level* of performance expected, the *strength* or certainty of those attainment beliefs, and the *generality* of those beliefs to other related tasks or domains. Bandura (1997) refined the definition of self-efficacy to encompass those beliefs regarding individuals' capabilities to produce performances that will lead to anticipated outcomes, and the term **self-regulatory efficacy** now encompasses a social cognitive approach that articulates the role cognition plays in performance above and beyond simple behavioral or skill beliefs.

Bandura (1986) has argued that (1) our efficacy beliefs mediate subsequent thought patterns, affective responses, and action and that (2) self-efficacy is positively related to positive motivational patterns. In general, sport research has shown that self-efficacy is a positive predictor of motor skill acquisition, execution, and competitive sport performance (Bandura, 1997; Feltz, Short, & Sullivan, 2007; Treasure, Monson, & Lox, 1996). Self-efficacy is one among a variety of mechanisms that is associated with higher performance. Athletes with high self-efficacy are more likely to try harder, choose challenging tasks, experience positive emotions, and be less anxious. The influence of self-efficacy on performance and other achievement-related behaviors also seems to be intertwined with the goal-setting process (see Chapter 13). That is, although self-efficacy may directly relate to variations in performance, its impact may be because of its effect on athletes' personal goal setting and the development and employment of self-regulation skills (Feltz, et al., 2007; Schunk, 1995).

It is interesting to note, however, that previous performance tends to be a better predictor of subsequent pretask self-efficacy than efficacy judgments are of ensuing performance (Feltz, et al., 2007). The athlete's incentives (whether intrinsic or extrinsic) to try to turn that self-efficacy into reality have an impact on the predictive utility of those initial task-specific confidence judgments. Further, if high performance is defined with respect to successful competitive outcomes, the athlete has relatively less control over achieving those outcomes than if the performance standard is self-referenced. That is, high self-efficacy does not always translate into a win. It does increase the probability, however, that the athlete will do well in terms of the facets of performance within her or his personal control which could contribute to winning. Coaches, sport psychologists, and athletes themselves would be wise to optimize efficacy judgments prior to the athletes' engagement in training or competitive-related activities. In other words, it is important for athletes to think (and act!) confidently if they want to perform optimally.

Implications for Practice

How do we increase an athlete's self-efficacy? Thankfully, existing theoretical frameworks and sport research provide some insight into the antecedents of task-specific confidence in the sport domain. Six key determinants of self-efficacy are emphasized (e.g., Bandura, 1997; Feltz et al., 2007) (Figure 4-1):

1. The most influential determinant of self-efficacy is *past performance*. Especially when the task is difficult, we tend to feel more confident about performing a particular task when we have demonstrated mastery of that activity before—success breeds success. Therefore, when learning a new aspect of technique or strategy or gaining experience in sport competitions, it is important for athletes to accumulate progressively more demanding accomplishments to build their sense of competence. Breaking down the task into manageable "chunks" or decreasing the difficulty of early-in-the-season opponents are two ways of increasing the probability of initial positive performance and, thus, fostering athletes' self-efficacy.

62   Chapter 4   **Motivational Processes and the Facilitation of Quality Engagement in Sport**

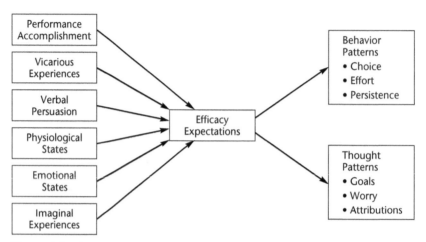

Figure 4-1 **The relationship between sources of self-efficacy, efficacy expectations, and behavior and thought patterns**
Source: Adapted from Feltz, 1988.

2. Another antecedent of athletes' efficacy judgments is *vicarious experience* (Bandura, 1986). For example, watching someone else successfully perform the activity, especially if this person is deemed to be similar to the athlete in question, can facilitate self-efficacy. This is a more salient source of efficacy information among younger athletes and those who have had limited experience with the task at hand. By watching or modeling others, athletes can learn how to do things. Also, if done in an informative rather than a comparative manner, coaches can use vicarious experiences to help athletes believe that "if he or she can do it, so can I!" Participation modeling, where the athlete engages in the task while observing someone else do it (and, thus, works his or her way through the activity), can be particularly appropriate for efficacy building (Feltz, et al., 2007).

3. It is important to remember that our heads are attached to our bodies (and vice versa!). With respect to formulating efficacy judgments, athletes also may look to their *physiological state* in deciding whether they can successfully meet specific task demands. More specifically, athletes appraise their physiological condition—state of autonomic arousal, fear,

pain, fatigue, and so on—and make judgments as to their readiness to "rise to the occasion." By mastering techniques such as progressive muscle relaxation and deep breathing, which help them modify physiological conditions such as the heightened muscle tension, heart rate, and respiration rate associated with stress (Chapter 15), athletes can facilitate their preperformance self-efficacy. Similarly, for those athletes who have difficulty "getting up" for competition, energizing strategies may be effective in increasing arousal levels that will, for example, enhance perceptions of precompetition self-efficacy.

4. *Verbal persuasion* from coaches, sport psychologists, and significant others is another antecedent of self-efficacy. This can be in the form of feedback ("Here's how to do this"; "You did this correctly") or motivational ("Come on, you can do it!") statements. If the person conveying the efficacy-enhancing information is considered credible and knowledgeable, the verbal persuasion is likely to be more influential. Athletes also often employ verbal persuasion (or positive self-talk, see Chapter 17) to help themselves feel efficacious about what they are about to do. As there is a tendency to act according to how we think, positive self- and task-related statements made by athletes can increase their self-efficacy, too.

5. Similar to a consideration of their physiological state, athletes also appraise their *emotional state,* or mood, prior to performing when they decide on their level of confidence (Maddux, 1995). Consequently, emotional control techniques should be helpful in enhancing task-specific confidence among athletes who find themselves being debilitated by anger, frustration, and other negative mood states. Our thoughts can precipitate different emotional responses, and cognitive interventions such as "negative thought stopping" (see Chapter 17) can also result in higher efficacy judgments among sport competitors, not only decreasing negative mood states but also, and perhaps more significantly, increasing positive mood states (Treasure et al., 1996).

6. Finally, *imaginal experiences* are assumed to have an impact on task-specific self-confidence (Maddux, 1995). If athletes go through the demands of a sport activity in their minds before performing, those demands might not seem so daunting or unfamiliar, and the athletes' perceptions of their ability to meet those demands should be increased. Seeing (and feeling) yourself doing something successfully before actually doing it can also enhance your perceptions of ability (see Chapter 16 on imagery in sport).

Keep in mind that these critical antecedents to self-efficacy can be interdependent. For example, an athlete can use imagery to help reduce over-activation (e.g., imaging a peaceful setting to diminish one's muscular tension or high heart rate) or to attenuate the cognitive anxiety associated with an upcoming competition. In this way imaginal strategies are employed to influence the physiological and emotional states that subsequently feed an athlete's preperformance efficacy judgments.

It is beyond the scope of the present chapter to go into depth regarding these constructs and their correlates, but sport researchers have also considered perceptions of task-specific confidence

in terms of teams and team leaders (i.e., coaches). *Collective efficacy* captures the degree of confidence team members have in their collective abilities to do what is necessary (e.g., play effective defense) to reach team goals (Feltz, et al., 2007). Perceptions of collective efficacy share many of the same antecedents as self-efficacy (Bandura, 1997), but these sources of confidence center on the team as a whole (e.g., previous team performance, verbal persuasion by the coach or spectators directed toward the team). According to Feltz and colleagues (Feltz, Chase, Moritz, & Sullivan, 1999, p. 765), *coaching efficacy* relates to the degree "to which coaches believe they have the capacity to affect the learning and performance of their athletes." Assumed to be multidimensional, overall coaching efficacy is held to be a function of coaches' judgments regarding their ability to teach and implement strategy, effectively motivate their athletes, diagnose and provide proper instruction regarding sport skills, and promote "character" and psychosocial maturity in their players. Previous coaching-related success, coaching experience and preparation, and the perceived skill and efficacy of one's athletes have been proposed as important antecedents of coaching efficacy (Feltz, et al., 2007).

Achievement Goals: The Importance of How We Judge Our Competence

> *I never played to get into the Hall of Fame. I only tried to be the best that I could be.*
>
> —*Walter Payton, member of the National Football League Hall of Fame*

Maintaining confidence is certainly important to exhibiting optimal motivated behaviors in sport settings. However, anyone with experience with training and competing in sport has witnessed athletes whose judgments of self-efficacy are more fragile than those of other athletes. We also have observed that not every competitor who has experienced setbacks (performance failure, losses) and is not feeling especially confident exhibits problems regarding the quantity or quality of his or her motivation. Why might that be so? Our contemporary understanding of sport motivation recognizes that adaptive versus problematic motivational patterns are not merely a function of whether an athlete has high or low self-efficacy. Rather, we need to also consider the criteria that athletes use to decide whether they are able or not. That is, how does the athlete define demonstrated competence?

Thus, another area of research that may assist athletes, coaches, and sport psychologists in understanding and enhancing motivation in sport is based on achievement goal frameworks. These frameworks assume that differences in goal perspectives, or the ways in which individuals judge their competence and perceive success, are the critical antecedents to variations in the direction and intensity of behavior. These models of motivation, similar to self-efficacy theory (Bandura, 1986), assume that perceptions of competence (how able we think we are) do relate to motivational patterns. However, achievement goal frameworks also state that how we decide whether we have been able or not is essential to the prediction of the quantity and quality of our motivation (Duda, 2001).

Fundamental to achievement goal models is that there are, at least, two central achievement goal perspectives (task and ego) that govern the way athletes think about achievement and guide subsequent decision making and action (Nicholls, 1989). According to Nicholls (1989), task and ego goal states entail distinct ways of processing an activity and can fluctuate throughout the course of an event. When task involved, an athlete's main purposes are to gain skill or knowledge, to exhibit effort, to perform at one's best, and to experience personal improvement. This athlete is focused on what he or she is doing and is thinking primarily about how to accomplish the task. If such purposes are achieved, the individual feels competent and successful. When ego-involved, athletes are preoccupied with the adequacy of their ability and the demonstration of superior competence compared to others. Perceptions of competence and subjective achievement, in this case, entail social comparisons with others. High ability is demonstrated for the ego-involved athlete when his or

her performance is perceived to exceed that of others or to be equivalent with less effort exerted. The athlete's focus is on whether he or she is good enough (if confidence is low) and how to prove (rather than improve) his or her high level of competence (if confidence is high).

When task involvement is manifested, it is assumed that the athlete will think, act, and feel in a motivated manner regardless of his or her level of perceived ability. Ego involvement, too, can correspond to positive achievement patterns (e.g., high performance, or persistence) as long as the athlete is quite certain that her or his ability is high. When an athlete is ego-involved and thinks the possibility of demonstrating superior competence is "slim to none," the achievement-related cognitions, emotions, and behaviors displayed are far less than optimal. That is, the quantity and, in particular, the quality of motivation is diminished.

Achievement goal theory states that an individual's goal perspective state—task or ego involvement—is the result of both individual differences and situational factors. With respect to the former, an athlete's proneness for task and ego involvement is thought to be captured by his or her dispositional task and ego goal orientations. We will first discuss the nature and implications of these goal orientations in the athletic domain.

Significance of Goal Orientations

Achievement goal orientations are not bipolar opposites (Nicholls, 1989). Rather, they are independent dimensions. As a result, an athlete can be high ego/low task, high task/low ego, high task/high ego, or low task/low ego. From both a theoretical and applied perspective, it is important to consider athletes' degree of proneness for both task and ego goals to get a more complete view of their motivational processes.

Findings from studies involving male and female athletes from a variety of competitive levels and age groups show that an adaptive achievement profile is one of high task and high ego orientation (Duda, 2001). But why might this be the case? Some researchers have suggested that a high task orientation might, to some degree, insulate highly ego-oriented individuals from the negative consequences of low perceived ability when they are performing poorly and, thus, be motivationally advantageous in the long run (Nicholls, 1989). Athletes who are high in both task and ego orientation have multiple sources of subjective success and perceived competence. They have the flexibility of focusing on either task or ego goals at different times in their training or competitions to enhance their motivation (Duda, 2001). We should note that there are some questions regarding whether a high-task/ high-ego orientation profile is most adaptive when the focus is on indexes of the *quality* of motivation (Duda, 2001). For example, research examining the subjective well-being and moral functioning of athletes suggests that high-task/ high-ego participants can be similar to their low-task/high-ego counterparts in views about and responses to sport (Reinboth & Duda, 2004).

In general, a significant body of research has revealed that task and ego goal orientations are associated with qualitatively different behavioral, cognitive, and affective patterns in sport that are likely to have an impact not only on short-term performance but also on the quantity and quality of long-term participation. Researchers have found a task orientation to be related to positive motivational outcomes—for example, the belief that effort is a cause of success, the use of problem-solving and adaptive learning strategies, enjoyment, satisfaction, and intrinsic interest (Duda, 2001, 2005; Roberts, Treasure, & Kavussanu, 1997). Previous work has also revealed a task orientation to be associated with the belief that one's level of physical ability is changeable or malleable (Sarrazin, Biddle, Famose, Cury, Fox, & Durand, 1996). This is very important in the context of sport, because elite level performers usually reach their potential only after years of training. If an athlete believed this commitment to training was not going to lead to increases in ability (i.e., given that he or she holds the view that sport ability is "fixed"), it is unlikely that the athlete would be optimally motivated to train over time.

In contrast, an ego orientation has been found to be associated with boredom, the belief

that deception is a cause of success, and reported anxiety (Duda, 2001; Roberts, et al., 1997). Ego orientation also has been found to be related to the belief that ability is an important determinant of success and the idea that sport competence is stable and a "gift" (Sarrazin et al., 1996). Such a belief system may lead an athlete who is questioning his or her ability not to be as motivated or committed to long-term training. These individuals believe that ultimately "You've either got it or you haven't," and the possession of "it" is deemed a prerequisite to sport achievement.

Achievement goal models state that individuals in a state of ego involvement who have high perceptions of perceived ability are likely to respond in a fashion similar to competitors who are task involved, regardless of whether their perceived competence is high or low. This has led a number of leading sport psychology researchers to contend that a high ego orientation may not be detrimental to performance. Indeed, it has been argued that it is hard to see how an individual could succeed, particularly at the elite level, without having a strong ego orientation. The assumption here is that elite athletes are primarily motivated by winning and outperforming others.

Although we would agree that all elite level athletes perceive success in an ego-involving fashion at certain times, we would caution those who want to *promote* ego orientation. Indeed, high levels of ego orientation may not be motivating at the elite level of sport as even these athletes sometimes doubt their ability (e.g., due to injury, during a performance slump). At such times, a predominant ego orientation coupled especially with moderate or low task orientation puts individuals at jeopardy for feeling incompetent because their focus is primarily on their performance compared to others (Duda, 2001; Nicholls, 1989). Because of the social comparative nature of sport and the high demands placed on competitors, both in training and competition, athletes (particularly those who are elite) are involved in an activity that is designed to challenge the adequacy of their perceived ability on a day-to-day basis.

Pertinent to any debate of the advantages or disadvantages of an ego orientation in sport are contemporary extensions of achievement goal models (e.g., Elliot, 1999; Elliot & McGregor, 2001). That is, recently some researchers have called for a reconsideration of dichotomous task/ego approaches to achievement goals and have instead advocated consideration of approach and avoidance aspects of an ego goal focus. An athlete would be considered ego-approach oriented when he or she is preoccupied with demonstrating superior ability compared to others. In contrast, an athlete emphasizing an ego-avoidance goal would be most concerned about not revealing his or her inferiority. For this athlete, the most important thing is to avoid showing that he or she does not possess adequate levels of ability. Central to this elaboration of the two-goal model of achievement goals (Nicholls, 1989) is the assumption that an ego approach goal orientation would positively relate to achievement striving, whereas an ego avoidance goal emphasis would be coupled with negative motivational outcomes.

Drawing from the existent research and similar to the findings of studies based on the dichotomous goal models, results regarding the presumed positive implications of ego-approach goals in sport-related settings have been equivocal (Adie, Duda, & Ntoumanis, 2008; Nien & Duda, 2008). Our understanding of the nature, antecedents, and consequences of ego-avoidance goals, especially in contrast to an ego-approach goal perspective, is still in its infancy (Duda, 2005). An ego-avoidance perspective on sport achievement has been linked to greater fear of failure, stronger beliefs that sport ability is fixed or unchangeable, perceptions of an ego-involving climate, heightened anxiety, lower intrinsic motivation, and greater amotivation (Conroy, et al., 2003, 2006; Cury, DaFonseca, Rufo, Peres, & Sarrazin, 2003; Morris & Kavussanu, 2006; Nien & Duda, 2008, in press).

Regardless of skill level, or whether their ego goal focus is approach or avoidance oriented, those who are particularly concerned about how they are doing compared to others (ego-involved athletes) are likely to become prime candidates for questioning their competence. This might be a regular occurrence for those of us who are less talented but could strike *any* athlete at *any* time. It is important at this point to remember that we are discussing *perceived* ability here, not *actual* ability. Although actual ability may not be altered during a game of tennis or a round of golf, athletes' perceptions of ability can and do change, often in a relatively short period of time, and are seldom stable over a long period of time. Indeed, recent lab-based research by Nien and Duda (2006) found that (in contrast to those focused on a task goal), the performance and affective responses of study participants who emphasized ego-approach goals were no different than what was observed for participants geared toward ego-avoidance goals following competitive losses in cycling races. Whether approach or avoidance-oriented, centering on ego goals translated into negative processes and outcomes when coupled with failure to demonstrate superiority. Such findings are not surprising when one considers that sport studies to date have found a strong positive correlation between ego approach and ego avoidance goal emphases (e.g., Nien & Duda, 2008). Moreover, aligned with theoretical expecations (Elliot, 1999), both ego-approach and ego-avoidance goals have been found to be tied to fear of failure in the sport domain (Nien & Duda, 2008).

How can ego involvement set the stage for performance impairment? Nicholls (1989) has suggested that the negative relationship between ego involvement and performance is instigated by the expectation an individual holds about looking incompetent. This expectation of looking low in ability can result in a decrease in performance in a number of ways. First, in an attempt to protect one's perceptions of competence, it may cause an athlete to select sport tasks that are too easy or too difficult. Although choosing to engage in less challenging tasks prevents the unhappy prospect of making errors and appearing to be less able, it simultaneously hinders an individual from developing a variety of sport skills to the maximum. Likewise, selecting tasks that are much too hard provides the athlete with a ready-made justification for the unsuccessful outcome as he or she is able to state, "I failed, but so did everyone else." This strategy, however, will be costly for the athlete in terms of maintaining or enhancing his or her skill development over time.

Second, the expectation of looking incompetent can result in a lack of trying when failure is looming and when it looks like one will appear less able compared to others. For example, athletes who back off at the end of a race because the outcome is already determined (i.e., they won't be the winner) and coast to the finish line or athletes who begin to engage in inappropriate achievement strategies or unsportspersonlike behavior when it looks like they will not be the best on that day are unlikely to ever reach their full potential.

Finally, if the expectation of demonstrating low ability becomes chronic, it may lead to regular and high levels of anxiety and, eventually, a devaluing of, and loss of interest in, the activity. If this chain of events occurs, it is likely that these athletes may find themselves in a state of amotivation (Vallerand, 2001). At the very least, if such high ego approach-oriented athletes stay in sport, we might expect them to become strongly ego avoidance goal-oriented over time (Duda, 2005).

Elliot and colleagues (Elliot & McGregor, 2001) have also distinguished between the approach and avoidance facets of task (or mastery-based) goals. This distinction has led to what is termed the 2 × 2 achievement goal framework. A task (or mastery) approach goal entails a focus on the development of personal competence and realization of task mastery. A task (or mastery) avoidance goal, on the other hand, centers on the avoidance of demonstrating self-referenced incompetence. To date, sport studies grounded in the 2 × 2 achievement goal model have pointed to the same advantages of a task approach goal as has been revealed in the multitude of studies based on dichotomous achievement goal frameworks (Duda, 2001, 2005; Dweck, 1999; Nicholls, 1989). Task approach goals have been found to correspond positively to perceptions of a task-involving climate, intrinsic motivation, and the belief that sport competence is an attribute that can be enhanced through training. Consonant with the predictions emanating from the 2 × 2 achievement goal model (Elliot & McGregor, 2001), task avoidance goals have been linked to

negative processes and outcomes such as amotivation, self-handicapping, fear of failure and anxiety (Nien & Duda, 2008).

Significance of the Sport Context

A key variable in determining the motivation of athletes is situational and relates to the salience of task- and ego-involving cues in the achievement context. The focus here is on how the *perceived* structure of the environment, often referred to as the **motivational climate** (Ames, 1992; Duda & Balaguer, 2007), can make it more or less likely that a particular goal state is manifested in training or competition. This perception of the motivational climate affects the achievement patterns of individuals through their view of what goals are reinforced in that setting (Treasure, 2001). In essence, perceptions of the goal perspectives emphasized in these social environments are assumed to be predictive of variability in motivational processes.

Sport research has shown that a perceived task-involving setting is characterized by the athletes' view that the coach does reinforce high effort, cooperation among team members, as well as learning and improvement, and the perception that everyone on the team (regardless of ability level) contributes to the team's achievements (Newton, Duda, & Zin, 1999). A perceived ego-involving team climate, in contrast, is marked by athletes perceiving that the coach punishes their mistakes, fosters rivalry among team members, and gives much of his or her attention to the most talented athletes on the team.

Research has shown a perceived task-involving climate to be associated with more adaptive motivational and affective patterns than perceptions of a performance or ego-involving climate in sport (Duda & Balaguer, 2007). For example, perceptions of task-involving coach-created environments have corresponded to greater enjoyment, more adaptive coping strategies, perceived competence, greater team cohesion and more positive peer relationships, and higher levels of moral functioning. Studies have also shown perceptions of a task involving climate to be negatively related to claimed self-handicapping behavior in elite level sport (e.g., Kuczka & Treasure, 2005). Self-handicapping is evident when athletes, who might be concerned about not performing well, "set the stage" to provide an excuse or "scapegoat" to explain their poor subsequent performance. In so doing, failure could be attributed to the "handicap" rather than any inadequacy in personal ability. Such a strategy also allows athletes to save face in front of others.

In contrast, perceptions of an ego-involving motivational climate have been linked to greater anxiety and performance-related worry, dropping out of sport, greater peer conflict, greater self-handicapping, and lower levels of moral functioning (Duda & Balaguer, 2007). Other work has found perceptions of an ego-involving climate to positively predict indexes of physical ill-being among athletes (e.g., reported physical exhaustion and symptoms; Reinboth & Duda, 2004). Moreover, the degree to which the sport environment is deemed ego-involving appears to have implications for athletes' level of self-esteem and the degree to which their self-worth is tied to athletic performance (Reinboth & Duda, 2004). When athletes train and compete in a highly ego-involving motivational climate and have some doubts about their sport competence, they also are more likely to question their worth as a person overall. When a highly ego-involving atmosphere is deemed to be operating on a team, athletes also perceive their coach to provide less social support and positive feedback and be more punishment oriented (Duda & Balaguer, 2007).

One of the key elements of achievement goal theory is that dispositional goal orientations and perceptions of the climate are considered two independent dimensions of motivation that interact to affect behavior (Nicholls, 1989). Specifically, the theory calls for examination of a Person X Situation interaction effect. For example, let us consider a basketball player with a predominantly ego-oriented goal orientation (high ego/low task) who finds herself in a situation where the task- and ego-involving cues are vague or weak. In this case it is likely that the athlete's goal orientation will be most predictive of her goal state. In a situation in which the cues are in favor of an ego-involving climate, it is likely that

these perceptions will complement the athlete's goal orientation in predicting a strong state of ego involvement. For a state of task involvement to emerge for this basketball player, the perceptions of a task-involving climate would have to be extremely strong. The stronger the goal orientation, the less probable it is to be overridden by situational cues and the stronger the situational cues must be. Alternatively, the weaker the disposition, the more easily it may be altered by situational cues (Newton & Duda, 1999).

Consideration of situational criteria would not be complete, particularly in the context of youth sport, without taking into account the influence peers (Vazou, Ntoumanis, & Duda, 2007) and parents (White, 1996) have in the development of children's and adolescents' achievement motivation. The majority of the work on the motivational climates created by such significant others in the sport setting has concentrated on parental influences. This research points to the benefits of task-involving parents and the negative implications of an ego-involving parental climate (Duda, 2001).

Implications for Practice

The existent research establishing links between task and ego goals (whether dispositional or situational in nature or approach or avoidance centred) and various motivational patterns has contributed to our understanding of motivational processes in sport. But how do we enhance motivation based on the research grounded in achievement goal frameworks? According to theoretical predictions and existing empirical findings, high ego/low task athletes are the most susceptible to motivational difficulties. The evidence suggests that a sport psychology consultant should try to enhance the dispositional task goal orientation for these athletes, perhaps by introducing process or performance centered goal-setting (see Chapter 11) and/or self-regulation techniques (Duda, Cumming, & Balaguer, 2005; Schunk, 1995; see Chapter 13). We should consider implementing strategies that encourage athletes to focus on gains in skill or knowledge, monitoring effort levels, and self-referenced criteria for success. It may be very difficult in the ego-involving milieu of sport to reduce an athlete's ego orientation, and it is likely that many athletes and coaches will be unwilling to moderate what they believe is a vital ingredient in developing motivation in sport—namely, focusing on winning and being superior. A high ego orientation is not necessarily detrimental to achievement striving (at least from a quantity of motivation perspective; Duda, 2001), but it is especially problematic when coupled with low task orientation and low perceived competence, and/or grounded in a fear of looking incompetent. All in all, techniques designed to increase task orientation are likely to be more readily accepted by practitioners in the sport world and probably will be a more effective strategy for an applied sport psychologist to pursue.

Focusing on the individual to enhance the quality of motivation by affecting his or her dispositional goal orientations may seem a viable option, but practically speaking this strategy may be most suitable for an elite athlete who has access to a sport psychologist on a regular basis. Concentrating on individual change in dispositional tendencies may not be the most efficient and feasible alternative for a team or, especially, in the youth sport setting where the goal should be the development of *all* players rather than the performance of a select few. However, in a relatively short period of time, a coach may be able to structure a context in such a way as to influence athletes' recognition that they participate in a more task-involving motivational climate. In so doing, the coach can have a positive impact on the quality of athletes' sport participation.

In addition to coaches, particularly youth coaches, interventions designed to enhance motivation should target the attitudes and behaviors of Moms and Dads and other significant people in the athletes' lives. By making certain types of goals and performance feedback salient, a parent can influence young athletes' views about themselves, perceptions of the sport activity per se, and the criteria they use to evaluate success and failure. For example, when a young sport participant returns from a weekly tennis game and a parent asks, "Did you win?" the athlete receives a rather clear message as to

what the parent considers most important. This message may counter or compromise the efforts of a coach or sport psychologist to enhance task involvement. We would suggest, therefore, that any intervention designed to promote task involvement in sport recognize the role parents and other significant adults (e.g., league officials) and peers (Vazou et al., 2007) may play in determining a young athlete's views on how to define sport success and the manner in which he or she tends to judge demonstrated competence.

By emphasizing certain cues, rewards, and performance expectations, a coach, parent, peer or teammate, or sport psychologist can encourage a particular goal state and in so doing affect the way an athlete perceives and responds to the sport. For the remaining discussion, the focus will be on intervention strategies relevant to adults in contrast to potential peer or teammate influences.

To enhance motivation, coaches, parents and sport psychologists should critically evaluate what they do and how they do it in terms of task and ego goals. For example, how do you define sport success for your players or children? Is it in terms of development and effort, or winning and losing? As a coach, do you design practice sessions that optimally challenge your players, or do you repeat well-learned skills that may delay or stifle development even though they increase the probability of winning? How do you evaluate performance? What behaviors do you consider desirable? Do you congratulate players and your children when they win and outperform others or when they try hard and improve? How do you react when the team, your athlete, or your child loses? If you feel that you coach, parent, or consult in a task-involving manner, then you are probably fostering the quality of athletes' motivation and promoting adaptive beliefs and positive achievement strategies. If your style of coaching, parenting, or consulting is ego-involving, you may be setting up more mature athletes or children, even those who are currently the most successful, for motivational difficulties in the future.

To assist the coach, parent, or sport psychologist in modifying the motivation-related atmosphere being created for athletes, Table 4-1

Table 4-1 **Description of TARGET Structures and Strategies That Enhance Task Involvement**

TARGET Structure	Strategies
Task. What athletes are asked to learn and what tasks they are given to complete (e.g., training activities, structure of practice conditions).	Provide the athlete with a variety of moderately demanding tasks that emphasize individual challenge and active involvement.
	Assist athletes in goal setting.
	Create a developmentally appropriate training environment by individualizing the demands of the tasks set.
Authority. The kind and frequency of participation in the decision-making process (e.g., athlete involvement in decisions concerning training, the setting and enforcing of rules).	Encourage participation by your athletes in the decision-making process.
	Develop opportunities for leadership roles.
	Get athletes to take responsibility for their own sport development by teaching self-management and self-monitoring skills.
Recognition. Procedures and practices used to motivate and recognize athletes for their progress and achievement (e.g., reasons for recognition, distribution of rewards, and opportunities for rewards).	Use private meetings between coach and athlete to focus on individual progress.
	Recognize individual progress, effort, and improvement.
	Ensure equal opportunities for rewards to all.
Grouping. How athletes are brought together or kept apart in training and competition (e.g., the way in-groups are created during practice).	Use flexible and mixed ability grouping arrangements.
	Provide multiple grouping arrangements (i.e., individual, small group, and large group activities).
	Emphasize cooperative solutions to training problems set.
Evaluation. Standards set for athletes' learning and performance and the procedures for monitoring and judging attainment of these standards.	Develop evaluation criteria based on effort, improvement, persistence, and progress toward individual goals.
	Involve athletes in self-evaluation.
	Make evaluation meaningful. Be consistent.
Timing. Appropriateness of the time demands placed on learning and per-formance (e.g., pace of learning and development, management of time and training schedule).	Training programs should recognize that athletes, even at the elite level, do not train, learn, or develop at the same rate.
	Provide sufficient time before moving on to the next stage in skill development.
	Spend equal time with all athletes.
	Assist athletes in establishing training and competition schedules.

lists some suggestions on how to develop a task-involving motivational climate (Duda & Balaguer, 2007; Treasure, 2001). These suggestions have been organized around the task, authority, recognition, grouping, evaluation, and timing (TARGET) situational structures Epstein (1989) has argued make up the "basic building blocks" of the achievement environment.

Doing It for the Joy: The Determinants of Intrinsic Motivation and Self-Determination

I love golf as much for its frankness as for those rare occasions when it rewards a wink with a smile.

—*Tiger Woods*

Sport is an achievement activity. Therefore, knowing how competent athletes perceive themselves and being aware of the criteria by which these athletes define their competence is relevant to their motivation in sport. Also relevant to motivational patterns are the reasons why athletes decide to participate in their selected sport activity.

When athletes are **intrinsically motivated,** they participate in sport for its own sake. That is, the motivation for sport engagement primarily revolves around the inherent pleasure of doing the activity. Someone or something else does not instigate athletes' sport participation in this case. Rather, they play sport out of personal choice. The motivation literature suggests that in various achievement activities, including sport, intrinsic motivation is associated with positive affect and maximal engagement.

Self-determination theory (SDT; Ryan & Deci, 2002) has become a very popular approach to understanding motivation and behavior in sport. Fundamentally, SDT distinguishes between behaviors that individuals perform freely or autonomously and those that they pursue for more or less extrinsic reasons. The theory examines why an individual acts (i.e., the level that

their motivation is more or less self-determined), how various types of motivation lead to different outcomes, and what social conditions support or undermine optimal functioning and well-being via the satisfaction of basic psychological needs.

There are different types of intrinsic and extrinsic motivation, and according to Deci and Ryan (2002) they vary along a self-determination continuum (Figure 4-2). We will start by describing the least self-determined types of motivation and move toward a portrayal of more autonomous motivational regulations (Vallerand, 2001). First are those athletes characterized by **amotivation.** These athletes have no sense of personal control with respect to their sport engagement, and there are no extrinsic (or intrinsic) reasons for doing the activity. Amotivated athletes are no longer sure of why they are playing their sport.

Next on the continuum come three forms of extrinsic motivation, with the least autonomous being **external regulation.** In this case, behavior is performed to satisfy an external demand or stems from the external rewards an athlete expects to secure. For example, an athlete might say "I'm going to practice today but only because my scholarship depends on it." With the second form of extrinsic motivation, **introjected regulation,** athletes participate because they feel they *have* to play sport. Such motivation is still extrinsic in nature; it only replaces the external source of control with an internalized contingency. For example, "I'm going to practice today because I can't deal with the guilt I will feel if I miss." With the third type of extrinsic motivation, **identified regulation,** behavior is undertaken out of free choice but as a means to an end, with the athlete often not considering the behavior itself pleasurable. For example, an athlete who wants to improve his fitness level chooses not to miss any sessions during off-season conditioning and preseason training, even though the activity is very demanding and unpleasant. At the opposite end of the self-determination continuum is the classic state of **intrinsic motivation,** in which an athlete participates in an activity for its inherent satisfactions. It is highly autonomous and represents the quintessential state of self-determination (Ryan & Deci, 2002).

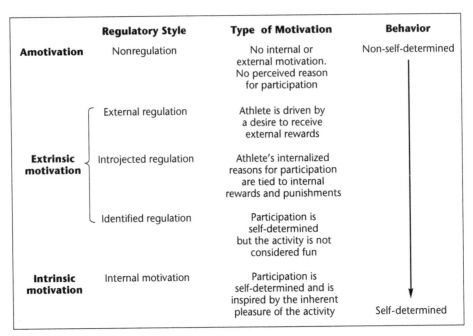

Figure 4-2 **The self-determination continuum**
Source: Deci & Ryan, 1985, 1992. With kind permission of Springer Science and Business Media.

Results of a recent qualitative study by Mallett and Hanrahan (2004) with elite Australian track and field athletes offers support for Deci and Ryan's (1985) multidimensional conceptualization of extrinsic motivation. Mallett and Hanrahan found that in addition to excitement, enjoyment, a love for competing at the highest level, and a sense of relatedness with fellow athletes, less self-determined motives for participation emerged. Specifically, these elite level athletes identified money and social recognition as motives while others spoke to the job aspect of the sport. The data showed, however, that the athletes had successfully managed to internalize and integrate the more self-determined extrinsic motivation regulations into their personal values as elite level performers. This is an important finding as motivation-related differences between athletes who engage in sport for more or less self-determined reasons are likely to be great.

A fundamental tenet of self-determination theory is that individuals engaged in an activity by choice will experience better consequences than those whose participation is less autonomous. Research has found a positive relationship between autonomous motivation and higher levels of task perseverance and psychological well-being and found it to be negatively related to feelings of stress, anxiety, and self-criticism in sport (e.g., Gagné, Ryan, & Bargmann, 2003; Krane, Greenleaf, & Snow, 1997). Consistent with this line of inquiry, recent studies have suggested that SDT may provide a useful framework to understand burnout in sport. In a sample of elite level swimmers, Lemyre, Treasure, and Roberts (2006) found that over the course of a competitive swimming season, susceptibility to burnout was more likely to occur when an athlete's reasons for participating shift to a more extrinsic motivation regulation representing a loss of autonomy. Aligned with the findings of

Lemyre and colleagues, a study by Cresswell and Eklund (2005) on burnout among top amateur rugby union players showed intrinsic motivation to be negatively associated, amotivation positively associated, and extrinsic regulation not related to reported burnout.

According to SDT, whether or not an athlete has more or less self-determined reasons for engaging in sport is dependent on his or her degree of basic need satisfaction. More specifically, Deci and Ryan (2002; Ryan & Deci, 2002) propose that all of us, athletes and nonathletes alike, need to feel competent (i.e., feel sufficiently efficacious to interact effectively with the environment), autonomous (i.e., perceive we are acting according to our own volition and have options and choices), and connected with others (i.e., view relationships with important individuals as being supportive and respectful) within our various life domains. When the sport environment meets these three basic needs, we expect to witness greater self determination, investment, as well as well-being in the athletic setting (Reinboth, Duda, & Ntoumanis, 2004). However, if one or more of the needs are not satisfied, ill-being and poor functioning are hypothesized to occur.

Understanding the social contexts that facilitate athletes' motivation, performance, and well-being via the satisfaction of these needs is an important line of inquiry. To this end, research in youth (e.g., Reinboth, et al., 2004; Sarrazin et al., 2002) and amateur as well as elite sport (e.g., Adie, Duda & Ntoumanis, in press; Balaguer, Castillo, & Duda, 2008; Reinboth & Duda, 2006; Treasure, Lemyre, Kuczka, & Standage, 2007) has shown that perceptions of autonomy support (and the degree of involvement or social support offered) from the coach positively predict the satisfaction of the participants' needs for competence, relatedness, and autonomy. The satisfaction of these needs hold implications for indexes of athletes' psychological, emotional, and physical health. In terms of parental support, Gagné and associates (2003) found, in a sample of 33 female subelite gymnasts between the ages of 7 and 18 years, that perceptions of both coach and parent autonomy support and involvement influenced the quality of the gymnasts' motivation in training. Specifically, the more the gymnasts perceived their parents and coaches to be autonomy supportive and involved, the more autonomously motivated the gymnasts were. Not surprisingly, parental involvement, parental autonomy support, and autonomous motivation had effects upon the athletes' practice attendance, which supports the assertion that autonomous forms of motivation not only influence the quality of an athlete's experiences, but also his or her behavior.

Intrinsic Motivation in the Often Extrinsic World of Sport

At all competitive levels, some athletes play sport for intrinsic reasons. The sources of that intrinsic interest may vary. It may be the continuous learning that sport affords, the possibility of personal accomplishment and mastery, or the opportunity to experience pleasant sensations whether they be sensory or aesthetic (Vallerand, 2001). All in all, intrinsically motivated athletes find sport pleasurable in and of itself and are maximally motivated both quantitatively and qualitatively. Indeed, we would argue that it is most unlikely that athletes, even multimillionaires, would be able to sustain high levels of motivation and commitment throughout their careers if they did not have high levels of intrinsic motivation for engaging in their sport, particularly during periods of adversity, duress, and poor performance.

From youth sport onward, competitive athletics is dominated by extrinsic reinforcements. One can win medals and trophies. Fame and fortune may be the consequences of sport involvement for some. Talented college athletes in the United States may be rewarded with scholarships. Athletes at the professional level are paid for their sport achievements. An interesting question, therefore, is, What is the effect of extrinsic rewards on intrinsic motivation? The answer to this question is, "It depends." Athletes who are intrinsically motivated and receive extrinsic rewards are not necessarily more motivated. Indeed, research has indicated that extrinsic rewards can diminish intrinsic interest

(Deci & Ryan, 1985). Rewards, however, also can foster intrinsic motivation. What seems to be critical in sport is to consider how extrinsic reinforcements are interpreted by individual athletes. That is, what do these rewards mean to the athlete?

Extrinsic rewards have a *controlling* aspect. The use of extrinsic reinforcements by coaches and parents can provide athletes with a sense of "who is pulling the strings" in terms of their sport involvement. Rewards are detrimental to intrinsic motivation when they take away from athletes' sense of self-determination. Consider how a coach might refer to an intercollegiate athlete's scholarship and the resulting impact on that athlete's intrinsic interest in the sport. Perhaps, during the recruitment process, the coach repeatedly used the scholarship to coax the athlete to come play for his or her team. In this case the athlete's decision to play for this coach might be more likely to be perceived as contingent on this external reward rather than being self-determined. When that athlete performs poorly, if the coach says, "How can you play like that? We're paying you to perform!", the athlete might think of his or her participation as more like work and less like an inherently enjoyable activity, which may lead to motivational difficulties.

It is important to keep in mind that sometimes rewards inform us about our level of competence and worth. When receiving the reward is contingent on personally controllable aspects of performance and an athlete obtains the reward, this should increase his or her perceived ability while not undermining self-determination. As a result, it should foster intrinsic motivation. The social environment that surrounds athletes (which is created by coaches, parents, sport psychologists, peers, the media, and fans) has a huge impact on the meaning of extrinsic rewards. Whether extrinsic reinforcements are likely to be viewed as controlling or informational regarding one's ability is a function of characteristics of these environments. In sport situations that allow athletes little autonomy, the rewards are more likely to be interpreted in a controlling manner.

Implications for Practice

The literature on intrinsic motivation and self-determination in sport provides another rationale for cultivating perceived competence as well as perceived personal control among sport participants. In essence, this research indicates that perceived adequate ability and autonomy are the fuel that fire athletes' intrinsic motivation. Caution in the use (and especially the *overuse*) of extrinsic reinforcements in athletic settings is required. Extrinsic rewards must be salient to the athletes to have any influence, positive or negative, and should be used sparingly so that athletes are less likely to construct a behavior–reward contingency (i.e., "If I do this, I will get that"). This can promote an external locus of control in the athlete's sport involvement. The goals cooperatively set between coach, sport psychologist, and athlete (see Chapter 13) should be performance rather than primarily outcome based and more task-involving. They also should be realistic, that is, optimally challenging with the exertion of effort. Achieving these goals will enhance perceptions of competence and are more within the athlete's personal control than goals tied to competitive outcomes.

Finally, coaches and other significant people in athletes' lives can foster their self-determination (Reinboth et al., 2004) in other ways. We have already discussed the motivational significance of a task- versus ego-involving sport environment. Drawing from the SDT literature, it is important to try to make the athletic environment as *autonomy supportive* as possible. Considering the athletes' perspective and allowing them to make choices in training and competition events should cultivate a greater sense of personal autonomy. SDT and related research also points to the relevance of *socially supportive* sport environments (Reinboth et al., 2004). Socially supportive coaches are there to assist athletes when they need help and convey that they care about their athletes as people rather than only as sport performers. Committed and compatible coach–athlete relationships (Olympiou, Jowett, & Duda, in press) and the fostering of positive social exchanges between and cooperation among team members should also lead to an enhanced sense of relatedness and social support.

Summary

Based on both anecdotal and scientific evidence, we know that elevated (or the quantity of) motivation is relevant to sport participation. Research and the wisdom gleaned from practice also suggest that motivational factors are fundamental to maximizing that involvement in terms of its quality. Sport allows for achievement, satisfaction, enjoyment, and interest, and athletes have an opportunity to develop in body, mind, and spirit. Motivation is a key ingredient in athletes' success, and we need to recognize that the quantity *and* quality of athletes' motivation is inferred from a constellation of behaviors, emotions, and cognitive variables—not from competitive sport performance alone. Indeed, indexes of athletes' mental and physical welfare and other indicators of optimal functioning (e.g., the ability to stay focused, enjoyment of one's sport) should be taken into account when we evaluate whether they are optimally motivated or not (Duda, 2001).

Athletes are more likely to exhibit an adaptive form of motivation when they perceive they have the necessary capabilities to match the psychological and physical challenges of the sport in question, have a sense of personal autonomy, and feel connected to others in regard to their sport involvement. Motivation deficits appear when an athlete doesn't think he or she "has what it takes," perceives him or herself to be like "a pawn on a chessboard," and/or feels disenfranchised from or not respected by relevant others in the sport setting. In other words, understanding variations in sport motivation implies that we pay attention to athletes' thoughts regarding issues of competence, personal control, and connectedness to others.

With respect to feeling competent, a number of elements contribute to athletes' perceived self-efficacy. For example, by providing effective models, "setting the stage" for success when athletes are learning a new skill or starting the competitive season, and efficacy-building verbal persuasion, coaches and sport psychologists can augment the confidence level of their athletes. Through learning and mastering psychological skills (e.g., arousal regulation, imagery), athletes make it more likely that their self-efficacy is elevated and more resistant to vacillation.

When sport participants feel competent and in charge of their own destiny, their motivation to participate is more likely to be more internalized. When athletes play sport for the love of the game and other self-determined reasons, they do not need external rewards to encourage or legitimize their involvement. As a consequence, coaches, sport psychologists, and other significant social agents in athletes' lives need to be careful when considering the use of extrinsic reinforcements as a means to increase motivation. These reinforcements can become the primary incentive for participation and diminish intrinsic interest. External reward contingencies can lead to self-determination if they inform athletes about their gains in competence, are not employed in overabundance, and are provided in an autonomy-supportive manner. Otherwise, they may cause more harm than good. For optimal engagement in sport, we would like athletes to primarily participate because they like and/or value sport rather than because of extrinsic rewards or a sense of guilt or compulsion.

Notwithstanding the importance of athletes' sense of autonomy and relatedness to others, perceptions of competence are a significant predictor of adaptive, more self-determined motivational patterns among athletes. However, research on achievement goals has indicated that how athletes judge their competence level is also critical to motivational processes and outcomes. A focus on task involvement in the athletic setting has several advantages, including that the source of subjective success is more within the athlete's direct influence and is less likely to result in feelings of incompetence. Defining sport competence in terms of self-referenced effort or task mastery criteria repeatedly stokes the motivation fire.

An emphasis on ego involvement can advance an athlete's desire to excel too, but it can also have its motivational costs. First, a strong ego focus, whether approach or avoidance oriented, means that others are individuals to be surpassed or from whom an athlete should hide his or her inadequacies. Opponents and teammates become primarily reference points for feeling more or less competent, rather than cohorts with whom we learn, collaborate to improve individually and collectively, or cooperate in competition. Thus, an emphasis on ego goals can jeopardize an athlete's sense of connectedness in the sport environment.

Second, when aiming to reach ego-centered goals, the criteria for success (showing superiority or avoiding the demonstration of inferiority) are less within the athlete's control. This means that maintaining an autonomous perspective on sport achievement is endangered when the athlete's inclination is toward ego-approach or ego-avoidance goals. The criteria underlying success, in both cases, are external to the athlete and her or his performance.

Finally, no matter the degree of athletic prowess or the competitive level of the athlete, emphasizing ego goals can prove detrimental if that individual's confidence starts to waiver and he or she possesses a weak task orientation. In this instance, the athlete desperately wants to be the best, fears he or she will not be, and has no other meaningful way of redefining his or her goals and sense of competence to feel good about the performance. Because the world of sport is competitive, challenging, and conducive to competence questioning, coaches, parents, and sport psychologists should encourage task involvement in an attempt to optimize sport motivation.

Study Questions

1. What are the behavioral characteristics that reflect whether an athlete's motivation is high or low?

2. What is the difference between the quantity and quality of motivation among athletes?

3. What is self-efficacy, and why is it supposed to affect motivation?

4. Provide examples for each of the six antecedents of self-efficacy in a sport setting.

5. How do task- and ego-involved athletes differ in the way they judge their competence and perceive success in sport?

6. What are the distinctions between and consequences of being more ego-approach or ego-avoidance goal-oriented?

7. Define and give an example of a task (or mastery) approach and task avoidance goal focus.

8. Illustrate how being primarily oriented to ego goals can set the stage for performance impairment and motivational difficulties.

9. What do we mean when we say that an athlete is intrinsically motivated in contrast to extrinsically motivated?

10. Describe the process by which external rewards can influence the intrinsic motivation of athletes.

11. What are ways in which we can make a sport environment more autonomy supportive?

References

Adie, J., Duda, J. L., & Ntoumanis, N. (2008). Achievement goals, competition appraisals and the psychological and emotional welfare of sport participants. *Journal of Sport and Exercise Psychology,30, 302–322.*

Adie, J., Duda, J. L., & Ntoumanis, N. (in press). Environmental support factors, basic need satisfaction and well-being among adult team sport participants: Tests of mediation and gender invariance. *Motivation and Emotion, 32, 189–199.*

Ames, C. (1992). Achievement goals, motivational climate, and motivational processes. In G. C. Roberts (Ed.), *Motivation in sport and exercise* (pp. 161–176). Champaign, IL: Human Kinetics.

Balaguer, I., Castillo, I., & Duda, J. L. (2008). Apoyo a la autonomia satisfacción de las necesidades, motivation, y bienestar en deportistas de competición: Un analysis de la teoria de la autodeterminación (Autonomy support, needs satisfaction, motivation and well-being in competitive athletes: A test of Self-Determination Theory). *Revista de Psicología del Deporte, 17, 123–139.*

Bandura, A. (1986). *Social foundations of thought and action: A social cognitive theory.* Englewood Cliffs, NJ: Prentice Hall.

Bandura, A. (1997). *Self-efficacy. The exercise of control.* New York: W. H. Freeman.

Conroy, D. E., Elliot, A. J., & Hofer, S. M. (2003). A 2 × 2 achievement goals questionnaire for sport: Evidence for factorial invariance, temporal stability, and external validity. *Journal of Sport and Exercise Psychology, 25, 456–476.*

Conroy, D. E., Kaye, M. P., & Coatsworth, J. D. (2006). Coaching climates and the destructive effects of mastery avoidance achievement goals on situational motivation. *Journal of Sport and Exercise Psychology, 28, 69–92.*

Cresswell, S. L., & Eklund, R. C. (2005). Motivation and burnout among top amateur rugby players. *Medicine and Science in Sports and Exercise, 37, 469–477.*

Cury, F., Da Fonseca, D., Rufo, M., Peres, C., & Sarrazin, P. (2003). The trichotomous model and investment in learning to prepare a sport test: A mediational analysis. *British Journal of Educational Psychology, 73, 529–543.*

Deci, E. L., & Ryan, R. M. (1985). *Intrinsic motivation and self-determination in human behavior.* New York: Plenum.

Deci, E. L., & Ryan, R. M. (2002). (Eds.). *Handbook of self-determination research.* Rochester, NY: University of Rochester Press.

Duda, J. L. (2001). Goal perspective research in sport: Pushing the boundaries and clarifying some misunderstandings. In G. C. Roberts (Ed.), *Advances in motivation in sport and exercise* (pp. 129–182). Champaign, IL: Human Kinetics.

Duda, J. L. (2005). Motivation in sport: The relevance of competence and achievement goals. In A. J. Elliot & C. S. Dweck (Eds.), *Handbook of competence and motivation* (pp. 318–335). New York: Guildford Publications.

Duda, J.L. & & Balaguer, I. (2007). The coach-created motivational climate. In S. Jowett & D. Lavalee (Eds.), *Social psychology of sport* (pp. 117–130). Champaign, IL: Human Kinetics.

Duda, J. L., Cumming, J., & Balaguer, I. (2005). Enhancing athletes' self regulation, task involvement, and self determination via psychological skills training. In D. Hackfort, J. Duda, & R. Lider (Eds.), *Handbook of applied sport psychology research* (pp. 159–181). Morgantown, WV: Fitness Information Technology.

Dweck, C. S. (1999). *Self-theories and goals: Their role in motivation, personality, and development.* Philadelphia, PA: Taylor & Francis.

Elliot, A. J. (1999). Approach and avoidance motivation and achievement goals. *Educational Psychologist, 34,* 169–189.

Elliot, A. J., & McGregor, H. A. (2001). A 2 × 2 achievement goal framework. *Journal of Personality and Social Psychology, 80,* 501–519.

Epstein, J. (1989). Family structures and student motivation: A developmental perspective. In C. Ames & R. Ames (Eds.), *Research on motivation in education: Vol. 3* (pp. 259–295). New York: Academic Press.

Feltz, D. L., Chase, M. A., Moritz, S. E., & Sullivan, P. J. (1999). Development of the multidimensional coaching efficacy scale. *Journal of Educational Psychology, 91,* 765–776.

Feltz, D. L., Short, S., & Sullivan, P. J. (2007). *Self-efficacy in sport: Research strategies for working with athletes, teams and coaches.* Champaign, IL: Human Kinetics.

Gagne, M., Ryan, R. M., & Bargmann, K. (2003). Autonomy support and need satisfaction in the motivation and well-being of gymnasts. *Journal of Applied Sport Psychology, 15,* 372–390.

Krane, V., Greenleaf, C. A., & Snow, J. (1997). Reaching for gold and the practice of glory: A motivational case study of an elite gymnast. *The Sport Psychologist, 11,* 53–71.

Kuczka, K., & Treasure, D. C. (2005). Self-handicapping in competitive sport: Influence of the motivational climate, self-efficacy and perceived importance. *Psychology of Sport and Exercise, 6,* 539–550.

Lemyre, P-N., Treasure, D. C., & Roberts, G. C. (2006). Influence of variability of motivation and affect on elite athlete burnout susceptibility. *Journal of Sport and Exercise Psychology, 28,* 32–48.

Maddux, J. E. (1995). Self-efficacy theory: An introduction. In J. E. Maddux (Ed.), *Self-efficacy, adaptation, and adjustment* (pp. 3–33). New York: Plenum.

Mallett, C. J., & Hanrahan, S. J. (2004). Elite athletes: Why does the 'fire' burn so brightly? *Psychology of Sport and Exercise, 5,* 183–200.

Morris, R., & Kavussanu, M. Antecedents of approach-avoidance goals in sport. *Journal of Sport Sciences, 26,* 465–476.

Newton, M., & Duda, J. L. (1999). The interaction of motivational climate, dispositional goal orientation and perceived ability in predicting indices of motivation. *International Journal of Sport Psychology, 30,* 63–82.

Newton, M. L., Duda, J. L., & Yin, Z. (2000). Examination of the psychometric properties of the perceived motivational climate in sport questionnaire-2 in a sample of female athletes. *Journal of Sports Sciences, 18,* 275–290.

Nicholls, J. (1989). *The competitive ethos and democratic education.* Cambridge, MA: Harvard University Press.

Olympiou, A., Jowett, S., & Duda, J. L. (2008). The psychological interface between the coach-created motivational climate and the coach-athlete relationship in team sports. *The Sport Psychologist, 22,* 423–438.

Nien, C-L. & Duda, J. L. (2006) The effect of situationally-emphasised achievement goals and win/loss on engagement in a cycle ergometer task. Presented at Annual Conference of the British Association of Sport and Exercise Sciences, Wolverhampton, UK. ISSN 0264-0414 print /ISSN1466-447X online.

Nien, C., & Duda, J. L. (2008). Antecedents and consequences of approach and avoidance achievement goals: A test of gender invariance. *Psychology of Sport and Exercise, 9,* 352–372.

Nien, C., & Duda, J. L. (in press). Construct validity of multiple achievement goals: A multitrait-multimethod approach. *International Journal of Sport and Exercise Psychology.*

Reinboth, M., & Duda, J. L. (2004). Relationship of the perceived motivational climate and perceptions of ability to psychological and physical well-being in team sports. *The Sport Psychologist, 18,* 237–251.

Reinboth, M., Duda, J. L., & Ntoumanis, N. (2004). Dimensions of coaching behavior, need satisfaction, and the psychological and physical welfare of young athletes. *Motivation and Emotion, 28,* 297–313.

Reinboth, M., & Duda, J. L. (2006). Perceived motivational climate, need satisfaction and indices of well-being in team sports: A longitudinal perspective. *Psychology of Sport and Exercise, 7,* 269–286.

Roberts, G. C., Treasure, D. C., & Kavussanu, M. (1997). Motivation in physical activity contexts: An achievement goal perspective. In M. L. Maehr & P. R. Pintrich (Eds.), *Advances in motivation and achievement. Vol. 10* (pp. 413–447). Greenwich, CT: JAI Press.

Ryan, R. M., & Deci, E. L. (2002). An overview of self-determination theory: An organismic-dialectical perspective. In E. L. Deci & R. M. Ryan (Eds.), *Handbook of self-determination research* (pp. 3–33). Rochester, NY: University of Rochester Press.

Ryan, R. M., & Deci, E. L. (2007). Active human nature: Self-determination theory and the promotion and maintenance of sport, exercise and health. In M. S. Haggar and N. L. D. Chatzisarantis (Eds.) *Intrinsic motivation and self-determination in exercise and sport,* (pp. 1–20). Champaign, IL: Human Kinetics.

Sarrazin, P., Biddle, S. J. H., Famose, J.-P., Cury, F., Fox, K. R., & Durand, M. (1996). Goal orientations and conceptions of sport ability in children: A social cognitive approach. *British Journal of Social Psychology, 35,* 399–414.

Sarrazin, P., Vallerand, R. J., Guillet, E., Pelletier, L. G., & Cury, F. (2002). Motivation and dropout in female handballers: A 21-month prospective study. *European Journal of Social Psychology, 32,* 395–418.

Schunk, D. H. (1995). Self-efficacy, motivation, and performance. *Journal of Applied Sport Psychology, 7*, 112–137.

Treasure, D. C. (2001). Enhancing young people's motivation in physical activity. In G. C. Roberts (Ed.), *Advances in motivation in sport and exercise* (pp. 79–100). Champaign, IL: Human Kinetics.

Treasure, D. C., Lemyre, P. N., Kuczka, K. K., & Standage, M. (2007). Motivation in elite level sport: A self-determination perspective. In M. S. Haggar and N. L. D. Chatzisarantis (Eds.) *Intrinsic motivation and self-determination in exercise and sport*, (pp. 153–166). Champaign, IL: Human Kinetics.

Treasure, D. C., Monson, J., & Lox, C. (1996). Relationship between self-efficacy, wrestling performance, and affect prior to competition. *The Sport Psychologist, 10*, 73–83.

Vallerand, R. (2001). A hierarchical model of intrinsic and extrinsic motivation in sport and exercise. In G. C. Roberts (Ed.), *Advances in motivation in sport and exercise* (pp. 263–320). Champaign, IL: Human Kinetics.

Vazou, S., Ntoumanis, N., & Duda, J. L. (2007). Perceptions of peer motivational climate in youth sport: Measurement development and implications for practice. In S. Jowett & D. Lavalee (Eds.), *Social psychology of sport* (pp. 145–156). Champaign, IL: Human Kinetics.

White, S. A. (1996). Goal orientation and perceptions of the motivational climate initiated by parents. *Pediatric Exercise Science, 8*, 122–129.

7 CHAPTER

Anxiety, Stress, and Mood Relationships

KEY TERMS

Affect
Alexithymia
Antecedent
Anxiety
Cognitive anxiety
Competitive situation
Competitive state
 anxiety
Conceptual model
 of mood
Distress
Drive
Drive theory
Dysfunctional
 perfectionism
Effect size
Emotion
Eustress
Functional
 perfectionism
Iceberg profile
Inverted-U theory
Mental health model
Meta-analysis
Mood
Mood profile
Mood state
Multidimensional

Organizational stress
Precompetitive mood
Precompetitive state
 anxiety
Primary appraisal
Profile of Mood States (POMS)
Secondary appraisal

Signal detection theory
Somatic anxiety
State anxiety
Stress
Stress process
Trait anxiety
Yerkes-Dodson law

The following story about a young athlete illustrates the potentially debilitating effects of anxiety on athletic performance. Ryan is a physically gifted 16-year-old athlete. He participates in several sports for his high school during the academic year and plays summer baseball as well. Some of the team sports he excels in are football, basketball, and baseball. However, his favorite sport is track and field, which is primarily an individual sport.

Ryan is a highly anxious young man with a tendency toward perfectionism. In Ryan's particular case, these traits had very little negative effect on his performance in the team sports he played. He would often get uptight about a big game, but he could always rely upon his teammates to help him out. The fact that team games involved other players seemed to help control the negative impact his anxiety could have had on his performance. Ryan occasionally "clutched" during baseball games, but the outcome of the game was rarely affected. Usually, only Ryan and Ryan's parents were aware of the anxiety and tension that were boiling within.

However, track and field was a different matter. Ryan was a sprinter and hurdler. His physical power and mesomorphic build made him especially well equipped for running and jumping events that required speed and leg power. Unfortunately, his basic anxiety and worry about failing had a serious effect on his performance during competition. During practice, Ryan always did well. In fact, during three years of high school Ryan had never lost a race to a teammate during practice. In actual competition, things were different. Ryan began preparing mentally for his races days in advance of the actual competition. During the days and hours preceding competition, his anxiety would rise to fearful levels. By the time actual competition came, Ryan could hardly walk, let alone run or jump. Several times he had to vomit before important races. His coach talked to him a great deal about learning to relax and not worry about the race, but didn't give him specific suggestions on how to accomplish this. Finally, the coach decided to remove Ryan from his favorite events because he was actually a detriment to the team. This was more than Ryan could take. He approached the coach one day and announced that he was going to give up athletics altogether and concentrate on his studies. This story has a successful conclusion, but it will be shared later, at the beginning of the cognitive and behavioral intervention section of the book (part 4).

In explaining the relationships among anxiety, stress, and mood, and their relationship to athletic performance, it is important to be introduced to a number of concepts and their relationships to each other. To accomplish this, this chapter is divided into the following eight sections: (a) differentiating among the terms *affect*, *emotion*, *anxiety*, *mood*, and *stress*, (b) multidimensional nature of anxiety, (c) stress process and antecedents of the state anxiety response, (d) measurement of anxiety, (e) time to event nature of precompetitive anxiety, (f) perfectionism in sport, (g) relationship between anxiety and performance, and (h) relationship between mood and performance.

Differentiating Among the Terms Affect, Emotion, Anxiety, Mood, and Stress

To begin with, **affect** is a generic term used to describe emotions, feelings, and moods. **Emotion** is a situation-specific affective response to the environment. Lazarus (2000a) defined emotion as "an organized psychophysiological reaction to ongoing relationships with the environment, most often, but not always interpersonal or social" (p. 230). Lazarus further identified 15 specific emotions and core themes associated with each emotion. The primary focus of this chapter is on just one of these emotions, specifically the emotion of **anxiety**, which he defined as "facing uncertain, existential threat" (p. 234). Other example emotions that might influence athletic performance include anger, guilt, shame, relief, happiness, and pride. Anxiety is the emotion that has been most studied and is believed

| 7.1 | CONCEPT & APPLICATION |

CONCEPT Anxiety is one of many emotions that may arise in response to a competitive situation. An emotion is associated with a physiological change, a subjective experience, and an action tendency. Conversely, a mood is more diffuse, longer lasting, and associated with life generally.

APPLICATION Athletes who experience the emotion of anxiety or anger do so in response to an environmental experience. The emotion will be associated with an increase in physiological arousal and with the tendency to take action of some sort. How the athlete responds to increased emotion is the topic of discussion in much of sections 3 and 4 of this book. For now, it is important to understand the difference between an emotion and a mood and that there are many different emotions.

to have the most influence upon athletic performance. This does not mean that powerful emotions such as anger, happiness, and hope do not influence performance, only that anxiety is the main focus of this chapter (Seve, Ria, Poizat, Saury, & Durand, 2007; Williams & Desteno, 2008; Woodman et al., 2009). To aid researchers in studying the effect of emotions on athletic performance, Jones, Lane, Bray, Uphill, and Catlin (2005) developed the Sport Emotion Questionnaire (2005). The study of emotion relative to the zone of optimal function (ZOF) in sport will be discussed as an alternative to inverted-U theory in chapter 8. In chapter 8 we will elaborate more on the influence of emotions generally on athletic performance. The balance of this chapter will focus on the emotion of anxiety and the effects of mood on performance. While emotions are instantaneous discrete responses to the environment that last only seconds, minutes, or perhaps hours, **moods** are more diffuse, and may last for weeks or even months (Jones, 2003; Vallerand & Blanchard, 2000). Furthermore, emotions are directed toward something associated with the environment (e.g., inside pitch in baseball), whereas moods are more diffuse, relate more to how we are doing in life and not easily associated with anything specific (Uphill & Jones, 2007). Jones (2003) further clarified that an emotion is composed of three main elements including a physiological change, a subjective experience, and an action tendency. Moods are generally referred to as mood states and are

often measured by sport psychologists using the Profile of Mood States (POMS), to be discussed later in this chapter.

The emotion of anxiety is closely related to Han Selye's concept of stress (pronounced "sale-ye"). Selye (1983, p. 2) defined **stress** as the "nonspecific response to the body to any demand made upon it." When aroused, the body is under stress regardless of whether the cause is something negative like anger or something positive like joy. Exercising at a high intensity would be classified as stressful to the body, because the heart is pumping faster and blood pressure is increased in the arteries and the veins. It can be argued, however, that anger and anxiety are much more stressful to the body than are joy and happiness. To take these factors into consideration, Selye allowed that there must be two different kinds of stress. He labeled the "good stress" **eustress** and the "bad stress" he labeled **distress.** In this chapter distress will be considered to be synonymous with the emotion of anxiety or what we will later refer to as situation-specific state anxiety.

The Multidimensional Nature of Anxiety

Anxiety is **multidimensional** in two different ways. Like all other emotions, anxiety has both a trait component and a state component. The trait component is like a personality disposition, whereas the state

FIGURE 7.1 | Both trait and state anxiety exhibit cognitive and somatic anxiety components.

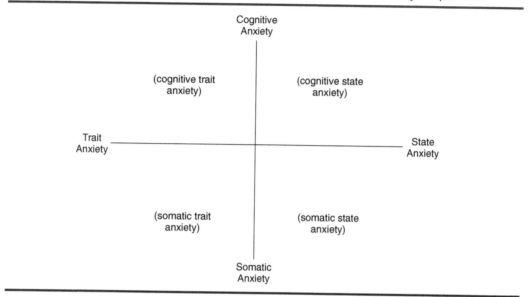

component is a situation-specific response. **State anxiety** is an immediate emotional state that is characterized by apprehension, fear, tension, and an increase in physiological arousal. Conversely, **trait anxiety** is a *predisposition* to perceive certain environmental situations as threatening and to respond to these situations with increased state anxiety (Spielberger, 1971). If an athlete has a high level of competitive trait anxiety, she is likely to respond to an actual competitive situation with a high level of competitive state anxiety.

Anxiety is also multidimensional in the sense that it is believed that there are both cognitive and somatic components to anxiety (Endler, Parker, Bagby, & Cox, 1991). **Cognitive anxiety** is the mental component of anxiety caused by such things as fear of negative social evaluation, fear of failure, and loss of self-esteem. **Somatic anxiety** is the physical component of anxiety and reflects the *perception* of such physiological responses as increased heart rate, respiration, and muscular tension. Both state and trait anxiety are believed to have cognitive and somatic components. In the

sport psychology literature, the notion that anxiety has both cognitive and somatic components is referred to as *multidimensional anxiety theory* (Martens, Vealey, & Burton, 1990). The bipolar, multidimensional nature of anxiety is illustrated in figure 7.1.

The Stress Process and Antecedents of the State Anxiety Response

The best way to understand stress is to conceptualize it as a process, as opposed to an outcome. The **stress process,** as illustrated in figure 7.2, is really the information processing model in action. The stress process begins with the stimulus (competitive situation) on the left and results in the response (stress response) on the right. In between the stimulus and the response is cognition, or thought processes. Cognition determines how the athlete will respond (Lazarus, 2000a, 2000b; Lazarus & Folkman, 1984).

FIGURE 7.2 | The stress process and not the competitive situation determines the extent of the stress response.

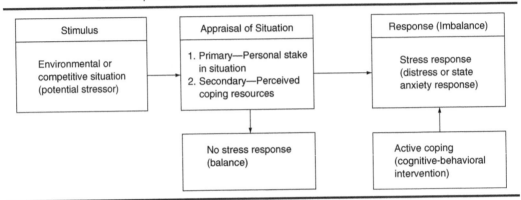

The stress process begins with the environmental or competitive situation on the left. This is the stimulus. The **competitive situation** is not by itself stressful. It is how the athlete interprets the situation that determines whether or not the situation is stressful. Consider the situation in which an athlete finds himself on the foul line in a basketball game with the outcome of the game resting upon his performance. To most people this would be an extremely stressful situation. However, to many basketball players this is exactly the kind of situation that they seek. The situation is not intimidating because they have supreme confidence in their skill and the thought of failure does not enter their minds.

In October of 2004, the Boston Red Sox made history by defeating the New York Yankees in seven games to get into baseball's World Series. There were many heroes in that series, but none greater than David Ortiz. What Ortiz accomplished in the face of potential extreme anxiety and tension speaks to his ability to manage the stress process. In game four of the American League Championship Series (ALCS), and down three games to none, David Ortiz hit a walk-off home run in the 12th inning to win the game and stave off what seemed to be a sure four-game sweep by the Yankees. Then, in game five, Ortiz hit a single in the bottom of the 14th inning to win the game and keep the seven-game series alive (Kepner, 2004).

Consider a nonathletic situation. Suppose you walk into an old abandoned home and notice that right on the ceiling above you is a very large spider. Does this evoke the stress response in your body? For most people it would, but not for all. Some individuals are not afraid of spiders because of their experiences with them. They know that most spiders are harmless and that this one is big and harmless. The difference is in perception. To understand this we look at the middle panel of figure 7.2.

Upon being confronted with a *potentially* stressful situation, the individual conducts an instantaneous appraisal or evaluation of the situation. Appraisal of the situation occurs on two levels. The first is referred to as primary appraisal, and the second as secondary appraisal. In **primary appraisal,** the athlete determines if she has a personal stake in the outcome. If the athlete determines that the outcome is very important to her, then secondary appraisal becomes important. In **secondary appraisal,** the athlete evaluates her personal coping resources to deal with the competitive situation. The outcomes of the primary and secondary appraisals determine whether the stress response will or will not occur.

CONCEPT & APPLICATION

CONCEPT   Whether or not an athlete responds to a threatening situation with high levels of state anxiety will depend entirely on the athlete's perception of the situation.

APPLICATION   Each athlete is unique and should be treated as an individual. Do not attempt to predict an athlete's anxiety response to a competitive situation based on your own perception of the same situation. The athlete's own perception of the situation will determine the level of anxiety response, if any.

If an athlete determines either that it makes no difference to him personally if he makes a play, or that he is perfectly capable of coping with the situation, then the stress response does not occur. In this case, we say that there is a *balance* between the stressful nature of the competitive situation and the athlete's perceived ability to cope with the situation. If, however, the athlete determines that he does not have the resources (skill, confidence, experience) to cope with the situation, the stress response will occur. In this case we say that there is an *imbalance* between the stressful nature of the competitive situation and the athlete's perceived ability to cope. The stress response is equated with Selye's concept of distress, or what we defined as state anxiety.

Also shown in figure 7.2 is a box labeled "active coping." If the state anxiety response proves to be detrimental to performance, it may become necessary to intervene in some way to reduce debilitating anxiety. We will discuss active coping, or cognitive-behavioral interventions, in part 4 of the text.

An anecdote related by Fisher (1976) serves to clarify the relationships illustrated in figure 7.2. Two researchers were studying the effects of fear of drowning on the physiological responses of a participant. The participant was strapped to the side of a swimming tank with the water steadily rising. For some reason the researchers left the test area and forgot about their participant. When they remembered, they were aghast and numb with fear. Dropping everything, they raced to the test area to find the water level dangerously high. Quickly, they unstrapped the participant and pulled him

from the water. Safe on the pool deck, they asked the participant if he was frightened. The participant responded that he wasn't at all worried, because it was just an experiment and he knew that the researchers wouldn't let any harm come to him! The participant perceived the test situation to be nonthreatening, and therefore the state anxiety reaction was not evoked.

To this point, all of our discussion on the stress process has focused on the individual athlete relative to figure 7.2, but there is another kind of stress that we have not talked about, and that is the stress placed on the athlete by the organizing body. **Organizational stress** is the stress placed on the athlete by the competitive sport environment, not just the coaches or a specific competitive event (Fletcher & Hanton, 2003). Fletcher and Hanton (2003) identified four sources of potential organizational stress: (a) environmental issues (selection, travel, accommodations, competitive environment, etc.), (b) personal issues (nutrition, injury, goals, expectations, etc.), (c) leadership issues (coaches and coaching style, etc.), and (d) team issues (team atmosphere, support network, roles, communication, etc.). Taken together, issues associated with organizational stress can take their toll on the athlete.

Competitive state anxiety that occurs prior to a competitive situation is referred to as **precompetitive state anxiety.** According to Endler (1983), there are five specific **antecedents,** or factors that lead to an increase in anxiety in anticipation of an achievement (competitive) situation. These five factors include fear of performance failure, fear of negative social evaluation, fear of physical harm,

| 7.3 | CONCEPT & APPLICATION |

CONCEPT   The primary cause or antecedent of competitive state anxiety in athletes relates to fear of failure and fear of negative social evaluation. Fear of harm, ambiguity, and disruption of routine are weaker predictors of anxiety in athletes.

APPLICATION   Knowing the factors that are most likely to cause a state anxiety response in an athlete should assist the coach in helping the athlete

overcome these fears. Fear of physical harm can be of major concern in certain sports and by certain athletes. For example, fear of physical injury in football by an athlete who has already sustained a season-ending injury could be of major concern. Situation ambiguity and disruption of routine are antecedents of anxiety that ought to be easily managed and controlled if the athlete and coach are aware of them.

situation ambiguity, and disruption of a well-learned routine. Thatcher and Day (2008) identified eight antecedents, but they are largely redundant to the five identified by Endler. It is these sources of stress and others that are appraised, as in figure 7.2, to determine if an imbalance exists between the stimulus and the athletes' perceived ability to deal with the stress.

Sport psychology researchers have been particularly interested in studying antecedents or sources of stress and anxiety in various sports and situations. For example, Dunn (1999) reported that fear of failure and negative social evaluation were sources of distress in ice hockey. High school basketball players experience high levels of anxiety relative to the perceived skill level of their opponents (Thuot, Kavouras, & Kenefick, 1998). In addition to perceived threat, perceived lack of control and coping resources are sources of stress (Hammereister & Burton, 2001). Personal sources of strain and stress experienced by British senior elite track-and-field athletes include lack of confidence, injury concerns, social evaluation, lack of social support, underperforming, and pressure to perform (McKay, Niven, Lavallee, & White, 2008). Personal appraisals of goal relevance, ego involvement, blame/credit, coping potential, and future expectations are associated with a wide range of emotions (including anxiety) in international athletes from various sports (Uphill & Jones, 2007).

Measurement of Anxiety

In recent years, the preferred method of measuring trait and state anxiety has been through the use of pencil-and-paper inventories. For your perusal a number of the most common anxiety inventories as used or developed by sport psychologists are listed in table 7.1.

While pencil-and-paper inventories are the most common measures of anxiety, behavioral and physiological assessment can be very effective. One category of behavioral measurement is direct observation, where the experimenter looks for objective signs of arousal in the subject and records them. Such things as nervous fidgeting, licking the lips, rubbing palms on pants or shirt, and change in respiration could all be interpreted as behavioral signs of activation. Such a system was developed and used by Lowe (1973) for ascertaining arousal through "on-deck activity" of batters in Little League baseball.

Along these lines, table 7.2 displays a list of overt behavioral responses that can be used by the athlete to identify indicators of distress, or state anxiety. The list is arranged in alphabetical order and may be used by the athlete as a checklist to monitor state anxiety response during practice, immediately before competition, and during competition.

From the perspective of applied (nonlaboratory) field research, pencil-and-paper inventories

TABLE 7.1 | Common Anxiety Inventories Utilized or Developed by Sport Psychologists

Trait/State	Dimension	Inventory	Reference
TRAIT	*Unidimensional*	Spielberger's Trait Anxiety Inventory (TAI) Sport Competition Anxiety Test (SCAT)	Spielberger (1983) Martens, Vealey, et al. (1990)
	Multidimensional	Cognitive Somatic Anxiety Questionnaire (CSAQ) Sport Anxiety Scale-2 (SAS-2)	Schwartz, Davidson, and Goleman (1978) Smith, Smoll, Cumming, and Grossbard (2006)
STATE	*Unidimensional*	Spielberger's State Anxiety Inventory (SAI) Competitive State Anxiety Inventory (CSAI)	Spielberger (1983) Martens (1977, 1982)
	Multidimensional	Activation-Deactivation Checklist (AD-ACL) Competitive State Anxiety Inventory-2 (CSAI-2) Revised Competitive State Anxiety Inventory-2 (CSAI-2R)	Thayer (1986) Martens, Vealey, et al. (1990) Cox, Martens, and Russell (2003)

TABLE 7.2 | Incomplete Checklist for Monitoring Distress-Related Behavioral Responses of the Athlete

_____ Clammy Hands		_____ Nausea
_____ Diarrhea		_____ Need to Urinate
_____ Dry Mouth		_____ Physical Fatigue
_____ Fidgeting		_____ Rapid Heart Rate
_____ Increased Respiration		_____ Scattered Attention
_____ Irritability		_____ Tense Muscles
_____ Jitters		_____ Tense Stomach
_____ Licking of Lips		_____ Trembling Legs
_____ Mental Confusion		_____ Unsettled Stomach
_____ Mental Fatigue		_____ Voice Distortion

and behavioral assessment techniques seem most feasible. This will remain true as long as electrophysiological indicators require expensive instruments. Advances in the field of applied psychophysiology, however, may change this perspective. Improvements in the use of telemetry will make it possible to monitor an athlete's heart rate, blood pressure, and muscular tension while he is competing in such dynamic activities as swimming, batting in baseball, and sprinting in track. It has long been argued that both physiological and psychological assessments of anxiety should be taken to measure anxiety and arousal. In this regard, however, it is important to point out

that the correlation between physiological and psychological measures of state anxiety is quite low (Karteroliotis & Gill, 1987). Consequently, if both physiological and psychological measures of state anxiety are recorded simultaneously, it is possible that conflicting results may be obtained (Tenenbaum, 1984).

Multidimensional anxiety theory has precipitated the development of anxiety inventories that measure both trait and state anxiety, as well as cognitive and somatic anxiety. Referring again to table 7.1, we can note that several of the inventories are identified as being multidimensional in nature, as opposed to unidimensional. A multidimensional

7.4 CONCEPT & APPLICATION

CONCEPT The state anxiety response to stressful situations can be observed and recorded through the use of a behavioral checklist.

APPLICATION The athlete should systematically chronicle anxiety-related behavioral responses. Once these are recorded, the coach will be able to help an athlete identify and control competitive stress.

measure of trait or state anxiety partitions the construct into at least two components: cognitive and somatic. A *unidimensional* measure of trait or state anxiety makes no attempt to partition the construct into multiple parts. Among the trait inventories, those that measure anxiety as a multidimensional construct include the Cognitive Somatic Anxiety Questionnaire (CSAQ) and the Sport Anxiety Scale-2 (SAS-2). Among the state inventories, those that measure anxiety as a multidimensional construct include the Activation-Deactivation Checklist (AD-ACL), the Competitive State Anxiety Inventory-2 (CSAI-2), and the Revised Competitive State Anxiety Inventory-2 (CSAI-2R).

Since 1990, the CSAI-2 has been the instrument of choice for measuring multidimensional competitive state anxiety. The CSAI-2 is composed of 27 items that measure cognitive state anxiety, somatic state anxiety, and self-confidence. Recent research with the CSAI-2, however, failed to confirm the hypothesized three-factor structure of the inventory (Cox, 2000; Lane, Sewell, Terry, Bertram, & Nesti, 1999). Consequently, the Revised Competitive State Anxiety Inventory–2 (CSAI-2R) was developed by Cox, Martens, et al. (2003). The CSAI-2R is composed of 17 items that measure the constructs of cognitive anxiety (5 items), somatic anxiety (7 items), and self-confidence (5 items). Items that were removed were items that tended to be highly correlated with more than one construct or subscale. A French version of the CSAI-2R was tested by Martinent, Ferrand, Guillet, and Gautheur (2010). While the three-factor structure of the CSAI-2R was confirmed, they suggested that the somatic factor could be improved by dropping the first somatic item in the inventory (i.e., "I feel

jittery"), reducing the CSAI-2R to 16 instead of 17 items.

Both the CSAI-2 and the CSAI-2R take several minutes to administer, so they can be a distraction to athletes who are preparing for competition. To address this shortcoming, several very short versions of the CSAI-2 have been developed. They include the Mental Readiness Form (Murphy, Greenspan, Jowdy, & Tammen, 1989); the Anxiety Rating Scale (Cox, Robb, & Russell, 2000, 2001); the Immediate Anxiety Measurement Scale (Thomas, Hanton, & Jones, 2002); the Sport Grid (Raedeke & Stein, 1994; Ward & Cox, 2004), and the Affect Grid (Russell, 2003; Russell, Weiss, & Mendelsohn, 1989).

A 15-item version of the CSAI-2 (CSAI-2C) has also been developed for children (Stadulis, Eidson, & MacCracken, 1994). Finally, the CSAI-2R can be modified to provide a multidimensional measure of competitive trait anxiety. This is accomplished through a simple modification of premeasurement instructions (Albrecht & Feltz, 1987). Instead of being asked to respond as to how she feels "at this moment" relative to a competition, the athlete is asked to respond to how she "usually feels" about competition in general.

Time-to-Event Nature of Precompetitive Anxiety

Our ability to obtain independent measures of cognitive and somatic state anxiety has greatly enhanced our knowledge about the athletic situation. One of the factors that is believed to significantly influence the quality of the athletic experience is the level of state anxiety during the time leading up to competition. We have already referred to this as precompetitive anxiety. We now know quite a bit

CONCEPT & APPLICATION

CONCEPT Pencil-and-paper inventories, behavioral checklists, and electrophysiological measures all provide somewhat independent measures of state anxiety.

APPLICATION Notwithstanding the lack of correlation among the various measures, it is useful to measure state anxiety from at least two perspectives. A pencil-and-paper inventory provides an easily administered assessment of state anxiety *prior* to the event, while the other two techniques theoretically assess state anxiety *during* the event.

CONCEPT & APPLICATION

CONCEPT Cognitive and somatic state anxiety are differentially manifested as the time to the competitive event approaches.

APPLICATION Bodily perceptions of increased sympathetic nervous system activity (somatic anxiety) are normal and healthy indicators of an approaching athletic contest. If allowed to dissipate, they should be viewed as indicators of physiological readiness. Conversely, cognitive state anxiety has the potential of causing a decrement in athletic performance if it is not controlled.

about the temporal changes in anxiety during the period of time leading up to and immediately following the beginning of the event. Precompetitive cognitive anxiety starts relatively high and remains high and stable as the time of the event approaches. Conversely, somatic anxiety remains relatively low until approximately 24 hours before the event, and then increases rapidly as the event approaches. Once performance begins, somatic anxiety dissipates rapidly, whereas cognitive state anxiety fluctuates throughout the contest as the probability of success/failure changes (Fenz, 1975; Hardy & Parfitt, 1991; Jones & Cale, 1989; Jones, Swain & Cale, 1991; Martens, Vealey, et al., 1990; Parfitt, Hardy, & Pates, 1995; Schedlowski & Tewes, 1992; Swain & Jones, 1992; Wiggins, 1998). The relationship between competitive state anxiety and time-to-event is graphically illustrated in figure 7.3.

In a related investigation (Woodman, Cazenave, & Le Scanff, 2008), the unidimensional state anxiety of two groups of female skydivers was ascertained 30 minutes before, 10 minutes after, and 70 minutes after their jump from their airplane. Results showed no time difference in state anxiety for the group of nonalexithymic skydivers, while time differences were significant for the group of alexithymic skydivers. For the alexithymic skydivers, state anxiety was high to begin with, dropped significantly right after the dive, but rose again 70–90 minutes after their jump. **Alexithymia** is defined as a difficulty in acknowledging one's own emotions and feelings along with the inability to express them to others. For this high-risk sport, alexithymic women's ability to express their emotions was facilitated.

FIGURE 7.3 | Changes in competitive state anxiety prior to competition (decline in cognitive anxiety fluctuates with probability of success/failure).

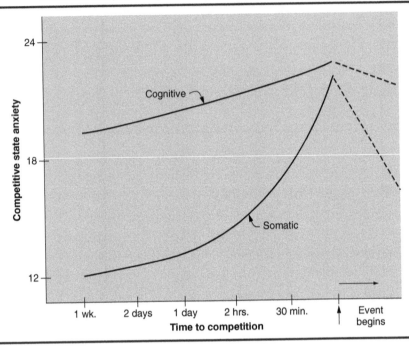

Perfectionism in Sport

Perfectionism and anxiety are not the same, but because they are sometimes strongly associated with each other, perfectionism in sport is discussed in this chapter (Hall, Kerr, & Matthews, 1998; Stoeber, Otto, Pescheck, Becker, & Stoll, 2007). Studies show that perfectionism is multidimensional and that the various factors attributed to perfectionism can be reduced down to two overarching factors (Sager & Stoeber, 2009). The first is functional perfectionism and the second is dysfunctional perfectionism. **Functional perfectionism** is positive in nature and considered to be adaptive. Functional perfectionism is characterized by perfectionistic strivings, high personal standards, desire for organization, self-oriented striving, and other oriented striving. Conversely, **dysfunctional perfectionism** is negative in nature and considered

to be maladaptive. Dysfunctional perfectionism includes such things as perfectionistic concerns, concern over mistakes, parental expectations, parental criticism, self-doubts about actions, and socially prescribed expectations (Anshel & Sutarso, 2010). Finally, research reported by Appleton, Hall, and Hill (2010) suggests that perfectionism in children is predicted by parental perfectionism.

Measuring Perfectionism

In the literature, four different but related inventories have been developed or utilized to measure perfectionism in athletes. We will discuss these briefly to help the student to understand the multidimensional nature of perfectionism. The *Frost Multidimensional Perfectionism Scale* (FMPS; Frost, Marten, Lahart, & Rosenblate, 1990) was composed of 35 items that measured six subscales of perfectionism including (a) personal standards, (b) organizational skills, (c) concern over mistakes, (d) doubts about actions, (e) parental expectations, and (f) parental criticism. Generally speaking, the first two can be classified under the heading of adaptive/functional perfectionistic strivings, while the last four can be classified under the heading of maladaptive/dysfunctional perfectionistic concerns. In a follow-up study by Khawaja and Armstrong (2005), the FMPS was reduced from 35 to 24 items. This psychometrically sound version of the FMPS was named the FMPS-24 and included four subscales of perfectionism including (a) personal standard (b) organizational skills, (c) concern over mistakes and doubts about actions, and (d) parental expectations and criticisms. Again, the first two can generally be classified as adaptive in nature, while the remaining two are maladaptive in nature. Finally, Khawaja and Armstrong (2005) introduced a third, 17-item version of the FMPS that they named the FMPS-Reduced (FMPS-R). The FMPS-R is composed of only two subscales named (a) functional perfectionism (adaptive), and (b) dysfunctional (maladaptive) perfectionism.

The *Hewitt Multidimensional Perfectionism Scale* (HMPS; Flett & Hewitt, 2006; Hewitt & Flett, 1991) is composed of 43 items and three subscales named (a) self-oriented perfectionism, (b) socially prescribed perfectionism, and (c) other-oriented perfectionism. It is a little harder to classify these three subscales as being adaptive or maladaptive, but generally speaking self-oriented perfectionism seems to be somewhat extreme, but more adaptive in nature. Conversely, socially prescribed perfectionism appears to be decidedly maladaptive. Other-oriented perfectionism does not relate to individual expectations, but to extreme dysfunctional expectations for others (Hill, Hall, & Appleton, 2010).

The final two inventories were designed specifically for sport and include the Sport Multidimensional Perfectionism Scale and the Multidimensional Inventory of Perfectionism in Sport. The *Sport Multidimensional Perfectionism Scale* (Sport-MPS; Dunn, Causgrove-Dunn, & Syrotuik,

2002) is composed of 30 items and four dimensions. The four dimensions of perfectionism measured included (a) personal standards, (b) concern over mistakes, (c) perceived parental pressure, and (d) perceived coach pressure. As with the other inventories, personal standards could generally be classified as functional in nature, while perceived parental pressure and concern over mistakes might be classified as maladaptive. It is difficult to classify perceived coach pressure as being adaptive or maladaptive, as athletes come to expect coaches to encourage good performance. Sound psychometric properties of the Sport-MPS have been reported by Dunn et al. (2006).

As with the Sport-MPS, the *Multidimensional Inventory of Perfectionism in Sport* (MIPS; Stoeber, Otto, & Stoll, 2004) was designed specifically for an athlete population. While the exact number of items and subscales associated with the MIPS is not clearly delineated, authors who have used the MIPS indicate that they selected 10 items from the full inventory that showed the highest factorial validity and consistency across samples (e.g., Stoeber & Becker, 2009). Five of the selected items measure striving for perfection (adaptive perfectionism), while the other five measure negative reactions to imperfection (maladaptive perfectionism).

Correlates of Perfectionism

Overall striving for perfection is associated with elevated cognitive and somatic state anxiety, but when functional and dysfunctional perfectionism is considered separately, a different result is obtained. Functional perfectionism predicts lower levels of state anxiety and higher levels of self-confidence, whereas dysfunctional perfectionism predicts elevated levels of somatic and cognitive state anxiety (Stoeber et al., 2007). Moreover, dysfunctional perfectionism predicts fear of failure and fear of experiencing shame and embarrassment. In addition, fear of failure mediates the relationship between dysfunctional perfectionism and negative affect following failure (Sager & Stoeber, 2009; Stoeber

7.7   CONCEPT & APPLICATION

CONCEPT   Perfectionism is multidimensional in nature and can be reduced to functional and dysfunctional components. The functional component is related to perfectionistic *strivings*, while the dysfunctional component is related to perfectionistic *concerns* about making mistakes.

APPLICATION   On the surface there would not seem to be anything dysfunctional about striving for perfection, but when these strivings become so all consuming that the athlete cannot tolerate imperfection in him- or herself or in others, it can become a problem. Dysfunctional perfectionism is also associated with increased anxiety, anger, dysfunctional goal orientations, controlling motivation, and maladaptive attributions. Because perfectionism is in many respects a personality disposition, great care must be taken to help an athlete develop coping skills to address these issues. Coping will be discussed in chapter 9.

& Becker, 2009). Whereas high trait anger is related to perfectionism generally, angry reaction to mistakes is specifically associated with dysfunctional perfectionism (Vallance, Dunn, & Dunn, 2006). In summary, dysfunctional perfectionism, but not functional perfectionism, is linked with elevated state anxiety, situation-specific anger, and fear of failure.

Perfectionism in sport is also related to various aspects of motivation. From the perspective of self-determination theory, functional perfectionism predicts a more autonomous form of self-determined motivation, whereas maladaptive perfectionism predicts a more controlling form of motivation (Gaudreau & Antl, 2008). From the perspective of attribution theory, functional perfectionism is positively associated with hope of success and to internal attributions to success, whereas dysfunctional perfectionism is negatively related to internal attributions to success and to external attributions to failure (Stoeber & Becker, 2009). From the perspective of goal perspective theory, functional perfectionism is predictive of mastery goal orientation, whereas dysfunctional perfectionism is predictive of an ego or performance goal orientation (Dunn et al., 2002). More specifically, when using a 2×2 goal orientation framework, functional perfectionism is associated with both mastery and performance approach goals, whereas dysfunctional perfectionism is associated with mastery and approach avoidance goals (Stoeber, Stoll, Pescheck, & Otto, 2008). In summary, functional perfectionism is linked to adaptive attributions, autonomous motivation, and adaptive goal orientations. Conversely, dysfunctional perfectionism is linked to maladaptive attributions, controlling motivation, and maladaptive goal orientations.

In terms of performance, research generally suggests that best performance is associated with functional perfectionism as opposed to dysfunctional perfectionism. In a study involving the ironman triathlon competition (swimming, biking, running), functional perfectionism was predictive of better performance (Stoeber, Uphill, & Hotham, 2009). In a study involving a new basketball training task, functional perfectionism was predictive of increased performance in learning the basketball task. When the effects of functional perfectionism were statistically controlled for, dysfunctional perfectionism was associated with weak initial but not subsequent performance. Athletes who were simultaneously high in both functional and dysfunctional perfectionism showed the greatest learning and performance increments (Stoll, Lau, & Stoeber, 2008). In summary, best learning and performance is generally, but not always, associated with functional perfectionism. In some cases, a combination of high functional and dysfunctional perfectionism yields best performance.

The Relationship Between Arousal and Athletic Performance

Throughout this chapter, an effort has been made to avoid confusing the terms *anxiety* and *arousal*. In this section, however, it will be necessary to use the term *arousal* as somewhat synonymous with *state anxiety*. This is the case because researchers have routinely employed a test of state anxiety as the primary means for determining a subject's arousal level. Consequently, most of the reported research will relate negative anxiety (state anxiety) to sport and motor performance. This practice, however, is consistent with our understanding that anxiety (emotion) is associated with a physiological change (Jones, 2003).

The primary focus of this section will be upon two main theories that purport to explain the relationship between arousal and athletic performance: inverted-U theory and drive theory.

Athlete exhibiting emotional response. Courtesy University of Missouri–Columbia Sports Information.

FIGURE 7.4 | Relationship between drive and inverted-U theories.

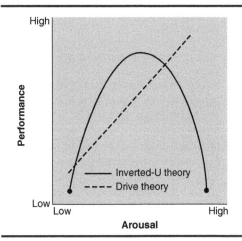

Inverted-U theory includes many subtheories that explain why the relationship between arousal and performance is curvilinear as opposed to linear in nature. Conversely, **drive theory** proposes a linear relationship between arousal and performance. In the most elementary case, the distinguishing characteristics of inverted-U and drive theory are illustrated in figure 7.4.

Inverted-U Theory

The inverted-U theory has been around for as long as the arousal/performance relationship has been studied. It simply states that the relationship between performance and arousal is curvilinear as opposed to linear, and takes the form of an inverted U (fig. 7.4). While it is described as a theory or hypothesis, researchers such as Duffy (1957) and Malmo (1959) considered it to be an observed fact.

One of the difficulties encountered in testing the inverted-U theory with humans is our inability to precisely measure arousal. For example, if in a particular study researchers fail to demonstrate that heightened arousal causes a decrement in performance, it is not particularly damaging to the

| 7.8 | CONCEPT & APPLICATION |

CONCEPT   The relationship between athletic performance and arousal takes the form of the inverted U.

APPLICATION   Preparing athletes for competition involves more than psyching them up. It involves finding the optimal level of arousal for each athlete.

theory. The reason for this is that it can always be argued that for that particular task, arousal was not high enough. If it had been higher, we may argue, performance would have declined. The problem is that from the perspective of protecting the human participant, the amount of arousal researchers can induce is limited. For example, if arousal is induced through electrical shock, how much can the researcher elevate the voltage without violating the participant's rights? Not very much.

The foundation for inverted-U theory is the classic work of Yerkes and Dodson (1908). Using dancing mice as subjects, Yerkes and Dodson set out to discover the relationship between arousal and task difficulty in their effect on performance. Performance was measured as the number of trials needed for the mice to select the brighter of two compartments. Arousal consisted of high, medium, and low intensities of electrical shock. Task difficulty was manipulated in terms of the differences in brightness between two compartments (high, medium, and low difficulty). Results showed that the amount of practice needed to learn the discrimination task increased as the difference in brightness between the two compartments diminished. These findings led to the **Yerkes-Dodson law,** which is this:

> an easily acquired habit, that is, one which does not demand difficult sense discrimination or complex associations, may readily be formed under strong stimulation, whereas a difficult habit may be acquired readily only under relatively weak stimulation (pp. 481–2).

The results of the Yerkes-Dodson research are illustrated in figure 7.5. As can be observed in this figure, the optimal level of electrical shock

FIGURE 7.5 | Results of the Yerkes-Dodson (1908) research showing the effect of arousal and task difficulty on performance.

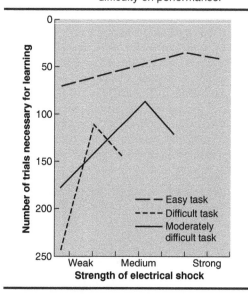

Source: From Yerkes, R. M., & Dodson, J. D. (1908). The relationship of strength of stimulus to rapidity of habit formation. *Journal of Comparative Neurology and Psychology, 18,* 459–482. Adapted with permission of Alan R. Liss, Inc., publisher and copyright holder.

(arousal) for a difficult task was much lower than that needed for an easy task. Additionally, an optimal level of arousal (electrical shock) is indicated for each task. Before and after the optimal point, performance drops off. This is the inverted U.

In terms of practical sport application, the Yerkes-Dodson law is illustrated in figure 7.6. This figure shows that as the complexity of a skill increases, the amount of arousal needed for optimal performance decreases.

FIGURE 7.6 | Application of the Yerkes-Dodson law in athletic events.

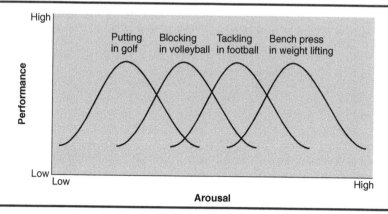

FIGURE 7.7 | Application of the Yerkes-Dodson law to tennis players at various skill levels.

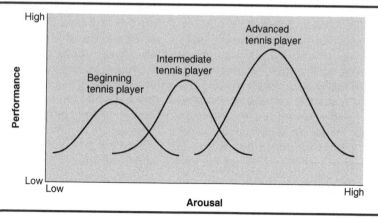

As can be observed in figure 7.6, a high level of arousal is necessary for the best performance in gross motor activities such as weight lifting. Conversely, a lower level of arousal is best for a fine motor task such as putting in golf. Each sport skill has its theoretical optimal level of arousal for best performance. Regardless of which type of skill is being performed, they all conform to the inverted-U principle. Specifically, performance is lowest when arousal is very high or very low, and highest when arousal is moderate, or optimum.

Another important consideration relating to the Yerkes-Dodson law is skill level. Just as putting in golf is a complex activity compared to weight lifting, learning to dribble a basketball is more difficult for a beginner than for someone performing the same task as an expert. The optimal level of arousal for a beginner should be considerably lower than the optimal level for an expert performing the same task. As illustrated in figure 7.7, this concept explains why highly skilled athletes often perform better in competitive situations than do novices.

CONCEPT   The optimal level of arousal varies as a function of the complexity of the task and the skill level of the athlete.

APPLICATION   Highly skilled athletes and athletes performing simple tasks need a moderately high level of arousal for maximum performance. Less skilled athletes and athletes performing complex tasks require a relatively low level of arousal for maximum performance.

Evidence of an inverted-U relationship between athletic performance and arousal has been well documented in the literature (Beuter & Duda, 1985; Burton, 1988; Gould, Petlichkoff, Simons, & Vevera, 1987; Klavora, 1978; Sonstroem & Bernado, 1982). The inverted-U relationship has also been documented between arousal and performance on laboratory tasks such as reaction time, auditory tracking, and hand steadiness (Arent & Landers, 2003; Lansing, Schwartz, & Lindsley, 1956; Martens & Landers, 1970; Stennet, 1957). Unrelated to the inverted-U hypothesis, several other interesting relationships between anxiety and performance have been recently reported. Utilizing college students as participants, Oudejans and Pijpers (2010) observed that training under mildly anxiety-producing conditions inoculated them against poor performance when performing later in high-stress conditions. Utilizing national-level female gymnasts as participants, Cottyn, de Clercq, Pannier, Crombez, & Lenoir (2006) observed that (a) significant increases in heart rate (HR) during training and competition is associated with reduced performance, (b) HR is higher during competition compared to training, and (c) falls and foibles are associated with significant increases in HR during training and competition. Finally, utilizing novice skiers as participants, Kunzell and Muller (2008) observed that early training with short and wide "bigfoot" skis results in lower anxiety toward skiing later in their instruction compared to a control group. Taken together, these studies all illustrate the critical relationship between anxiety and arousal with athletic performance.

While it seems relatively clear that the nature of the relationship between athletic performance and arousal takes the form of the inverted U, it is not clear why this occurs. In the following subsections, three theories that predict the inverted-U relationship will be briefly reviewed.

Easterbrook's Cue Utilization Theory
Easterbrook's (1959) notion of cue utilization theory was introduced in chapter 6 and illustrated in figure 6.4. The basic premise of cue utilization or attentional narrowing theory is that *as arousal increases, attention narrows*. The narrowing of attention results in some cues being gated out, first irrelevant cues and later relevant cues. From figure 6.4 it should be clear that attentional narrowing predicts an inverted-U relationship between arousal and performance. When arousal is low, the attentional band is wide, and both irrelevant and relevant cues are available. The presence of the irrelevant cues is distracting and causes a decrement in performance. At a moderate, or optimal, level of arousal, only the irrelevant cues are eliminated, and therefore performance is high. Finally, when arousal is high, attentional focus is narrow, and both relevant and irrelevant cues are gated out. This results in a decrement in performance, as predicted by the inverted-U theory.

Cue utilization theory also addresses the problem of task complexity and learning. With a complex or unlearned motor skill, there are a greater number of task-relevant cues to manage. Consequently, with increased arousal, the probability of error increases at a faster rate than it would for a simple motor skill. Because there are

CONCEPT & APPLICATION

CONCEPT Increased arousal has the effect of narrowing an athlete's attention.

APPLICATION Athletes who participate in a sport that requires broad attentional awareness

need lower levels of arousal for best performance. The setter in volleyball must be particularly aware of all aspects of the game. Narrow vision would seem to be particularly damaging to the setter's play selection.

CONCEPT & APPLICATION

CONCEPT Decreased arousal has the effect of broadening an athlete's attentional focus.

APPLICATION Athletes who participate in a sport that requires narrow attentional focus need

appropriately increased levels of arousal for optimal performance. An athlete attempting a single feat of power and force will need a narrowed focus of attention.

---

so many task-relevant cues to manage, the relevant as well as irrelevant cues get gated out as arousal increases and attention narrows.

Signal Detection Theory Another theory that predicts a curvilinear relationship between arousal and performance is signal detection theory (SDT). **Signal detection theory** is a theory of perception that predicts that increased decision errors will occur when an individual is either insensitive to a physical stimulus (stringent response criterion) or supersensitive to a physical stimulus (lenient response criterion). The lowest number of decision errors should occur with an optimal, or balanced, sensitivity to stimuli.

According to signal detection theory, the response criterion, or sensitivity to a physical stimulus, changes as a function of physiological arousal. At a very low level of arousal, the individual exhibits a stringent response criterion and is insensitive to signals from the environment (errors of omission). At a very high level of arousal, the individual exhibits a lenient response criterion and is

very sensitive to signals from the environment (errors of commission). At a moderate level of arousal, the individual exhibits an optimal, or balanced, response criterion (fewer errors). Thus, low and high levels of arousal are associated with a large number of signal detection errors, while an optimal or moderate level of arousal is associated with fewer signal detection errors. This pattern of errors is consistent with inverted-U theory.

Consider an example in American football. The defensive lineman is interested in exploding out of his ready position and across the line of scrimmage when he detects the ball has been snapped. There is considerable advantage to be gained from exploding across the line of scrimmage before the offensive line can block movement. If the linesman is underaroused, he will not get across the line as quickly as he should; this represents an error of omission. If the linesman is overaroused, he will explode across the line of scrimmage too quickly and be called for being offside. This would be an error of commission. If the linesman is optimally aroused with a moderate

$$\boxed{7.12} \quad \textbf{CONCEPT \& APPLICATION}$$

CONCEPT   Athletes in sports that require instant decisions require a moderate level of arousal to avoid errors of commission or omission.

APPLICATION   An overly aroused batter in baseball will tend to swing at bad pitches (error of commission), while an underaroused hitter will allow called strikes (error of omission). A moderate level of arousal will tend to balance out the two kinds of decision errors.

---

level of arousal, he will move with the snap of the ball and make fewer errors of either commission or omission. For a detailed review of signal detection theory applied to sport, see Cox (1998).

Information Processing Theory   The basic predictions of information processing theory for the arousal/performance relationship are identical to those of signal detection theory. Both theories predict the inverted-U relationship between performance and arousal, and both support the Yerkes-Dodson law. Welford (1962, 1965) gives a basic outline of the theory's predictions.

According to Welford (1962, 1973), brain cells become active with increased levels of arousal, and they begin to fire. As this happens, the information processing system becomes noisy, and its channel capacity is reduced. At low levels of arousal, the system is relatively inert and performance is low. At high levels of arousal, a performance decrement occurs because of the reduced information processing capacity of the channels. At some optimal level of arousal, the information processing capacity of the system is at its maximum, and performance is at its best.

Drive Theory

Perhaps the great contribution of drive theory is that it helps to explain the relationships between learning and arousal, and between performance and arousal. Many young athletes are just beginning the process of becoming skilled performers. The effect of arousal upon a beginner may be different from its effect upon a skilled performer. The basic relationship between arousal and an athlete's performance at any skill level is given in the following formula:

$$\text{Performance} = \text{Arousal} \times \text{Skill Level}$$

As developed by Hull (1943, 1951) and Spence (1956), drive theory is a complex stimulus-response theory of motivation and learning. It is a theory of competing responses, in which increased **drive** (arousal) facilitates the elicitation of the dominant response. The basic tenets of drive theory are as follows:

1. Increased arousal (drive) will elicit the dominant response.

2. The response associated with the strongest potential to respond is the dominant response.

3. Early in learning or for complex tasks, the dominant response is the incorrect response.

4. Late in learning or for simple tasks, the dominant response is the correct response.

We can make several practical applications of these drive theory tenets. First, heightened levels of arousal should benefit the skilled performer, but hamper the beginner. The coach with a relatively young team should strive to create an atmosphere relatively low in anxiety and arousal. Low levels of arousal should increase the beginner's chances of a successful performance. In turn, the experience of success should strengthen self-confidence. Skilled athletes, on the other hand, will benefit from an

CONCEPT & APPLICATION

CONCEPT   The effect of increased arousal on an athlete performing a complex task or learning a novel task will be to elicit an incorrect response, which is the dominant response.

APPLICATION   With beginners it is important that the environment be one of low arousal and stress. Young athletes tend to make more mistakes if they become excited and overly activated.

CONCEPT & APPLICATION

CONCEPT   The effect of increased arousal on an athlete performing a simple or well-learned task will be to elicit a correct response, which is the dominant response.

APPLICATION   Highly skilled athletes will often benefit from increased arousal. Psyching up a basketball star like Michael Jordan, Kobe Bryant, or Le Bron James could have grave consequences for the opposing team.

increase in arousal. Similar applications can be made to the performance of simple and complex tasks. For example, a complex task, such as throwing a knuckleball in baseball, will always require a low level of arousal. Conversely, a very simple task, such as doing a high number of push-ups, would seem to benefit from arousal. A case in point is a study reported by Davis and Harvey (1992). Utilizing drive theory predictions, the researchers hypothesized that increased arousal caused by major league baseball pressure situations would cause a decrement in batting (a complex task). Four late-game pressure situations were compared with nonpressure situations relative to batting performance. Results showed a decrement in batting performance associated with increased arousal, as predicted by drive theory.

Drive theory received tremendous amounts of attention from researchers between 1943 and 1970. However, since then, interest in the theory has diminished significantly. The theory was extremely difficult to test, and the tests that were conducted often yielded conflicting results. For an in-depth review of research associated with drive theory, the reader is referred to Cox (1990).

Mood State and Athletic Performance

As introduced in the beginning of this chapter, a **mood state** differs from an emotion in that it is more diffuse and may last for weeks or even months. Emotions are instantaneous discrete responses to the environment and last for only seconds, minutes, or perhaps hours. While a mood state is more stable than an emotion, both differ from a personality disposition in that they are not enduring traits. Mellalieu (2003) differentiated between emotions and moods as follows:

> Emotions are suggested to be relatively brief but intense experiences activated by cognitive appraisal of situation factors, while moods are deemed less intense, more prolonged experiences that relate to the individual rather than the situation. (Mellalier, 2003, p. 100)

As we learned in chapter 2, there has been a great deal of interest in discovering if a relationship exists between personality and athletic performance. Similarly, researchers have been interested in discovering if a predictive relationship exists between mood states and athletic performance. In the pages that follow, we will discuss (a) measurement of mood state, (b) Morgan's mental health model, and (c) mood state relationships in sport.

Measurement of Mood State

While other inventories have been developed for measuring mood states, the inventory most commonly used by sport psychologists is the **Profile of Mood States** (POMS; McNair, Lorr, & Droppleman, 1992). The POMS is published by the Educational and Industrial Testing Service (EDITS). LeUnes and Burger (1998) noted that the POMS was first used in 1975 by sport psychologists, and was used with 257 published articles between 1975 and 1998. More recently, McNair, Heuchert, and Shilony (2003) documented the use of the POMS in more than 5,000 educational and industrial studies between 1964 and 2002.

The most commonly used version of the POMS is the original 65-item version that measures the following six mood states: tension, depression, anger, vigor, fatigue, and confusion. Five of these mood states are negative in nature, while one is positive (vigor). Since the original development of the 65-item version of POMS, two additional EDITS versions have been developed. One of them was a bipolar 72-item version, and the other a short 30-item version. Recent psychometric analyses of the POMS reveal that compared to the 65-item version, the 30-item short version of the POMS is the superior instrument. The factorial

Does this highly successful collegiate athlete exhibit the mood state "iceberg profile" of the elite athlete? Courtesy University of Missouri–Columbia Sports Information.

integrity of the 65-item POMS was called into question because of failure of the confusion factor to fit the data as hypothesized (Bourgeois, LeUnes, & Myers, 2010).

In addition to the three authorized versions of the POMS mentioned above, independent researchers have developed four other shortened

TABLE 7.3 | Authorized and Independently Developed Versions of the Profile of Mood States (POMS)

Category	Items	POMS Version
Authorized	65	Profile of Mood States (McNair et al., 1971, 1981, 1992)
	72	Profile of Mood States—Bipolar (Lorr & McNair, 1988)
	30	Profile of Mood States—Short version (McNair et al., 1992)
Independent	37	Shortened Version of POMS (Shacham, 1983)
	40	Abbreviated POMS (Grove & Prapavessis, 1992)
	27	Short POMS for Young Athletes (Terry, Keohane, & Lane, 1996)
	06	Brief Assessment of Mood (Whelan & Meyers, 1998)

versions (LeUnes & Burger, 2000; Terry, 1995). These four versions, along with the three authorized versions of the POMS are listed in table 7.3. Research has shown that all of the shortened versions are correlated with the 65-item POMS (Bourgeois, LeUnes, & Myers, 2010).

The Profile of Mood States and Morgan's Mental Health Model

It appears that Morgan (1979) was one of the first to utilize the Profile of Mood States (POMS) in sport- and exercise-related research. Morgan plotted standardized POMS scores for elite athletes and noted that (a) elite athletes exhibited a **mood profile** that was lower in negative moods and higher in vigor than a normative sample, and (b) elite athletes also exhibited a more mentally healthy mood profile than less successful athletes. Morgan referred to the notion that the successful athlete exhibits a more healthy mood profile than less successful athletes or a normative population as the **mental health model.** According to this model, the successful athlete is viewed as a mentally healthy individual relative to psychological mood. When the standardized POMS scores of the elite athlete are plotted as in figure 7.8, they take the form of an iceberg, with all of the negative moods falling below the population norm and the vigor

score falling well above the norm. This mood profile has come to be referred to as the **iceberg profile.**

Research has been very supportive of the notion that the successful athlete exhibits an iceberg profile relative to the population norm (average of the population), but not so supportive in terms of discriminating between successful and less successful athletes. We will discuss the issue of discriminating among athletes in the next section.

Terry and Lane (2000), however, found strong support for the notion that the athlete exhibits a mood profile that is superior to that of the population norm. They administered the POMS to 2,086 athletes and found differences between the athletic sample and the existing population norm for all mood subscales. Consistent with the mental health model, athletes exhibit lower negative mood states and a higher vigor score compared to a POMS normative sample of a similar age group.

Mood State Relationships in Sport

As with personality research, investigators have been interested in studying the relationship between **precompetitive mood** and athletic performance. One approach has been to determine if athletes belonging to different achievement levels can be differentiated based on mood state measures. A

FIGURE 7.8 | Illustration of the iceberg profile of the elite athlete.

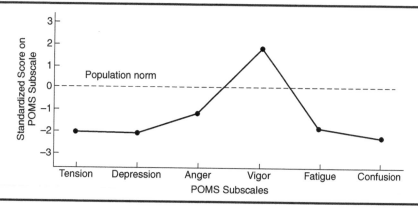
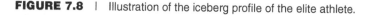

7.15	CONCEPT & APPLICATION

CONCEPT Researchers cannot consistently and effectively discriminate between athletes of differing skill level on the basis of mood state scores alone.

APPLICATION You will note that we observed a similar outcome when we tried to discriminate between athletes of different skill level based on personality. While the mental health model does discriminate between athletes and nonathletes, it is not a reliable predictor of whether an athlete belongs to a high achievement group or a low achievement group. As with personality, coaches should not use POMS scores to make personnel decisions.

7.16	CONCEPT & APPLICATION

CONCEPT A weak to moderate relationship exists between precompetitive mood and performance outcome. This relationship is enhanced when performance is measured subjectively as opposed to objectively.

APPLICATION An athlete's mood prior to an athletic contest is related to athletic performance. The less negative mood and the more positive mood the athlete experiences, the better he is likely to perform. This relationship is not so strong, however, that the coach should use it to predict objective performance outcome.

second approach has been to determine if performance outcome can be predicted based on precompetitive mood. In this section, we will consider both of these approaches. In addition, a conceptual model for studying the relationship between mood and performance will be considered.

Mood States and Achievement Levels In this line of research, investigators attempted to show that scores on the POMS could discriminate among groups of athletes of different skill levels. That is, can mood differentiate between starters and nonstarters on an athletic team? This is a situation in which athletes of clearly different skill levels are given the POMS to see if the scores of the differently skilled groups differ.

Beedie, Terry, and Lane (2000) reported the results of a **meta-analysis** (statistical summary of studies) that included 13 studies, 90 effect sizes (mean comparisons), and 2,285 participants. The overall **effect size** for this investigation was .10, which is considered to be very low (Cohen, 1992). Except for a small difference in vigor scores, athletes at different levels of achievement report essentially the same moods. These results are consistent with earlier reviews by Landers (1991); Rowley, Landers, Kyllo, and Etnier (1995); and Prapavessis (2000). Apparently, it is not possible to consistently differentiate between athletes of differing skill level, as earlier suggested by Morgan and the mental health model.

Mood States and Performance Outcome In the previous section, we considered whether athletes of differing achievement or skill levels could be differentiated on the basis of POMS scores. In this section we consider whether the performance outcome of athletes of a similar skill level

CONCEPT & APPLICATION

CONCEPT Depression moderates the relationship between the other mood states and athletic performance. In the presence of depression, the increased levels of negative mood will have a debilitating effect on performance. Increased depression is also associated with reduced vigor, which results in a reduced facilitative effect.

APPLICATION Coaches and athletes must be concerned about the debilitating levels of depression. Depression can negatively influence the other moods, as well as performance. If high levels of depression are suspected, the athlete may need to seek professional help from a counseling or clinical sport psychologist.

can be predicted based on POMS scores. If I know an athlete's precompetitive mood profile, can I use it to predict how she will do in the competition?

Beedie et al. (2000) reported the results of a second meta-analysis that included 16 studies, 102 effect sizes, and 1,126 participants. The overall effect size for this investigation was .35, which is considered to be small to medium. In addition, some moderating variables were identified. A moderating variable is a variable that determines the relationship between two other variables. Moderating variables to be considered here included type of sport and how performance was measured.

Type of Sport Performance was predicted a little better in open skills as opposed to closed skills. Closed skills are believed to be closed to the environment (e.g., bowling, clean-and-jerk), while open skills are believed to be open to the environment (e.g., tennis, soccer). Effects were slightly larger for individual sports compared to team sports, and effects were larger for short-duration sports (rowing, wrestling) compared to long-duration sports (e.g., basketball, volleyball).

Measurement of Performance Effects were larger when performance outcome was conceptualized as subjective and self-referenced, as opposed to objective. An objective outcome would be whether you won or lost a contest, or whether you recorded a better time than another athlete in a contest. Examples of subjective self-referenced outcomes include (a) a post-event self-rating of performance, (b) percentage of a personal best, and

(c) comparison to expectations. In post-event self-rating, an athlete has an opportunity to subjectively indicate how she feels she performed independent of objective outcome (win/loss). In the percentage of personal best method, performance is measured as a percentage of how the athlete did compared to her personal best. If she lost a race, but performed at 95 percent of her personal best, this may be a better performance outcome than the 90 percent of personal best displayed by the winner. Finally, in the comparison to expectations method, the athlete compares her performance with how she expected to perform. For example, an athlete's expected performance in golf is her golf handicap. If she normally shoots seven over par and she shoots four over par today, she has had a good performance, regardless of objective outcome.

A stronger relationship exists between mood and performance when performance is measured subjectively than when it is measured objectively. If you are simply trying to predict whether an athlete wins or loses a contest or finishes higher than another runner in a race, mood is a relatively weak predictor of performance (effect size = .28). If you are trying to predict if an athlete will perform up to personal expectations and past performance, then the relationship between mood and performance is a little stronger (effect size = .37). Cohen (1992) has indicated that effect sizes of .20, .50, and .80 are considered to be small, medium, and large, respectively.

A Conceptual Model for Predicting Performance Based on the literature, Lane and

Terry (2000) proposed a **conceptual model of mood** for explaining the relationship between precompetitive mood and performance. At the present time the model should be considered to be theoretical in nature. A theory allows investigators to test various aspects of a model to either modify it, verify it, or reject it. For this reason, a testable theory is very important to the advancement of science.

Lane and Terry propose that depression is a moderator between other manifestations of mood and athletic performance. As can be observed in figure 7.9, *high levels of depression are associated with increased anger, tension, confusion, and fatigue, but with reduced vigor.* The increased levels of negative mood have a debilitative effect upon performance, while

FIGURE 7.9 | Lane and Terry's (2000) conceptual model to predict performance from precompetitive mood.

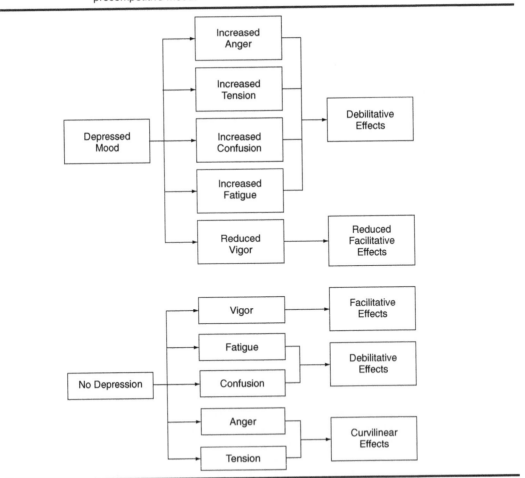

Source: Reproduced with permission.

reduced vigor has a reduced facilitative effect upon performance.

In the *absence of depression,* vigor will have a facilitative effect on performance, fatigue and confusion will have a debilitative effect upon performance, and anger and tension will have a curvilinear effect upon performance. Note that fatigue and confusion are predicted to have a debilitative effect upon performance regardless of whether the athlete is depressed or not. Anger and tension, in the absence of depression, can actually facilitate performance up to a point, but when they get too high they will cause a decrement in performance.

Some of the tenets of the conceptual model were tested by Lane, Terry, Beedie, Curry, and Clark (2002) utilizing a large sample (N = 451) of school-age children. Mood was assessed, using an adolescent version of the POMS, 10 minutes prior to a running competition in which participants completed a self-referenced race for distance or time. Consistent with the conceptual model, participants categorized as depressed scored higher on anger, confusion, fatigue and tension, but lower in vigor compared to the nondepressed group. Also

consistent with the conceptual model, larger correlations were observed among the moods of anger, tension, confusion, fatigue, and vigor for the depressed mood group compared to the nondepressed group. As predicted, vigor significantly predicted increased performance regardless of level of depression; however, confusion and fatigue did not lead to a reduction in perfonnance as expected. Finally, in the depressed group, anger predicted reduced performance as expected, but anger in the no-depression group and tension in both groups failed to influence performance as expected. Overall, this study provided support for some aspects of the Lane and Terry (2000) conceptual model, partial support for others, and no support for the notion that a curvilinear relationship would exist between anger and tension with performance in the no-depression group. Finally, it is important to note that while many predicted relationships were signiﬁcant, due to a large sample size, many of the significant effects were very weak. Clearly, the model needs further testing before we can conclude that depression acts as a moderator of the relationship between mood state and athletic performance.

Summary

Affect is a generic term used to describe emotions, feelings, and moods. Emotion is a situation specific affective response to the environment. Anxiety is one example of 15 specific emotions identified by Lazarus. While emotions are instantaneous discrete responses to the environment, moods are more diffuse and may last for weeks or months. Selye defined stress as the "nonspecific response to the body to any demand placed upon it." Distress and eustress are two manifestations of stress; distress is equated with state anxiety.

Anxiety is multidimensional in two different ways. First, anxiety can be conceptualized as a

personality disposition (trait anxiety) or as situation-specific emotional response to an environmental stimulus (state anxiety). Secondly, both trait and state anxiety can be conceptualized as being cognitive (cognitive anxiety) or somatic (somatic anxiety) in nature. A number of unidimensional and multidimensional inventories have been developed for measuring state and trait anxiety prior to and during competition.

The best way to understand stress is to conceptualize it as a process, as opposed to an outcome. The stress process begins with a stimulus and ends with the potential of a response. Distress and state anxiety (stress response) only occurs if an imbalance is perceived between the stimulus and the individual's perceived ability to cope with the stimulus threat. Competitive state anxiety that occurs prior to a competitive situation is referred to as precompetitive state anxiety. Antecedents that precede the competitive state anxiety response include such things as fear of performance failure, fear of negative social evaluation, fear of physical harm, situation ambiguity, and disruption of a well-learned routine.

Precompetitive cognitive anxiety starts relatively high and remains high and stable as the time-to-event approaches. Conversely, somatic anxiety remains relatively low until approximately 24 hours before the event, and then increases rapidly as the event approaches. Once performance begins, somatic anxiety dissipates rapidly, whereas cognitive state anxiety fluctuates throughout the contest as the probability of success/failure changes.

Perfectionism is multidimensional in nature and can be reduced to two overarching factors named functional perfectionism and dysfunctional perfectionism. Four inventories are identified that measure multidimensional perfectionism. These include the Frost Multidimensional Perfectionism Scale (FMPS), the Hewitt Multidimensional Perfectionism Scale (HMPS), the Sport Multidimensional Perfectionism Scale (Sport-MPS), and the Multidimensional Inventory of Perfectionism in Sport. Overall striving for perfection is associated with elevated cognitive and somatic state anxiety, but when functional and dysfunctional perfectionism are considered separately, a different result is obtained. Functional perfectionism predicts lower levels of state anxiety and higher levels of self-confidence, whereas dysfunctional perfectionism predicts elevated levels of somatic and cognitive state anxiety.

The relationship between arousal/anxiety and athletic performance is represented best by the inverted-U curve. The foundation of inverted-U theory is the classic work of Yerkes and Dodson (1908). Three theories that predict a curvilinear relationship between performance and arousal are cue utilization, signal detection theory, and information processing theory. Conversely, drive theory posits a linear relationship between arousal and performance. Perhaps the greatest contribution of drive theory is that it helps to explain the relationship between arousal and learning as well as arousal and performance.

As introduced in the beginning of the chapter, a mood state differs from an emotion in that it is more diffuse and may last for weeks or even months. While other inventories have been developed for measuring mood states, the most commonly used inventory used in sport is the Profile of Mood States (POMS). The POMS measure the moods of tension, depression, anger, vigor, fatigue, and confusion. The mental health model and the iceberg profile of the elite athlete all describe a mood profile in which negative moods are low and positive mood is high. It is not recommended that any attempt be made to distinguish between athletes' differing skill levels based on POMS scores. However, it may be possible to make a modest prediction of performance outcome based on precompetitive POMS scores if sport type and method of defining success are taken into consideration. Lane and Terry (2000) proposed a conceptual model of mood as a theoretical approach to predicting mood effects on performance outcome. The theory identifies the mood of depression as a moderator variable in the model.

Critical Thought Questions

1. Differentiate among the terms *emotion*, *anxiety*, *stress*, and *mood*. Provide examples of each showing differences and why they are different.

2. Discuss and clarify Selye's notion of stress relative to your answer to question number one.

3. Discuss the stress process, and give examples of each stage of the process. What is the importance of appraisal and coping in the model? What is meant by a balance between the stressful nature of a competitive situation and the athlete's perceived ability to cope with the situation?

4. Provide some practical application suggestions about research associated with the time to event nature of precompetitive anxiety.

5. Differentiate between functional and dysfunctional perfectionism and relate perfectionism to anxiety and motivation (e.g., autonomous motivation, goal orientation, attribution).

6. How is mood state measured and how does mood relate to athletic performance?

Glossary

affect A generic term used to describe emotions, feelings, and moods.

alexithymia Difficulty in acknowledging ones' own emotions and feelings along with inability to express them to others.

antecedent A preceding event or predictor of a later event.

anxiety Facing uncertain, existential threat.

cognitive anxiety The mental component of anxiety, caused by such things as fear of negative social evaluation, fear of failure, and loss of self-esteem.

competitive situation Situation-specific achievement environment that involves competition.

competitive state anxiety State anxiety associated with a competitive situation.

conceptual model of mood Theoretical model that explains how mood predicts performance, and one in which depression is a moderator variable that determines how the other moods affect performance.

distress According to Selye, bad stress, as represented by such things as anger and anxiety.

drive Represented by arousal and anxiety within the drive theory model.

drive theory A complex theory of learning that predicts a linear relationship between drive (arousal) and learning or performance.

dysfunctional perfectionism Perfectionism that is negative in nature and considered to be maladaptive.

effect size The number of times that a pooled standard deviation can be divided into the difference between two means.

emotion Instantaneous discrete response to the environment that lasts only seconds, minutes, or perhaps hours.

eustress According to Selye, good stress, as represented by such things as joy and happiness.

functional perfectionism Perfectionism that is positive in nature and considered to be adaptive.

iceberg profile A profile of the elite athlete on the six mood states measured by the POMS. Vigor is the only mood state for which elite athletes score well above the population mean, causing the profile to resemble an iceberg when charted on a graph.

inverted-U theory A model describing the hypothesized curvilinear relationship between arousal and performance. The term originates from the shape of the curve that results when this relationship is plotted on a graph.

mental health model Developed by Morgan, a model that proposes that the elite athlete is a mentally healthy individual.

meta-analysis Based on effect sizes, a statistical summary and comparison of independent samples associated with a literature review.

mood While emotions are directed toward something associated with the environment, moods are more diffuse and relate to how we are doing in our life.

mood profile Plotting of standardized mood state scores on a graph.

mood state Differs from an emotion in that it is more diffuse and may last for weeks or even months.

multidimensional The notion that a particular concept or psychological construct is composed of several different dimensions as opposed to just one.

organizational stress Stress placed on an athlete by the competitive sport environment, not just the coaches or a specific competitive event.

precompetitive mood An athlete's mood immediately before a competitive event.

precompetitive state anxiety Competitive state anxiety that occurs prior to or in anticipation of competition.

primary appraisal The first state of appraisal in the stress process, in which the individual determines the personal importance of the outcome of a situation.

profile of Mood States (POMS) A 65-item inventory designed to measure a person's mood state on six subscales.

secondary appraisal The second stage of appraisal in the stress process which involves appraisal of the individual's coping resources.

signal detection theory A theory of perception that predicts that increased decision errors will occur when an individual is either insensitive or supersensitive to a physical stimulus.

somatic anxiety The physical component of anxiety that reflects the perception of such physiological responses as increased heart rate, respiration, and muscular tension.

state anxiety An immediate emotional state that is characterized by apprehension, fear, tension, and an increase in physiological arousal.

stress The nonspecific response of the body to any demand made upon it.

stress process The process by which a potential stressful event elicits a stress response following an unfavorable appraisal of coping resources.

trait anxiety A predisposition to perceive certain environmental situations as threatening and to respond to these situations with increased state anxiety.

Yerkes-Dodson law A principle based on the classic work by Yerkes and Dodson (1908) that predicts an inverted-U relationship between arousal and performance.

Bioenergetics

■ Objectives

By studying this chapter, you should be able to do the following:

1. Discuss the function of the cell membrane, nucleus, and mitochondria.

2. Define the following terms: (1) *endergonic reactions*, (2) *exergonic reactions*, (3) *coupled reactions*, and (4) *bioenergetics*.

3. Describe the role of enzymes as catalysts in cellular chemical reactions.

4. List and discuss the nutrients that are used as fuels during exercise.

5. Identify the high-energy phosphates.

6. Discuss the biochemical pathways involved in anaerobic ATP production.

7. Discuss the aerobic production of ATP.

8. Describe the general scheme used to regulate metabolic pathways involved in bioenergetics.

9. Discuss the interaction between aerobic and anaerobic ATP production during exercise.

10. Identify the enzymes that are considered rate limiting in glycolysis and the Krebs cycle.

■ Outline

■ Key Terms

acetyl-CoA
activation energy
adenosine diphosphate
   (ADP)
adenosine triphosphate
   (ATP)
aerobic
anaerobic
ATPase
ATP-PC system
beta oxidation
bioenergetics
cell membrane
chemiosmotic hypothesis
coupled reactions
cytoplasm
electron transport chain
endergonic reactions
energy of activation
enzymes
exergonic reactions
flavin adenine
   dinucleotide (FAD)

glucose
glycogen
glycogenolysis
glycolysis
inorganic
inorganic phosphate (P_i)
isocitrate dehydrogenase
Krebs cycle
lactate
metabolism
mitochondrion
molecular biology
nicotinamide adenine
   dinucleotide (NAD$^+$)
nucleus
organic
oxidation
oxidative phosphorylation
phosphocreatine (PC)
phosphofructokinase (PFK)
reduction

Thousands of chemical reactions occur throughout the body during each minute of the day. Collectively, these reactions are called **metabolism.** Metabolism is broadly defined as the total of all cellular reactions and includes chemical pathways that result in the synthesis of molecules (anabolic reactions) as well as the breakdown of molecules (catabolic reactions).

Because energy is required by all cells, it is not surprising that cells possess chemical pathways that are capable of converting foodstuffs (i.e., fats, proteins, carbohydrates) into a biologically usable form of energy. This metabolic process is termed **bioenergetics.** For you to run, jump, or swim, skeletal muscle cells must be able to continuously extract energy from food nutrients. In fact, the inability to transform energy contained in foodstuffs into usable biological energy would limit performance in endurance activities. The explanation for this is simple. To continue to contract, muscle cells must have a continuous source of energy. When energy is not readily available, muscular contraction is not possible, and thus work must stop. Therefore, given the importance of cellular energy production during exercise, it is critical that students of exercise physiology develop a thorough understanding of bioenergetics. It is the purpose of this chapter to introduce both general and specific concepts associated with bioenergetics.

CELL STRUCTURE

Cells were discovered in the seventeenth century by the English scientist Robert Hooke. Advancements in the microscope over the past 300 years have led to improvements in our understanding of cell structure and function. To understand bioenergetics, it is important to have some appreciation of cell structure and function. Four elements (an element is a basic chemical substance) compose over 95% of the human body. These include oxygen (65%), carbon (18%), hydrogen (10%), and nitrogen (3%) (10). Additional elements found in rather small amounts in the body include sodium, iron, zinc, potassium, magnesium, chloride, and calcium. These various elements are linked by chemical bonds to form molecules or compounds. Compounds that contain carbon are called **organic** compounds, whereas those that do not contain carbon are termed **inorganic.** For example, water (H_2O) lacks carbon and is thus inorganic. In contrast, proteins, fats, and carbohydrates contain carbon and are organic compounds.

As the basic functional unit of the body, the cell is a highly organized factory capable of synthesizing the large number of compounds necessary for normal cellular function. Figure 3.1 illustrates the structure of a muscle cell (muscle cells are typically called muscle fibers). Note that not all cells are alike, nor do they all

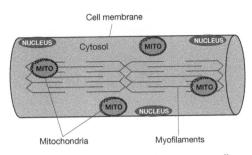

Figure 3.1 A muscle cell (fiber) and its major organelles.

perform the same functions. Nonetheless, in general, cell structure can be divided into three major parts:

1. **Cell membrane** The cell membrane (also called the *sarcolemma* in skeletal muscle fibers) is a semipermeable barrier that separates the cell from the extracellular environment. The two most important functions of the cell membrane are to enclose the components of the cell and to regulate the passage of various types of substances in and out of the cell (1, 10, 21).

2. **Nucleus** The nucleus is a large, round body within the cell that contains the cellular genetic components (genes). Genes are composed of double strands of deoxyribonucleic acids (DNA), which serve as the basis for the genetic code. In short, genes regulate protein synthesis, which determines cell composition and controls cellular activity. The field of **molecular biology** is concerned with understanding the composition and regulation of genes and is introduced in A Closer Look 3.1. Note that although most cells have only one nucleus, skeletal muscle cells have many nuclei along the entire length of the muscle fiber.

3. **Cytoplasm** (called *sarcoplasm* in muscle cells) This is the fluid portion of the cell between the nucleus and the cell membrane. Contained within the cytoplasm are various organelles (minute structures) that are concerned with specific cellular functions. One such organelle, the **mitochondrion,** is often called the powerhouse of the cell and is involved in the oxidative conversion of foodstuffs into usable cellular energy. Also contained in the cytoplasm are the enzymes that regulate the breakdown of glucose (i.e., glycolysis).

BIOLOGICAL ENERGY TRANSFORMATION

All energy on earth comes from the sun. Plants use light energy from the sun to drive chemical reactions to form carbohydrates, fats, and proteins. Animals (including

A CLOSER LOOK 3.1

Molecular Biology and Exercise Physiology

Molecular biology is defined as the study of biology at the molecular level. That is, molecular biology is the study of molecular structures and events underlying biological processes. Moreover, molecular biology is concerned with understanding the relationship between genes and the cellular characteristics that they determine. The field of molecular biology overlaps with other areas of biology, including physiology, biochemistry, and genetics (figure 3.2).

Recall from chapter 2 that each gene is responsible for the synthesis of a specific cellular protein. Cellular signals regulate protein synthesis by "turning on" or "turning off" specific genes. Therefore, understanding those factors that act as signals to promote or inhibit protein synthesis is of importance to exercise physiologists.

The technical revolution in the field of molecular biology offers another opportunity to make use of scientific information for the improvement of

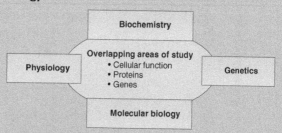

FIGURE 3.2   The different fields of biology have overlapping areas of study.

human performance. For example, exercise training results in modifications in the amounts and types of proteins synthesized in the exercised muscles (see chapter 13 for details). Indeed, it is well known that regular strength training results in an increase in muscle size due to an increase in contractile proteins. The techniques of molecular biology

provide the exercise physiologist with the "tools" to understand how exercise controls gene function and the synthesis of new proteins. Ultimately, understanding how exercise promotes the synthesis of specific proteins in muscles will allow the exercise scientist to design the most effective training program to achieve the desired training effects.

humans) then eat plants and other animals to obtain the energy required to maintain cellular activities.

Energy exists in several forms (e.g., electrical, mechanical, chemical), and all forms of energy are interchangeable (21). For example, muscle fibers convert chemical energy obtained from carbohydrates, fats, or proteins into mechanical energy to perform movement. The bioenergetic process of converting chemical energy to mechanical energy requires a series of tightly controlled chemical reactions. Before discussing the specific reactions involved, we provide an overview of cellular chemical reactions.

Cellular Chemical Reactions

Energy transfer in the body occurs via the releasing of energy trapped within chemical bonds of various molecules. Chemical bonds that contain relatively large amounts of potential energy are often referred to as "high-energy bonds." As mentioned previously, bioenergetics is concerned with the transfer of energy from foodstuffs into a biologically usable form. This energy transfer in the cell occurs as a result of a series of

chemical reactions. Many of these reactions require that energy be added to the reactants (**endergonic reactions**) before the reaction will "proceed." However, because energy is added to the reaction, the products contain more free energy than the original reactants.

Reactions that give off energy as a result of chemical process are known as **exergonic reactions.** Note that the words *endergonic* and *endothermic* can be used interchangeably. The same applies for the words *exergonic* and *exothermic*. Figure 3.3 illustrates that the amount of total energy released via exergonic reactions is the same whether the energy is released in one single reaction (combustion) or many small, controlled steps that usually occur in cells (cellular oxidation).

Coupled Reactions   Many of the chemical reactions that occur within the cell are called **coupled reactions.** Coupled reactions are reactions that are linked, with the liberation of free energy in one reaction being used to "drive" a second reaction. Figure 3.4 illustrates this point. In this example, energy released by an exergonic reaction is used to drive an energy-requiring reaction

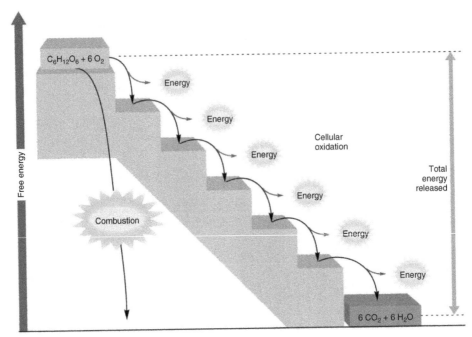

Figure 3.3 The breakdown of glucose into carbon dioxide and water via cellular oxidation results in a release of energy. Reactions that result in a release of free energy are termed exergonic.

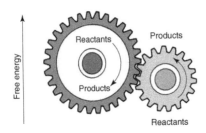

Exergonic reactions   Endergonic reactions

Figure 3.4 Model showing the coupling of exergonic and endergonic reactions. Note that the energy given off by the exergonic reaction (drive shaft) powers the endergonic reactions (smaller gear).

IN SUMMARY

■ Metabolism is defined as the total of all cellular reactions that occur in cells of the body; this includes both the synthesis of molecules and the breakdown of molecules. Cell structure includes the following three major parts: (1) cell membrane, (2) nucleus, and (3) cytoplasm (called *sarcoplasm* in muscle).

■ The cell membrane provides a protective barrier between the interior of the cell and the extra-cellular fluid.

■ Genes (located within the nucleus) regulate protein synthesis within the cell.

■ The cytoplasm is the fluid portion of the cell and contains numerous organelles.

(endergonic reaction) in the cell. This is like two meshed gears in which the turning of one (energy-releasing, exergonic gear) causes the movement of the second (endergonic gear). In other words, energy-liberating reactions are "coupled" to energy-requiring reactions. Oxidation-reduction reactions are an important type of coupled reaction and are discussed in the next section.

Oxidation-Reduction Reactions

The process of removing an electron from an atom or molecule is called **oxidation.** The addition of an electron to an atom or molecule is referred to as **reduction.** Oxidation and reduction are always coupled reactions because a molecule cannot be oxidized unless it donates electrons to another atom. The molecule that donates the electron is known as the *reducing agent,* whereas the one that accepts the electrons is called an *oxidizing agent*. Note that a molecule can act as both an oxidizing agent and a reducing agent. For example, when molecules play both roles, they can gain electrons in one reaction and then pass these electrons to another molecule to produce an oxidation-reduction reaction. Hence, coupled oxidation-reduction reactions are analogous to a bucket brigade, with electrons being passed along in the buckets.

Note that the term *oxidation* does not mean that oxygen participates in the reaction. This term is derived from the fact that oxygen tends to accept electrons and therefore acts as an oxidizing agent. This important property of oxygen is used by cells to produce a usable form of energy and is discussed in detail in the section "Electron Transport Chain."

Keep in mind that oxidation-reduction reactions in cells often involve the transfer of hydrogen atoms (with their electrons) rather than free electrons. This occurs because a hydrogen atom contains one electron and one proton in the nucleus. Therefore, a molecule that loses a hydrogen atom also loses an electron and therefore is oxidized; the molecule that gains the hydrogen (and electron) is reduced. In many biological oxidation-reduction reactions, pairs of electrons are passed along between molecules as free electrons or as pairs of hydrogen atoms.

Two molecules that play important roles in the transfer of electrons are 1) **nicotinamide adenine dinucleotide** and 2) **flavin adenine dinucleotide.** Nicotinamide adenine dinucleotide is derived from the vitamin niacin (vitamin B_3), whereas flavin adenine dinucleotide comes from the vitamin riboflavin (B_2). The oxidized form of nicotinamide adenine dinucleotide is written as NAD^+, whereas the reduced form is written as NADH. Similarly, the oxidized form of flavin adenine dinucleotide is written as FAD, and the reduced form is abbreviated as FADH. Note that FADH can also accept a second hydrogen, forming $FADH_2$. Therefore, FADH and $FADH_2$ can be thought of as the same molecule because they undergo the same reactions. An illustration of how NADH is formed from the reduction of NAD^+ during a coupled oxidation-reduction reaction is shown in figure 3.5. Details of how NAD^+ and FAD function as "carrier molecules" during bioenergetic reactions are discussed later in this chapter in the section "Electron Transport Chain."

Enzymes

The speed of cellular chemical reactions is regulated by catalysts called **enzymes.** Enzymes are proteins that play a major role in the regulation of metabolic pathways in the cell. Enzymes do not cause a reaction

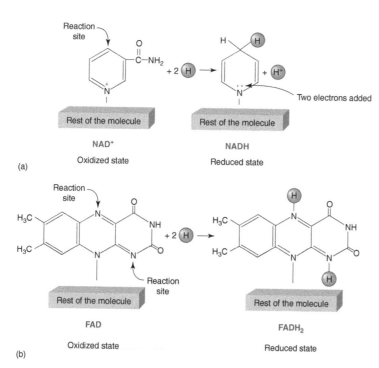

Figure 3.5 Structural formulas for NAD^+, NADH, FAD, and $FADH_2$. (a) When NAD^+ reacts with two hydrogen atoms, it binds to one of them and accepts the electron from the other. This is shown by two dots above the nitrogen (Ṅ) in the formula for NADH. (b) When FAD reacts with two hydrogen atoms to form $FADH_2$, it binds each of them to a nitrogen atom at the reaction sites.

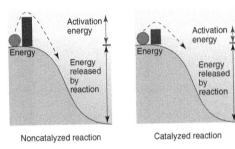

Figure 3.6 Enzymes catalyze reactions by lowering the energy of activation. That is, the energy required to start the reaction is reduced. Note the difference in the energy of activation in the catalyzed reaction versus the noncatalyzed reaction.

to occur, but simply regulate the rate or speed at which the reaction takes place. Further, the enzyme does not change the nature of the reaction nor its final result.

Chemical reactions occur when the reactants have sufficient energy to proceed. The energy required to initiate chemical reactions is called the **activation energy** (8, 31). Enzymes work as catalysts by lowering the activation energy. The end result is to increase the rate at which these reactions take place. Figure 3.6 illustrates this concept. Note that the activation energy is greater in the noncatalyzed reaction on the left when compared to the enzyme-catalyzed reaction pictured on the right. By reducing the activation energy, enzymes increase the speed of chemical reactions and therefore increase the rate of product formation.

The ability of enzymes to lower the activation energy results from unique structural characteristics. In general, enzymes are large protein molecules with a three-dimensional shape. Each type of enzyme has characteristic ridges and grooves. The pockets that are formed from the ridges or grooves located on the enzyme are called active sites. These active sites are important because it is the unique shape of the active site that causes a specific enzyme to adhere to a particular reactant molecule (called a *substrate*). The concept of how enzymes fit with a particular substrate molecule is analogous to the idea of a lock and key (figure 3.7). The shape of the enzyme's active site is specific for the shape of a particular substrate, which allows the two molecules (enzyme + substrate) to form a complex known as the enzyme-substrate complex. After the formation of the enzyme-substrate complex, the energy of activation needed for the reaction to occur is lowered, and the reaction is more easily brought to completion. This is followed by the dissociation of the enzyme and the product. The ability of an enzyme to work as a catalyst is not constant and can be modified by several factors; this will be discussed shortly.

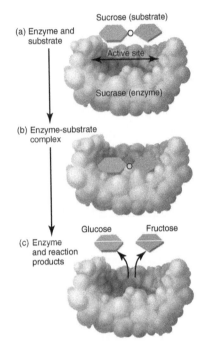

Figure 3.7 The lock-and-key model of enzyme action: (a) The substrate (i.e., sucrose) approaches a pocket on the enzyme called the active site. (b) The substrate fits into the active site in the enzyme, forming an enzyme-substrate complex. (c) The enzyme then breaks the bond between the two sugars in sucrose and releases glucose and fructose (i.e., reaction products). The enzyme remains unchanged and is free to be used again.

Note that cellular enzymes can often play a key role in diagnosing specific illnesses. For example, when tissues become damaged as a result of diseases, dead cells within these tissues can release enzymes into the blood. Many of these enzymes are not normally found in blood and therefore provide a clinical "clue" to diagnose the source of the illness. Details about the use of blood enzyme levels in the diagnosis of diseases are contained in Clinical Applications 3.1.

Classification of Enzymes   In the early days of biochemistry, enzymes were named by the scientist who discovered the enzyme. Often these names did not provide a clue to the function of the enzyme. Therefore, to reduce confusion, an international committee developed a systematic naming system that names the enzyme according to the type of chemical reaction it catalyzes. In this scheme, enzymes are provided a systematic name and a numerical identification. In addition, a shorter version of the systematic name, called the recommended name, was provided for everyday use. With the exception of some older

CLINICAL APPLICATIONS 3.1

Diagnostic Value of Measuring Enzyme Activity in the Blood

When tissues become diseased, dead cells often break open and release their enzymes into the blood. Because many of these intracellular enzymes are not normally found in blood, the presence of a specific enzyme in blood provides important diagnostic information regarding the source of the medical problem. In practice, the diagnostic test proceeds as follows. A doctor obtains a blood sample from the patient and forwards the sample to a clinical laboratory for analysis. The laboratory then determines the activity of a specific enzyme in a test tube by addition of the blood sample and appropriate substrates for the enzyme. The results of this test can often assist in making a diagnosis. For example, the finding that the blood sample contains high levels of the enzyme lactate dehydrogenase would suggest that the patient experienced a myocardial infarction (i.e., heart attack). Similarly, elevated blood levels of the enzyme creatine kinase would also indicate cardiac injury and would provide additional evidence that the patient suffered a heart attack. See table 3.1 for additional examples of the diagnostic usage for specific enzymes found in blood.

TABLE 3.1   Examples of the Diagnostic Value of Enzymes Found in Blood

Enzyme	Diseases Associated with High Blood Levels of Enzyme
Lactate dehydrogenase (cardiac-specific isoform)	Myocardial infarction
Creatine kinase	Myocardial infarction, muscular dystrophy
Alkaline phosphatase	Carcinoma of bone, Paget's disease, obstructive jaundice
Amylase	Pancreatitis, perforated peptic ulcer
Aldolase	Muscular dystrophy

enzyme names (e.g., pepsin, trysin, and rennin) all enzyme names end with the suffix "ase" and reflect both the job category of the enzyme and the reaction it catalyzes. For example, enzymes called kinases add a phosphate group (i.e., phosphorylate), a specific molecule. Other enzyme categories include dehydrogenases, which remove hydrogen atoms from their substrates, and oxidases, which catalyze oxidation-reduction reactions involving molecular oxygen. Enzymes called isomerases rearrange atoms within their substrate molecules to form structural isomers (i.e., molecules with the same molecular formula but with a different structural formula).

Factors That Alter Enzyme Activity   The activity of an enzyme, as measured by the rate at which its substrates are converted into products, is influenced by several factors. Two of the more important factors include temperature and pH (pH is a measure of acidity or alkalinity) of the solution.

Individual enzymes have an optimum temperature at which they are most active. In general, a small rise in body temperature above normal (i.e., 37° C) increases the activity of most enzymes. This is useful during exercise because muscular work results in an increase in body temperature. The resulting elevation in enzyme activity would enhance bioenergetics (ATP production)

by speeding up the rate of reactions involved in the production of biologically useful energy. This point is illustrated in figure 3.8. Notice that enzyme activity is less than maximum at normal body temperature (37° C). Also, note that an exercise-induced increase in body temperature (e.g., 40° C) results in a temperature-induced increase in enzyme activity.

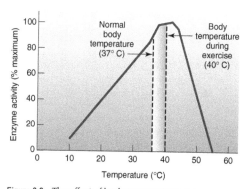

Figure 3.8   The effect of body temperature on enzyme activity. Notice that an optimal range of temperatures exists for enzyme activity. An increase or decrease in temperature away from the optimal temperature range results in diminished enzyme activity.

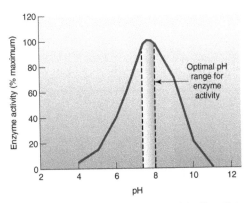

Figure 3.9 The effect of pH on enzyme activity. Note that every enzyme has a narrow range of optimal pH. An increase or decrease of pH away from this optimum range results in a decrease in enzyme activity.

The pH of body fluids also has a large effect on enzyme activity. The relationship between pH and enzyme activity is similar to the temperature/enzyme activity relationship; that is, individual enzymes have a pH optimum. If the pH is altered from the optimum, the enzyme activity is reduced (figure 3.9). This has important implications during exercise. For example, during intense exercise, skeletal muscles can produce large amounts of hydrogen ions (34). Accumulation of large quantities of hydrogen ions results in a decrease in the pH of body fluids below the optimum pH of important bioenergetic enzymes. The end result is a decreased ability to provide the energy (i.e., ATP) required for muscular contraction. In fact, extreme acidity is an important limiting factor in various types of intense exercise. This will be discussed again in chapters 10 and 19.

IN SUMMARY

- Enzymes that serve as catalysts for these reactions regulate the speed of chemical reactions.
- Enzymes are classified into categories based upon the type of reaction that the enzyme performs.
- Two important factors that regulate enzyme activity are temperature and pH. Individual enzymes have an optimum temperature and pH at which they are most active.

FUELS FOR EXERCISE

The body uses carbohydrate, fat, and protein nutrients consumed daily to provide the necessary energy to maintain cellular activities both at rest and during exercise. During exercise, the primary nutrients used for energy are fats and carbohydrates, with protein contributing a small amount of the total energy used (3).

Carbohydrates

Carbohydrates are composed of atoms of carbon, hydrogen, and oxygen. Stored carbohydrates provide the body with a rapidly available form of energy, with 1 gram of carbohydrate yielding approximately 4 kcal of energy (36). As mentioned earlier, plants synthesize carbohydrates from the interaction of CO_2, water, and solar energy in a process called photosynthesis. Carbohydrates exist in three forms (36): (1) monosaccharides, (2) disaccharides, and (3) polysaccharides. Monosaccharides are simple sugars such as glucose and fructose. **Glucose** is familiar to most of us and is often referred to as "blood sugar." It can be found in foods or can be formed in the digestive tract as a result of cleavage of more complex carbohydrates. Fructose is contained in fruits or honey and is considered to be the sweetest of the simple carbohydrates (33).

Disaccharides are formed by combining two monosaccharides. For example, table sugar is called sucrose and is composed of glucose and fructose. Maltose, also a disaccharide, is composed of two glucose molecules. Sucrose is considered to be the most common dietary disaccharide in the United States and constitutes approximately 25% of the total caloric intake of most Americans (28). It occurs naturally in many carbohydrates, such as cane sugar, beets, honey, and maple syrup.

Polysaccharides are complex carbohydrates that contain three or more monosaccharides. Polysaccharides may be rather small molecules (i.e., three monosaccharides) or relatively large molecules containing hundreds of monosaccharides. In general, polysaccharides are classified as either plant or animal polysaccharides. The two most common forms of plant polysaccharides are cellulose and starch. Humans lack the digestive enzymes necessary to digest cellulose, and thus cellulose is discarded as waste in the fecal material. On the other hand, starch—found in corn, grains, beans, potatoes, and peas—is easily digested by humans and is an important source of carbohydrate in the American diet (28). After ingestion, starch is broken down to form monosaccharides and may be used as energy immediately by cells or stored in another form within cells for future energy needs.

Glycogen is the term used for the polysaccharide stored in animal tissue. It is synthesized within cells by linking glucose molecules using the action of the enzyme glycogen synthase. Glycogen molecules are generally large and may consist of hundreds to thousands of glucose molecules. Cells store glycogen as a means of supplying carbohydrates as an energy source. For example, during exercise, individual muscle cells break down glycogen into glucose (this process is called **glycogenolysis**) and use the glucose as a source of energy for contraction. On the other hand, glycogenolysis also occurs in the liver, with the free glucose being released into the bloodstream and transported to tissues throughout the body.

Important to exercise metabolism is that glycogen is stored in both muscle fibers and the liver. However, total glycogen stores in the body are relatively small and can be depleted within a few hours as a result of prolonged exercise. Therefore, glycogen synthesis is an ongoing process within cells. Diets low in carbohydrates tend to hamper glycogen synthesis, whereas high-carbohydrate diets enhance glycogen synthesis (see chapter 23).

Fats

Although fats contain the same chemical elements as carbohydrates, the ratio of carbon to oxygen in fats is much greater than that found in carbohydrates. Stored body fat is an ideal fuel for prolonged exercise because fat molecules contain large quantities of energy per unit of weight. One gram of fat contains about 9 kcal of energy, which is more than twice the energy content of either carbohydrates or protein (33). Fats are insoluble in water and can be found in both plants and animals. In general, fats can be classified into four general groups: (1) fatty acids, (2) triglycerides, (3) phospholipids, and (4) steroids. Fatty acids consist of long chains of carbon atoms linked to a carboxyl group at one end (a carboxyl group contains a carbon, oxygen, and hydrogen group). Importantly, fatty acids are the primary type of fat used by muscle cells for energy.

Fatty acids are stored in the body as triglycerides. Triglycerides are composed of three molecules of fatty acids and one molecule of glycerol (not a fat but a type of alcohol). Although the largest storage site for triglycerides is fat cells, these molecules are also stored in many cell types, including skeletal muscle. In times of need, they can be broken down into their component parts, with fatty acids being used as energy substrates by muscle and other tissues. The process of breaking down triglycerides into fatty acids and glycerol is termed *lipolysis* and is regulated by a family of enzymes called *lipases*. The glycerol released by lipolysis is not a direct energy source for muscle, but can be used by the liver to synthesize glucose. Therefore, the entire triglyceride molecule is a useful source of energy for the body.

Phospholipids are not used as an energy source by skeletal muscle during exercise (17). Phospholipids are lipids combined with phosphoric acid and are synthesized in virtually every cell in the body. The biological roles of phospholipids vary from providing the structural integrity of cell membranes to providing an insulating sheath around nerve fibers (10).

The final classification of fats is the steroids. Again, these fats are not used as energy sources during exercise, but will be mentioned briefly to provide a clearer understanding of the nature of biological fats. The most common steroid is cholesterol. Cholesterol is a component of all cell membranes. It can be synthesized in every cell in the body and, of course, can be consumed in foods. In addition to its role in membrane structure, cholesterol is needed for the synthesis of the sex hormones estrogen, progesterone, and testosterone (10). Although cholesterol has many "useful" biological functions, high blood cholesterol levels have been implicated in the development of coronary artery disease (38) (see chapter 18).

Proteins

Proteins are composed of many tiny subunits called amino acids. At least twenty types of amino acids are needed by the body to form various tissues, enzymes, blood proteins, and so on. Nine amino acids, called essential amino acids, cannot be synthesized by the body and therefore must be consumed in foods. Proteins are formed by linking amino acids by chemical bonds called peptide bonds. As a potential fuel source, proteins contain approximately 4 kcal per gram (8). For proteins to be used as substrates for the formation of high-energy compounds, they must be broken down into their constituent amino acids. Proteins can contribute energy for exercise in two ways. First, the amino acid alanine can be converted in the liver to glucose, which can then be used to synthesize glycogen. Liver glycogen can be degraded into glucose and transported to working skeletal muscle via the circulation. Second, many amino acids (e.g., isoleucine, alanine, leucine, valine) can be converted into metabolic intermediates (i.e., compounds that may directly participate in bioenergetics) in muscle cells and directly contribute as fuel in the bioenergetic pathways (12).

IN SUMMARY

- The body uses carbohydrate, fat, and protein nutrients consumed daily to provide the necessary energy to maintain cellular activities both at rest and during exercise. During exercise, the primary nutrients used for energy are fats and carbohydrates, with protein contributing a relatively small amount of the total energy used.
- Glucose is stored in animal cells as a polysaccharide called glycogen.
- Fatty acids are the primary form of fat used as an energy source in cells. Fatty acids are stored as triglycerides in muscle and fat cells.
- Proteins are composed of amino acids, and twenty different amino acids are required to form the various proteins contained in cells. The use of protein as an energy source requires that cellular proteins be broken down into amino acids.

HIGH-ENERGY PHOSPHATES

The immediate source of energy for muscular contraction is the high-energy phosphate compound **adenosine triphosphate (ATP)** (33). Although ATP is not the only energy-carrying molecule in the cell, it is the most important one, and without sufficient amounts of ATP most cells die quickly.

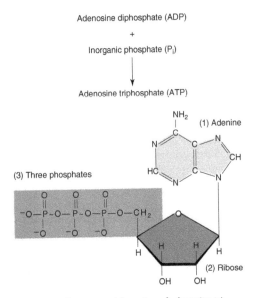

Figure 3.10   The structural formation of adenosine triphosphate (ATP).

The structure of ATP consists of three main parts: (1) an adenine portion, (2) a ribose portion, and (3) three linked phosphates (figure 3.10). The formation of ATP occurs by combining **adenosine diphosphate (ADP)** and **inorganic phosphate (P_i)** and requires a rather large amount of energy. Some of this energy is stored in the chemical bond joining ADP and P_i. Accordingly, this bond is called a high-energy bond. When the enzyme **ATPase** breaks this bond, energy is released, and this energy can be used to do work (e.g., muscular contraction):

$$ATP \xrightarrow{\text{ATPase}} ADP + P_i + Energy$$

ATP is often called the universal energy donor. It couples the energy released from the breakdown of foodstuffs into a usable form of energy required by all cells. For example, figure 3.11 presents a model depicting ATP as the universal energy donor in the cell. The cell uses exergonic reactions (breakdown of foodstuffs) to form ATP via endergonic reactions. This newly formed ATP can then be used to drive the energy-requiring processes in the cell. Therefore, energy-liberating reactions are linked to energy-requiring reactions like two meshed gears.

BIOENERGETICS

Muscle cells store limited amounts of ATP. Therefore, because muscular exercise requires a constant supply of ATP to provide the energy needed for contraction, metabolic pathways must exist in the cell with the capability to produce ATP rapidly. Indeed, muscle cells can produce ATP by any one or a combination of

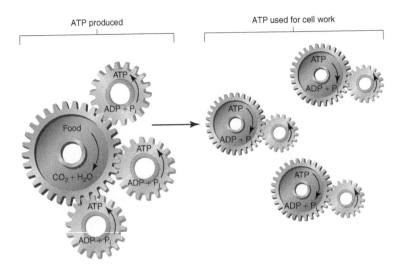

Figure 3.11   A model of ATP as the universal energy carrier of the cell. Exergonic reactions are shown as blue gears with arrows going down (these reactions produce a decrease in free energy); endergonic reactions are shown as green gears with arrows going up (these reaction produced an increase in free energy).

three metabolic pathways: (1) formation of ATP by **phosphocreatine (PC)** breakdown, (2) formation of ATP via the degradation of glucose or glycogen (called glycolysis), and (3) oxidative formation of ATP. Formation of ATP via the PC pathway and glycolysis does not involve the use of O_2; these pathways are called **anaerobic** (without O_2) pathways. Oxidative formation of ATP by the use of O_2 is termed **aerobic** metabolism. A detailed discussion of the operation of the three metabolic pathways involved in the formation of ATP during exercise follows.

Anaerobic ATP Production

The simplest and, consequently, the most rapid method of producing ATP involves the donation of a phosphate group and its bond energy from PC to ADP to form ATP (33, 36, 37):

$$PC + ADP \xrightarrow[\text{Creatine kinase}]{} ATP + C$$

The reaction is catalyzed by the enzyme creatine kinase. As rapidly as ATP is broken down to ADP + P_i

at the onset of exercise, ATP is resynthesized via the PC reaction. However, muscle cells store only small amounts of PC, and thus the total amount of ATP that can be formed via this reaction is limited. The combination of stored ATP and PC is called the **ATP-PC system** or the "phosphagen system." It provides energy for muscular contraction at the onset of exercise and during short-term, high-intensity exercise (i.e., lasting fewer than 5 seconds). PC reformation requires ATP and occurs only during recovery from exercise (11).

The importance of the ATP-PC system in athletics can be appreciated by considering short-term, intense exercise such as sprinting 50 meters, high jumping, performing a rapid weight-lifting move, or a football player racing 10 yards downfield. All these activities require only a few seconds to complete and thus need a rapid supply of ATP. The ATP-PC system provides a simple one-enzyme reaction to produce ATP for these types of activities. The fact that depletion of PC is likely to limit short-term, high-intensity exercise has led to the suggestion that ingesting large amounts of creatine can improve exercise performance (see The Winning Edge 3.1).

THE WINNING EDGE 3.1

Exercise Physiology Applied to Sports

Does Creatine Supplementation Improve Exercise Performance?
The depletion of phosphocreatine (PC) may limit exercise performance during short-term, high-intensity exercise (e.g., 100- to 200-meter dash) because the depletion of PC results in a reduction in the rate of ATP production by the ATP-PC system. Studies have shown that ingestion of large amounts of creatine monohydrate (20 grams/day) over a 5-day period results in increased stores of muscle PC (2, 6, 14, 19, 26, 39). This creatine supplementation has been shown to improve performance in laboratory settings during short-duration (e.g., 30 seconds), high-intensity stationary cycling exercise (14, 19, 24, 26, 39). However, results on the influence of creatine supplementation on performance during short-duration running and swimming are not consistent (2, 14, 19, 26, 39). This may be due to the fact that creatine supplementation results in a weight gain due to water retention. Therefore,

this increase in body weight may impair performance in weight-bearing activities such as running.

Studies suggest that creatine supplementation in conjunction with resistance exercise training results in an enhanced physiologic adaptation to weight training (2, 5, 15, 23, 32, 39). Specifically, these studies indicate that creatine supplementation combined with resistance training promotes an increase in both dynamic muscular strength and fat-free mass. Nonetheless, whether creatine supplementation improves isokinetic or isometric muscular strength remains controversial (2).

Does oral creatine supplementation result in adverse physiological side effects and pose health risks? Unfortunately, a definitive answer to this question is not available. Although anecdotal reports indicate that creatine supplementation can be associated with negative side effects such as nausea, neurological dysfunction, minor gastrointestinal distress, and muscle cramping, these reports are not well documented

(2, 7, 14, 20, 39). At present, due to limited data, a firm conclusion about the long-term health risks of creatine supplementation cannot be reached. However, current evidence suggests that creatine supplementation for up to eight weeks does not appear to produce major health risks, but the safety of more prolonged creatine supplementation has not been established.

An important issue related to the use of creatine and other dietary supplements is the possibility of contamination within the product; that is, the supplement product may contain other chemical compounds in addition to creatine (27). Indeed, this is an important safety issue in the "over-the-counter supplement" industry because a large study has reported a high level of variability in the purity of over-the-counter products (27). For more information on creatine and exercise performance, see Bemben and Lamont (2005) and Hespel and Derave (2007) in the Suggested Readings.

A CLOSER LOOK 3.2

Lactic Acid or Lactate?

In many textbooks, the terms "lactic acid" and "lactate" are used interchangeably. This is often confusing to students who ask, "Are lactic acid and lactate the same molecule?" The answer is that lactic acid and lactate are related but are technically different molecules. Here's the explanation: The term *lactate* refers to the salt of lactic acid (figure 3.12) (4). You may recall from another science course that when acids dissociate and release hydrogen ions, the remaining molecule is called the *conjugate base* of the acid. It follows that lactate is the conjugate base of lactic acid. Because of the close relationship between lactic acid and lactate, many authors use these terms interchangeably (3). Remembering the relationship between lactic acid and lactate will reduce confusion when you read about these molecules in future chapters within this text.

FIGURE 3.12 The ionization of lactic acid forms the conjugate base called lactate. At normal body pH, lactic acid will rapidly dissociate to form lactate.

A second metabolic pathway capable of producing ATP rapidly without the involvement of O_2 is termed **glycolysis.** Glycolysis involves the breakdown of glucose or glycogen to form two molecules of pyruvate or **lactate** (figure 3.13). Simply stated, glycolysis is an anaerobic pathway used to transfer bond energy from glucose to rejoin P_i to ADP. This process involves a series of enzymatically catalyzed, coupled reactions. Glycolysis occurs in the sarcoplasm of the muscle cell and produces a net gain of two molecules of ATP and two molecules of pyruvate or lactate per glucose molecule (see A Closer Look 3.2).

Let's consider glycolysis in more detail. First, the reactions between glucose and pyruvate can be considered as two distinct phases: (1) an energy investment phase, and (2) an energy generation phase (figure 3.13). The first five reactions make up the "energy investment phase" where stored ATP must be used to form sugar phosphates. Although the end result of glycolysis is energy producing (exergonic), glycolysis must be "primed" by the addition of ATP at two points at the beginning of the pathway (figures 3.14 and 3.15). The purpose of the ATP priming is to add phosphate groups (called phosphorylation) to glucose and to fructose 6-phosphate. Note that if glycolysis begins with glycogen as the substrate, the addition of only one ATP is required. That is, glycogen does not require phosphorylation by ATP, but is phosphorylated by inorganic phosphate instead (figure 3.14). The last five reactions of glycolysis represent the "energy generation phase" of glycolysis. Figure 3.15 points out that two molecules of ATP are produced at each of two separate reactions near the

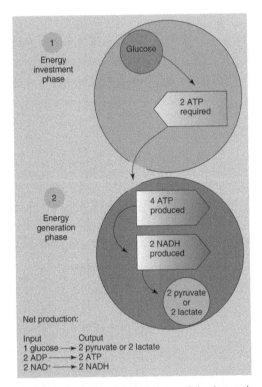

Figure 3.13 Illustration of the two phases of glycolysis and the products of glycolysis. From *Biochemistry* by Mathews and van Holde. Copyright © 1990 by The Benjamin/Cummings Publishing Company. Reprinted by permission.

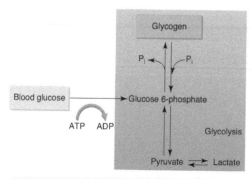

Figure 3.14   Illustration of the interaction between blood glucose and muscle glycogen for the provision of glucose for glycolysis. Regardless of the source of glucose for glycolysis, glucose must be phosphorylated to form glucose 6-phosphate as the first step in glycolysis. Note, however, that phosphorylation of glucose obtained from the blood requires 1 ATP, whereas the phosphorylation of glucose obtained from glycogen is achieved by using inorganic phosphate (Pᵢ) located in the cell.

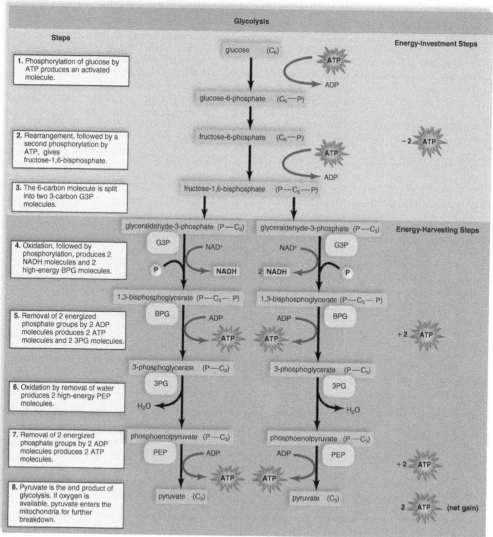

Figure 3.15   Summary of the anaerobic metabolism of glucose. Note that the end result of the anaerobic breakdown of one molecule of glucose is the production of two molecules of ATP and two molecules of pyruvate.

A CLOSER LOOK 3.3

NADH Is "Shuttled" into Mitochondria

NADH generated during glycolysis must be converted back to NAD$^+$ if glycolysis is to continue. As discussed in the text, the conversion of NADH to NAD$^+$ can occur by pyruvate accepting the hydrogens (forming lactate) or "shuttling" the hydrogens from NADH across the mitochondrial membrane. The "shuttling" of hydrogens across the mitochondrial membrane requires a specific transport system. Figure 4.9 (see chapter 4) illustrates this process. This transport system is located within the mitochondrial membrane and transfers NADH-released hydrogens from the cytosol into the mitochondria, where they can enter the electron transport chain.

---

end of the glycolytic pathway; thus, the net gain of glycolysis is two ATP if glucose is the substrate and three ATP if glycogen is the substrate.

Hydrogens are frequently removed from nutrient substrates in bioenergetic pathways and are transported by "carrier molecules." Two biologically important carrier molecules are nicotinamide adenine dinucleotide (NAD$^+$) and flavin adenine dinucleotide (FAD). Both NAD$^+$ and FAD transport hydrogens and their associated electrons to be used for later generation of ATP in the mitochondrion via aerobic processes. For the chemical reactions in glycolysis to proceed, two hydrogens must be removed from glyceraldehyde 3-phosphate, which then combines with inorganic phosphate (P$_i$) to form 1,3-diphosphoglycerate. The hydrogen acceptor in this reaction is NAD$^+$ (figure 3.15). Here, NAD$^+$ accepts one of the hydrogens, while the remaining hydrogen is free in solution. Upon accepting the hydrogen, NAD$^+$ is converted to its reduced form, NADH. Adequate amounts of NAD$^+$ must be available to accept the hydrogen atoms that must be removed from glyceraldehyde 3-phosphate if glycolysis is to continue (3, 31). How is NAD$^+$ reformed from NADH? There are two ways that the cell restores NAD$^+$ from NADH. First, if sufficient oxygen (O$_2$) is available, the hydrogens from NADH can be "shuttled" into the mitochondria of the cell and can contribute to the aerobic production of ATP (see A Closer Look 3.3). Second, if O$_2$ is not available to accept the hydrogens in the mitochondria, pyruvate can accept the hydrogens

to form lactate (figure 3.16). The enzyme that catalyzes this reaction is lactate dehydrogenase (LDH), with the end result being the formation of lactate and the reformation of NAD$^+$. Therefore, the reason for lactate formation is the "recycling" of NAD$^+$ (i.e., NADH converted to NAD$^+$) so that glycolysis can continue.

Again, glycolysis is the breakdown of glucose into pyruvate or lactate with the net production of two or three ATP, depending on whether the pathway began with glucose or glycogen, respectively. Figure 3.15 summarizes glycolysis in a simple flowchart. Glucose is a six-carbon molecule, and pyruvate and lactate are three-carbon molecules. This explains the production of two molecules of pyruvate or lactate from one molecule of glucose. Because O$_2$ is not directly involved in glycolysis, the pathway is considered anaerobic. However, in the presence of O$_2$ in the mitochondria, pyruvate can participate in the aerobic production of ATP. Thus, in addition to being an anaerobic pathway capable of producing ATP without O$_2$, glycolysis can be considered the first step in the aerobic degradation of carbohydrates. This will be discussed in detail in the next section, "Aerobic ATP Production."

IN SUMMARY

- The immediate source of energy for muscular contraction is the high-energy phosphate ATP. ATP is degraded via the enzyme ATPase as follows:

$$ATP \xrightarrow{\text{ATPase}} ADP + P_i + Energy$$

- Formation of ATP without the use of O$_2$ is termed *anaerobic metabolism*. In contrast, the production of ATP using O$_2$ as the final electron acceptor is referred to as *aerobic metabolism*.
- Muscle cells can produce ATP by any one or a combination of three metabolic pathways: (1) ATP-PC system, (2) glycolysis, and (3) oxidative formation of ATP.
- The ATP-PC system and glycolysis are two anaerobic metabolic pathways that are capable of producing ATP without O$_2$.

Figure 3.16 The addition of hydrogen atoms to pyruvate forms lactate and NAD$^+$, which can be used again in glycolysis. The reaction is catalyzed by the enzyme lactate dehydrogenase (LDH).

A LOOK BACK—IMPORTANT PEOPLE IN SCIENCE

Hans Krebs and the Discovery of the "Krebs Cycle"

Hans Krebs (1900–1981) received the Nobel Prize for Physiology or Medicine in 1953 for his research on a series of important chemical reactions in cells that became known as the "Krebs cycle." Krebs was born in Germany and earned his MD degree from the University of Hamburg in 1925. After graduation from medical school, he moved to Berlin to study chemistry and became actively involved in biochemical research. The son of a Jewish physician, Hans Krebs was forced to leave Nazi Germany in 1933 for England. Upon arrival in England, Dr. Krebs continued his research at Cambridge University and later at the University of Sheffield and Oxford University.

During his distinguished research career, Hans Krebs made many impor-tant contributions to physiology and biochemistry. One of his first signifi-cant areas of research was how protein is metabolized in cells. An important outcome of this early work was the finding that the liver produces a nitrogenous waste product of protein metabolism called urea. Further work by Dr. Krebs and his colleague Kurt Henseleit (another German biochem-ist) led to the discovery of the series of reactions that produce urea (later known as the urea cycle).

Although Dr. Krebs's research on protein metabolism was important, he is best known for his discovery of the cellular reactions involving the sub-stances formed from the breakdown of carbohydrates, fats, and proteins in the body. Specifically, in 1937, Dr. Krebs discovered the existence of a cycle of chemical reactions that com-bines the end product of carbohydrate breakdown (this product was later named acetyl-CoA) with oxaloacetic acid to form citric acid. Dr. Krebs's work showed that this cycle regenerates oxaloacetic acid through a series of intermediate compounds while liber-ating carbon dioxide and electrons. This cycle has been known by three different names, including the citric acid cycle and the tricarboxylic acid cycle. However, many biochemists (and this textbook) refer to this cycle as the Krebs cycle in recognition of Hans Krebs's contribution to this important discovery. The discovery of the Krebs cycle and how chemical foodstuffs are converted into usable energy was of vital importance to our basic understanding of cellular energy metabolism and paved the way for exercise physiologists to further inves-tigate skeletal muscle bioenergetics during exercise.

Aerobic ATP Production

Aerobic production of ATP occurs inside the mitochon-dria and involves the interaction of two cooperating metabolic pathways: (1) the **Krebs cycle** and (2) the **electron transport chain.** The primary function of the Krebs cycle (also called the citric acid cycle) is to com-plete the oxidation (hydrogen removal) of carbohy-drates, fats, or proteins using NAD^+ and FAD as hydrogen (energy) carriers. The importance of hydro-gen removal is that hydrogens (by virtue of the elec-trons that they possess) contain the potential energy in the food molecules. This energy can be used in the electron transport chain to combine ADP + P_i to reform ATP. Oxygen does not participate in the reactions of the Krebs cycle but is the final hydrogen acceptor at the end of the electron transport chain (i.e., water is formed, $H_2 + O \rightarrow H_2O$). The process of aerobic pro-duction of ATP is termed oxidative phosphorylation. It is convenient to think of aerobic ATP production as a three-stage process (figure 3.17). Stage 1 is the genera-tion of a key two-carbon molecule, acetyl-CoA. Stage 2 is the oxidation of acetyl-CoA in the Krebs cycle. Stage 3 is the process of **oxidative phosphorylation** (i.e., ATP formation) in the electron transport chain (i.e., respira-tory chain). A detailed look at the Krebs cycle and elec-tron transport chain follows.

Krebs Cycle The Krebs cycle is named after the biochemist Hans Krebs, whose pioneering research has increased our understanding of this rather com-plex pathway (see A Look Back—Important People in Science). Entry into the Krebs cycle requires pre-paration of a two-carbon molecule, acetyl-CoA. **Acetyl-CoA** can be formed from the breakdown of carbohydrates, fats, or proteins (figure 3.17). For the moment, let's focus on the formation of acetyl-CoA from pyruvate (pyruvate can be formed from both carbohydrates and proteins). Figure 3.18 depicts the cyclic nature of the reactions involved in the Krebs cycle. Note that pyruvate (three-carbon molecule) is broken down to form acetyl-CoA (two-carbon mole-cule), and the remaining carbon is given off as CO_2. Next, acetyl-CoA combines with oxaloacetate (four-carbon molecule) to form citrate (six carbons). What follows is a series of reactions to regenerate oxaloac-etate and two molecules of CO_2, and the pathway begins all over again.

For every molecule of glucose entering glycoly-sis, two molecules of pyruvate are formed, and in the presence of O_2, they are converted to two molecules of acetyl-CoA. This means that each molecule of glucose results in two turns of the Krebs cycle. With this in mind, let's examine the Krebs cycle in more detail. The primary function of the Krebs cycle is to

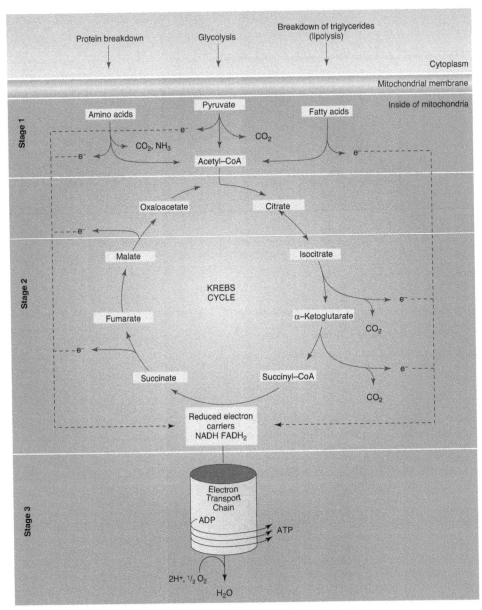

Figure 3.17 The three stages of oxidative phosphorylation. From Mathews and van Holde, *Biochemistry*, Diane Bowen, Ed. Copyright © 1990 Benjamin/Cummings Publishing Company, Menlo Park, CA. Reprinted by permission.

remove hydrogens and the energy associated with those hydrogens from various substrates involved in the cycle. Figure 3.18 illustrates that during each turn of the Krebs cycle, three molecules of NADH and one molecule of FADH are formed. For every pair of electrons passed through the electron transport chain from NADH to oxygen, enough energy is available to form 2.5 molecules of ATP (10). For every FADH molecule that is formed, enough energy is available to produce 1.5 molecules of ATP. Thus, in terms of ATP production, FADH is not as energy rich as NADH.

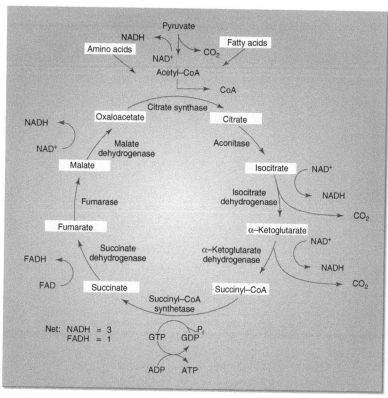

Figure 3.18 Compounds, enzymes, and reactions involved in the Krebs cycle. Note the formation of three molecules of NADH and one molecule of FADH per turn of the cycle.

In addition to the production of NADH and FADH, the Krebs cycle results in direct formation of an energy-rich compound, guanosine triphosphate (GTP) (figure 3.18). GTP is a high-energy compound that can transfer its terminal phosphate group to ADP to form ATP. The direct formation of GTP in the Krebs cycle is called substrate-level phosphorylation. It accounts for only a small amount of the total energy conversion in the Krebs cycle because most of the Krebs cycle energy yield (i.e., NADH and FADH) is taken to the electron transport chain to form ATP.

Up to this point we have focused on the role that carbohydrates play in producing acetyl-CoA to enter the Krebs cycle. How do fats and proteins undergo aerobic metabolism? The answer can be found in figure 3.19. Note that fats (triglycerides) are broken down to form fatty acids and glycerol. These fatty acids can then undergo a series of reactions to form acetyl-CoA (called beta oxidation; see A Closer Look 3.4 for details) and thus enter the Krebs cycle (8). Although glycerol can be converted into an intermediate of glycolysis in the liver, this

does not occur to a great extent in human skeletal muscle. Therefore, glycerol is not an important direct muscle fuel source during exercise (13, 16).

As mentioned previously, protein is not considered a major fuel source during exercise, because it contributes only 2% to 15% of the fuel during exercise (9, 13, 25). Proteins can enter bioenergetic pathways in a variety of places. However, the first step is the breakdown of the protein into its amino acid subunits. What happens next depends on which amino acid is involved. For example, some amino acids can be converted to glucose or pyruvate, some to acetyl-CoA, and still others to Krebs-cycle intermediates. The role of proteins in bioenergetics is summarized in figure 3.19.

In summary, the Krebs cycle completes the oxidation of carbohydrates, fats, or proteins; produces CO_2; and supplies electrons to be passed through the electron transport chain to provide the energy for the aerobic production of ATP. Enzymes catalyzing Krebs-cycle reactions are located inside the mitochondria.

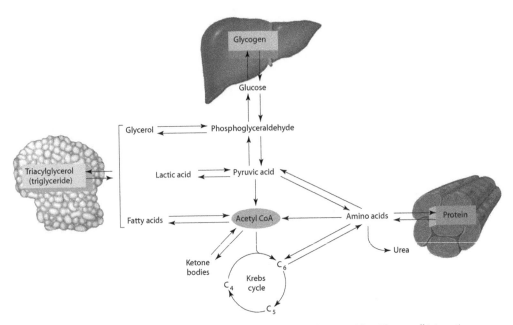

Figure 3.19   The relationships among the metabolism of proteins, carbohydrates, and fats. The overall interaction between the metabolic breakdown of these three foodstuffs is often referred to as the metabolic pool.

Electron Transport Chain   The aerobic production of ATP (called oxidative phosphorylation) occurs in the mitochondria. The pathway responsible for this process is called the **electron transport chain** (also called the respiratory chain or cytochrome chain). Aerobic production of ATP is possible due to a mechanism that uses the potential energy available in reduced hydrogen carriers such as NADH and FADH to rephosphorylate ADP to ATP. The reduced hydrogen carriers do not directly react with oxygen. Instead, electrons removed from the hydrogen atoms are passed down a series of electron carriers known as cytochromes. During this passage of electrons down the cytochrome chain, enough energy is released to rephosphorylate ADP to form ATP at three sites (8) (figure 3.20). Interestingly, as electrons pass down the electron transport chain, highly reactive molecules called *free radicals* are formed. However, increased rates of electron flow through the electron transport chain do not increase in the rate of radical production in the mitochondrion (see Research Focus 3.1).

The hydrogen carriers that bring the electrons to the electron transport chain come from a variety of sources. Recall that two NADH are formed per glucose molecule that is degraded via glycolysis (figure 3.15). These NADH are outside the mitochondria, and their hydrogens must be transported across the mitochondrial membrane by special

"shuttle" mechanisms. However, the bulk of the electrons that enter the electron transport chain come from those NADH and FADH molecules formed as a result of Krebs-cycle oxidation.

Figure 3.20 outlines the pathway for electrons entering the electron transport chain. Pairs of electrons from NADH or FADH are passed down a series of compounds that undergo oxidation and reduction, with enough energy being released to synthesize ATP at three places along the way. Notice that FADH enters the cytochrome pathway at a point just below the entry level for NADH (figure 3.20). This is important because the level of FADH entry bypasses one of the sites of ATP formation, and thus each molecule of FADH that enters the electron transport chain has enough energy to form only 1.5 ATP. In contrast, NADH entry into the electron transport chain results in the formation of 2.5 ATP (details will be mentioned later). At the end of the electron transport chain, oxygen accepts the electrons that are passed along and combines with hydrogen to form water. If O_2 is not available to accept those electrons, oxidative phosphorylation is not possible, and ATP formation in the cell must occur via anaerobic metabolism.

How does this ATP formation occur? The mechanism to explain the aerobic formation of ATP is known as the **chemiosmotic hypothesis.** As electrons are

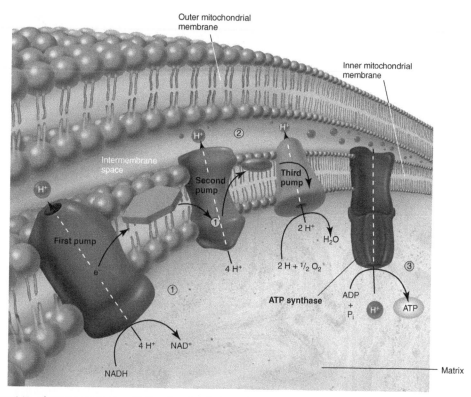

Figure 3.20 The steps leading to oxidative phosphorylation in the mitochondria. (1) Molecules within the electron transport chain function to pump H^+ from the mitochondrial matrix into the intermembrane space. (2) This results in an increased concentration of H^+ ions in the intermembrane space and therefore, a large H^+ gradient between the intermembrane space and the matrix of the mitochondria. (3) The movement of H^+ through the ATP synthase provides the energy required to produce ATP.

RESEARCH FOCUS 3.1

Free Radicals Are Formed in the Mitochondria

Although the passage of electrons down the electron transport chain performs an essential role in the process of aerobic ATP production, this pathway also produces free radicals (30) . Free radicals are molecules that have an unpaired electron in their outer orbital, which makes them highly reactive. That is, free radicals quickly react with other molecules in the cell, and this combi-nation results in damage to the molecule combining with the radical.

Historically, it was believed that increased aerobic metabolism during exercise promotes increased production of free radicals in the mitochondria of the working muscles (30). However, new research indicates that this is not the case. Indeed, although exercise results in increased produc-tion of free radicals in the active skeletal muscles, this increase in muscle free radical production is not due to oxidative phosphorylation in the mito-chondrion (22). For additional information on the sources of free radical production during exercise, see Powers et al. (2008) in the Suggested Readings.

A CLOSER LOOK 3.4

Beta Oxidation Is the Process of Converting Fatty Acids to Acetyl-CoA

Fats are stored in the body in the form of triglycerides within fat cells or in the muscle fiber itself. Release of fat from these storage depots occurs by the breakdown of triglycerides, which results in the liberation of fatty acids (see chapter 4). However, for fatty acids to be used as a fuel during aerobic metabolism, they must first be converted to acetyl-CoA. **Beta oxidation** is the process of oxidizing fatty acids to form acetyl-CoA. This occurs in the mitochondria and involves a series of enzymatically catalyzed steps, starting with an "activated fatty acid" and ending with the production of acetyl-CoA.

A simple illustration of this process is presented in figure 3.21. This process begins with the "activation" of the fatty acid; the activated fatty acid is then transported into the mitochondria, where the process of beta oxidation begins. In short, beta oxidation is a sequence of four reactions that "chops" fatty acids into two carbon fragments forming acetyl-CoA. Once formed, acetyl-CoA then becomes a fuel source for the Krebs cycle and leads to the production of ATP via the electron transport chain.

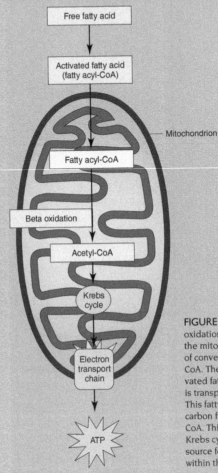

FIGURE 3.21 Illustration of beta oxidation. Beta oxidation occurs in the mitochondria and is the process of converting fatty acids into acetyl-CoA. The process begins after an activated fatty acid (i.e., fatty acyl-CoA) is transported into the mitochondria. This fatty acyl-CoA is broken into two carbon fragments, forming acetyl-CoA. This acetyl-CoA then enters the Krebs cycle and provides an energy source for the production of ATP within the electron transport chain.

transferred along the cytochrome chain, the energy released is used to "pump" hydrogens (protons; H^+) released from NADH and FADH from the inside of the mitochondria across the inner mitochondrial membrane (figure 3.20). This results in an accumulation of hydrogen ions within the space between the inner and outer mitochondrial membranes. The accumulation of H^+ is a source of potential energy that can be captured and used to recombine P_i with ADP to form ATP (17). For example, this collection of H^+ is similar to the potential energy of water at the top of a dam; when the water accumulates and runs over the top of the dam, falling water becomes kinetic energy, which can be used to do work (17).

Three pumps move H^+ (i.e., protons) from mitochondrial matrix to the intermembrane space (figure 3.20). The first pump (using NADH) moves four H^+ into the intermembrane space for every two electrons that move along the electron transport chain. The second pump also transports four H^+ into the intermembrane space, while the third pump moves only two H^+ into the intermembrane space. As a result, there is a higher concentration of H^+ within the intermembrane space compared to that in the matrix; this gradient creates a strong drive for these H^+ to diffuse back into the matrix. However, because the inner mitochondrial membrane is not permeable to H^+, these ions can cross the membrane only through specialized H^+ channels (called *respiratory assemblies*). This idea is illustrated in figure 3.20. Notice that as H^+ cross the inner mitochondrial membrane through these channels, ATP is formed from the addition of phosphate to ADP (called *phosphorylation*). This occurs because the movement of H^+ across the inner mitochondrial membrane activates the enzyme ATP synthase, which is responsible for catalyzing the reaction:

$$ADP + P_i \rightarrow ATP$$

So, why is oxygen essential for the aerobic production of ATP? Remember that the purpose of the electron transport chain is to move electrons down a series of cytochromes to provide energy to drive ATP production in the mitochondria. This process, illustrated in figure 3.20, requires each element in the electron transport chain to undergo a series of oxidation-reduction reactions. If the last cytochrome (i.e., cytochrome a_3) remains in a reduced state, it would be unable to accept more electrons, and the electron transport chain would stop. However, when oxygen is present, the last cytochrome in the chain can be oxidized by oxygen. That is, oxygen, derived from the air we breathe, allows electron transport to continue by functioning as the final electron acceptor of the electron transport chain. This oxidizes cytochrome a3 and allows electron transport and oxidative phosphorylation to continue. At the last step in the electron transport chain, oxygen accepts two electrons that were passed along the electron transport chain from either NADH or FADH. This reduced oxygen mol-

ecule now binds with two protons (H^+) to form water (figure 3.20).

As mentioned earlier, NADH and FADH differ in the amount of ATP that can be formed from each of these molecules. Each NADH formed in the mitochondria donates two electrons to the electron transport system at the first proton pump (figure 3.20). These electrons are then passed to the second and third proton pumps until these electrons are finally passed along to oxygen. The first and second electron pumps transport four protons each, whereas the third electron pump transports two protons, for a total of ten. Because four protons are required to produce and transport one ATP from the mitochondria to the cytoplasm, the total ATP production from one NADH molecule is 2.5 ATP (10 protons/4 protons per ATP = 2.5 ATP). Note that ATP molecules do not exist in halves and that the decimal fraction of ATP indicates an average number of ATP molecules that are produced per NADH.

Compared to NADH, each FADH molecule produces less ATP because the electrons from FADH are donated later in the electron transport chain than those by NADH (figure 3.20). Therefore, the electrons from FADH activate only the second and third proton pumps. Because the first proton pump is bypassed, the electrons from FADH result in the pumping of six protons (four by the second pump and two by the third pump). Because four protons are required to produce and transport one ATP from the mitochondria to the cytoplasm, the total ATP production from one FAD molecule is 1.5 ATP (6 protons/4 protons per ATP = 1.5 ATP). See A Closer Look 3.5 for more details on the quantity of ATP produced in cells.

A CLOSER LOOK 3.5

A New Look at the ATP Balance Sheet

Historically, it was believed that aerobic metabolism of one molecule of glucose resulted in the production of thirty-eight ATP. However, more recent evidence indicates that this number overestimates the total ATP production and that only thirty-two molecules of ATP actually reach the cytoplasm . The explanation for this conclusion is that new evidence indicates that the energy provided by NADH and FADH is required not only for ATP production but also to transport ATP across the mitochondrial

membrane. This added energy cost of ATP metabolism reduces the estimates of the total ATP yield from glucose. Specific details of this process follow.

For many years it was believed that for every three H^+ produced, one molecule of ATP was produced and could be used for cellular energy. Although it is true that approximately three H^+ must pass through the H^+ channels (i.e., respiratory assemblies) to produce one ATP, it is now known that another H^+ is required to move the ATP molecule

across the mitochondrial membrane into the cytoplasm. The ATP and H^+ are transported into the cytoplasm in exchange for ADP and P_i, which are transported into the mitochondria to resynthesize ATP. Therefore, while the theoretical yield of ATP from glucose is thirty-eight molecules, the actual ATP yield, allowing for the energy cost of transport, is only thirty-two molecules of ATP per glucose. For details of how these numbers are obtained, see the section "Aerobic ATP Tally."

- Oxidative phosphorylation or aerobic ATP production occurs in the mitochondria as a result of a complex interaction between the Krebs cycle and the electron transport chain. The primary role of the Krebs cycle is to complete the oxidation of substrates and form NADH and FADH to enter the electron transport chain. The end result of the electron transport chain is the formation of ATP and water. Water is formed by oxygen-accepting electrons; hence, the reason we breathe oxygen is to use it as the final acceptor of electrons in aerobic metabolism.

AEROBIC ATP TALLY

It is now possible to compute the overall ATP production as a result of the aerobic breakdown of glucose or glycogen. Let's begin by counting the total energy yield of glycolysis. Recall that the net ATP production of glycolysis was two ATP per glucose molecule. Further, when O_2 is present in the mitochondria, two NADH produced by glycolysis can then be shuttled into the mitochondria with the energy used to synthesize an additional five ATP (table 3.2). Thus, glycolysis can produce two ATP directly via substrate-level phosphorylation and an additional five ATP by the energy contained in the two molecules of NADH.

How many ATP are produced as a result of the oxidation-reduction activities of the Krebs cycle? Table 3.3 shows that two NADH are formed when pyruvate is converted to acetyl-CoA, which results in the formation of 5 ATP. Note that two GTP (similar to ATP) are produced via substrate-level phosphorylation. A total of six NADH and two FADH are produced in the Krebs cycle from one glucose molecule. Hence, the six NADH formed via the Krebs cycle results in the production of a total of 15 ATP (6 NADH × 2.5 ATP per NADH = 15 ATP), with three ATP being produced from the two FADH. Therefore, the total ATP yield for the aerobic degradation of glucose is thirty-two ATP. The aerobic ATP yield for glycogen breakdown is thirty-three ATP, because the net glycolytic production of ATP by glycogen is one ATP more than that of glucose.

EFFICIENCY OF OXIDATIVE PHOSPHORYLATION

How efficient is oxidative phosphorylation as a system of converting energy from foodstuffs into biologically usable energy? This can be calculated by computing the ratio of the energy contained in the

TABLE 3.2   Aerobic ATP Tally from the Breakdown of One Molecule of Glucose

Metabolic Process	High-Energy Products	ATP from Oxidative Phosphorylation	ATP Subtotal
Glycolysis	2 ATP	—	2 (total if anaerobic)
	2 NADH*	5	7 (if aerobic)
Pyruvate to acetyl-CoA	2 NADH	5	12
Krebs cycle	2 GTP	—	14
	6 NADH	15	29
	2 FADH**	3	32
			Grand total: 32 ATP

*2.5 ATP per NADH
**1.5 ATP per FADH

TABLE 3.3   Factors Known to Affect the Activity of Rate-Limiting Enzymes of Metabolic Pathways Involved in Bioenergetics

Pathway	Rate-Limiting Enzyme	Stimulators	Inhibitors
ATP-PC system	Creatine kinase	ADP	ATP
Glycolysis	Phosphofructokinase	AMP, ADP, P_i, pH↑	ATP, CP, citrate, pH↓
Krebs cycle	Isocitrate dehydrogenase	ADP, Ca^{++}, NAD^+	ATP, NADH
Electron transport chain	Cytochrome oxidase	ADP, P_i	ATP

ATP molecules produced via aerobic respiration divided by the total potential energy contained in the glucose molecule. For example, a mole (a mole is 1 gram molecular weight) of ATP, when broken down, has an energy yield of 7.3 kcal. The potential energy released from the oxidation of a mole of glucose is 686 kcal. Thus, an efficiency figure for aerobic respiration can be computed as follows (18):

$$\text{Efficiency of respiration} =$$
$$\frac{32 \text{ moles ATP/mole glucose} \times 7.3 \text{ kcal/mole ATP}}{686 \text{ kcal/mole glucose}}$$

Therefore, the efficiency of aerobic respiration is approximately 34%, with the remaining 66% of the free energy of glucose oxidation being released as heat.

IN SUMMARY

- The aerobic metabolism of one molecule of glucose results in the production of 32 ATP molecules, whereas the aerobic ATP yield for glycogen breakdown is 33 ATP.
- The overall efficiency of aerobic respiration is approximately 34%, with the remaining 66% of the energy being released as heat.

CONTROL OF BIOENERGETICS

The biochemical pathways that result in the production of ATP are regulated by very precise control systems. Each of these pathways contains a number of reactions that are catalyzed by specific enzymes. In general, if ample substrate is available, an increase in the number of enzymes present results in an increased rate of chemical reactions. Therefore, the regulation of one or more enzymes in a biochemical pathway would provide a means of controlling the rate of that particular pathway. Indeed, metabolism is regulated by the control of enzymatic activity. Most metabolic pathways have one enzyme that is considered "rate limiting." This rate-limiting enzyme determines the speed of the particular metabolic pathway involved.

How does a rate-limiting enzyme control the speed of reactions? First, as a rule, rate-limiting enzymes are found early in a metabolic pathway. This position is important because products of the pathway might accumulate if the rate-limiting enzyme were located near the end of a pathway. Second, the activity of rate-limiting enzymes is regulated by modulators. Modulators are substances that increase or decrease enzyme activity. Enzymes that are regulated by modulators are called *allosteric enzymes*. In the control of energy metabolism, ATP is the classic example of an inhibitor, whereas ADP and P_i are examples of substances that stimulate enzymatic activity (31). The

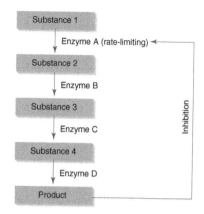

Figure 3.22 An example of a "rate-limiting" enzyme in a simple metabolic pathway. Here, a buildup of the product serves to inhibit the rate-limiting enzyme, which in turn slows down the reactions involved in the pathway.

fact that large amounts of cellular ATP would inhibit the metabolic production of ATP is logical because large amounts of ATP would indicate that ATP usage in the cell is low. An example of this type of negative feedback is illustrated in figure 3.22. In contrast, an increase in cell levels of ADP and P_i (low ATP) would indicate that ATP utilization is high. Therefore, it makes sense that ADP and P_i stimulate the production of ATP to meet the increased energy need.

Control of ATP-PC System

Phosphocreatine breakdown is regulated by creatine kinase activity. Creatine kinase is activated when sarcoplasmic concentrations of ADP increase and is inhibited by high levels of ATP. At the onset of exercise, ATP is split into ADP + P_i to provide energy for muscular contraction. This immediate increase in ADP concentrations stimulates creatine kinase to trigger the breakdown of PC to resynthesize ATP. If exercise is continued, glycolysis and finally aerobic metabolism begin to produce adequate ATP to meet the muscles' energy needs. The increase in ATP concentration, coupled with a reduction in ADP concentration, inhibits creatine kinase activity (table 3.3). Regulation of the ATP-PC system is an example of a "negative feedback" control system, which was introduced in chapter 2.

Control of Glycolysis

Although several factors control glycolysis, the most important rate-limiting enzyme in glycolysis is **phosphofructokinase (PFK)** (1). Note that PFK is located near the beginning of glycolysis (figure 3.15).

Table 3.3 lists known regulators of PFK. When exercise begins, ADP + P_i levels rise and enhance PFK activity, which serves to increase the rate of glycolysis. In contrast, at rest, when cellular ATP levels are high, PFK activity is inhibited and glycolytic activity is slowed. Further, high cellular levels of hydrogen ions or citrate (produced via Krebs cycle) also inhibit PFK activity (35). Similar to the control of the ATP-PC system, regulation of PFK activity operates via negative feedback.

Another important regulatory enzyme in carbohydrate metabolism is phosphorylase, which is responsible for degrading glycogen to glucose. Although this enzyme is not technically considered a glycolytic enzyme, the reaction catalyzed by phosphorylase plays an important role in providing the glycolytic pathway with the necessary glucose at the origin of the pathway. With each muscle contraction, calcium (Ca^{++}) is released from the sarcoplasmic reticulum in muscle. This rise in sarcoplasmic Ca^{++} concentration indirectly activates phosphorylase, which immediately begins to break down glycogen to glucose for entry into glycolysis. Additionally, phosphorylase activity may be stimulated by high levels of the hormone epinephrine. Epinephrine is released at a faster rate during heavy exercise and results in the formation of the compound cyclic AMP (see chapter 5). It is cyclic AMP, not epinephrine, that directly activates phosphorylase. Thus, the influence of epinephrine on phosphorylase is indirect.

Control of Krebs Cycle and Electron Transport Chain

The Krebs cycle, like glycolysis, is subject to enzymatic regulation. Although several Krebs cycle enzymes are regulated, the rate-limiting enzyme is **isocitrate dehydrogenase.** Isocitrate dehydrogenase, like PFK, is inhibited by ATP and stimulated by increasing levels of ADP + P_i (31). Further, growing evidence suggests that increased levels of calcium (Ca^{++}) in the mitochondria also stimulates isocitrate dehydrogenase activity (29). This is a logical signal to turn on energy metabolism in muscle cells, because an increase in free calcium in muscle is the signal to begin muscular contraction (see chapter 8).

The electron transport chain is also regulated by the amount of ATP and ADP + P_i present (31). The rate-limiting enzyme in the electron transport chain is cytochrome oxidase. When exercise begins, ATP levels decline, ADP + P_i levels increase, and cytochrome oxidase is stimulated to begin aerobic production of ATP. When exercise stops, cellular levels of ATP increase and ADP + P_i concentrations decline, and thus the electron transport activity is reduced when normal levels of ATP, ADP, and P_i are reached.

IN SUMMARY

- Metabolism is regulated by enzymatic activity. An enzyme that controls the rate of a metabolic pathway is termed the *rate-limiting enzyme.*
- The rate-limiting enzyme for glycolysis is phosphofructokinase, and the rate-limiting enzymes for the Krebs cycle and electron transport chain are isocitrate dehydrogenase and cytochrome oxidase, respectively.
- In general, cellular levels of ATP and ADP + P_i regulate the rate of metabolic pathways involved in the production of ATP. High levels of ATP inhibit further ATP production, whereas low levels of ATP and high levels of ADP + P_i stimulate ATP production. Evidence also exists that calcium may stimulate aerobic energy metabolism.

INTERACTION BETWEEN AEROBIC/ANAEROBIC ATP PRODUCTION

It is important to emphasize the interaction of anaerobic and aerobic metabolic pathways in the production of ATP during exercise. Although it is common to hear someone speak of aerobic versus anaerobic exercise, in reality the energy to perform most types of exercise comes from a combination of anaerobic and aerobic sources (11). This point is illustrated in The Winning Edge 3.2. Notice that the contribution of anaerobic ATP production is greater in short-term, high-intensity activities, whereas aerobic metabolism predominates in longer activities. For example, approximately 90% of the energy required to perform a 100-meter dash would come from anaerobic sources, with most of the energy coming via the ATP-PC system. Similarly, energy to run 400 meters (i.e., 55 seconds) would be largely anaerobic (70–75%). However, ATP and PC stores are limited, and thus glycolysis must supply much of the ATP during this type of event(11).

On the other end of the energy spectrum, events like the marathon (i.e., 26.2-mile race) rely on aerobic production of ATP for the bulk of the needed energy. Where does the energy come from in events of moderate length (i.e., 2 to 30 minutes)? The Winning Edge 3.2 provides an estimation of the percentage anaerobic/aerobic yield in events over a wide range of durations. Although these estimates are based on laboratory measurements of running or exercising on a cycle ergometer, they can be related

THE WINNING EDGE 3.2

Exercise Physiology Applied to Sports

Contributions of Anaerobic/ Aerobic Energy Production During Various Sporting Events
Because sports differ widely in both the intensity and the duration of physical effort, it is not surprising that the source of energy production differs widely among sporting events. Figure 3.23 provides an illustration of the anaerobic versus aerobic energy production during selected sports. Knowledge of the interaction between the anaerobic and aerobic energy production in exercise is useful to coaches and trainers in planning conditioning programs for athletes. See chapter 21 for more details.

FIGURE 3.23 Contribution of anaerobic and aerobically produced ATP for use during sports.

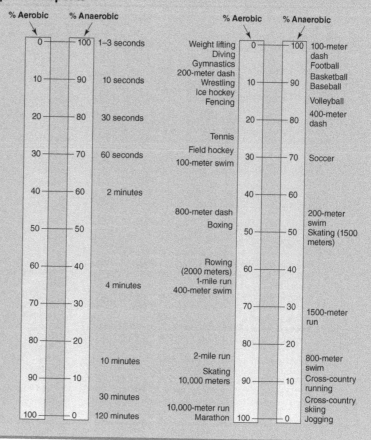

to other athletic events that require intense effort by comparing the length of time spent in the activity. In review, the shorter the duration of all-out activity, the greater the contribution of anaerobic energy production; conversely, the longer the duration, the greater the contribution of aerobic energy production. A more detailed discussion of the metabolic responses to various types of exercise is presented in chapter 4.

IN SUMMARY

- Energy to perform exercise comes from an interaction of anaerobic and aerobic pathways.
- In general, the shorter the activity (high intensity), the greater the contribution of anaerobic energy production. In contrast, long-term activities (low to moderate intensity) utilize ATP produced from aerobic sources.

STUDY QUESTIONS

1. List and briefly discuss the function of the three major components of cell structure.
2. Briefly explain the concept of coupled reactions.
3. Define the following terms: (1) *bioenergetics*, (2) *endergonic reactions*, and (3) *exergonic reactions*.
4. Discuss the role of enzymes as catalysts. What is meant by the expression "energy of activation"?
5. Where does glycolysis, the Krebs cycle, and oxidative phosphorylation take place in the cell?
6. Define the terms *glycogen*, *glycogenolysis*, and *glycolysis*.

7. What are high-energy phosphates? Explain the statement that "ATP is the universal energy donor."
8. Define the terms *aerobic* and *anaerobic*.
9. Briefly discuss the function of glycolysis in bioenergetics. What role does NAD$^+$ play in glycolysis?
10. Discuss the operation of the Krebs cycle and the electron transport chain in the aerobic production of ATP. What is the function of NAD$^+$ and FAD in these pathways?
11. What is the efficiency of the aerobic degradation of glucose?
12. What is the role of oxygen in aerobic metabolism?

13. What are the rate-limiting enzymes for the following metabolic pathways? ATP-PC system? Glycolysis? Krebs cycle? Electron transport chain?
14. Briefly discuss the interaction of anaerobic versus aerobic ATP production during exercise.
15. Discuss the chemiosmotic theory of ATP production.
16. Briefly discuss the impact of changes in both temperature and pH on enzyme activity.
17. Discuss the relationship between lactic acid and lactate.

SUGGESTED READINGS

Bemben, M., and H. Lamont. 2005. Creatine supplementation and exercise performance. *Sports Medicine* 35:107–25.

Fox, S. 2009. *Human Physiology*. New York, NY: McGraw-Hill Companies.

Hespel P., and W. Derave. 2007. Ergogenic effects of creatine in sports and rehabilitation. *Sub-cellular Biochemistry* 46: 245–59.

Houston, M. 2006. *Biochemistry Primer for Exercise Science*. Champaign, IL: Human Kinetics.

Karp, G. 2009. *Cell and Molecular Biology: Concepts and Experiments*. Hoboken, NJ. Wiley Publishers.

Powers, S., and M. Jackson. 2008. Exercise-induced oxidative stress: Cellular mechanisms and impact on muscle force production. *Physiological Review* 88: 1243–76.

Widmaier, E., H. Raff, and K. Strang. 2008. *Vander's Human Physiology*. New York, NY. McGraw-Hill.

REFERENCES

1. **Alberts B, Johnson A, Lewis J, Raff M, Roberts K, and Walter P.** *Molecular Biology of the Cell*. New York: Garland Science, 2007.
2. **Bemben MG, and Lamont HS.** Creatine supplementation and exercise performance: recent findings. *Sports Medicine (Auckland, NZ)* 35: 107–125, 2005.
3. **Brooks G, Fahey T, and Baldwin K.** *Exercise Physiology: Human Bioenergetics and Its Applications*. New York: McGraw-Hill, 2005.
4. **Brooks GA.** Cell-cell and intracellular lactate shuttles. *The Journal of Physiology* 587: 5591–5600, 2009.
5. **Camic CL, Hendrix CR, Housh TJ, Zuniga JM, Mielke M, Johnson GO, Schmidt RJ, and Housh DJ.** The effects of polyethylene glycosylated creatine supplementation on muscular strength and power. *Journal of Strength and Conditioning Research/National Strength & Conditioning Association* 24: 3343–3351, 2010.
6. **Cribb PJ, Williams AD, Stathis CG, Carey MF, and Hayes A.** Effects of whey isolate, creatine, and resistance training on muscle hypertrophy. *Medicine and Science in Sports and Exercise* 39: 298–307, 2007.
7. **Dalbo VJ, Roberts MD, Stout JR, and Kerksick CM.** Putting to rest the myth of creatine supplementation leading to muscle cramps and dehydration. *British Journal of Sports Medicine* 42: 567–573, 2008.
8. **Devlin T.** *Textbook of Biochemistry with Clinical Correlations*. Hoboken: Wiley, 2010.
9. **Dolny DG, and Lemon PW.** Effect of ambient temperature on protein breakdown during prolonged exercise. *J Appl Physiol* 64: 550–555, 1988.
10. **Fox S.** *Human Physiology*. New York: McGraw-Hill, 2009.
11. **Gastin PB.** Energy system interaction and relative contribution during maximal exercise. *Sports Medicine (Auckland, NZ)* 31: 725–741, 2001.
12. **Gibala MJ.** Protein metabolism and endurance exercise. *Sports Medicine (Auckland, NZ)* 37: 337–340, 2007.
13. **Gollnick PD.** Metabolism of substrates: energy substrate metabolism during exercise and as modified by training. *Fed Proc* 44: 353–357, 1985.
14. **Greenhaff PL.** Creatine and its application as an ergogenic aid. *Int J Sport Nutr* 5 Suppl: S100–110, 1995.
15. **Hespel P, and Derave W.** Ergogenic effects of creatine in sports and rehabilitation. *Sub-cellular Biochemistry* 46: 245–259, 2007.
16. **Holloszy JO, and Coyle EF.** Adaptations of skeletal muscle to endurance exercise and their metabolic consequences. *J Appl Physiol* 56: 831–838, 1984.
17. **Houston M.** *Biochemistry Primer for Exercise Science*. Champaign: Human Kinetics, 2006.
18. **Jequier E, and Flatt J.** Recent advances in human bioenergetics. *News in Physiological Sciences* 1: 112–114, 1986.
19. **Juhn MS, and Tarnopolsky M.** Oral creatine supplementation and athletic performance: a critical review. *Clin J Sport Med* 8: 286–297, 1998.
20. **Juhn MS, and Tarnopolsky M.** Potential side effects of oral creatine supplementation: a critical review. *Clin J Sport Med* 8: 298–304, 1998.
21. **Karp G.** *Cell and Molecular Biology: Concepts and Experiments*. Hoboken, NJ: Wiley, 2009.
22. **Kavazis AN, Talbert EE, Smuder AJ, Hudson MB, Nelson WB, and Powers SK.** Mechanical ventilation induces diaphragmatic mitochondrial dysfunction and increased oxidant production. *Free Radical Biology & Medicine* 46: 842–850, 2009.
23. **Kerksick CM, Wilborn CD, Campbell WI, Harvey TM, Marcello BM, Roberts MD, Parker AG, Byars AG, Greenwood LD, Almada AL, Kreider RB, and Greenwood M.** The effects of creatine monohydrate supplementation with and without D-pinitol on resistance training adaptations. *Journal of Strength and Conditioning Research/National Strength & Conditioning Association* 23: 2673–2682, 2009.
24. **Law YL, Ong WS, GillianYap TL, Lim SC, and Von Chia E.** Effects of two and five days of creatine loading on muscular strength and anaerobic power in trained athletes. *Journal of Strength and Conditioning Research/National Strength & Conditioning Association* 23: 906–914, 2009.

25. **Lemon PW, and Mullin JP.** Effect of initial muscle glycogen levels on protein catabolism during exercise. *J Appl Physiol* 48: 624–629, 1980.

26. **Maughan RJ.** Creatine supplementation and exercise performance. *Int J Sport Nutr* 5: 94–101, 1995.

27. **Maughan RJ, King DS, and Lea T.** Dietary supplements. *J Sports Sci* 22: 95–113, 2004.

28. **McArdle W, Katch F, and Katch V.** *Exercise Physiology: Energy, Nutrition, and Human Performance.* Baltimore: Lippincott Williams & Wilkins, 2006.

29. **McCormack J, and Denton R.** Signal transduction by intramitochondrial calcium in mammalian energy metabolism. *News in Physiological Sciences* 9: 71–76, 1994.

30. **Powers SK, and Jackson MJ.** Exercise-induced oxidative stress: cellular mechanisms and impact on muscle force production. *Physiological Reviews* 88: 1243–1276, 2008.

31. **Pratt CW, and Cornely, K.** *Essential Biochemistry.* Hoboken: Wiley, 2011.

32. **Rawson ES, and Volek JS.** Effects of creatine supplementation and resistance training on muscle strength and weightlifting performance. *Journal of Strength and Conditioning Research/National Strength & Conditioning Association* 17: 822–831, 2003.

33. **Reed S.** *Essential Physiological Biochemistry: An Organ-Based Approach.* Hoboken: Wiley, 2010.

34. **Roberts RA, Ghiasvand F, and Parker D.** Biochemistry of exercise-induced metabolic acidosis. *American Journal of Physiology* 287: R502–516, 2004.

35. **Spriet LL.** Phosphofructokinase activity and acidosis during short-term tetanic contractions. *Can J Physiol Pharmacol* 69: 298–304, 1991.

36. **Tymoczko J, Berg J, and Stryer L.** *Biochemistry: A Short Course.* New York: W. H. Freeman, 2009.

37. **Voet D, and Voet JG.** *Biochemistry.* Hoboken: Wiley, 2010.

38. **West J.** *Best and Taylor's Physiological Basis of Medical Practice.* Baltimore: Lippincott Williams & Wilkins, 2001.

39. **Williams MH, and Branch JD.** Creatine supplementation and exercise performance: an update. *J Am Coll Nutr* 17: 216–234, 1998.

Systemic Response to Exercise

CHAPTER 5

Neuromuscular Function and Adaptations to Exercise

hen we move our body or body parts, we require very complex functions of nerves and skeletal muscle to be performed in fractions of a second. For certain activities, these events are repeated for several seconds, minutes, and even hours depending upon the duration of exercise or physical activity. In addition, some contractions need to be weak and finely controlled (e.g., handwriting), whereas others are required to be as forceful as possible (e.g., throwing the shot put). Some movements that we perform do not require us to think about them, such as the muscle contractions required in talking and breathing, and some actions that protect us when we fall (using our arms for improved balance or protection). Other movements that we voluntarily perform require conscious effort, such as throwing a ball, kicking a football, or jumping a fence. Clearly, our brain must organize nerve and skeletal muscle function differently depending on the type of movements required. The purpose of this chapter is to identify the important interactions that exist between nerves and skeletal muscle, explain the process of skeletal muscle contraction, document the different neural and muscle metabolic properties of the human neuromuscular system, and identify the acute and chronic adaptations of neuromuscular structure and function that result from exercise.

OBJECTIVES

After studying this chapter, you should be able to:

- Explain how nerves and skeletal muscle combine to control muscle contraction.
- Explain the molecular events that occur during the contraction of skeletal muscle.
- Define and explain the function of motor units and muscle fiber types.
- List the neural, contractile, and metabolic differences among motor units.
- Draw the different curves of muscle torque and power for changes in contraction velocity.
- Explain the multiple functions of the muscle spindle.
- Describe the potential changes in muscle fiber type proportions after endurance, strength, or power training.
- Explain the definitions of the terms hypertrophy, hyperplasia, and atrophy.

KEY TERMS

nerves	myofibrils	electromyography
action potential	sarcomere	(EMG)
axon	myosin	muscle biopsy
synapse	actin	fiber type
neurotransmitter	tropomyosin	muscle spindle
receptors	troponin	flexibility
motor cortex	motor unit	alpha-gamma
neuromuscular	concentric	coactivation
junction	eccentric	hypertrophy
muscle fibers	isometric	hyperplasia
sarcolemma	isokinetic	atrophy

The Nervous System

*T*he nervous system of the body provides the means to have rapid communication between the brain and the different tissues and organs of the body. **Nerves** are special cells that function to conduct a rapid change in the charge across a membrane (**action potential**) along a long thin component of the cell (**axon**). The nerve axon extends the nerve from one part of the body to another, thereby conducting the action potential to a specific location. Where a nerve connects to another nerve, or the target tissue, is called a **synapse.** At the synapse, a special chemical (**neurotransmitter**) is released that results in the transmission of the action potential to the connecting tissue. This process is facilitated by the presence of specific proteins (**receptors**) on the connecting-tissue (postsynaptic) membrane that bind the neurotransmitter and regenerate the action potential (table 5.1). When the action potential reaches the target tissue, the binding of the neurotransmitter to the specific receptor of the postsynaptic membrane instigates a cell/tissue response that is very specific to the receptor. For example, such events can cause the contraction of skeletal muscle, relaxation of certain smooth muscle, release of certain hormones, acceleration of heart rate, or alteration in function of enzymes within specific metabolically active tissues. These events can occur in as little as 5 msec, which is a clear example of the speed of neural communication within the body.

Functional and Anatomical Divisions

The nervous system can be divided into functional and anatomic divisions. The functional divisions of the nervous system can be divided into involuntary and voluntary control divisions. The voluntary, or *somatic*, nervous system is best exemplified by the nerves that innervate skeletal muscle. We have voluntary control over whether to use these nerves, giving us voluntary control over our movement. The involuntary, or *autonomic*, nervous system is composed of two divisions that our body uses to regulate cellular, tissue, and organ functions—sympathetic and parasympathetic. These subdivisions exist because of differences in anatomy and *neurotransmitter* release, *and not necessarily function*. For example, the parasympathetic nerves all leave the central nervous system (CNS) at the lower brain level, whereas the nerves of the sympathetic division leave the spinal cord at levels that generally reflect the anatomical location of the organs and tissues they innervate. In addition, all parasympathetic nerves release the neurotransmitter acetylcholine on their target tissues, whereas sympathetic nerves mostly release norepinephrine (table 5.1). Depending on the type of receptor on the target cell membrane, the cellular response to parasympathetic and sympathetic innervation may differ, or may be similar, such as blood vessel vasoconstriction or vasodilation.

The parasympathetic division works in combination with the sympathetic division to control such things as heart rate and heart muscle (myocardium) contraction velocity; the contraction of the smooth muscle surrounding certain blood vessels, the bladder, and sweat glands; and the release of hormones from certain glands. The importance of the autonomic nervous system will be discussed and exemplified in later chapters of the book concerning muscle metabolism (chapter 6), cardiovascular functions (chapter 7), and hormone functions (chapter 9).

Anatomically, the nervous system is composed of the central and peripheral systems (fig. 5.1), where the CNS consists of the brain and spinal cord. The peripheral nervous system comprises sensory nerves, nerves from the parasympathetic and sympathetic divisions of the autonomic nervous system, and motor nerves. Within the peripheral nervous system, nerves that leave the CNS and direct action potentials

TABLE 5.1		
Examples of the fast-acting* neurotransmitters of the nervous system, the main regions of the nervous system in which they occur, and examples of their importance during exercise		
NEUROTRANSMITTER	**LOCATIONS**	**FUNCTIONS DURING EXERCISE**
Acetylcholine	Motor cortex, basal ganglia, Aα motor nerves, some nerves of the autonomic nervous system	↑ Muscle contraction, ↑ sweating
Norepinephrine	Brain stem, hypothalamus, most post-ganglionic nerves of the sympathetic nervous system	↑ Heart rate, cardiovascular regulation, blood glucose regulation, ↑ muscle metabolism
Epinephrine	Adrenal medulla	↑ Heart rate, cardiovascular regulation, blood glucose regulation, ↑ muscle metabolism
Dopamine	Basal ganglia	Motor coordination
Serotonin	Brain stem, spinal cord, hypothalamus	↑ Perceptions of fatigue
γ-aminobutyric acid (GABA)	Brain stem, spinal cord, cerebellum, cortex	Motor coordination

*The nervous system also uses slow-acting neurotransmitters, or neuropeptides, that are synthesized in the soma of a nerve and not in the presynaptic region of the nerve.

FIGURE 5.1

The anatomical (structural) and functional divisions of the nervous system.

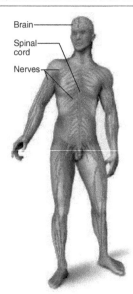

Major structural divisions of the nervous system

Central nervous system (CNS)	Brain	Gray matter
		White matter
	Spinal cord	Gray matter
		White matter
Peripheral nervous system (PNS)	Nerves	Cranial nerves (12 pairs)
		Spinal nerves (31 pairs)
	Ganglia	

Functional classes of peripheral nerve fibers

Somatic	Sensory
	Motor
Autonomic	Sensory
	Motor

---

to peripheral tissue are termed *efferent* nerves. Additionally, nerves that originate in specialized sensory structures (receptors) in peripheral tissues that direct action potentials to the CNS are termed *afferent* nerves.

Nerve-Muscle Interactions

When you move your body, your first awareness of the results of this action comes when you feel or see your muscles contract and your limbs move. However, the movement is really the end result of a sequence of neural and muscular events. Complex neural events take place before your skeletal muscles contract, and to learn and understand why muscles contract, we must first focus on the functions of the central nervous system that initiate muscle contraction.

Initiating Movement

The neural events that eventually cause muscle contraction begin in several locations in the brain, with the involvement of each location dependent on the complexity of movement. If you think hard about what is needed from the brain to orchestrate movement, you come to the conclusion that movement is a remarkable feat of life. Multiple muscles must be stimulated to contract, and some relax, in a well-timed sequence, with added control over the magnitude and speed of muscle force development. For the 100-m sprint runner, bouts of muscle contraction and opposing muscle relaxation are occurring

several times per second. For the gymnast, rapid muscle contractions are also required, but with an overall emphasis on grace, and biomechanical and aesthetic perfection. How is it possible for the human body to accomplish such tasks?

In a localized region of the outer layers of the brain (cortex), anterior to the main convoluted fold (gyrus) of the brain, is a region called the **motor cortex** (fig. 5.2). This cortical matter is responsible for developing neural patterns that

---

nerves the cells of the nervous systems that conduct action potentials

action potential the rapid change in the membrane potential of excitable cells that is conducted along an excitable membrane

axon (ak'son) the long component of a nerve that conducts the action potential from one location to another within the body

synapse (sin'aps) the junction between two nerves

neurotransmitter (nu'ro-trans-mit'er) a chemical released at a synapse in response to the depolarization of the presynaptic membrane

receptors (re-sep'tors) proteins located within a membrane that are able to bind another molecule (typically a hormone or neurotransmitter)

motor cortex the cortex region of the precentral gyrus responsible for the origin of the neural processing that instigates most contraction of skeletal muscle

FIGURE 5.2

The anatomical and functional association between the neuromuscular components involved in body movement. The basal ganglia are several nuclei within the mid and lower brain that receive nerves from the motor cortex, and primarily return nerves back to the cortex. Skilled movements and movements requiring cognitive input such as throwing, kicking, shoveling, and writing require the presence of the basal ganglia. The main nucleus of the basal ganglia, the caudate nucleus, receives input from numerous regions of the brain and combines these inputs to "inform" the motor cortex of appropriate movement patterns, or the appropriate speed at which movement patterns should occur. The red nucleus is responsible for assisting the motor cortex in causing refined movement of the distal muscles of the body, such as the forearms and lower leg. The red nucleus has a spatial arrangement similar to the motor cortex.

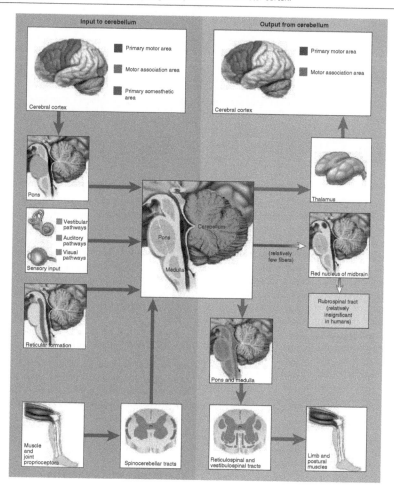

eventually cause muscle contraction. The three-dimensional area of the motor cortex is divided into regions that are specific to different muscles of the body. The greater the number of motor units of the muscle, and the more intricate the neural control over a given muscle's contraction, the greater the area of the cortex that is assigned to that muscle. Thus, muscles that we use to cause intricate movement patterns, such as the forearm and hand for writing, typing and painting, or the muscles of the face for expression and talking, all occupy a relatively large area of the motor cortex. Not

surprisingly, more than 50% of the motor cortex concerns the muscles of the hands and face (35).

The nerves that leave the motor cortex group together at the level of the lower brain and pass down the spinal cord in the *corticospinal tract* (or pyrimidal tract). The nerves of the corticospinal tract cross in the medulla, so that the right side of the motor cortex controls movement on the left side of the body, and vice versa. This is best seen in patients who have suffered a stroke, as a stroke on the left side of the brain affects movement of the right side of the body, and vice versa.

FIGURE 5.3

Electron micrographs of neuromuscular junctions. *(a)* A scanning electron micrograph of a motor nerve axon and its neuromuscular junction. The neuromuscular junction is an enlarged end region of the nerve axon that extends in many directions across the surface of the muscle fiber. *(b)* When the axon and neural components of the neuromuscular junction are removed, invaginations can be seen in the muscle fiber, within which are further clefts and folds.

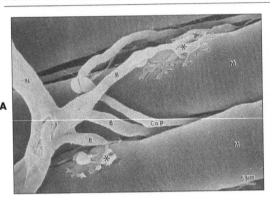

Before nerve action potentials leave the brain and pass along the spinal cord, many patterns are modified in other sections of the brain. This modification is essential for refinement, correction, and sudden changes that are required in the movement. Why have a system that requires a change to be made in the motor cortex, when adjustments can occur faster, with less mental effort, somewhere else? One of the main locations of the refinement of movement patterns is called the cerebellum. In addition, the cerebellum is important for the preparation of future motor patterns, and for storing correct movement sequences (35). For example, after considerable training of a particular movement, more of the details of the movement can be retrieved from the cerebellum, leaving less need of the motor cortex. This is akin to requiring less conscious effort to do a particular task. In sports, this would mean that a person is able to concentrate on other aspects of performance, such as tactics, teamwork, or the ability to anticipate future events. These are the neurological facts behind the saying "Practice makes perfect."

As illustrated in figure 5.2, all the components of the motor control regions of the brain operate together in a complex manner that results in the controlled and precisely orchestrated series of action potentials that are propagated to the appropriate Aα motor nerves of the spinal cord. Nerves are classified by their axon diameter, degree of myelination, and conduction velocity. The motor nerve has the largest diameter and highest conduction velocity, and the letters "Aα" indicate this. *Many nerves innervate the soma of an Aα motor nerve*, as efferent nerves from the different components of the motor control system of the brain can synapse either directly or indirectly on the Aα nerve. In addition, afferent nerves function to invoke inhibition or excitation of the Aα motor nerve, thus providing important refinement at the level of the spinal cord.

The distribution of Aα motor nerves down the spinal cord is somewhat organized into a *segmental distribution*, where the Aα motor nerves leave the spinal cord at a vertebral level that reflects the anatomical position of the skeletal muscle (13). For example, the Aα motor nerves from the motor units of the muscles of the shoulder girdle, abdominal muscles, and muscles from the upper and lower leg leave the spinal cord at various levels of the cervical, thoracic, and sacral vertebrae, respectively.

Instigating Movement

The stimulation of the Aα motor nerves results in the propagation of action potentials to the skeletal muscle fibers of the muscles required to contract during the given movement. The divergence of the Aα motor nerve results in the formation of many junctions between the nerve and skeletal muscle fibers. These junctions are special synapses, and as such are referred to as *neuromuscular junctions*.

The Neuromuscular Junction

As for the synapse, the function of the **neuromuscular junction** is to transmit the action potential across a synaptic cleft. Unlike the synapse, the postsynaptic membrane is not a nerve but the *sarcolemma* of a skeletal muscle fiber.

Electron micrographs of tissue preparations containing neuromuscular junctions are presented in figure 5.3*a* and *b*. Some muscle fibers have more than one neuromuscular junction, each neuromuscular junction is an enlarged structure that extends over an area far greater than the cross-sectional area of the Aα motor nerve axon, and an extensive invagination exists in the skeletal muscle fiber under the neural extensions of the junction.

FIGURE 5.4

FIGURE 5.4

An illustration of the cross section of a neuromuscular junction. The intracellular structures and membrane channels that are involved in neuromuscular transmission of the action potential are included, as are the membrane features of the postsynaptic membrane.

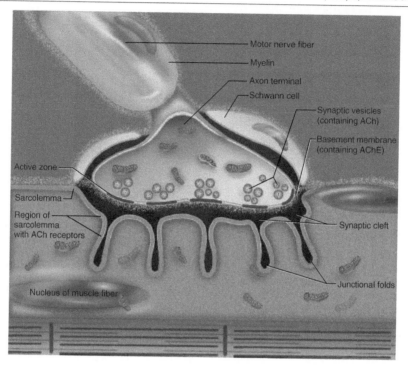

An enlarged simplified illustration of the cross section of a neuromuscular junction is presented in figure 5.4. The postsynaptic region of the sarcolemma, sometimes termed the *motor endplate,* is not only a large invagination, but within it exist numerous other invaginations that serve to increase the cross-sectional area exposed to the release of acetylcholine. As with the postsynaptic membrane of a nerve synapse, the region of the sarcolemma at the neuromuscular junction contains special Na^+ channels that open when bound by acetylcholine. The sarcolemma is then depolarized, and an action potential spreads across the sarcolemma and down special tubules that eventually lead to the molecular events of muscle contraction.

Skeletal Muscle Contraction

Skeletal muscle is one of three types of muscle in the human body: *skeletal muscle, cardiac muscle,* and *smooth muscle.* The individual cells in each muscle type are referred to as **muscle fibers,** and the specialized excitable cell membrane of skeletal muscle fibers is called the **sarcolemma.** Skeletal muscle, as with all the types of muscle, can receive an action potential, and can conduct the action potential across and

within muscle fibers. This property is termed *excitability.* In addition, skeletal muscle can respond to action potentials by contracting (*contractility*), and then return to its precontraction length because of the property of *elasticity.*

Skeletal muscle functions to contract and cause either body movement or the stability of body posture. Skeletal muscle contraction must be able to be performed with a decrease or increase in muscle length. In performing these functions, *skeletal muscle is required to contract and generate tension throughout the length of the muscle.* Depending on the muscle and movement, skeletal muscle must also be able to develop a wide range of tensions, with the ability to alter tension in small increments. These general requirements necessitate a structure with enormous capacity to change length, and be structurally and functionally organized to contract and generate both minutely small and extremely large forces.

neuromuscular junction the connection between a branch of an alpha motor nerve and a skeletal muscle fiber

muscle fibers muscle cells

sarcolemma (sar'ko-lem'ah) the cell membrane of a muscle fiber

Fundamentals of Sport and Exercise Science

Structure

When viewed in transverse section (fig. 5.5), the striated appearance of skeletal muscle fibers results from the organized arrangement of proteins. The main proteins of skeletal muscle are myosin, actin, tropomyosin, and troponin: *myosin and actin are involved in the process of muscle contraction; troponin and tropomyosin are involved in the regulation of muscle contraction.*

Striated muscle proteins are organized into subcellular structures called **myofibrils,** which extend along the length of the muscle fiber. The myofibrils are aligned beside each other, resulting in a similar three-dimensional pattern of the contractile proteins within the entire fiber. Within a myofibril, the contractile proteins are arranged in units called **sarcomeres** (fig. 5.6). The sarcomere is bordered by proteins that form the Z-lines. F-actin molecules extend from each Z-line toward the middle of the sarcomere. The myosin molecules do not extend to each Z-line, and are maintained in the central region of the sarcomere by proteins that form the M-line (81). When viewed three-dimensionally, each myosin molecule is associated with six different F-actin molecules in a hexagonal structure.

The different visual regions of the sarcomere have been named. The darkly stained region indicating the region of myosin is termed the A-band. Located centrally within the A-band is a less darkly stained region where no actin is associated with the myosin, termed the H-band. On either side of the Z-lines are unstained (clear) regions composed solely of actin molecules, termed the I-band.

The contractile proteins of the myofibrils differ in structure and function (fig. 5.7). **Myosin,** the largest of the proteins, is a two-stranded helical structure, and consists of two forms of myosin (light and heavy). In vivo the two heavy chains contain a hinged region, a linear end region, and two globular heads (S_1 units) at one end. The S_1 units contain the enzyme myosin ATPase.

Actin is a globular protein (G-actin), however, in vivo it aggregates to form a two-stranded helical structure (F-actin).

FIGURE 5.6

The organization of the contractile proteins in skeletal muscle as viewed through an electron microscope.

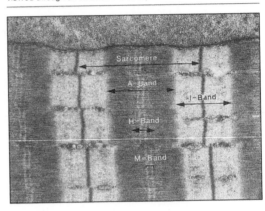

Associated with the F-actin is a rod-shaped molecule called **tropomyosin,** which exists as multiple strands, each of which associates with six or seven G-actin molecules along the length of the F-actin (8, 43, 44). At the end of each tropomyosin molecule is bound a **troponin** molecule, which is involved in the regulation of skeletal muscle contraction.

Contraction and Regulation

For one muscle, hundreds of separate Aα nerves may be stimulated, and for a given Aα motor nerve, divergence of the main axon into hundreds of branches results in the innervation of hundreds of muscle fibers. The muscle fibers and the Aα motor nerve that innervates them make up what is called a **motor unit** (fig. 5.8). When stimulated, a motor unit responds by contracting maximally. Therefore, *the motor unit is the functional unit of muscle contraction.* Contraction of a skeletal muscle results from the combined contraction of many motor units.

FIGURE 5.5

A transverse section of human skeletal muscle, illustrating the striated appearance of skeletal muscle fibers.

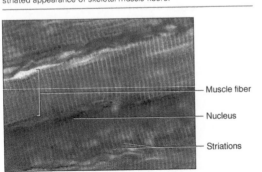

— Muscle fiber

— Nucleus

— Striations

myofibril (mi'o-fi'bril) the longitudinal anatomical unit within skeletal and cardiac muscle fibers that contains the contractile proteins

sarcomere (sar'ko-mere) the smallest contractile unit of skeletal muscle, consisting of the contractile proteins between two Z-lines

myosin (mi'o-sin) the largest of the contractile proteins of skeletal muscle

actin (ac'tin) a contractile protein of skeletal muscle

tropomyosin (tro'po-my'osin) a contractile protein of striated muscle

troponin (tro'po'nin) the regulatory calcium binding contractile protein of striated muscle

motor unit an alpha motor nerve and the muscle fibers that it innervates

FIGURE 5.7

The molecular structure of the contractile proteins of skeletal and cardiac muscle. Filamentous actin (F-actin) is made up of separate units of G-actin. Troponin and tropomyosin are located along the F-actin filament. Myosin is a more complex molecule than actin. Myosin can be enzymatically cleaved at two sites. The long tail is termed light meromyosin (LMM), and the remaining hinge and two-head structure is termed heavy meromyosin (HMM). HMM can be further divided into two S_1 units, with each S_1 unit having two light chains. One of the light chains from each S_1 head is a regulatory light chain. The enzyme myosin ATPase is also located on each S_1 unit.

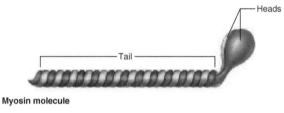

Heads

Tail

Myosin molecule

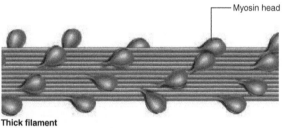

Myosin head

Thick filament

Tropomyosin

Troponin complex

G actin

Thin filament

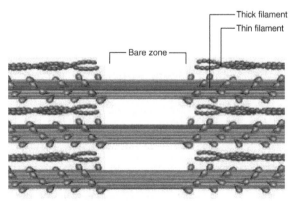

Thick filament

Thin filament

Bare zone

Portion of a sarcomere showing the overlap of thick and thin filaments

FIGURE 5.8

The motor nerve and muscle fiber components of the motor unit.

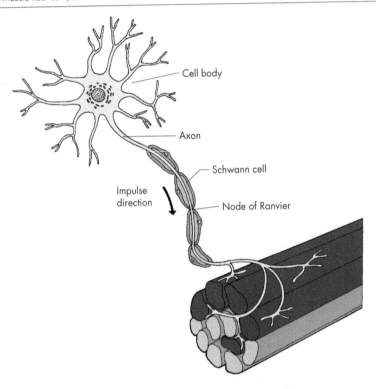

TABLE 5.2

The sequence of events during contraction in striated muscle

When striated muscle is relaxed, ADP and Pi are bound to the S_1 unit of myosin, the myosin head is in the vertical "strained" position, there is a low intracellular calcium concentration, and therefore negligible actin-myosin binding and contraction.

1. The depolarization is received at the sarcolemma and is propagated down the t-tubule network to the sarcoplasmic reticulum (SR).
2. Depolarization of the SR in the region of the triad initiates the release of calcium from the SR and an increase in intracellular calcium.
3. Increased intracellular calcium increases calcium binding to troponin.
4. The troponin-calcium complex causes a structural change in the position of troponin and tropomyosin on the F-actin polymer, enabling actin to bind to the S_1 units of myosin.
5. Actin-myosin binding enables the S_1 units to immediately move to their "less strained" or "favorable" position, thus causing the movement of the attached actin toward the central region of the sarcomere. During this process, ADP and Pi are released from each S_1 unit. This constitutes muscle contraction.
6. Because actin is connected to the Z-lines, actin movement results in the shortening of each sarcomere within the fibers of the stimulated motor unit, resulting in muscle contraction.
7. Provided ATP is continually replenished at the myosin-actin sites of the sarcomere, ATP molecules once again bind to the myosin S_1 units, which causes the release of each S_1 unit from actin. During the release of actin and myosin, ATP is hydrolyzed to ADP and Pi and the S_1 units change conformation to a vertical "strained" position. The ATP hydrolysis is believed to provide the free energy needed to move the S_1 units to the "strained" position.
8. If the increased intracellular calcium concentration is maintained (because of continued neural stimulation), the myosin S_1 units will continue the cyclical attachment and detachment to actin, termed *contraction cycling*.
9. Relaxation occurs when the action potentials are not received by the neurmuscular junction and calcium is actively "pumped" back into the SR.

FIGURE 5.9

The sequence of events during skeletal and cardiac muscle contraction. The depolarization of the sarcolemma is propagated down the t-tubules and causes calcium release from the SR *(a)*. As long as calcium is not pumped back into the SR, the sequence of events from A to E continues, and represents c nit binding sites. *(c)* Binding of actin and the S_1 units of myosin causes the translation of the actin and myosin, causing contraction. *(d)* The regeneration of ATP from metabolism enables a new ATP molecule to bind to the S_1 unit, which causes the deattatchment of actin and the S_1 units of myosin. *(e)* The S_1 units of myosin return to the vertical or "strained" position, powered by the free energy of ATP dephosphorylation.

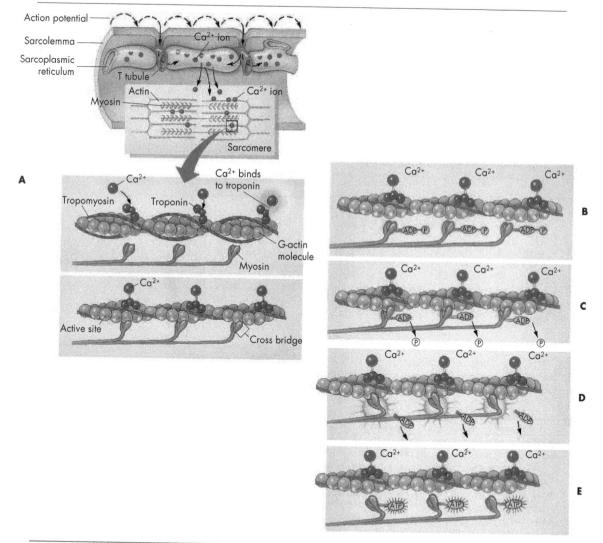

The electrochemical and molecular events during muscle contraction are listed in sequential order in table 5.2 and illustrated in figure 5.9. When an action potential is transmitted to and propagated along the sarcolemma, the depolarization is internalized within the fiber by the *t-tubule* network. When the wave of depolarization reaches the junction of the t-tubule and sarcoplasmic reticulum *(triad)*, calcium is re-

leased from the *sarcoplasmic reticulum* (SR) and increases the concentration of free calcium within the fiber.

The binding of the calcium ions to the troponin molecules induces a conformational shift in the actin-troponin-tropomyosin association. This shift in three-dimensional molecular structure exposes a site which enables the association of actin and the S_1 units of myosin. The position of the

FIGURE 5.10

The different types of skeletal muscle contraction. Concentric contractions occur with a rapid increase in *external force* application. However, because of the influence of joint angle on force development, *contractile tension* varies during a full joint range of motion contraction. During eccentric contractions the *external force* profile is similar to that of concentric contractions; however, muscle tension development is greatest when the force of gravity is perpendicular to the lever arm. Greater forces can be developed during eccentric contractions than for concentric contractions.

FIGURE 5.11

Isokinetic contractions performed with maximal effort produce a variable force. The data presented are for maximal isokinetic knee flexion and extension, and show force curves during the range of motion during flexion and extension. Force production is less for the start and end of a contraction, where musculoskeletal mechanics (joint angles) limit force generation. Training muscle for strength and power using isokinetic equipment has received support for its ability to maximize resistance at optimal joint angles, and for the ability to set specific contraction velocities. However, the isolation of specific muscles and muscle groups decreases the suitability of this training to actions that involve multiple muscle groups (adapted from Thorstensson A., G. Grimby and J. Karlsson. Force-velocity relations and fiber composition in human knee extensor muscles. *J. Appl. Physiol.* 40(1):12–16, 1976).

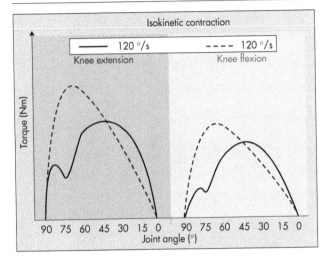

myosin S_1 units prior to calcium release from the SR is often illustrated as a vertical structure, and represents the "unfavorable" or "strained" position of the S_1 unit.

The binding of the S_1 units to actin enables the release of the ADP (adenosine diphosphate) and Pi (inorganic phosphate) molecules, which strengthens the actin-myosin complex (58). During this event, the S_1 units return to their "less strained" or "favored" position, causing shortening of the sarcomere. The myosin and actin association is broken by the binding of ATP (adenosine triphosphate) to the myosin S_1 heads and the release of the ADP. The hydrolysis of ATP then provides the free energy to move the S_1 units of myosin to their strained position. The presence of ADP and Pi on the S_1 units retains the S_1 units in this position until calcium ions bind to troponin. Consequently, if free calcium is still present within the myofibrillar apparatus and calcium remains bound to troponin, as soon as the S_1 units are returned to their strained position, the contraction process will occur once again. The continued cycling of the S_1 units, which *requires the presence of calcium and the continual production and hydrolysis of ATP*, is termed *contraction cycling*. Contraction cycling accounts for the ability of skeletal muscle to generate force despite no (isometric) or minimal changes in

length, and for the ATP and metabolic demands of these contractions. The summation of contraction cycling and sarcomere shortening within a myofibril, muscle fiber, and motor unit, and among multiple motor units, results in the shortening of muscle during dynamic muscle contraction.

Function

Types of Contractions   Skeletal muscle can contract in a variety of ways. Contractions causing a change in muscle length are called *isotonic* contractions. When the muscle length shortens, the isotonic contraction is referred to as a **concentric** contraction. When the muscle length increases during contraction, the isotonic contraction is referred to as **eccentric** (fig. 5.10). However, by definition a contraction involves muscle shortening. For this reason many researchers now refer to an eccentric contraction as an eccentric action. Nevertheless, because the American College of Sports Medicine recommends that the word "contraction" be retained because of the broad acceptance and application of its nonspecific meaning (62), it will be used in this text. Eccentric muscle contractions can generate greater force than concentric contractions (82), with the difference due to combined effects of gravity assistance

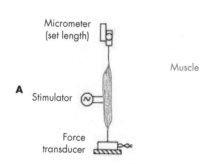

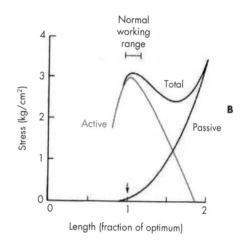

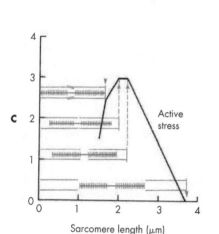

FIGURE 5.12

(a) In vitro research of muscle contraction has produced curves illustrating the relationship between muscle length and tension development (b). Active tension is the tension remaining after the passive tension component is removed, and reflects the molecular interaction between actin and myosin (c).

(when performed with gravity), stored elastic energy, and the passive tension of the contractile proteins and musculotendinous junctions (Up Close 5.1). Muscle contractions causing no change in muscle length are called **isometric** contractions.

A third type of contraction (muscle action) is **isokinetic.** Isokinetic contractions are a special type of concentric contraction, where the velocity of muscle shortening remains constant (hence the prefix "iso"). These contractions require specialized and expensive equipment that instantaneously modifies resistance in proportion to the force generated at specific joint angles (refer to fig. 1.6). The result of this is to provide maximal resistance when musculoskeletal mechanics allow maximal force production and vice versa (fig. 5.11).

Length-Tension Relationship

For a given muscle, the force of a maximal concentric contraction depends on the length of the muscle (8). When a muscle is removed from the body, with one end connected to a micrometer and the other end connected to a force transducer, stimulation of the muscle will cause contraction without shortening (isometric) and the development of tension on the force transducer (fig. 5.12a). By stimulating the muscle and recording the resulting forces for various muscle lengths,

the data can be graphed as a length-tension curve (fig. 5.12b). However, because simply stretching the muscle generates *passive tension*, this passive component must be subtracted from the *total tension* measured, resulting in the *active tension*. Muscle length influences tension development because excessive stretch and inadequate length decrease actin and myosin interaction (fig. 5.12c). These facts have direct application to exercise because warm-up and flexibility preparation prior to an event optimize the length-tension relationship of skeletal muscle, allow increased force production and power generation, and may improve performance.

concentric (kon-sen'trik) in reference to skeletal muscle contraction; a contraction involving the shortening of muscle

eccentric (e-sen'trik) in reference to skeletal muscle contraction; a contraction involving the lengthening of muscle

isometric (i-so-met'rik) in reference to skeletal muscle contraction; a contraction involving no change in the length of muscle

isokinetic (i-so-ki-net'ik) in reference to skeletal muscle contraction; a contraction involving a constant velocity

UP CLOSE 5.1

Eccentric Contraction-Induced Skeletal Muscle Injury

When exercise is performed that involves eccentric muscle contractions, especially when the muscle is unaccustomed to the exercise duration or intensity, microscopic muscle damage occurs. This damage is associated with the development of elevated serum creatine kinase activity, swelling, soreness, and restricted range of motion during the ensuing 48 h (14, 18, 21, 41). Originally, this condition was termed delayed onset muscle soreness (DOMS); however, research conducted since the early 1980s has indicated that the muscle damage that accompanies DOMS can be quite severe, induces an immune response, and increases calcium release from muscle, which in turn can activate many protein-degrading enzymes and exacerbate the microtrauma to skeletal muscle. The biochemical events that accompany these responses probably induce the inflammation and soreness. In short, delayed onset muscle soreness is a nondescript term for the condition, and the term *exercise-induced muscle damage* is becoming more accepted.

Figure 5.13 presents an electron micrograph of damaged skeletal muscle. The disruption of the Z-lines is termed Z-line streaming, and probably results from damage to proteins that stabilize the actin molecules to the Z-line proteins. After approximately 12 h, infiltration of the damaged muscle region by macrophages and lymphocytes occurs, resulting in the destruction of the damaged region of muscle. It is theorized that chemicals released from the immune response induce both the swelling and pain symptoms, and that the influx of calcium into the damaged cells may activate enzymes that degrade protein and further accentuate the muscle damage.

Clarkson and Tremblay (18) have documented that recovery from even a single bout of exposure to eccentric muscle contractions protects the muscle from the same damage during a second bout of eccentric muscle contractions. This rapid adaptability to eccentric contractions is remarkable; however, the cellular events and changes that lead to this tolerance are unknown.

FIGURE 5.13

Microscopic skeletal muscle damage resulting from eccentric exercise. The disruption of the Z-line has caused this damage to be termed "Z-line streaming."

Force-Velocity and Power-Velocity Relationships

Skeletal muscle tension development is also known to vary with the velocity of the shortening. Greatest tension development occurs at zero-shortening velocity (isometric) contractions. The force developed during maximal isometric contractions is referred to as the *maximal voluntary contraction* (MVC) force. As contraction velocity increases, peak tension development decreases (fig. 5.14a). The force-velocity curve can differ among muscles with training/detraining, and among individuals who differ in fiber type proportions. The skeletal muscle force-power curve reveals that an optimal velocity exists for developing power (fig. 5.14b).

During repeated maximal effort contractions, muscle fatigues. Fatigue is illustrated as a decay in force generation with subsequent contractions (fig. 5.14c). Interestingly, muscles with greater force generation capabilities, or muscles trained to increase strength, exhibit more rapid decrements in muscle force. Conversely, muscles trained for long-term endurance have smaller maximal force capabilities and less force decrement during fatigue.

Summation and Tetanus The skeletal muscle twitch response is extremely long (150 to 250 ms) compared to the action potential (< 5 ms). As previously explained, skeletal muscle contraction results from the combined contraction of many motor units. The long contraction time and short stimulation time provide opportunity for additional neural stimulation prior to the complete relaxation of the muscle or motor unit. In these circumstances, the force of the total muscle or motor unit twitch can increase with increased stimulation frequency, and is called *summation*. As stimulation frequency increases, twitch tension also increases until a smooth maximal tension is reached, which is called *tetanus*. Tetanus is not a normal occurrence during voluntary muscle contraction, but exemplifies the ability of skeletal muscle to respond to high-frequency stimulation. Furthermore, during abnormal muscle function, such as during a cramp, the resulting response is similar to tetanus and can often exceed the maximal voluntary contraction force.

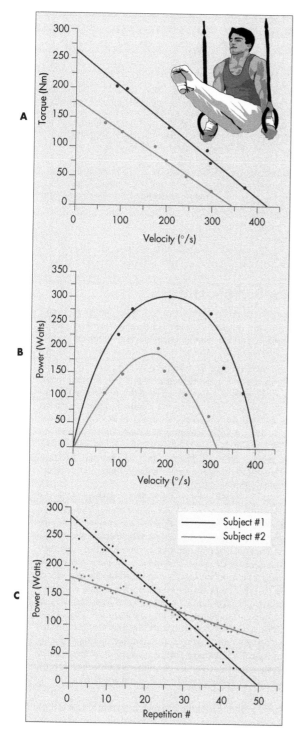

FIGURE 5.14

(a) The relationship between muscle contraction force and contraction velocity. Data is shown from two subjects that have different maximal force capabilities of the quadriceps. Subject 1 is an untrained individual, and subject 2 is a nationally competitive triathlete. Even though subject 2 was endurance trained for prolonged exercise, subject 1 had greater maximal force. *(b)* The relationship between muscle power and contraction velocity of the quadriceps for the same two subjects. Subject 1 had greater power, with both subjects having the optimal power-velocity relationship at velocities between 150 and 200°/s. *(c)* The decrease in power during multiple contractions of skeletal muscle in the same two subjects. Subject 2 had far greater endurance (less decrease in power).

Resting Muscle Tone   At rest a small amount of muscle motor unit contraction occurs to maintain firmness or *tone* of skeletal muscle. The resting muscle tone is known to be caused by neural stimulation because neurally isolated muscles are flaccid. In addition, when afferent nerves from muscle are cut, thereby preventing feedback from muscles to the central nervous system, muscle tone is lost (8). This fact illustrates that resting muscle tone is caused by afferent nerve feedback from muscle to the spinal cord, which then stimulates efferent fibers that innervate a small number of skeletal muscle motor units (8).

Identifying Motor Units and Muscle Fiber Types

Research of neuromuscular function was first conducted using samples from animals. The earliest animal models used to research nerve function and muscle contraction were the triceps surae and gastrocnemius muscles of the cat (10, 11, 12, 36, 38). This research identified that differences existed in the morphology and function among the nerves of certain motor units, and that the metabolic and contractile characteristics of muscle fibers innervated by different nerves were also different. The complete classification of a motor unit requires data of nerve and muscle morphology and physiology, and differences in these characteristics have resulted in motor unit classifications based on nerve recruitment order and conduction velocity, muscle contraction velocity and force, or muscle fiber metabolic capacities (table 5.3). Motor units exist in human muscle that are fast-twitch and slow-twitch. Within the fast-twitch category are two subdivisions that differ in oxidative capacity.

Nerve and Recruitment Characteristics

The attainment of a threshold membrane potential of the soma of the nerve occurs more rapidly in an SO (slow-twitch oxidative) motor unit than in either the FOG (fast-twitch oxidative glycolic) or FG (fast-twitch glycolic) motor unit, resulting in a recruitment order of motor units. *SO motor units are recruited first during incremental exercise,*

TABLE 5.3

The classification nomenclature of mammalian skeletal muscle motor units

CLASSIFICATION METHOD	NOMENCLATURE			
Visual	Red		White	
Contractile velocity (Hennemen and Mendell [40])	Slow-twitch		Fast-twitch	
Contractile velocity and metabolism (Brooke and Kaiser [9])	I Slow-twitch	IIab Fast-twitch intermediate	IIa Fast-twitch fatigue resistant	IIb Fast-twitch fatigable
Contractile velocity and metabolism (Burke et al. [11, 13])	S Slow-twitch	F(int) Fast-twitch intermediate	FR Fast-twitch fatigue resistant	FF Fast-twitch fatigable
Contractile velocity and metabolism (Peter et al. [59])	Slow-twitch oxidative (SO)		Fast-twitch oxidative glycolytic (FOG)	Fast-twitch glycolytic (FG)

Source: Adapted from Burke (13) and Peter et al. (59).

A more complex classification, resulting in additional subdivisions, can be found in Pette and Straron (60)

followed by a progressive increase in FOG and FG motor unit recruitment as exercise intensity increases. This pattern of recruitment has been termed the *size principle*, and causes SO motor units to be recruited predominantly during low to moderate exercise intensities, and each of SO, FOG, and FG motor units to be recruited during intense exercise requiring contractions against high resistance or fast muscle contractions (27, 38, 39, 40, 67). *During contractions of increased velocity; the size principal is still retained;* however, the difference in recruitment order among the different types of motor units is less pronounced (27).

Apart from the soma and recruitment order, the Aα motor nerves of different motor units also differ in size, conduction velocity, and stimulation characteristics (fig. 5.15). The area dimensions of the soma and cross-sectional area of the axon of the Aα motor nerve are larger in the FG motor unit than in the SO motor unit (13, 40, 66). In addition, the Aα motor nerve has a higher conduction velocity in the FG motor unit than in the SO motor unit, and SO motor units are stimulated in a more consistent manner compared to the rapid and intermittent manner of the FG motor units (40). However, because of considerable overlap among motor units for these characteristics, Burke (13) has commented that motor units cannot be classified based on nerve characteristics alone.

The contribution of human motor unit recruitment to muscle function has been indirectly studied using **electromyography (EMG)**. The signal obtained from EMG is proportional to electrical activity, which in turn is proportional to the number of muscle fibers, and therefore, the number of motor units stimulated to contract (6). EMG has revealed the increase in electrical activity that occurs when muscle contractions develop increased tension, and the different electrical activity and recruitment patterns for concentric, eccentric, and isokinetic muscle contractions (Up Close 5.2).

Muscle Characteristics

The muscle fibers of a motor unit have biochemical and contractile capacities that influence how the motor unit is suited to different exercise intensities and durations.

Contractile Force and Velocity

The contractile force of muscle within the different motor units increases in a progression from SO, to FOG, to FG motor units (fig. 5.15), whereas the duration of the contraction decreases in the progression from SO, to FOG, to FG motor units. The force of contraction of a motor unit is determined by the size of the muscle fibers within a motor unit, and by the number of muscle fibers within a motor unit. FT (fast-twitch) motor units generally contain more muscle fibers than ST (slow-twitch) motor units.

Contractile velocity of motor units is determined by the conduction velocity of the Aα motor nerves and the type of myosin proteins and myosin ATPase enzyme within the muscle fibers. The myosin heavy and light chains and ATPase enzyme are known to result from separate genes, and their expression is therefore determined by gene translation, which is believed to be differentiated within the first year of life (13). Different structures of the myosin light chains are known to be present in FT compared to ST muscle fibers, as are different structures of the enzyme myosin ATPase. These differences result in faster contraction times in FT compared to ST motor units; however, the contribution from other determinants to contractile velocity, such as neuromuscular transmission, t-tubule and sarcoplasmic reticulum density, and calcium pump characterstics, is unknown (67).

Muscle Fiber Biochemical and Enzymatic Capacities

Skeletal muscle fibers from SO motor units have a high oxidative capacity. In other words, they possess relatively

FIGURE 5.15

The different neural, stimulatory, contractile, and metabolic differences among the three main types of motor units of human skeletal muscle. SO = slow-twitch oxidative, FOG = fast-twitch oxidative glycolytic, FG = fast-twitch glycolytic.

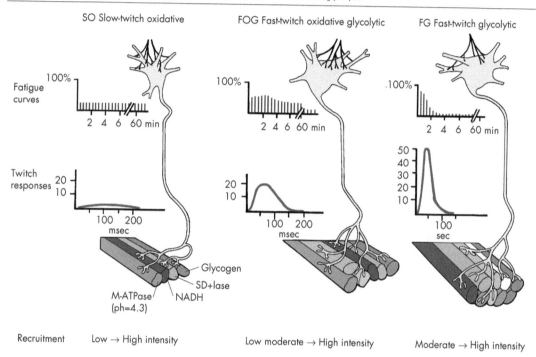

high concentrations of myoglobin, high mitochondrial membrane density, and, therefore, relatively high concentrations of the enzymes of the TCA (tricarboxylic acid) cycle, β-oxidation, and electron transport chain. The added myoglobin and mitochondria of SO muscle compared to FG muscle are the reasons for the "red" appearance and "white" appearance of the respective muscle types. Muscle fibers from FOG motor units have moderate concentrations of these molecules and enzymes, with muscle from FG motor units having the lowest concentrations. However, the differentiation of muscle fibers based on metabolic capacities is by far less sensitive than that of histochemical staining based in the different pH stability of myosin ATPase, and has been interpreted as evidence of a metabolic continuum that exists within and between muscle fibers of different motor units (see Up Close 5.3) (9, 12, 13, 32, 66, 67).

These metabolic differences make SO motor units more suited to prolonged exercise, and allow muscle catabolism of lipid and carbohydrate via mitochondrial respiration. Conversely, the low mitochondrial density of the skeletal muscle fibers from FG motor units makes these muscle fibers reliant on glycolytic catabolism, and therefore the production of lactate and the development of acidosis (25, 31). Muscle fibers

from SO motor units are therefore termed *fatigue resistant*, whereas muscle fibers from FG motor units are *fatigable*.

Researchers have documented the metabolic differences among muscle fibers from different motor units by several methods. An increasingly common but laborious technique is to isolate individual muscle fibers from a biopsy sample, determine their fiber type by an enzymatic assay, pool the fibers into different fiber type populations, and then assay the muscle samples for the activity of additional enzymes of either glycolysis, β-oxidation, the TCA cycle, or the electron transport chain (16, 46). Researchers can also analyze whole muscle biopsy samples, and based on additional myosin ATPase fiber typing, compare enzyme activities among samples that have differing percentages of ST and FT muscle fibers. Another method is to histochemically assay sections of muscle biopsy samples for specific enyzme activities.

Based on single-fiber research, muscle fibers from the different motor units have distinctive enzymatic capacities that are best discriminated by the activity of mitochondrial

electromyography (EMG) (e-lek'tro-mi'og-ra'fi) study of neuromuscular electrical activity at rest and during muscle contraction

Electromyography: Measuring Neuromuscular Electrical Activity During Muscle Contraction

What Is Electromyography?

Electromyography (EMG) is the study of muscle function from the detection of electrical activity emanating from the depolarization of nerves and muscle membranes that accompany contraction (7). The electrical activity is detected by the placement of one or more electrodes over the contracting muscle(s) of interest. The type of electrodes can be either needle or surface, where needle electrodes are inserted into a muscle belly or a specific nerve, and surface electrodes are placed on the skin over the muscle(s) of interest (fig. 5.16).

The EMG Signal

The observed unprocessed signal is the composite of all neural and muscle membrane depolarization, and as such consists of signals from Aα motor nerves of the recruited motor units, muscle receptors, and afferent nerves. Understandably, the EMG signal can be very complex! The raw signal can be processed by adding the squared deviations from the baseline signal. This signal processing, when expressed relative to the duration of the signal, is referred to as *integrated EMG*. Another method of analysis is to record the

frequency of individual spikes in the EMG signal. Increased frequency of EMG signals indicates increased conduction velocities (and/or increased FT recruitment), whereas a decrease in frequency represents muscle fatigue (7). In addition, the ability of skeletal muscle to increase force application after exercise training, despite no increase in EMG signal, has been used to indicate a neural component to training adaptation, such as an increased synchronization of motor unit firing (28, 56).

EMG Evidence of Motor Unit Recruitment

The use of the EMG to detect changes in motor unit recruitment has been based on an increase in signal amplitude and an increase in integrated EMG signal (fig. 5.17). Both parameters increase in an exponential manner as the muscle contraction force increases.

The increase in integrated EMG signal with increases in the strength of muscle contraction.

Photograph of an EMG with surface electrodes attached to a subject.

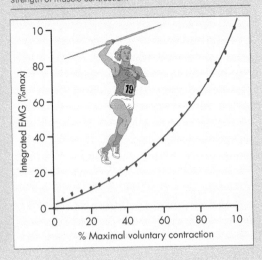

enzymes, or by ratios of activities from enzymes of glycolytic versus mitochondrial pathways (60). When using histochemical methods to detect differences in the quantity of NADH in muscle fibers, SO fibers stain darkest and a progressive decrease in stain intensity occurs for the FOG and FG fibers.

Muscle Glycogen Stores   Muscle glycogen stores have been reported to be higher in FT than ST muscle fibers prior

to exercise (47, 63, 69, 78, 79, 80). However, because of the recruitment order of motor units and the bias to ST muscle metabolism that would exist in daily locomotion requirements, this finding may be due to an activity-related lowering of muscle glycogen in ST muscle fibers rather than a difference in glycogen storage. This interpretation is understandable given the predominance of carbohydrate catabolism in skeletal muscle during both intense prolonged exercise and short-term intense exercise.

Capillary Density

Research on the density of capillaries in rodent skeletal muscle has revealed that within a muscle of homogenous fiber type, a greater capillary density is evident in slow-twitch compared to fast-twitch muscle. Because human muscle is heterogenous in fiber type, a similar investigation cannot be completed. Nevertheless, Anderson (3) studied the capillary density of human muscle relative to the area occupied by either of the fiber types. Greatest capillary density occurred around SO muscle fibers, and there was no difference in capillary density between FG and FOG muscle fibers. Consequently, even in human muscle with a heterogenous distribution of fiber types, there appear to be *more capillaries surrounding SO muscle fibers.*

Fiber Type Proportions

The differences in biochemical capacities and myosin ATPase pH stability among the muscle fibers of differing motor units have enabled histochemical methods to become those predominantly used to determine motor unit proportions in human **muscle biopsy** samples (Up Close 5.3) from skeletal muscle. However, as the myosin ATPase histochemical procedure involves only the muscle fiber component of the motor unit, the term **fiber type** has often replaced the more correct expressions SO, FOG, and FG *motor unit* proportions. This is unfortunate, as evidence exists to indicate that muscle fibers have a greater potential for diversity than do the neural components of the entire motor unit. For example, at least eight different muscle fiber types based on the myosin ATPase stain have been shown (32) and, as will be discussed in later sections of this chapter, exercise training can alter the genetic function of skeletal muscle fibers resulting in the transcription of myosin light chains that typically occur in other fiber type subcategories (60). Consequently, changes in fiber type proportions may not reflect actual motor unit changes, and it remains unclear whether fiber type changes are more important than nerve changes for the function of motor units during exercise.

Sensory Functions

During rest and exercise conditions, neural functions of our body are continually operating to provide feedback to the CNS of the conditions experienced by our internal organs and peripheral tissues. The neural information is derived from specialized *sensory receptors* that convert a biochemical (e.g., reactions altered by light in retina of the eye), physical (e.g., temperature), or mechanical (joint movement) stimulus into an action potential that is propagated to the CNS. The main sensory receptors that function during exercise are listed in table 5.4. Of these, the receptors of importance to neuromuscular function are the muscle spindle, golgi tendon organ, and joint receptors.

General Function of Sensory Receptors

The function of receptors and their afferent nerves is to "inform" the CNS of changes in local conditions. To do this ef-

TABLE 5.4	
The sensory receptors of the body most pertinent to exercise	
RECEPTOR	**FUNCTION DURING EXERCISE**
Mechanoreceptors	
Muscle spindle	Smooth muscle contractions; kinesthesis
Golgi tendon organ	Prevention of muscle injury
Pacinian corpuscles	Pressure sensation
Joint receptors	$\uparrow$ Ventilation rate
Free nerve endings	$\uparrow$ Blood pressure and heart rate
Cochlea	Sound
Vestibular apparatus	Equilibrium and balance
Baroreceptors	Blood pressure and blood volume regulation
Atrial stretch receptors	Blood pressure and blood volume regulation
Skeletal muscle	Cardiovascular response/ regulation
Thermoreceptors	
Cold receptors	Thermoregulation
Warm receptors	Thermoregulation
Electromagnetic receptors	
Rod and cone cells	Vision
Chemoreceptors	
Aortic and carotid bodies	Blood O_2 and CO_2 concentrations, ventilatory regulation
Osmoreceptors	Blood osmolality, fluid balance, kidney function, and blood volume regulation
CNS blood CO_2 sensors	Ventilatory regulation, blood acid-base regulation
Glucose receptors	Blood glucose regulation, carbohydrate metabolism
Skeletal muscle	Cardiovascular response/ regulation

Source: Adapted from Guyton (35).

fectively, there must be a means to (1) detect these changes and (2) relay neural information of the magnitude of these changes.

The Receptor Potential A given receptor has a specialized structure that enables a specific sensory stimulus (modality) to alter the membrane potential. The depolarization of

muscle biopsy the procedure of removing a sample of skeletal muscle from an individual

fiber type a categorization of muscle fibers based on their enzymatic and metabolic characteristics

UP CLOSE 5.3

Applications of Muscle Biopsy to Exercise Physiology

The Muscle Biopsy Procedure

Human muscle biopsy is an invasive procedure that removes a small piece of muscle tissue from the human body. It is performed by first injecting a local anaesthetic into the skin and underlying connective tissue where the biopsy is to be performed. Once the anaesthetic has taken effect, a small incision (usually 1 cm long) is made through the skin and down through the fascia sheath covering the muscle (fig. 5.18). The biopsy needle (fig. 5.19) is then forced into the

opening. When in place, the center plunge and guillotine is raised and, to increase the size of the biopsy sample, suction is generated within the needle to force muscle into the window of the needle (26). The guillotine is then forcefully lowered, cutting the muscle. The needle is then withdrawn, with the muscle specimen inside.

How Are Muscle Biopsy Specimens Processed and Analyzed?

When the muscle specimen is removed from the needle, it can be processed in several ways. For biochemical assay, the muscle specimen is frozen in liquid nitrogen as rapidly as possible. Some researchers place the needle, with the muscle sample still inside, immediately into liquid nitrogen to prevent the added delay in removing the muscle from the needle! If the specimen is to be used for histological preparations, the rapidity of freezing is less important (see below).

Freeze Drying vs. Wet Weight

When frozen, the muscle specimen either can be stored as is, or the water content of the tissue can be removed by vacuum sublimation (freeze drying). If the muscle is left frozen in its raw form, it contains a large amount of water, which dilutes the concentration of metabolites. Conversely, freeze drying enables the water to be removed, increasing the concentration of metabolites, and thereby improving the ability to detect metabolites by enzymatic assays. The drawback to freeze drying is that metabolites are not in their true in vivo concentration; however, dividing metabolite concentrations

FIGURE 5.18

Muscle tissue needle biopsy procedure performed under local anesthesia.

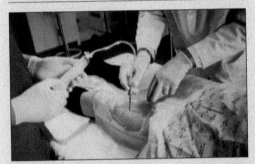

(Photo courtesy of Henry Ford Health System.)

FIGURE 5.19

Biopsy needle.

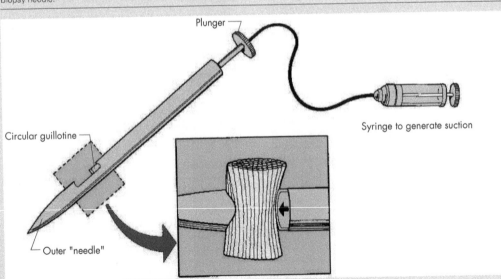

expressed relative to muscle dry weight (e.g., mmol/kg dry wt) by 4.11 will give a concentration close to wet weight values (depending on the original tissue hydration).

Enzymatic Biochemistry

Muscle metabolites and enzyme activities are most frequently determined by first homogenizing the muscle in a solution containing buffers and electrolytes. For the assay of metabolites, a sample of this homogenate is then added to test tubes containing appropriate enzymes, substrates, and enzyme activators to induce reactions that will eventually increase the concentration of a suitable end product that can be measured via an indirect technique (usually NADH, which can be measured by spectrophotometry or fluorometry).

Histology

For histological preparation, the muscle specimen needs to be cleaned of excess blood and connective tissue, and then mounted within a special paste on a small platform (usually cork). The mounted specimen is then frozen slowly in an organic solvent (e.g., isopentane) to prevent damage to the specimen that occurs during rapid freezing, and is then stored in liquid nitrogen for later histological preparation.

Microscopically thin slices of frozen tissue are obtained in a *cryostat*. Serial sections of the tissue are then placed in solutions containing chemicals that specifically favor a given reaction, or selectively denature enzymes in given muscle fiber types. For example, the periodic acid-Schiff stain produces a pink color, with the color intensity being proportional to muscle carbohydrate (glycogen) (fig. 5.20*b*).

The myosin ATPase stain, if it involves a preincubation of the sections in an acid medium of pH = 4.3, denatures the myosin ATPase enzyme in fast-twitch muscle fibers and allows the following incubation and reactions to deposit cobalt in the slow-twitch fibers whose myosin ATPase is still active. This stains slow-twitch fibers black, and leaves fast-twitch fibers unstained (white) when viewed by light microscopy. A preincubation in a solution of pH = 10.3 will denature the myosin ATPase from slow-twitch muscle fibers, thus allowing subsequent incubations to stain the fast-twitch muscle fibers which have active myosin ATPase. Consequently, when preincubated at pH = 10.2, fast-twitch fibers stain black and slow-twitch fibers remain unstained. If the preincubation is at a moderately low pH (pH = 4.6), some muscle fibers that are classified as fast-twitch by either of the 4.3 or 10.3 preincubation procedures retain some myosin ATPase activity (fig. 5.20*a*). These fibers reveal a slight stain from the incubation and reactions that follow, and have been classified as fast-twitch oxidative (IIa or FOG) fibers.

FIGURE 5.20

Sections of skeletal muscle stained for *(a)* myosin ATPase activity after a preincubation pH of 4.6, and *(b)* carbohydrate content by the periodic acid Schiff (PAS) stain. The PAS stain section is from a postexercise condition. The difference in stain intensity (glycogen content) for the muscle fibers is evident. For the ATPase stain section, there are multiple shades of staining for many fast-twitch fibers. Note that these are not serial sections.

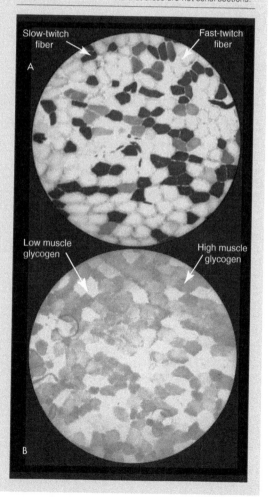

the receptor membrane is called a *receptor potential*. As with the postsynaptic membrane, or the soma of a nerve, if the receptor potential exceeds a *threshold* value, an action potential is generated and propagated toward the CNS.

The magnitude of the stimulus to a receptor is relayed to the CNS by the rate of action potentials leaving the receptor. *The greater the stimulus strength, the larger the receptor potential and, if above threshold, the greater the rate of action potentials leaving the receptor.*

The Muscle Spindle During exercise, where many muscles are contracting during very complex movements, it is easy to overlook the complex interactions that must exist between nerves and muscle. In fact, the contraction of skeletal muscle is only one of several neuromuscular interactions during movement. During muscle contraction and the movement of the body, there is continual feedback by afferent nerves that originate in receptors within skeletal muscle. The main skeletal muscle receptor of interest is the **muscle spindle,** which continually *allows neural information to be relayed back to the CNS of muscle stretch, muscle length, and the rate of change in muscle length.* These functions are a result of the anatomical arrangement between afferent and efferent nerves and the components of the muscle spindle (fig. 5.21).

The muscle spindle contains specialized muscle fibers, which are collectively termed *intrafusal fibers.* These fibers run parallel to the normal skeletal muscle fibers, which for the sake of clarity are termed *extrafusal fibers.* There are two types of intrafusal fibers, which are termed *nuclear bag* and *nuclear chain* fibers, and the typical spindle has several of each type, with the chain fiber being more numerous (12, 27, 35).

The nuclear bag and chain fibers get their names from their anatomical appearances. Nuclear bag fibers are the larger of the two, and have multiple nuclei clustered centrally within the fiber. Nuclear chain fibers also have multiple nuclei, yet because of their smaller diameter the nuclei are aligned in a single line, resembling a chain in the central region of the fiber. The intrafusal fibers also differ with regard to efferent and afferent nerve connections. The bag fiber has a Ia afferent nerve that encapsulates the central nuclear region. The multiple encapsulation of the Ia nerve around the bag fiber is termed an *annulospiral ending* (actually the origin or receptor of the afferent nerve). The chain fibers also have annulospiral Ia afferent nerve connections and, in addition, have group II afferent connections (flower spray endings) located distally and proximally to the central region of the fiber. The Ia afferent nerves have a greater conduction velocity than the group II afferents and therefore relay information faster to the CNS. Both the bag and chain fibers have γ efferent nerves innervating the distal and proximal ends of each fiber where the contractile proteins are located.

Functions of the Spindle The muscle spindle is sensitive to static stretch, dynamic stretch, and to changes in muscle length.

Static Stretch During static stretch the central regions of the bag and chain fibers are forcefully elongated and cause receptor potentials in the annulospiral and flower spray endings of the type Ia afferents of the bag and chain fibers and type II afferent nerves of the chain fibers. These action potentials are propagated back to the spinal cord, where they synapse directly to a type Aα motor nerve. This nerve innervates the stretched muscle, causing a contraction of the fibers innervated by the motor nerve. This stretch

response is termed the *static stretch reflex* because it is performed at the spinal cord level without the involvement of the higher-level centers of the CNS. The static stretch reflex is maintained for as long as the muscle is stretched.

Dynamic Stretch The neuromuscular response to dynamic stretch is slightly different from the static stretch reflex. A sudden stretch of a skeletal muscle induces a receptor potential solely in the type Ia annulospiral endings from the bag and chain fibers. The ensuing reflex is rapid, causing a forceful contraction of the stretched muscle, and is completed in a fraction of a second.

The applications of static and dynamic functions of the muscle spindle are clearly seen in the measurement and training of flexibility (Personal Trainer 5.1).

Changes in Muscle Length During muscle contraction and relaxation there is a repeated increase and decrease in the length of the extrafusal fibers. If the muscle spindle is to remain effective in responding to changes in muscle length, at differing initial lengths, the spindle must also change length in concert with the extrafusal fibers. This does happen, and represents a very important additional function of the γ efferent nerves. When Aα nerves are stimulated, γ nerves are also stimulated so that the change in length of the intrafusal fibers matches that of the extrafusal fibers. This process is called **alpha-gamma coactivation,** and allows the spindle to be at near-optimal sensitivity regardless of the changing length of the extrafusal muscle fibers. Alpha-gamma coactivation enables continual afferent feedback from the contracting muscle that informs the CNS of muscle length almost continually during a contraction. This dynamic sense has been termed *kinesthesis,* whereas the term *proprioception* is used to describe the general state of body awareness in the resting state. Our abilities of proprioception and kinesthesis are used in daily activities, as well as in exercise and athletic performance.

Other Muscle Receptors

As well as the muscle spindle, other receptors exist that connect to afferent nerves and the CNS. As the name implies, the *Golgi tendon organs* are located in the tendons of skeletal muscle. They are receptive to tension generated in the tendon during excessively strong muscle contractions, and action potentials are directed to the spinal cord by type Ib afferent nerves, where they synapse on an inhibitory interneuron, which then inhibits the respective Aα motor nerve(s).

muscle spindle the sensory receptor within skeletal muscle that is sensitive to static and dynamic changes in muscle length

alpha-gamma coactivation the interaction between alpha and gamma motor nerves and type I and II afferent nerves of skeletal muscle and muscle spindles that results in smooth and controlled dynamic muscle contractions

FIGURE 5.21

The skeletal muscle spindle. The muscle spindle is located parallel to the extrafusal fibers of a muscle. The spindle consists of several smaller, and relatively more specialized, intrafusal fibers which are encapsulated in a connective tissue sheath. As explained in the text, the differentiation between afferent and efferent nerve association in the intrafusal fibers is integral to the multiple functions of the spindle.

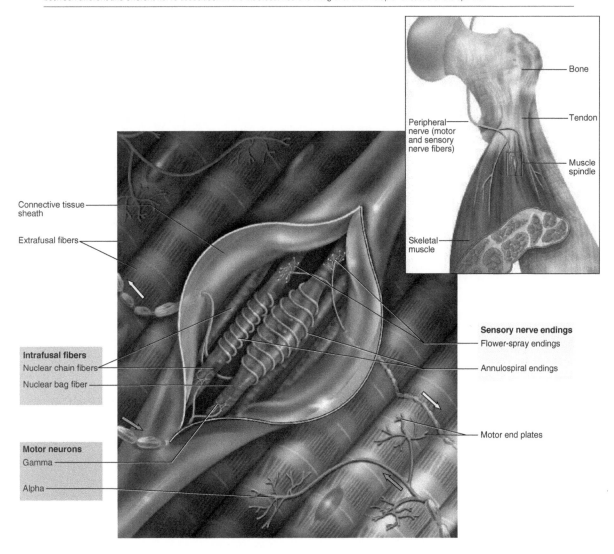

Research has documented the existence of other muscle afferents that are probably either special mechanoreceptors or receptors sensitive to metabolites from metabolism, or both. Muscle contraction is known to elicit increases in cardiovascular parameters, such as heart rate and blood pressure, and to increase ventilation. These afferent nerves are believed to be type III and IV nerves, and therefore have a slower conduction velocity compared to the Ia and Ib nerves of the spindle and golgi tendon organ (35). These added receptors provide evidence for the role of nerves in orchestrating extremely rapid multisystemic responses to muscle contraction, and therefore partially account for how the body can rapidly adapt to exercise stress.

Fundamentals of Sport and Exercise Science

Flexibility is an important and often overlooked component of physical fitness. The two types of flexibility are *static* and *dynamic*. Static flexibility concerns the range of motion about a joint, and is typically measured by devices that quantify the angular degrees of joint motion, such as a goniometer or a flexometer (fig. 5.22).

The flexibility of a joint is influenced by (1) bone structures, (2) muscle, (3) ligaments and tendons, and (4) skin. The bone and joint characteristics obviously set major limits to joint motion. However, within these limits, the soft tissue constraints are the most limiting to flexibility. For example, of the soft tissue structures, it has been estimated that the joint capsule provides 47% of the opposition to flexibility, with an additional 41% coming from muscle, 10% from tendons, and 2% from skin (42, 65).

Developing Flexibility

Given that the major constraints to flexibility involve soft tissue, there is potential to improve flexibility, as well as potential for flexibility to be further impaired by these structures. Unfortunately, most adults in the United States, as well as in other developed countries, have a high incidence of lower back pain caused primarily by a lack of flexibility on the muscles of the thigh, hamstrings, and gluteals. Flexibility is a component of fitness that should not be ignored, and requires training. Despite this importance, minimal research has been completed on training for flexibility.

The generic term for exercises performed to improve flexibility is *stretching*.

FIGURE 5.22

The Leighton flexometer.

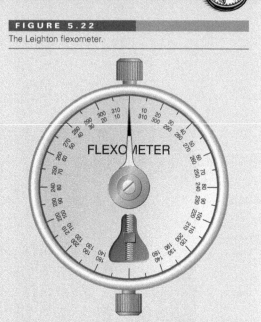

(Figure from Measurement in Physical Education, Fourth Edition, by Donald K. Mathews, copyright © 1973 by Saunders College Publishing, reprinted by permission of the publisher.)

Neuromuscular Adaptations to Exercise

The Metabolic Contribution of Muscle Fiber Types during Exercise

The dissimilar metabolic capacities of muscle fibers from different motor units, combined with the recruitment transition of slow- to fast-twitch motor units during increases in exercise intensity, emphasize the need to interpret metabolic changes during and following exercise relative to the specific contributions from specific types of muscle fibers. Because of these facts, the following sections are structured to present research on specific contributions of fiber type to muscle metabolism relative to the intensity of exercise and specific metabolic pathways.

Steady-State Exercise and Intense Exercise

Glycogenolysis   During exercise at intensities that can be sustained for periods of time in excess of 30 min, there is greater use of glycogen from SO compared to FG and FOG muscle fibers (30, 49, 69, 78). After 60 min of cycling at

43% VO_{2max}, muscle biopsy specimens revealed that SO muscle fibers contributed 80% of the change in muscle glycogen, with the remainder due to FOG fiber recruitment. The FOG contribution to glycogen breakdown increased at 61% VO_{2max}, and at 91% VO_{2max} glycogen breakdown continued to occur in SO and FOG fibers, and also in FG fibers (78). In similar research of muscle glycogen changes during an active recovery at 40% VO_{2max}, muscle glycogen increased in FOG and FG muscle fibers, which were presumably not recruited during the low-intensity exercise (57). Collectively, this evidence is used to indirectly indicate preferential recruitment of SO motor units during low-intensity long-duration exercise.

The previous evidence does not mean that fast-twitch motor units are never recruited during low-intensity exercises. As muscle glycogen is depleted from SO muscle fibers and exercise is continued, FOG and FG motor units are recruited to allow for continued activity (78). However, the level of motor skill often diminishes during these conditions

flexibility the range of motion about a joint

FIGURE 5.23

The proportions of ST and FT muscle fibers in elite athletes from different events. The more long term the activity, the greater the proportion of ST muscle fibers in select muscles of the athletes.

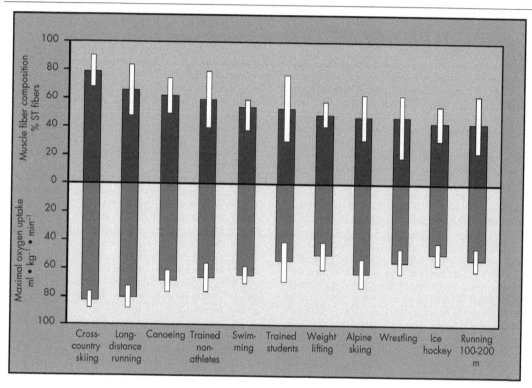

because the larger number of muscle fibers of the FOG and FG motor units decreases refinement in the gradations of contractile strength. In addition, as will be explained in chapter 6, decreases in muscle glycogen are associated with decreases in liver glycogen and blood glucose, which are conditions that invoke additional metabolic adaptations that decrease the ability to maintain relatively high steady-state exercise intensities.

Muscle Lactate Accumulation   As will be discussed in chapter 6, during prolonged steady-state exercise, where slow-twitch motor unit recruitment predominates, minimal lactate is produced (45). However, as exercise intensity increases above the lactate threshold (see chapter 6), lactate production increases. The cause for increased lactate production is partly due to the recruitment of fast-twitch glycolytic motor units (46).

Fiber Type and Exercise Performance

The metabolic and contractile differences between slow- and fast-twitch motor units can not only alter metabolic responses to exercise, but also influence exercise performance.

For elite athletes, where muscle metabolic capacities are highly developed, genetically determined motor unit proportions can limit the magnitude of training adaptations.

Long-Term Endurance Exercise

A summary of research on human muscle fiber type proportions in elite athletes from different activities is presented in figure 5.23. Based on this compilation of cross-sectional data, the elite athletes who are involved in long-term activities, such as distance running, cycling, or swimming, have predominantly SO muscle fibers in the muscles that contribute most to their respective exercise. Conversely, the proportion of FG and FOG muscle fibers predominate in athletes who have excelled in activities more reliant on muscle strength and power. These data are derived from genetically favored individuals and *should not be interpreted as evidence for muscle fiber type changes that are specific to the intensity and duration of exercise training* (see section entitled "Training Adaptations").

Experimental evidence exists to provide a mechanistic association between fiber type proportions and exercise performance. For example, a high SO proportion in muscle causes a high mitochondrial capacity, a high capacity for oxygen consumption (45), a high lactate threshold (see chapter 6), and superior distance running and cycling performance (20, 45).

Short-Term Intense Exercise

A high FG proportion in muscle is accompanied by the continued ability to generate power at increasing contraction velocities (34, 77), and superior performance in explosive activities (19, 22, 34). It has often been accepted that such a bias toward FG proportions would favor all types of intense exercise; however, research exists to question this. Collian-der and colleagues (19) investigated performance during three bouts of intense single-leg knee extensions performed at 180°/s, with each bout separated by 1 min of recovery. Individuals with high FG fiber type proportions generated greater *torque* than those with predominantly SO proportions during the first bout of contractions; however, torque was no different between groups for bouts two and three. Individuals with greater SO fiber type proportions in their vastus lateralis had greater metabolic recovery between bouts. The results indicated that when multiple bouts of intense exercise are to be performed, SO muscle fibers are important for allowing recovery between bouts. Conversely, individuals with greater FG fiber proportions will probably perform better during single bouts of intense exercise, or if they are allowed longer recovery intervals between successive bouts of intense exercise.

Training Adaptations

The following sections will focus on how exercise training affects the characteristics of muscle fibers that are important in distinguishing their classification as SO, FOG, and FG fiber types. These characteristics are central nervous system activation and neuromuscular function, fiber size and number, myosin ATPase and myosin isozyme content, and capillary density. Specific comment and reference to different exercise intensities will be provided in each section.

Fiber Size and Number

The increase in size, or more specifically the cross-sectional area, of muscle fibers is termed **hypertrophy**. In endurance-trained individuals, the size of the SO muscle fibers can be larger than either of the FOG or FG muscle fibers (29), with considerable variation in size within a fiber type in the same muscle (15). These findings indicate some degree of selective hypertrophy of muscle fibers from different motor units, and is presumably a result of an increased mitochondrial and membranous mass and increased muscle filaments within the fibers.

During more intense exercise, such as sprinting or weight lifting, muscle hypertrophy is greater than for endurance activities (17, 23). The fiber type hypertrophy is not as selec-

tive as for endurance exercise, because all motor unit types are recruited in these activities (53).

Animal research has indicated the potential for muscle fibers to split and form new fibers during intense training (4). Although there are various animal models, those involving voluntary exercise, and therefore most similar to human exercise, have repeatedly reported increases in muscle fiber numbers from 5 to 15% after long-term resistance training (> 10 weeks) (33, 73). The increase in the number of muscle fibers is termed **hyperplasia.** It is unclear whether hyperplasia occurs from the splitting of existing fibers or the generation of new fibers.

Although there is no experimental evidence for hyperplasia in human muscle following training for long-term muscular endurance, Antonio and Gonyea (4) have very meticulously detailed the large body of indirect evidence for hyperplasia. When entire muscles have been obtained postmortem, comparison between left and right tibialis anterior muscles from previously healthy men revealed a 10% difference in fiber numbers (68). Research that has compared muscle fiber areas between hypertrophied trained athletes and sedentary controls has revealed no difference in fiber areas, yet large differences in muscle size (2, 48, 70, 74, 75, 76). However, a similar body of research exists that has shown the muscle fiber hypertrophy can account for differences in muscle cross-sectional area between trained and untrained individuals (36, 54, 61, 68).

The generally accepted interpretation of these findings is that *muscle fiber hypertrophy accounts for the largest increases in muscle cross-sectional area,* with a small contribution that may occur from hyperplasia.

Central Nervous System Activation, Neuromuscular Function, and Muscular Strength

Generally speaking, maximal force development during muscle contractions (muscular strength) is proportional to the cross-sectional area of skeletal muscle. Consequently, training that increases muscle mass will increase muscular strength. However, research indicates that muscular strength is not just dependent on muscle mass, as the neural components of motor unit recruitment are also important. For example, during the initial weeks of a strength-training program, muscular strength increases, yet there is no evidence of muscle hypertrophy. Results from research using isokinetic training and electromyography indicate that such strength gains without changes in muscle size are because of alterations in motor unit recruitment (15, 22). Alterations in motor unit recruitment involve an

hypertrophy (hi-per'tro-fi) the increase in size of skeletal muscle due to the increased size of individual muscle fibers

hyperplasia (hi'per-pla'zi-ah) the increase in muscle fiber number in skeletal muscle

Making Paralyzed Muscle Contract Again

Individuals who suffer injury causing a complete break of their spinal cord experience many symptoms of impaired neuromuscular, cardiac, and pulmonary function. Additionally, the muscles that are now *deinnervated* from the injury experience severe wasting. Such wasting is aesthetically unappealing to the individual. However, despite a large loss of muscle, if the remaining muscle is retrained and used to assist in exercise, the risk for developing risk factors for coronary artery disease could decrease, resulting in improved health and quality of life.

Research has been conducted on the effects of artificial electrical stimulation on the paralyzed muscle of individuals with spinal cord injury (SCI).

Artificial Electrical Stimulation

Artificial electrical stimulation (AES) of skeletal muscle involves the placement of surface or needle electrodes on/in muscles of interest, and the stimulation of these muscles with a small electric current at predetermined intervals. This stimulation results in the synchronous contraction of all motor unit types, with the number of motor units recruited dependent on the strength (voltage) of the stimulation.

Researchers from Wayne State University in Detroit, Michigan, have further developed AES to enable individuals with complete spinal cord injury to perform cycle ergometry or walking by providing computer-controlled AES to several muscles. For example, correctly programmed AES to the quadraceps, hamstrings, and gluteal muscles can result in movement of the lower legs similar to voluntary cycling. Such use of AES has been termed computerized functional electrical stimulation (CFES) (fig. 5.24) and has enabled many individuals with complete spinal cord injury to once again experience the movement pattern of riding a bike.

Human Paralyzed Muscle Training by Electrical Stimulation

Deinnervated muscle eventually experiences a decrease in fiber number, and an unusually large fiber cross-sectional areas with inconsistent myosin ATPase staining. Paralyzed muscle also experiences an increase in fast-twitch fiber type expression (55). Collectively, these alterations decrease the contractile function and endurance of the muscle, as indicated by the minimal endurance and strength capabilities of paralyzed muscle when initially exposed to AES (47).

AES and CFES have been shown to increase the endurance capacity of paralyzed muscle (47). When AES is used as a means of exercise training, there is an increase in slow-twitch muscle fiber type expression toward normal values, and associated increases in mitochondrial enzyme activity

(55). In addition, if multiple muscles are stimulated and therefore the muscle mass stimulated is large, there is a considerable production of lactate that can raise systemic blood lactate concentrations above 4 mmol/L—even for extremely low exercise intensities (47).

Initial application of AES to paralyzed muscle causes muscle fatigue and contractile failure within as little as 1 min, with the fatigue probably due to neuromuscular or intramuscular electrochemical impairment. However, when an individual with SCI is trained by CFES, muscle endurance increases dramatically, as does the person's ability to increase his or her peak heart rate and VO_2 during exercise (47).

FIGURE 5.24

An individual with spinal cord injury receiving computerized functional electrical stimulation (CFES) that enables her to perform cycle ergometry.

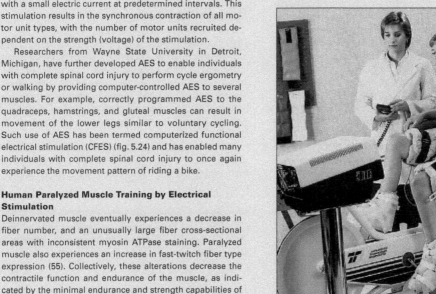

increase in the number of motor units recruited and the stimulation of these motor units in a manner such that more are stimulated at the same time (more synchronous) (15, 22, 77).

The neural component of muscular strength is important because it explains why some individuals can generate large contractile forces without large muscles and, as previously explained, accounts for the initial strength gains during resistance training. Furthermore, the training findings indicate that the central nervous system can be trained to improve function (motor unit recruitment).

Research has also addressed the best way to train to optimize muscle strength gains. Greatest strength gains result from training using concentric and eccentric muscle actions (24, 37). It remains unclear why an eccentric component is needed to optimize muscular strength during concentric contractions. However, is has been theorized that the microscopic damage to skeletal muscle that occurs during the eccentric phases might further increase the cellular stimulus for muscular hypertrophy.

Myosin ATPase and Myosin Structures

Animal research has clearly documented the importance of neural activation and muscle contraction as determinants of the altered expression of myosin and myosin ATPase in skeletal muscle fiber types. Both nerve cross reinnervation and artificial electrical stimulation of motor nerves have been shown to reverse the metabolic and contractile profiles of muscle fibers (64). Connecting muscle fibers to an opposite motor nerve, or stimulating a nerve in the opposite frequency and intensity, converts the muscle fibers to reflect the characteristics of the muscle normally innervated by the nerve and stimulation profile (64). However, these interventions are extreme and not reflective of voluntary activation of human motor units in patterns that reflect low-intensity or high-intensity muscle contractions.

In humans, exercise training for improvement in long-term muscular endurance, strength, or power lifting causes changes in the genetic expression of myosin ATPase, certain structural components of the myosin molecule (heavy and light chains), and the contractile function of myosin in select populations of muscle fibers (1). These changes result in altered contractile function that favor the specific demand of training. However, in human voluntary exercise training, these changes do not alter the basic proportions of slow- and fast-twitch muscle fibers. Rather, the relative proportions of the FG and FOG fiber types change so that endurance training increases the proportion of FT fibers that stain as FOG fibers (decreased FG fibers), whereas pure strength training may either increase (71) or decrease (1, 5, 54, 55) the proportion of muscle fibers that stain as FG fibers (decreased FOG).

Capillary Density

Exercise training for long-term muscular endurance also increases the number of capillaries per cross-sectional area of muscle. As previously mentioned, Anderson (3) documented a selective increase in capillary density around SO muscle fibers in human muscle samples that have a heterogenous distribution of fiber types. Exercise training for long-term endurance further increases capillary density, thus providing more potential for blood flow to and from the contracting muscle fibers. As these new capillaries cannot be totally associated with only SO muscle fibers, this adaptation also provides a more oxygen-rich microenvironment to certain FG and FOG fibers, thus further supporting the potential for increased capacities for mitochondrial respiration in these fibers.

Disuse Atrophy

During detraining, muscle mitochondrial metabolic capacities are lost at a fast rate and those of glycolysis remain unchanged or increase slightly (51, 52). However, alterations in fiber type proportions require more severe disuse, like forced bed rest and immobilization of a limb (e.g., limb casts) (52), or deinnervation (e.g., spinal cord injury) (53) (Up Close 5.4). Generally, there is a shift in fiber type from SO to FOG to FG; however, the shift is not consistent in all muscles that are affected by the intervention (64, 72). Increased activity can reverse this **atrophy** response, even by artificial electrical stimulation of the immoblized muscle(s) (55).

> **atrophy (a-tro′fi)** the degeneration of muscle, often resulting in a decrease in size and functional capacities

SUMMARY

- **Nerves,** like all excitable tissues, can generate a rapid change in their membrane potential, called an **action potential.** Action potentials are conducted along the **axon** of a nerve, and are transmitted from one nerve to another, or from a nerve to a target tissue/organ via a **synapse.**

- Almost all the synapses of the body function by releasing a chemical substance from the *presynaptic membrane* that diffuses across the space between nerves, or *synaptic cleft,* where the chemical binds to special **receptors** on the *postsynaptic membrane.* Such chemicals are called **neurotransmitters.** All synapses function unidirectionally.

- All the components of the motor control regions of the brain operate together in a complex manner that results in the controlled and precisely orchestrated series of action potentials that are propagated from the **motor cortex** or other regions to the appropriate Aα motor nerves of the spinal cord. The distribution of Aα motor nerves down the spinal cord is somewhat organized into a *segmental distribution.* The Aα motor nerves leave the spinal cord at a vertebral level that reflects the anatomical position of the skeletal muscle.

- As for the synapse, the function of the **neuromuscular junction** is to transmit the action potential across a synaptic cleft. Unlike the synapse, the postsynaptic membrane is not a nerve but the sarcolemma of a skeletal muscle fiber.

- The individual cells in each muscle type are referred to as **muscle fibers,** and the specialized excitable cell membrane of skeletal muscle fibers is called the **sarcolemma.** Striated muscle proteins are organized into subcellular structures called **myofibrils,** which extend along the length of the muscle fiber. The myofibrils are aligned beside each other resulting in a similar three-dimensional pattern of the contractile proteins within the entire fiber. Within a myofibril, the contractile proteins are arranged in units called **sarcomeres.**

- The contractile proteins of the myofibrils differ in structure and function. **Myosin** is the largest of the proteins, is a two-stranded helical structure, and consists of two forms of myosin (light and heavy). In vivo the two heavy chains contain a hinged region, a linear end region, and two globular heads (S_1 units) at one end. The S_1 units contain the enzyme myosin ATPase. The activity of myosin ATPase is believed to be influenced by the myosin light chains. **Actin** is a globular protein (G-actin); however, in vivo it aggregates to form a two-stranded helical structure (F-actin). Associated with the F-actin is a rod-shaped molecule called **tropomyosin,** which exists as multiple strands, each of which associates with six or seven G-actin molecules along the length of the F-actin. At the end of each tropomyosin molecule is bound a **troponin** molecule, which is involved in the regulation of skeletal muscle contraction.

- The muscle fibers and the Aα motor nerve that innervates them comprise what is called a **motor unit.** When stimulated, a motor unit responds by contracting maximally. Therefore, *the motor unit is the functional unit of muscle contraction.* Contraction of a skeletal muscle results from the combined contraction of many motor units.

- Skeletal muscle can contract in a variety of ways. Contractions causing a change in muscle length are called *isotonic* contractions. When the muscle length shortens, the isotonic contraction is referred to as a **concentric** contraction. When the muscle length increases during contraction, the isotonic contraction is referred to as **eccentric.** Muscle contractions causing no change in muscle length are called **isometric** contractions. **Isokinetic** contractions are a special type of concentric contraction, where the velocity of muscle shortening remains constant (hence the term *isokinetic*).

- The long contraction time and short stimulation time of skeletal muscle motor units provide opportunity for additional neural stimulation prior to the complete relaxation

of the muscle or motor unit. In these circumstances, the force of the total muscle or motor unit twitch can increase with increased stimulation frequency and is called *summation.* As stimulation frequency increases, twitch tension also increases until a smooth maximal tension is reached, which is called *tetanus.*

- The earlier attainment of a threshold membrane potential of the soma of the nerve of an SO motor unit than of either an FOG or FG motor unit results in a recruitment order of motor units. *SO motor units are recruited first during incremental exercise, followed by a progressive increase in FOG and FG motor unit recruitment as exercise intensity increases.* This pattern of recruitment has been termed the *size principle,* and causes SO motor units to be recruited predominantly during low to moderate exercise intensities, and SO, FOG, and FG motor units to be recruited during exercise requiring intense contractions against high resistance or fast muscle contractions.

- **Electromyography (EMG)** is the study of muscle function from the detection of electrical activity emanating from the depolarization of nerves and muscle membranes that accompany contraction. The electrical activity is detected by the placement of one or more electrodes over the contracting muscle(s) of interest.

- The contractile force of muscle within the different motor units increases in a progression from SO, to FOG, to FG motor units, and the duration of the contraction decreases in the progression from SO, to FOG, to FG motor units. Contractile velocity of motor units is determined by the conduction velocity of the Aα motor nerves and the type of myosin proteins and mysoin ATPase enzyme within the muscle fibers.

- Skeletal muscle fibers from SO motor units have a high oxidative capacity. In other words, they possess relatively high concentrations of myoglobin, high mitochondrial membrane density, and therefore relatively high concentrations of the enzymes of the TCA cycle, β-oxidation, and electron transport chain. The added myoglobin and mitochondria of SO muscle compared to FG muscle are the reasons for the "red" appearance and "white" appearance of the respective muscle types. Muscle fibers from FOG motor units have moderate concentrations of these molecules and enzymes, with muscle from FG motor units having the lowest concentrations.

- The differences in biochemical capacities and myosin ATPase pH stability among the muscle fibers of differing motor units have enabled histochemical methods to become predominantly used to determine motor unit proportions in human **muscle biopsy** samples from skeletal muscle. However, as the myosin ATPase histochemical procedure involves only the muscle fiber component of the motor unit, the term **fiber type** has often replaced the more correct expressions SO, FOG, and FG motor unit proportions.

▪ The main skeletal muscle receptor is the **muscle spindle,** which continually *allows neural information to be relayed back to the CNS of muscle stretch, muscle length, and the rate of change in muscle length.* These functions are a result of the anatomical arrangement between afferent and efferent nerves and the components of the muscle spindle. When Aα nerves are stimulated, γ nerves are also stimulated so that the change in length of the intrafusal fibers matches that of the extrafusal fibers. This process is called **alpha-gamma coactivation,** and allows the spindle to be at near-optimal sensitivity regardless of the changing length of the extrafusal muscle fibers.

▪ During exercise at intensities that can be sustained for periods of time in excess of 30 min, there is greater use of glycogen from SO compared to FG and FOG muscle fibers. As muscle glycogen is depleted from SO muscle fibers and exercise is continued, FOG and FG motor units are recruited to allow for continued activity. During low-intensity exercise, where slow-twitch motor unit recruitment predominates, minimal lactate is produced.

▪ The increase in size, or more specifically the cross-sectional area, of muscle fibers is termed **hypertrophy.** The increase in the number of muscle fibers is termed **hyperplasia.** It is unclear whether hyperplasia occurs from the splitting of existing fibers or the generation of new fibers. *Muscle fiber hypertrophy accounts for the largest increases in muscle cross-sectional area,* with a small contribution that may occur from hyperplasia. Disuse of skeletal muscle causes a decrease, or **atrophy,** of muscle.

▪ In humans, exercise training for improvement in long-term muscular endurance, strength, or power lifting results in altered contractile function that favors the specific demands of training. However, in human voluntary exercise training, *these changes do not alter the basic proportions of slow- and fast-twitch muscle fibers.* Rather, endurance training increases the proportion of FT muscle that stains as FOG fibers, whereas strength/power training increases the proportion of muscle fibers that stain as FG fibers.

STUDY QUESTIONS

1. How can the nervous system be divided based on both structure and function?

2. Detail and sequence the molecular events of skeletal and cardiac muscle contraction.

3. Explain the differences among concentric, eccentric, and isokinetic muscle contractions.

4. How does the velocity of skeletal muscle contraction affect force and power development?

5. What are the functions of the muscle spindle?

6. What is a motor unit, how many different types are there, and how do they differ within and between different muscles of the body?

7. What is a fiber type, and how are they determined in research?

8. What is electromyography, and how has it been used in exercise-related research?

9. Can extremes in fiber type proportions influence an individual's potential for success in given types of exercise or sports competition? Explain.

10. What are the changes in muscle fiber type proportions that one should expect from training for either endurance or muscular power?

11. When muscles increase in cross-sectional area, is the increase due to hypertrophy or hyperplasia?

12. What muscle fiber changes occur during severe disuse, like that of immobilization of a limb or deinnervation?

APPLICATIONS

1. During episodes of skeletal muscle cramp, relief is often promoted by immediate massage and the stretching of the muscle. Propose explanations for why these immediate treatment modalities might be effective.

2. Why do electrolyte imbalances in blood (Na^+, K^+, Ca^{++}) impair the ability of muscle to respond appropriately to neural stimulation?

3. How might the preferential decrease in muscle glycogen from SO muscle fibers influence performance during exercise lasting in excess of 2 h?

4. How would you recommend that people train to increase flexibility?

REFERENCES

1. Abernethy, P. J., J. Jurimae, P. A. Logan, A. W. Taylor, and R. E. Thayer. Acute and chronic response of skeletal muscle to resistance exercise. *Sports Medicine* 17(1):22–38, 1994.

2. Alway, S. E., W. H. Grumbt, J. Stray-Gundersen, and W. J. Gonyea. Effects of resistance training on elbow flexors of highly competitive bodybuilders. *J. Appl. Physiol.* 72(4):1512–1521, 1992.

3. Anderson, P. Capillary density in skeletal muscle of man. *Acta Physiol. Scand.* 95:203–205, 1975.

4. Antonio, J. A., and W. J. Gonyea. Skeletal muscle fiber hyperplasia. *Med. Sci. Sports Exerc.* 25(12):1333–1345, 1993.

5. Baldwin, K. M., G. H. Klinkerfuss, R. L. Terjung, P. A. Mole, and J. O. Holloszy. Respiratory capacity of white, red, and intermediate muscle: Adaptive response to exercise. *Am. J. Physiol.* 222:373–378, 1972.

6. Bandy W. D., J. M. Iron, and M. Briggler. The effect of stretch and dynamic range of motion training on the flexibility of the hamstring muscles. *J. Orthop. Sports Phys. Ther.* 27(4):295–300, 1998.

7. Basmajian, J. V., and C. J. DeLuca. *Muscles alive: Their functions revealed by electromyography,* 5th ed. Williams & Wilkins, Baltimore, 1985.

8. Berne, R. M., and M. N. Levy. *Physiology,* 3d ed. Mosby-Year Book, St. Louis, 1993.

9. Brooke, M. H., and K. Kaiser. Three "myosin adenosine triphosphatase" systems: The nature of their pH lability and sulfhydryl dependence. *J. Histochem. Cytochem.* 18:670–672, 1970.

10. Burke, R. E. Firing patterns of gastrocnemius motor units in the decerebrate cat. *J. Physiol.* 196:631–654, 1968.

11. Burke, R. E., D. N. Levine, P. Tsairis, and F. E. Zajac. Physiological types and histochemical profiles in motor units of the cat gastrocnemius. *J. Physiol. London* 234:723–748, 1973.

12. Burke, R. E., and V. R. Edgerton. Motor unit properties and selective involvement in movement. *Exerc. Sport Sci. Rev.* 3:31–81, 1975.

13. Burke, R. E. Motor units: Anatomy, physiology and functional organization. In V. B. Brooks (ed.), *Handbook of physiology: The nervous system,* Sec. 1, Vol. 11. The American Physiological Society, Bethesda, MD, 1981, pp. 345–422.

14. Byrnes, W. C., P. M. Clarkson, J. Spencer White, S. S. Hsieh, P. N. Frykman, and R. J. Maughan. Delayed onset muscle soreness following repeated bouts of downhill running. *J. Appl. Physiol.* 59:710–715, 1985.

15. Caiozzo, V. J., J. J. Perrine, and V. R. Edgerton. Training-induced alterations of the in vivo force-velocity relationship of human muscle. *J. Appl. Physiol.* 51(3):750–754, 1981.

16. Chi, M. M.-Y., et al. Effects of detraining on enzymes of energy metabolism in individual human muscle fibers. *Am. J. Physiol.* 244:C276–C287, 1983.

17. Clarke, D. H. Adaptations in strength and muscular endurance resulting from exercise. *Exerc. Sports Sci. Rev.* 1:73–102, 1973.

18. Clarkson, P. M., and I. Tremblay. Exercise-induced muscle damage, repair and adaptation in humans. *J. Appl. Physiol.* 65(1):1–6, 1988.

19. Collainder, E. B., G. A. Dudley, and P. A. Tesch. Skeletal muscle fiber composition and performance during repeated bouts of maximal, concentric contractions. *Eur. J. Appl. Physiol.* 58:81–86, 1988.

20. Costill, D. L., W. J. Fink, and M. L. Pollock. Muscle fiber composition and enzyme activities of elite distance runners. *Med. Sci. Sports Exerc.* 8(2):96–100, 1976.

21. Costill, D. L., D. D. Pascoe, W. J. Fink, R. A. Robergs, and S. I. Barr. Muscle glycogen resynthesis after eccentric exercise. *J. Appl. Physiol.* 69:46–50, 1990.

22. Coyle, E. F., et al. Specificity of power improvements through slow and fast isokinetic training. *J. Appl. Physiol.* 51(6):1437–1442, 1981.

23. Dons, B., K. Bollerup, F. Bonde-Petersen, and S. Hancke. The effect of weight lifting exercise related to muscle fiber composition and muscle cross-sectional area in humans. *Eur. J. Appl. Physiol.* 40:95–106, 1979.

24. Dudley, G. A., P. A. Tesch, B. J. Miller, and P. Buchanan. Importance of eccentric actions in performance adaptations to resistance training. *Aviation Space Environ. Med.* 62:543–550, 1991.

25. Essen, B., E. Jansson, J. Henriksson, A. W. Taylor, and B. Saltin. Metabolic characteristics of fiber types in human skeletal muscle. *Acta Physiol. Scand.* 95:153–165, 1975.

26. Evans, W. J., S. J. Phinney, and V. R. Young. Suction applied to muscle biopsy maximizes sample size. *Med. Sci. Sports Exerc.* 14:101–102, 1982.

27. Freund, H. J. Motor unit and muscle activity in voluntary motor control. *Physiol. Rev.* 63:387–436, 1983.

28. Garfinkel, S., and E. Cafarelli. Relative changes in maximal force, EMG, and muscle cross-sectional area after isometric training. *Med. Sci. Sports Exerc.* 24(11):1220–1227, 1992.

29. Gollnick, P. D., R. B. Armstrong, C. W. Saubert, K. Piehl, and B. Saltin. Enzyme activity and fiber composition in skeletal muscle of untrained and trained men. *J. Appl. Physiol.* 33(3):312–319, 1972.

30. Gollnick, P. D., K. Piehl, and B. Saltin. Selective glycogen depletion pattern in human skeletal muscle fibers after exercise of varying intensity and at varying pedal rates. *J. Physiol.* 241:45–57, 1974.

31. Gollnick, P. D., M. Reidy, J. J. Quintinskie, and L. A. Bertocci. Differences in metabolic potential of skeletal muscle fibers and their significance for metabolic control. *J. Exp. Biol.* 115:91–199, 1985.

32. Gollnick, P. D., and R. D. Hodgson. The identification of fiber types in human skeletal muscle: A continual dilemma. *Exercise. Sport Sciences Reviews.* 14:81–104, 1986.

33. Gonyea, W. J., D. G. Sale, F. B. Gonyea, and A. Mikesky. Exercise-induced increases in muscle fiber number. *Eur. J. Appl. Physiol.* 55:137–141, 1986.

34. Gregor, R. J., V. R. Edgerton, J. J. Perrine, D. S. Campion, and C. DeBus. Torque-velocity relationships and muscle fiber composition in elite female athletes. *J. Appl. Physiol.* 47(2):388–392, 1979.

35. Guyton, A. C. *Textbook of medical physiology,* 8th ed. Saunders, Philadelphia, 1991, chap. 8, pp. 87–95.

36. Haggmark, T., E. Jansson, and B. Svane. Cross-sectional area of the thigh muscle in man measured by computed tomography. *Scn. J. Clin. Lab. Invest.* 38:355–360, 1978.

37. Hather, B. M., P. A. Tesch, P. Buchanan, and G. A. Dudley. Influence of eccentric actions on skeletal muscle adaptations to resistance training. *Acta Physiol. Scand.* 143:177–185, 1991.

38. Henneman, E., G. Somjen, and D. O. Carpenter. Functional significance of cell size in spinal motor neurons. *J. Neurophysiol.* 28:560–580, 1965.

39. Henneman, E., G. Somjen, and D. O. Carpenter. Excitability and inhibitability of motor neurons of different sizes. *J. Neurophysiol.* 28:599–620, 1965.

40. Henneman, E., and L. M. Mendell. Functional organization of motorneurone pool and its inputs. In V. B. Brooks (ed.), *Handbook of physiology: The nervous system,* Sec. 1, Vol. 11. The American Physiological Society, Bethesda, MD, 1981, pp. 345–422.

41. Hortobagyi, T., and T. Denaham. Variability in creatine kinase: Methodological, exercise, and clinically related factors. *Int. J. Sports Med.* 10:69–80, 1989.

42. Hortobagyi T., J. Faludi, J. Tihanyi, and B. Merkely. Effects of intense "stretching": flexibility training on the mechanical profile of the knee extensors and on the range of motion of the hip joint. *Int. J. Sports Med.* 6(6):317–321, 1985.

43. Huxley, H. E. Molecular basis of contraction in cross-striated muscle. In G. H. Bourke (ed.), *The structure and function of muscle,* Vol. 1, Part 1. Academic Press, New York, 1972, pp. 302–388.

44. Ishikawa, H., H. Sawada, and E. Yamada. Surface and internal morphology of skeletal muscle. In L. D. Peachey, R. H. Adrian, and S. R. Geiger (eds.), *Handbook of physiology: Sec. 10, Skeletal muscle.* American Physiological Society, Bethesda, MD, 1983, pp. 1–22.

45. Ivy, J. L., R. T. Withers, P. J. Van Handel, D. H. Elger, and D. L. Costill. Muscle respiratory capacity and fiber type as determinants of the lactate threshold. *J. Appl. Physiol.* 48(3):523–527, 1980.

46. Ivy, J. L., M.M.-Y Chi, C. S. Hintz, W. M. Sherman, R. P. Hellendall, and O. H. Lowry. Progressive metabolite changes in individual human muscle fibers with increasing work rates. *Am. J. Physiol.* 252(21):C630–C639, 1987.

47. Kraus, J., et al. Cardiorespiratory effects of computerized functional electrical stimulation (CFES) and hybrid training in individuals with spinal cord injury. *Med. Sci. Sports Exerc.* 25(9):1054–1061, 1993.

48. Larsson, L., and P. A. Tesch. Motor unit fiber density in extremely hypertrophied skeletal muscles in man. *Eur. J. Appl. Physiol.* 55:130–136, 1986.

49. Lesmes, G. R., D. W. Benham, D. L. Costill, and W. J. Fink. Glycogen utilization in fast- and slow-twitch muscle fibers during maximal isokinetic exercise. *Ann. Sports Med.* 1:105–108, 1983.

50. Lowey, S., and D. Risby. Light chains from fast and slow muscle myosins. *Nature* 234:81–85, 1971.

51. MacDougall, J. D., G. R. Ward, D. G. Sale, and J. R. Sutton. Biochemical adaptation of human skeletal muscle to heavy resistance training and immobilization. *J. Appl. Physiol.* 43:700–703, 1977.

52. MacDougall, J. D., E. C. B. Elder, D. G. Sale, J. R. Moroz, and J. R. Sutton. Effects of strength training and immobilization on human muscle fibers. *Eur. J. Appl. Physiol.* 43:25–34, 1980.

53. MacDougall, J. D., D. G. Sale, E. C. B. Elder, and J. R. Sutton. Muscle ultrastructural characteristics of elite power lifters and body builders. *Eur. J. Appl. Physiol.* 48:117–126, 1982.

54. MacDougall, J. D., D. G. Sale, S. E. Elway, and J. R. Sutton. Muscle fiber number in biceps brachia in body builders and control subjects. *J. Appl. Physiol.* 57:1399–1403, 1984.

55. Martin, T. P., R. B. Stein, P. H. Hoeppner, and D. C. Reid. Influence of electrical stimulation on the morphological and metabolic properties of paralyzed muscle. *J. Appl. Physiol.* 72(4):1401–1406, 1992.

56. Narici, M., G. Roi, L. Landoni, M. Minetti, and P. Cerretelli. Changes in force, cross-sectional area, and neural activation during strength training and detraining of the human quadriceps. *Eur. J. Appl. Physiol.* 59:310–319, 1989.

57. Nordheim, K., and N. K. Vollestad. Glycogen and lactate metabolism during low-intensity exercise in man. *Acta Physiol. Scand.* 139:475–484, 1990.

58. Pate, E., and R. Cooke. A model of crossbridge action: The effects of ATP, ADP, and Pi. *J. Muscle Res. Cell Motility* 10:181–196, 1989.

59. Peter, J. B., R. J. Barnard, V. R. Edgerton, C. A. Gillespie, and K. E. Stempel. Metabolic profiles of three types of skeletal muscle in guinea pigs and rabbits. *Biochemistry* 11:2627–2633, 1972.

60. Pette, D., and R. S. Staron. Cellular and molecular diversities of mammalian skeletal muscle fibers. *Rev. Physiol. Biochem. Pharmacol.* 116:2–76, 1990.

61. Prince, F. P., R. S. Hikida, and F. C. Hagerman. Human muscle fiber types in power lifters, distance runners and untrained subjects. *Pflugers Archives* 363:19–26, 1976.

62. Raven, P. B. Editorial. *Med. Sci. Sports Exerc.* 23(7):777–778, 1991.

63. Robergs, R. A., et al. Muscle glycogenolysis during differing intensities of weight-resistance exercise. *J. Appl. Physiol.* 70(4):1700–1706, 1991.

64. Roy, R. R., K. M. Baldwin, and V. R. Edgerton. The plasticity of skeletal muscle: Effects of neuromuscular activity. *Exercise and Sport Sciences Reviews* 19:269–312, 1991.

65. Sady, S. P., M. Wortman, and M. Blanke. Flexibility training: Ballistic, static or proprioceptive neuromuscular facilitation? *Arch. Phys. Med. Rehabil.* 63(6):261–263, 1982.

66. Saltin, B., J. Henriksson, E. Nygaard, and P. Anderson. Fiber types and metabolic potentials of skeletal muscles in sedentary man and endurance runners. *Annals New York Acad. of Sci.* 301:3–29, 1977.

67. Saltin, B., and P. D. Gollnick. Skeletal muscle adaptability: Significance for metabolism and performance. In *Handbook of physiology: Sec. 10, Skeletal muscle.* American Physiological Society, Bethesda, MD, 1983, pp. 555–631.

68. Schantz, P., E. Randall Fox, P. Norgen, and A. Tyden. The relationship between muscle fiber area and the muscle cross-sectional area of the thigh in subjects with large differences in thigh girth. *Acta Physiol. Scand.* 113:537–539, 1981.

69. Secher, N. H., and N. E. Jenssen. Glycogen depletion patterns in type I, IIA, and IIB muscle fibers during maximal voluntary static and dynamic exercise. *Acta Physiol. Scand.* (Suppl. 440):174–181, 1976.

70. Sjostrom, M., J. Lexell, A. Eriksson, and C. C. Taylor. Evidence of fiber hyperplasia in human skeletal muscles from healthy young men? *Eur. J. Appl. Physiol.* 62:301–304, 1992.

71. Staron, R. S., E. S. Malicky, M. J. Leonardi, J. E. Falkel, F. C. Hagerman, and G. A. Dudley. Muscle hypertrophy and fast fiber type conversions in heavy resistance-trained women. *Eur. J. Appl. Physiol.* 60:71–79, 1990.

72. Stephens, J. A., and T. P. Usherwood. The mechanical properties of human motor units with special reference to their fatigabililty and recruitment threshold. *Brain Research* 125:91–97, 1977.

73. Tamaki, T., S. Uchiyama, and S. Nakano. A weight-lifting exercise model for inducing hypertrophy in the hindlimb muscles of rats. *Med. Sci. Sports Exerc.* 24:881–886, 1992.

74. Tesch, P. A., A. Thorsson, and P. Kaiser. Muscle capillary supply and fiber type characteristics in weight and power lifters. *J. Appl. Physiol.* 56(1):35–38, 1984.

75. Tesch, P. A., and L. Larsson. Muscle hypertrophy in body builders. *Eur. J. Appl. Physiol.* 49:301–306, 1984.

76. Tesch, P. A., A. Thorsson, and P. Kaiser. Muscle capillary supply and fiber type characteristics in weight and power lifters. *J. Appl. Physiol.* 56(1):35–38, 1984.

77. Thorstensson, A., G. Grimby, and J. Karlsson. Force-velocity relations and fiber composition in human knee extensor muscles. *J. Appl. Physiol.* 40(1):12–16, 1976.

78. Vollestad, N. K., O. Vaage, and L. Hermansen. Muscle glycogen depletion pattern in type I and subgroups of type II fibers during prolonged severe exercise. *Acta Physiol. Scand.* 122:433–440, 1984.

79. Vollestad, N. K., and P. C. S. Blom. Effect of varying exercise intensity on glycogen depletion in human muscle fibers. *Acta Physiol. Scand.* 125:395–405, 1985.

80. Vollestad, N. K., P. C. S. Blom, and O. Gronnerod. Resynthesis of glycogen in different muscle fiber types after prolonged exhaustive exercise in man. *Acta Physiol. Scand.* 137:15–21, 1989.

81. Wang, K. Sarcomere-associate cytoskeletal lattices in striated muscle. In J.W. Shay (ed.), *Cell muscle motility,* Vol. 6. Plenum, New York, 1985, pp. 315–369.

82. Westing, S. H., and Y. Segar. Eccentric and concentric torque-velocity characteristics, torque output comparisons and gravity effect torque corrections for quadriceps and hamstring muscles in females. *Int. J. Sports Med.* 10:175–180, 1989.

RECOMMENDED READINGS

Antonio, J. A., and W. J. Gonyea. Skeletal muscle fiber hyperplasia. *Med. Sci. Sports Exerc.* 25(12):1333–1345, 1993.

Clarkson, P. M., and I. Tremblay. Exercise-induced muscle damage, repair and adaptation in humans. *J. Appl. Physiol.* 65(1):1–6, 1988.

Coyle, E. F., et al. Specificity of power improvements through slow and fast isokinetic training. *J. Appl. Physiol.* 51(6):1437–1442, 1981.

Gollnick, P. D., and R. D. Hodgson. The identification of fiber types in human skeletal muscle: A continual dilemma. *Exec. Sport Sci. Rev.* 14:81–104, 1986.

Gollnick, P. D., M. Reidy, J. J. Quintinskie, and L. A. Bertocci. Differences in metabolic potential of skeletal muscle fibers and their significance for metabolic control. *J. Exp. Biol.* 115:91–199, 1985.

Hortobagyi, T., and T. Denaham. Variability in creatine kinase: Methodological, exercise, and clinically related factors. *Int. J. Sports Med.* 10:69–80, 1989.

Kraus, J., et al. Cardiorespiratory effects of computerized functional electrical stimulation (CFES) and hybrid training in individuals with spinal cord injury. *Med. Sci. Sports Exerc.* 25(9):1054–1061, 1993.

Martin, T. P., R. B. Stein, P. H. Hoeppner, and D. C. Reid. Influence of electrical stimulation on the morphological and metabolic properties of paralyzed muscle. *J. Appl. Physiol.* 72(4):1401–1406, 1992.

Peter, J. B., R. J. Barnard, V. R. Edgerton, C. A. Gillespie, and K. E. Stempel. Metabolic profiles of three types of skeletal muscle in guinea pigs and rabbits. *Biochemistry* 11:2627–2633, 1972.

Thorstensson, A., G. Grimby, and J. Karlsson. Force-velocity relations and fiber composition in human knee extensor muscles. *J. Appl. Physiol.* 40(1):12–16, 1976.

Vollestad, N. K., O. Vaage, and L. Hermansen. Muscle glycogen depletion pattern in type I and subgroups of type II fibers during prolonged severe exercise. *Acta Physiol. Scand.* 122:433–440, 1984.

CHAPTER 7

Cardiovascular Function and Adaptation to Exercise

ach day, everyone partici- pates in some type of physical activity. For some, this may mean making their bed or preparing meals. For others, this might entail high-intensity exertion, such as running a 1500-m race. Common to all activities is the involvement of the cardiovas- cular system. The cardiovascular responses that take place can be brief and "relatively" mi- nor, such as an increase in heart rate as one stands up from sitting in a chair and walks from one room to another. Alternately, cardio- vascular responses can be quite complex, to the extent that blood flow during intense mountain biking is increased and preferentially directed toward the more metabolically active skeletal muscles. In the latter example, the car- diovascular system plays an important role in helping transfer oxygen from room air to the active muscle cells. It also helps transfer the heat generated in the muscle to the external environment. Because the cardiovascular sys- tem is integral in the regulation of blood oxy- gen transport, body temperature, fluid balance, and blood pressure, and exercise alters each of these functions, the cardiovascular responses to exercise represent a crucial body of knowl- edge in exercise physiology. The purpose of this chapter is to briefly outline the compo- nents of the cardiovascular system, explain the regulation of cardiovascular function during exercise, and detail the acute and chronic adaptations of cardiovascular structure and function to exercise.

OBJECTIVES

After studying this chapter, you should be able to:

- List the components of the cardiovascular system.
- Describe the diverse functions of blood and its importance to the optimal function of the cardiovascular system.
- Identify approximate volumes of blood and plasma and their relationships to fitness and body mass.
- Identify the changes that occur for cardiac output, stroke volume, and heart rate during different exercise conditions.
- List the several factors that regulate blood flow to skeletal muscle.
- Explain how cardiovascular structure and function changes in response to endurance and strength training.

KEY TERMS

cardiovascular system	osmolality	Fick equation
systemic circulation	chronotropic	vasoconstriction
	cardiac cycle	vasodilation
blood	stroke volume	hemoconcentration
hematocrit	preload	hyperemia
anemia	inotropic	cardiovascular drift
polycythemia	ejection fraction	blood pressure
erythrocytes	cardiac output	Korotkoff sounds

Components of the Cardiovascular System

Anatomical and functional aspects of the heart are referred to as *cardiac*, whereas the anatomical and functional aspects of the circulation of blood are referred to as *vascular*, hence the term *cardiovascular*. The **cardiovascular system** (or *circulatory system*) is composed of blood, the heart, and the blood vessels (i.e., vasculature) within which blood is pumped throughout the body. The heart is a biological pump that generates the pressure needed to drive blood throughout the vasculature. Within the cardiovascular system exists the *pulmonary circulation* of the lungs, and the **systemic circulation** for the remainder of the body. Within the systemic circulation are local circulation beds, such as the head and brain (*cranial* circulation), liver (*hepatic* circulation), kidney (*renal* circulation), abdominal viscera and intestinal tract (*splanchnic* circulation), skin (*cutaneous* circulation), and *skeletal muscle* circulation. The combined function of the cardiovascular and pulmonary systems (chapter 8) is referred to as *cardiorespiratory* function.

This chapter reviews several of the components of the cardiovascular system, so that the full implications of cardiovascular function during exercise can be appreciated. Please note that a more detailed description of the blood supply and electrocardiographic (ECG) characteristics associated with the heart are provided in chapter 20.

Blood

Blood is the liquid medium that circulates within the vascular system. The blood volume of the average adult is ~5 L, or 8% of total body mass. Blood volume is greater for larger, more endurance trained and altitude-acclimated people. The increase in blood volume that occurs with training can approach 400–500 mL.

Blood can be divided into cellular and noncellular components, as illustrated in figure 7.1. The general functions of these components are presented in table 7.1.

It is clear that blood serves many functions, and that although the transport of O_2 and CO_2 is crucial to life, other functions of blood can be equally important during rest (e.g., immune functions) and certain exercise conditions (e.g., thermoregulation, water exchange).

Cellular Components

The cell content of blood (**hematocrit**) constitutes approximately 45% of the total blood volume. Hematocrit is lower in females than males, and will vary with hydration status. In **anemia** (figure 7.1), a condition where the number of red blood cells falls below normal, hematocrit may approach 24%. Causes of anemia might include an inadequate iron intake, excessive bleeding, or an exaggerated destruction of red blood cells. On the other hand, in the rare conditions

TABLE 7.1	
The main functions of the cellular and liquid components of blood	
COMPONENT	**FUNCTIONS**
Cellular	Transport of oxygen and carbon dioxide
	Blood clotting
	Acid-base buffering
	Immune functions
	Tissue repair and destruction
Liquid (plasma)	Blood clotting
	Circulation of cellular components and their contents
	Maintenance of blood pressure
	Heat transfer and thermoregulation
	Water exchange and transport
	Circulation of hormones
	Acid-base buffering
	Circulation of metabolites, nutrients, and waste products

associated with too many red blood cells (i.e., **polycythemia**), hematocrit may exceed 60%—a dangerously high level.

Blood consists of several types of cells which all emanate from a stem cell located in bone marrow. The original stem cell can differentiate into precursors of white blood cells *(leukocytes)*, red blood cells (**erythrocytes**), or cell fragments known as *platelets*. During the synthesis of erythrocytes *(erythropoiesis)*, the stem cell is differentiated into nucleated cells that synthesize hemoglobin. These cells are released into the circulation when they have lost their nucleus, and are then termed *reticulocytes*. The reticulocyte has remnants of RNA and continues to synthesize hemoglobin.

cardiovascular system the heart and blood vessels of the body

systemic circulation the vasculature of the body other than the pulmonary circulation

blood the fluid medium that contains cells that function to transport oxygen and carbon dioxide, cells involved in immunity, certain proteins involved in blood clotting and the transport of nutrients, and electrolytes necessary for optimal cell function

hematocrit (hem'a-to-krit) the ratio of the volume of blood cells and formed elements of blood to total blood volume; usually expressed as a percentage

anemia (a-ne'mi-ah) abnormally low erythrocyte content, hemoglobin concentration, or hematocrit of the blood

polycythemia (pol'i-si-the'mi-ah) above-normal increase in the erythrocyte content of the blood

erythrocyte (e-rith'ro-syt) red blood cell

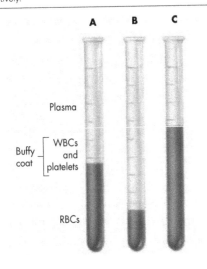

Plasma

Buffy coat ⎡ WBCs
            ⎢ and
            ⎣ platelets

RBCs

Hemoglobin is a complex molecule containing iron (heme) and protein (globin). Hemoglobin's affinity or ability to combine with O_2 is related to the heme component. Hemoglobin also assists with CO_2 transport and provides a buffering function for protons. The stimulation of erythropoiesis is under the control of the hormone *erythropoietin*, as will be discussed in chapter 9.

The shape of the erythrocyte resembles a biconcaved disk, with molecules of hemoglobin located on and inside the membrane surface of the cell. Erythrocytes have an average life span of 120 days, with the iron from the hemoglobin of destroyed erythrocytes recycled by the liver. This iron, along with the dietary iron, is transported in the blood bound to *transferrin* (iron-binding globulin). Iron can also be stored in plasma and certain tissues (heart, liver, spleen) as *ferritin*, which is a complex of water-soluble protein and reduced iron (ferrous hydroxide).

Liquid Component

The liquid component of blood is termed *plasma*. Plasma is the medium within which the blood cells, metabolites, hormones, and nutrients are circulated around the body, body heat and water are redistributed, and certain reactions occur. When blood is drawn from the body, the clotting process forms fibrinogen and the remaining fluid component of blood is termed *serum*.

Because plasma represents 55% of total blood volume [1.00 − 0.45 (hematocrit) = 0.55], it approximates a volume of 3 L in the average adult. Plasma volume varies in proportion with the lean body mass, more so than either of total body mass or even fitness (39). However, plasma volume is highly variable and changes very rapidly with alterations in posture, exercise, dehydration, and acute altitude exposure. For healthy young men (age range 18–35), plasma volume at seated rest can be estimated from the following equation (39). Unfortunately, an equation specific to females has not yet been produced.

7.1 $$PV = 0.042 (LBM) + 0.567$$

where

PV = plasma volume (L)

LBM = lean body mass (kg)

The presence of electrolytes (e.g. Na^+, Cl^-) and proteins in plasma generates an osmotic force to attract and retain water within the vessels of the cardiovascular system. This osmotic force is best reflected by the number of particles in solution, which is termed **osmolality.** Changes in osmolality are detected by several specialized receptors in the central nervous system and also in peripheral tissues such as the kidney. Changes in osmolality are important for the processes involved in the control of hydration and kidney function (see chapter 9).

The Heart

The heart is illustrated in figure 7.2 to reveal the flow of blood through the four chambers. Blood returns to the right atrium of the heart via the superior and inferior vena cava veins, passes into the right ventricle through the tricuspid valve, and is pumped by the right ventricle through the pulmonary valve into the *pulmonary circulation.* After being oxygenated in the lungs, blood returns to the left atrium of the heart. The blood then passes through the mitral valve into the left ventricle, where it is pumped though the aorta artery to the remainder of the body, or *systemic circulation.* *The heart functions as a double pump,* with special one-way valves that prevent the backflow of blood. One pump, the right side of the heart, receives blood from the systemic circulation and pumps it through the pulmonary circulation of the lungs. The other pump, the left side of the heart, receives blood from the pulmonary circulation and pumps it through the systemic circulation. The right and left sides of the heart contract and pump blood at the same time, resulting in a closed-loop circulation. As a closed-loop pump, the volume of blood pumped by the right and left sides of the heart must be equal, or else a backlog of blood would develop in either the pulmonary or systemic circulations. Any such backlog would lead to harmful impairments in pulmonary and cellular respiration.

The heart is a muscular organ that contracts without voluntary control. Let's estimate the number of times your heart beats in a lifetime. Assume an average of 100 b/min over 75 years, and you'll experience almost 4 trillion beats in your lifetime. What is all the more amazing about the heart is that it can be regulated to rapidly increase its rate of beating (heart rate) from what could be a resting value of

FIGURE 7.2

Blood flow through the valves and chambers of the heart to the pulmonary and systemic circulations.

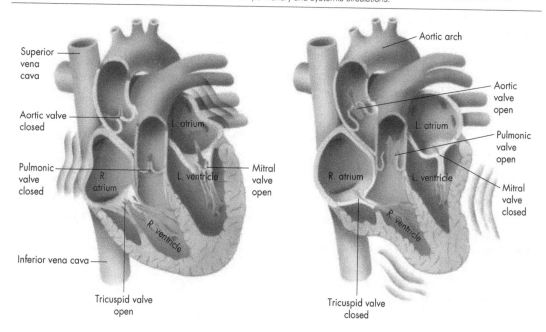

50 b/min to a maximal value of 200 b/min. The use of heart rate to guide exercise intensity is described in Personal Trainer 7.1.

While pumping blood, the healthy heart can generate average circulation pressures that increase from 90 to over 140 mmHg, without signs or symptoms of impaired function. The ability to generate pressure is critical for the function of the heart and all other bodily functions, and will be explained in more detail later in this chapter. For the time being, keep in mind that pressure is needed for blood to flow, and blood flows or circulates down a pressure gradient. Blood pressure is highest where blood leaves the left side of the heart and lowest where blood returns to the right side of the heart (i.e., right atrium). As shown in figure 7.3, a thicker wall/mass surrounds the left ventricle. This is needed for the heart to generate a sufficient amount of pressure to circulate blood throughout the body.

The Cardiac Cycle

The previous description of blood flow through the heart and vasculature is referred to as the **cardiac cycle.** During the cardiac cycle, the volumes and pressures of blood in the atria and ventricles change in an organized and repeatable fashion, as do the blood pressures within the systemic and pulmonary circulations.

The phase of the cardiac cycle when the myocardium is relaxed is termed *diastole,* and blood flows passively into the right and left atrium and then into the respective ventricles.

When the atria contract, termed *atrial systole* (or "atrial kick"), an additional 30% of total ventricular filling occurs. The volume of blood in each ventricle at the end of diastole is referred to as *end-diastolic volume* (EDV). Soon after EDV is achieved, the ventricles contract (i.e., systole), following which the cycle repeats itself—thousands of times each day. At rest, systole and diastole represent one-third and two-thirds of the cardiac cycle, respectively.

Cardiac Performance

In addition to heart rate, another main determinant of cardiac performance at rest and during exercise is stroke volume. **Stroke volume** is the amount of blood pumped per stroke or beat of the heart. The resting stroke volume of untrained male subjects' hearts averages between 70 and 90 mL/beat. With training it may approach 100 to 120 mL/beat. Stroke volume is generally lower in women.

osmolality (oz'mo-lal'i-ti) the number of particles per kilogram of solvent

cardiac cycle the electrical, pressure and volume changes that occur in a functional heart between successive heart beats

stroke volume the volume of blood ejected from the ventricle each beat

Throughout our daily lives we are constantly reminded about the important role that heart rate plays in cadiac performance. The pounding in our chest we feel after slamming on the car brakes to avoid a traffic accident or the rapid beating or flutter we feel while waiting for an important job interview represent only a few of many such examples.

When discussing heart rate it is important to familiarize yourself with the term **chronotropic.** Any agent or technique that increases heart rate is said to have a positive chronotropic effect. Conversely, any agent or factor that decreases heart rate has a negative chronotropic effect. For example, associated with a program of regular endurance exercise is a decrease in resting heart rate; therefore, exercise training is said to have a negative chronotropic effect.

Measurement of heart rate in the laboratory or in the field is relatively simple. And, given the direct relationship between heart rate and $\dot{V}O_2$ (or work rate), one can see why it represents the single most used index of circulatory function during exercise. As a trainer, coach, researcher, or clinician, one can use heart rate response to (1) guide intensity or severity of exercise and (2) assess the effects of an exercise training regimen. However, these uses should be applied on an individual basis only, because heart rate responses to both acute exercise and exercise training can (and do) vary considerably from one person to another.

One contemporary device to monitor heart rate uses a conductive chest strap to detect the small voltage changes from heart contraction that are conducted to the surface of the skin. These small voltage changes are converted to a radio signal and transferred through the air to a watch worn on the wrist by a process termed *telemetry.* The watch has computer software which then converts the received signals to heart rates that are displayed, and can be stored in the watch memory, in previously programmed intervals. This method of using the body's voltage changes during muscle contraction is the basis of the science of electrocardiography, and will be discussed in chapter 20.

The use of a personal heart rate monitor is a relatively simple and inexpensive method for the recording of heart rates during exercise. The heart rate monitor also allows many athletes to bring the laboratory to their training track. In the absence of a heart rate monitor, one can measure pulse rate, which refers to the frequency of pulses we are able to palpate (feel) in any artery (e.g., radial in wrist or carotid in neck) or on the chest wall (apical pulse). Heart rate and pulse rate are usually the same. However, among patients with a very slow or very fast rate or an irregular rhythm, not all contractions of the heart are forceful enough so that an equal number of pulse beats are felt in the peripheral artery.

Finally, care must be used when interpreting heart rate or pulse rate. Although heart rate does increase in proportion with increases in exercise intensity, other factors also alter the heart rate response to exercise—such as exercise duration, hydration, body temperature, terrestrial altitude, air pollution, overtraining, illness, and to a lesser extent the phase of the menstrual cycle. All these additional factors must be considered when interpreting the heart or pulse rate response to exercise.

Stroke volume can be computed in several ways. One such way uses the following equation:

$$\text{Stroke volume} = \text{end-diastolic volume (EDV)} - \text{end-systolic volume (ESV)}$$

EDV was defined earlier as the amount of blood that remains in the ventricle after diastole is finished. For most people this value is around 120 mL; however, in some individuals it may approach 180 mL. Long-term endurance training is known to increase EDV. ESV is the volume of blood that remains in the ventricle after the heart has finished contracting. For the person with a resting EDV of 120 mL and an ESV of 50 mL, stroke volume at rest would be 70 mL.

The stretch or load that blood exerts on the cardiac muscle fibers is called **preload.** As figure 7.4 shows, moving along any one of the four curves in the figure is associated with a change in EDV and a corresponding change in cardiac performance. This relationship between EDV and cardiac performance is known as the *Frank-Starling law* of the heart (Otto Frank and Ernest Starling).

In addition to changes in EDV, another major factor controlling stroke volume is inotropicity or contractility. **Inotropic** is defined as a shift of the Frank-Starling curve either upward to the left (increased contractility or positive inotropic effect) or downward to the right (decreased contractility or negative inotropic effect) (figure 7.4). A change in inotropic state means a greater or lesser force of contraction at a given end-diastolic volume (preload). The end result is that more blood (positive effect) or less blood (negative effect) is squeezed out, which leads to an increase or decrease in stroke volume, respectively.

For example, the catecholamine norepinephrine is known to affect the heart by increasing the force of contraction without any change in end-diastolic volume. This exemplifies why catecholamines are said to have a positive inotropic effect. A change in ejection fraction is sometimes used as a marker or index of a change in inotropic state or contractility.

Ejection fraction is the percentage of EDV ejected with each contraction (ejection fraction = stroke volume/EDV). The ejection fraction for a healthy heart at rest approximates

FIGURE 7.3

A cross section of the heart, showing the larger muscle mass surrounding the left compared with the right ventricle. RA = right atrium, LA = left atrium, IVS = interventricular septum.

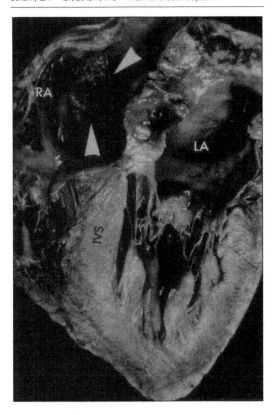

FIGURE 7.4

The relationship between end-diastolic volume (EDV), myocardial performance, and contractility. Increasing EDV (increasing venous return) causes an increase in myocardial performance (i.e., stroke volume). In addition, stimulation by catecholamines generates a different curve for EDV, due to increasing contractility.

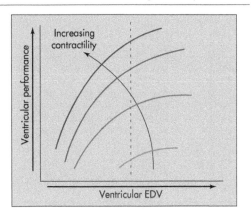

exceptions to this rule in tissues such as the pituitary gland and liver, where one capillary bed is connected to another by an intermediate vein, and each of these special circulation beds is referred to as a *portal circulation*.

The artery has the thickest wall and the greatest ability to stretch and then recoil to its original dimension, a property termed *elasticity*. Conversely, arteries have a limited ability to be distended and increase their vascular volume, a property termed *compliance*. Arterioles possess similar properties to arteries, but in addition are often surrounded circumferentially by layers of smooth muscle fibers. This smooth muscle is regulated by nerves, hormones present in circulation, local metabolites, and perhaps even local pressure and electrical changes that result in either the constriction or relaxation of the muscle (2, 18, 19, 25). Contraction of smooth muscle surrounding an arteriole will decrease the diameter of the lumen, increase resistance to blood flow, and thereby

0.55 to 0.6, or 55% to 60%. As will be discussed in later sections, the ejection fraction can increase to 80% during exercise. The product of stroke volume and heart rate (HR) quantifies the volume of blood pumped by the heart per unit time, and is referred to as **cardiac output** (Q).

7.2 $Q \text{ (L/min)} = SV \text{ (L)} \times HR \text{ (b/min)}$

At rest, the normal value for cardiac output approximates 5 L/min, but may increase in excess of 35 L/min during the exercise intensities at or close to VO_{2max}. See Up Close 7.1 for a discussion of the relationship between cardiac output and VO_2.

The Vasculature

The flow of blood through almost all the circulatory beds within the body proceeds in the order of arteries, arterioles, capillaries, venules, and veins. However, there are a few

chronotrophic an agent or technique that increases or decreases heart rate

preload the load to which a muscle is subjected just before shortening; usually explained as the stretch induced on the myocardium at end-diastole—due to filling of the ventricles

inotropic relative to the heart, a greater or lesser force of contraction at a given end-diastolic volume

ejection fraction the percentage of blood pumped by the heart per beat, expressed as a percentage of left ventricular end-diastolic volume

cardiac output the blood volume pumped by the heart each minute

UP CLOSE 7.1

Application of the Fick Equation to Understanding Cardiovascular Function

The function of the central cardiovascular system during rest and exercise can be understood by application of the Fick principle (Adolph Fick, 1870). The Fick principle is based on simple physiological concepts. The consumption of oxygen by the whole body or in any defined body segment is dependent on blood flow and the amount of oxygen extracted from blood, which is expressed as the arterial-venous oxygen difference (a-vO$_2\Delta$). Applied to the whole body, VO$_2$ represents total body oxygen consumption (as calculated by indirect gas analysis calorimetry, see chapter 4), cardiac output (Q) represents blood flow, and the difference between arterial and mixed venous blood oxygen content represents the a-vO$_2\Delta$.

7.3 $VO_2 = Q \times a\text{-}vO_2\Delta$

7.4 $Q = VO_2/a\text{-}vO_2\Delta$

The **Fick equation** can also be applied to regional circulations. Because all blood flow to the contracting thigh and lower leg muscles is provided by the femoral artery, and all blood flow from the leg drains through the femoral vein, sampling blood from each vessel would provide an oxygen content difference that reflects oxygen extraction by the leg. For example, when blood flow to the leg is measured in the femoral artery and blood is sampled from the femoral artery and vein for measurement of oxygen content, the a-vO$_2\Delta$ across the leg can be calculated. Using the Fick equation, VO$_2$ can then be calculated for that leg.

A classic example of the application of the Fick equation to exercise physiology is a study published by Knight and associates (26). These researchers wanted to verify that the exercising muscle mass contributed most to the increase in VO$_2$ during exercise. Consequently, the researchers measured total body VO$_2$ during cycle ergometry by indirect calorimetry, while simultaneously sampling blood from the femoral artery and vein of one leg and measuring blood flow in the femoral artery. In the process of accounting for both legs, they noted that the increase in VO$_2$ from rest to maximum during cycle ergometry could be more than 90% accounted for by the VO$_2$ measured across the legs. The remaining VO$_2$ was accounted for by additional muscles used in posture and ventilation.

---

decrease flow, a process termed **vasoconstriction.** Conversely, relaxation of smooth muscle around an arteriole will increase the diameter, decrease resistance, and increase blood flow, a process termed **vasodilation.**

Capillaries are the smallest-diameter blood vessels, and possess a wall composed of a single cell layer. The cells of the capillary wall are not tightly connected, and pores exist that allow for the movement of fluid, certain cells, small proteins and metabolites into and from the vascular compartment. In certain circulatory beds, smooth muscle may also be present around the junctions between arterioles and capillaries. The walls of venules and veins are not as thick as those of arteries or arterioles, do not have high elasticity, but have high compliance. Veins are also surrounded by smooth muscle which, because of the compliance characteristic of the venous circulation, function to regulate the cross-sectional dimensions of the veins and therefore the volume of blood that is in the venous circulation.

Acute Adaptations to Exercise

During exercise the metabolically more active skeletal muscles contribute more than 90% of the increased demand for oxygen consumption (26). The faster that oxygen is circulated to the contracting muscle, the more rapid will be the increase in VO$_2$, and the lower the oxygen deficit, as was discussed in chapter 6. The immediate response of the cardiovascular system to different types of exercise will now be discussed relative to changes in heart (cardiac) function, blood, hemoglobin concentration, and peripheral blood flow.

Cardiac Function

The heart responds to exercise by increasing heart rate, stroke volume, and cardiac output. Heart rate is controlled by neural and hormonal changes to the intrinsic discharge from the pacemaker or sino-atrial (SA) node of the heart (see chapter 20). Parasympathetic innervation causes the SA node to become hyperpolarized, leading to a slower rate of discharge and a lower heart rate. Conversely, sympathetic stimulation from neural secretion of norepinephrine or hormonal stimulation by circulating norepinephrine and epinephrine increases the permiability of the SA node tissue to sodium and leads to an increase in heart rate. Sympathetic stimulation also increases the excitability of the atrioventricular (AV) node, resulting in less of a delay in the propagation of the action potential from the atrium and to the ventricular myocardium.

Increases in stroke volume result from increases in contractility (ejection fraction) and the maintenance of blood flow back to the heart *(venous return)* (fig. 7.4).

Changes in Cardiac Function During Exercise

Not all exercise elicits the same cardiac response. Dynamic exercise induces increases in heart rate, stroke volume, cardiac output, and blood pressures that differ from those of

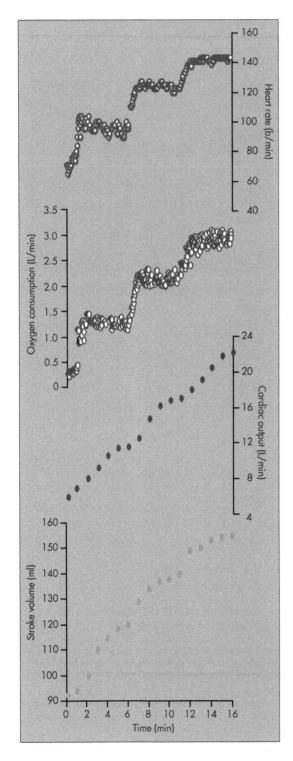

FIGURE 7.5

The changes in oxygen consumption (VO_2), heart rate, stroke volume, and cardiac output during several intermittent steady-state exercise intensities. The sudden increases and decreases in heart rate reflect its intricate regulation. When the steady-state heart rate and VO_2 responses are graphed, both measures increase linearly with intensity.

isometric exercise. Similarly, dynamic upper-body exercise, which involves a smaller muscle mass, elicits a slightly unique cardiac response when compared with dynamic exercise with the legs.

Dynamic Lower-Body Exercise Heart Rate Figure 7.5 presents the increases in heart rate, oxygen consumption (VO_2), cardiac output, and stroke volume during several submaximal steady-state exercise intensities during cycle ergometry. The rapidity of the increases in heart rate and oxygen consumption are obvious. When viewing the steady-state values for VO_2 and heart rate, it is clear that both appear to increase linearly with intensity. However, when looking at the heart rate response during incremental exercise to evaluate the relationship between heart rate and exercise intensity, many individuals have only a small portion of the heart rate curve that is truly linear (16, 35, 44) (fig. 7.6). Furthermore, there is also individual variation in the curvilinear heart rate response to increasing exercise intensities (44), and it is therefore not surprising that considerable error exists in evaluating exercise intensity or predicting VO_2 (a more linear response) from heart rate (see chapter 13).

Stroke Volume and Cardiac Output The dramatic increase in muscle metabolic demand during exercise is complemented by near-immediate increases in cardiac output. This increased blood flow helps increase venous return, which in turn helps increase or maintain EDV at preexercise levels. Other factors responsible for increasing venous return during exercise include the skeletal muscle pump, the respiratory and abdominal pumps, and venoconstriction. As skeletal muscles in the legs contract and compress surrounding veins (i.e., muscle pump), blood within the veins is propelled toward the heart (37).

Also, during breathing, changes in intrathoracic pressure and the flattening of the diaphragm during inhalation cause the veins to empty or propel blood toward the heart. Finally, recall that veins are capacitance vessels in that they have the

Fick equation the equation based on the Fick principle, where $VO_2 = Q \times a\text{-}vO_2\Delta$

vasoconstriction (vas'o-kon-strik'shun) narrowing of the lumen diameter of blood vessels

vasodilation (vas'o-di-la'shun) widening of the lumen diameter of blood vessels

FIGURE 7.6

With increases in exercise intensity to VO_{2max}, the majority of individuals demonstrate a slightly nonlinear increase in heart rate.

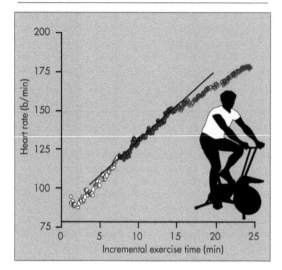

FIGURE 7.7

The increase in stroke volume during incremental exercise to VO_{2max} differs between untrained (blue line) and endurance-trained individuals. Untrained individuals experience a plateau in stroke volume at relative intensities approximating 50% VO_{2max}. Endurance training enables the heart to increase stroke volume to VO_{2max}, and thereby allows for further increases in cardiac output and improved exercise performance.

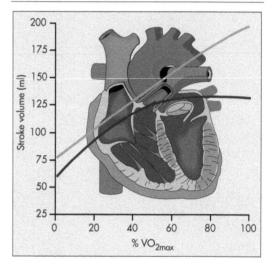

ability to "store" blood. During exercise there is a venoconstriction or narrowing of the small veins and venules in the legs, causing blood to be moved out toward the heart.

In addition, because of changes in the autonomic nervous system and hormones, there is increased contractility of the ventricular myocardium. This causes an increased ejection fraction of the heart during exercise that further increases stroke volume. For example, at rest ejection fraction approximates 60% and stroke volume may equal 80 mL. During exercise at 60% VO_{2max}, ejection fraction is 85% and stroke volume can equal 150 mL. As will be explained, endurance training and genetics can influence the maximal values of these capacities.

As shown in figure 7.7, stroke volume increases as exercise intensity increases from rest to approximately 50% VO_{2max}. In relatively untrained individuals, stroke volume then plateaus through peak exercise. In trained individuals, stroke volume continues to increase to VO_{2max}, which coincides with the significant increases in maximal cardiac output and VO_{2max} observed in these people (13, 27). These responses are only typical for exercise performed in the vertical position. Individuals exercising in a recumbent or supine position achieve maximal stroke volumes at the onset of exercise (29), presumably because of lower hydrostatic pressures which decrease the resistance to venous return to the heart.

The increased heart rate and stroke volumes that accompany exercise result in an increase in cardiac output. This increase in blood flow is linear with increases in exercise intensity and plateaus close to maximal heart rate and VO_{2max}.

Given these demands on the heart during exercise, it is no surprise that individuals with heart disease, or previous damage to the heart from myocardial infarction, have a much lower capacity to exercise than individuals with a healthy cardiovascular system.

Blood Pressure   The increasing cardiac output that occurs during exercise has the potential to increase blood pressure. The potential to increase blood pressure can be explored in the following equation:

7.5 $Q \ (L/min) = P_m(mmHg) \ / \ PVR \ (arbitrary \ units)$

where

P_m = mean blood pressure

PVR = peripheral vascular resistance.

Under resting conditions, Q approximates 6 L/min, and P_m approximates 95 mmHg. Thus, PVR approximates 15.8 units. With exercise to VO_{2max}, Q may increase to 25 L/min, and mBP may increase to 110 mmHg. At this P_m, and to accommodate such an increase in Q, PVR must decrease to approximately 4.5 units—more than a threefold decrease.

Figure 7.8 presents the change in systolic, diastolic, and mean arterial blood pressures during an incremental exercise test. Mean arterial blood pressure is not the average of systolic (SBP) and diastolic (DBP) blood pressures, because the

FIGURE 7.8

The change in arterial systolic (upper line), diastolic (lower line), and mean blood pressures during an incremental cycle ergometer test. Note the generally steady diastolic blood pressure. The increase in mean arterial blood pressure is therefore due to the increase in systolic blood pressure.

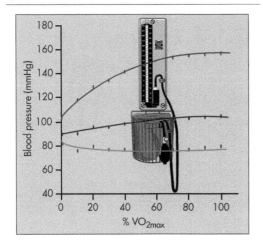

duration of systole and diastole differ. At rest, P_m can be estimated from the calculation:

7.6 $$P_m \text{ (mmHg)} = DBP + [(SBP - DBP)/3]$$

This calculation is based on the duration of diastole being approximately threefold that of systole. However, this time relationship changes with increases in heart rate, in that diastolic filling time shortens. During exercise, arterial systolic and mean pressures increase, and diastolic pressure remains close to resting values (< 80 mmHg) (14). Therefore, during conditions of increasing cardiac output, ejection of blood from the left ventricle exceeds the compliant properties of the arterial vasculature, yet the reduced peripheral vascular resistance maintains a low diastolic pressure. This occurs despite the reduced interval between successive ejections from the left ventricle.

During even intense exercise, there is only a minimal increase in pulmonary P_m of approximately 10 mmHg. This is understandable, given the proximity of the pulmonary vasculature to the heart, its large capillary network, and therefore the low resistance to flow that would exist even at high flow rates.

Upper-Body Exercise The cardiovascular responses to upper-body dynamic exercise invoke a different heart rate, stroke volume, and blood pressure response compared with lower-body dynamic exercise (fig. 7.9).

For a given submaximal steady-state work rate or VO_2, heart rate, ventilation, and systemic blood pressures are all higher during arm ergometry than during lower-body exercise

(34, 22, 23). Cardiac output is the same, and understandably stroke volume is lower. The higher blood pressures are due to the small muscle mass involved in arm exercise, and the large lower-body vasculature that remains unchanged or more vasoconstricted—providing resistance to peripheral circulation (42). For a given submaximal exercise intensity expressed relative to heart rate, muscle blood flow is similar between upper- and lower-body exercise; however, the VO_2 is lower because of a lower extraction of oxygen as indicated by a-v$O_2\Delta$ (46). Conversely, for a given VO_2, heart rate is higher during upper-body exercise.

During maximal upper-body exercise, exercise cardiac output is 30% lower, heart rate is 10% lower, stroke volume is 30–40% lower, and ventilation is 25% lower than what is achieved during lower-body exercise. Despite these differences, systemic blood pressures are similar.

Isometric Exercise Muscle blood flow, systemic blood pressures, and central cardiac function also differ between dynamic and static, or isometric, exercise. Sustained isometric contractions are characterized by increased vascular resistance within the exercising muscle. The intensity of isometric contractions is expressed relative to the maximal voluntary contraction (MVC) of the muscle(s) concerned. Sustained contractions at 20% or more MVC induce a rapid increase in both systolic and diastolic blood pressures, whereas blood pressure responses during dynamic exercise with loads of 10% MVC are much lower.

When isometric exercise is performed, additional increases in blood pressure may also occur if the person attempts to exhale against a closed trachea. This maneuver is similar to a clinical procedure known as the *Valsalva maneuver*, where subjects exhale at greatly increased airway pressures. This increases thoracic pressures because of the added muscular contraction of the muscles of expiration against a near-constant lung volume. These pressures raise systemic diastolic arterial blood pressure, lower stroke volume, and make the heart work harder for a given cardiac output.

Blood

An acute effect of exercise on blood is the movement of fluid out of the vascular compartment, which decreases the volume of plasma and blood. This fluid loss from the plasma causes the hematocrit and plasma metabolite concentrations to increase, which is termed **hemoconcentration.** In fact, a significant hemoconcentration even occurs when moving from a supine to vertical posture. The added hemoconcentration of exercise is predominantly confined to the transition from rest to exercise (6, 12, 28, 31). This response is followed by a more gradual hemoconcentration that occurs

hemoconcentration increased hematocrit due to the loss of plasma volume

FIGURE 7.9

Difference between the cardiovascular responses to upper-body and lower-body exercise at a similar VO₂.

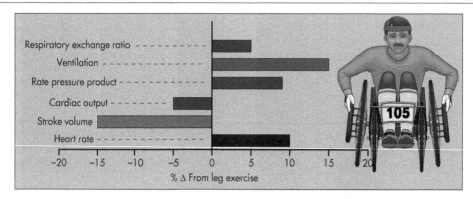

with increases in exercise intensity (fig. 7.10), and these changes are greater with the larger blood pressures associated with resistance exercise than during more prolonged dynamic exercise.

Peripheral Blood Flow

The finite blood volume of the body and limited increase in cardiac output present potential limitations to increased blood flow to peripheral tissues. For example, at rest a cardiac output of 5 L/min and a blood volume of 5 L requires the complete recirculation of the entire blood volume every minute. During exercise, cardiac output may increase to 30 L/min, and the blood volume must be recirculated six times per minute. Compared with the potential 20-fold increase in the body's demand for oxygen during exercise, as six- or sevenfold increase in blood flow appears meager.

We can accommodate the increased metabolic demands of intense exercise because the systemic circulation is regulated to *redistribute blood flow* to the more metabolically active skeletal muscle tissue. In addition, the acute metabolic adaptations that occur in skeletal muscle result in an *increased extraction of oxygen* from the capillary blood, causing an increased a-vO₂Δ (see Up Close 7.1).

Blood Flow Redistribution

Figure 7.11 compares the relative contribution of the cardiac output to the main tissue beds of the body at rest and during exercise. During exercise, the vasoconstriction of arterioles supplying the brain, gut, and kidney reduces the percentage of the cardiac output that perfuses these tissues. However, because of the increased cardiac output, actual blood flow to these organs remains the same or increases slightly. This redistribution allows for an increasing percentage of total blood flow to be directed to the working skeletal muscle. Consequently, blood flow to skeletal muscle (assuming 20 kg

FIGURE 7.10

Exercise and the accompanied increases in blood pressure force fluid from plasma out of the vascular system. This response causes an increase in hematocrit and osmolality, which is termed hemoconcentration.

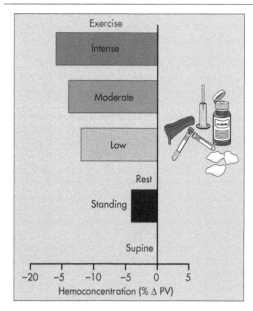

of muscle) can increase from 50 mL/kg of muscle/min at rest to over 1,000 mL/kg/min at peak exercise. This translates to blood flow increasing from 15% at rest to over 80% at peak exertion. Furthermore, when exercising a smaller muscle mass, maximal muscle blood flow has been measured at over 2000 mL/kg/min (2).

FIGURE 7.11

The distribution of cardiac output to the main tissues of the body at rest and during exercise.

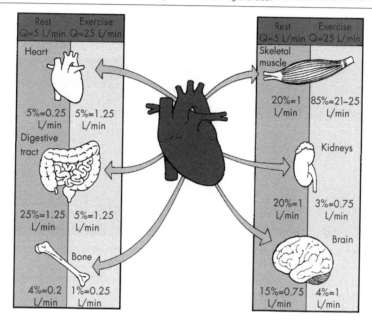

Peripheral Artery and Skeletal Muscle Blood Flow

As with cardiac output, both peripheral artery and muscle blood flow increase linearly with increases in exercise intensity. However, this response should not be interpreted to indicate a uniform flow to skeletal muscle, or that the entire skeletal muscle mass is uniformly perfused. Animal research suggests a marked blood flow heterogeneity within contracting skeletal muscle, resulting in regions that are over- and underperfused. This inequality can result in regions of the muscle that do not receive adequate oxygenation, and may compromise muscle metabolism. Because of methodological constraints, it is unclear whether this nonuniform perfusion occurs in human muscle.

Variation in blood flow during contractions have been documented in humans. Walloe and Wesche (46) reported that intense muscle contractions compress the vasculature within the muscle, causing a reduction in blood flow. Immediately following there is increased flow, called **hyperemia,** during muscle relaxation. Similar findings have been reported for dynamic exercise of the forearm musculature (36) (fig. 7.12) and show that blood flow to muscle is influenced by the contracting muscle.

Increased Oxygen Extraction

Under resting conditions, blood flow from the central arterial to central venous circulation is associated with a reduction in the partial pressure of oxygen in the blood from 100 mmHg

to 40 mmHg (see chapter 8). Use of the oxy-hemoglobin dissociation curve reveals that such a pressure difference amounts to a 50 mL/L change in oxygen content (200−150 mL O_2/L blood), which is the arterial-mixed venous difference in oxygen content (a-v$O_2\Delta$). During exercise, the a-v$O_2\Delta$ reflects the added uptake of oxygen by the skeletal muscle, and can increase to over 150 mL/L during running and cycling in highly trained endurance athletes.

However, the use of central blood concentration measures for arterial (CaO_2) and venous (CvO_2) values can be misleading. For example, the above central blood volume values for a-v$O_2\Delta$ suggest that the body is unable to extract all the oxygen from the blood. This is not true for the localized microvasculature, where muscle PO_2 values have been estimated to be as low as 2 mmHg (40, 42). If equilibration between capillary and tissue PO_2 is assumed, a value of 2 mmHg indicates an almost complete uptake of oxygen from the capillary circulation. Why then, is CvO_2 as high as 150 mL/L blood? The answer is due to the fact that blood in central circulation represents a combination of blood from both active and inactive tissues. Also, there is both spatial and temporal heterogeneity in blood flow within the exercised muscle mass (17).

> **hyperemia (hi-per-e′mi-ah)** increased blood flow above normal; usually expressed relative to a particular tissue

When blood flow is measured by a Doppler Flowmetry, an uneven blood flow to skeletal muscle during dynamic muscle contractions is seen. Beat-to-beat variation in the volume of blood pumped to contracting muscle is dependent on the phase of the contraction cycle: rest, concentric contraction, eccentric contraction. It is clear that as exercise intensity increases, the amount of blood able to flow to the muscle is dramatically reduced during the concentric phase of the contraction because of an increase in intramuscular pressure. Conversely, during the recovery phases there is an exaggerated increase in blood flow, or hyperemia.

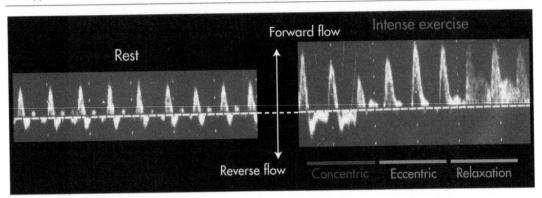

The near complete extraction of oxygen from the capillaries perfusing active muscle engaged in intense exercise provides further evidence of the high capacity of the muscle fibers to extract oxygen. It also indicates that it is the transport and provision of oxygen to the muscles that is the limiting factor to maximal oxygen consumption. In fact, research that has artificially increased muscle blood flow (3, 4, 5) or artificially increased red blood cell numbers in the circulation *(erythrocythemia)*, showed an increased capacity to extract oxygen from the blood (41). This is why blood doping and injections of erythropoietin to stimulate polycythemia work, yet are banned practices in athletic events.

Cutaneous Circulation

The adjustments to skin (cutaneous) blood flow during exercise in a hot environment (see chapter 17) are integral components of the body's ability to dissipate heat to the surroundings. Unlike the splanchnic, renal, and portal circulations, which vasoconstrict during exercise, the start of exercise initially induces an adrenergic vasoconstriction of the skin, which is then followed by a sympathetic cholinergic vasodilation (20, 21). During incremental exercise, skin blood flow decreases as exercise intensity increases above approximately 80% VO_{2max}. This response is likely due to both increased levels of catecholamines (24), and increased systemic blood pressures that stimulate the baroreceptors and inhibit the cholinergic vasodilator response (20, 21).

Hemodynamics During Prolonged Exercise— Cardiovascular Drift

Changes in cardiac output, stroke volume, and heart rate for *short-term submaximal* exercise were shown in figure 7.5. During prolonged submaximal work (over 30 to 60 min),

cardiac output is maintained over the course of the exercise, but stroke volume and heart rate are not. As shown in figure 7.14, stroke volume gradually decreases and heart rate gradually increases as exercise progresses. This is referred to as **cardiovascular drift** (8). Because the changes are opposite in direction and equal in magnitude, cardiac output remains fairly constant. Thus, in prolonged efforts, it is not surprising to find near maximal heart rates by the end of the performance.

The long-held and still prevailing belief is that cardiovascular drift is due to an increase in cutaneous blood flow, which would ultimately result in a decrease in end-diastolic volume and, therefore, a decrease in stroke volume. Therefore, the increase in heart rate was felt to be a compensatory response.

Although it may be true that an increase in cutaneous blood flow during exercise, especially if done in a warm environment, is partly related to the decrease in stroke volume, more recent evidence suggests that the decrease in stroke volume primarily occurs because there is an increase in heart rate. An increase in heart rate shortens the amount of time available for the ventricle to fill during diastole. The increase in heart rate appears to be primarily due to either the direct effect of the increase in body temperature on the SA node or an indirect effect on increasing sympathetic outflow (8).

A Summary of Acute Cardiovascular Adaptation to Exercise

Figure 7.13 summarizes the acute responses of the cardiovascular system to exercise. Once again, components of the Fick equation (Q and a-$\bar{v}O_2\Delta$) are used to differentiate the parameters responsible for increasing VO_2 at the systemic and the peripheral levels of function.

Chapter 7 ▪ Cardiovascular Function and Adaptation to Exercise   **153**

FIGURE 7.13

FIGURE 7.13

A summary of the acute cardiovascular adaptations that combine to increase oxygen consumption during exercise.

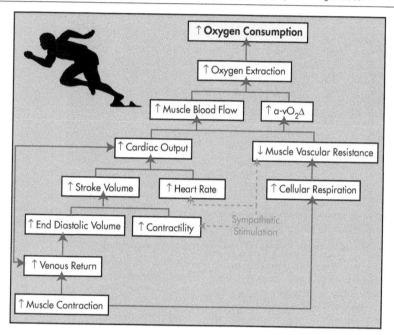

FIGURE 7.14

During prolonged exercise, heart rate increases steadily while stroke volume decreases. This is referred to as "cardiovascular drift." Because these changes are equal in magnitude and opposite in direction, cardiac output remains stable.

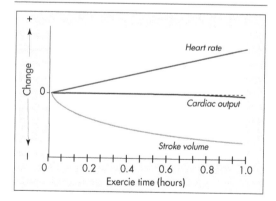

O_2 consumed during maximal exercise (3100 mL/min) is ten times greater than that found during rest (300 mL/min). This increase is accomplished by a 3.6-fold increase in cardiac output, brought about by a 1.5-fold increase in stroke volume and a 2.4-fold increase in heart rate. Additionally, there is a 2.8-fold increase in the a-vO$_2\Delta$ (48.8 to 138 mL/L).

Be sure to also notice the differences between the untrained and highly trained endurance athletes at maximal exercise. The endurance athletes were international competitors in long-distance and cross-country running and cycling. They were members of the Swedish National teams and had been training for several years. In this comparison, maximal heart rate was quite similar between the two groups (190 b/min vs. 200 b/min), and there is only a modest increase (12%) in maximal a-vO$_2\Delta$ for the endurance trained athletes. However, the biggest difference is in the magnitude of the stroke volume. The stroke volume in the endurance athletes (189 mL/beat) is 70% higher than that of the untrained subjects (112 mL/beat)! Such a large difference clearly points out that the most important component of the oxygen transport system is stroke volume.

Some examples of O_2 transport and utilization at rest and during maximal exercise for untrained and endurance trained male subjects are given in table 7.2. Notice how each variable contributes toward increasing the amount of O_2 consumed. Using the untrained subjects as an example, the

Cardiovascular drift the gradual increase in heart rate and decrease in stroke volume during prolonged endurance exercise

TABLE 7.2

Components of the oxygen transport system at rest and during maximal exercise for untrained subjects and endurance athletes

CONDITION	VO$_2$ (mL/min)	=	STROKE VOLUME (L/Beat)	×	HEART RATE (Beats/min)	×	a-vO$_2$Δ (mL/L)
Untrained							
Rest	300	=	0.075*	×	82	×	48.8
Maximal exercise	3100	=	0.112	×	200	×	138.0
Endurance athletes							
Maximal exercise	5570	=	0.189	×	190	×	155.0

*Usually expressed in mL/beat, e.g., 0.075 L/beat = 75 mL/beat.

Chronic Adaptations to Exercise

Prolonged and repeated exposures to exercise can cause structural and functional changes in the cardiovascular system. The extent of these changes is dependent upon the type and quality of exercise training, and the changes are known to differ between training for long-term cardiorespiratory endurance and training for short-term muscular endurance, strength, and power. The following description of chronic training adaptations is organized by the type of exercise training and by the component of the cardiovascular system.

Adaptations from Training for Long-Term Endurance

Cardiac Structure and Function

Data from both experimental and cross-sectional research, studies that compare two or more groups that differ in training status, indicate that heart dimensions and end-diastolic volumes (i.e., cavity size) are greater in endurance athletes than in nonendurance athletes (33) (fig. 7.15). This information has developed the notion of an *athletic heart*, which is larger than that of sedentary individuals. Endurance training has also been shown to elicit increases in cardiac mass and function in previously sedentary individuals (10). The end-diastolic volume of the left ventricle (LVEDV) increases after 9 weeks of endurance training in males, and similar responses have been shown in females (38).

These adaptations can occur rapidly, with measures of ventricular dimensions increasing with as little as 1 week of endurance training; whereas myocardial mass responds more slowly (11). As discussed next, the rapid increase in cardiac dimensions is primarily due to a rapid increase in plasma and blood volume (9, 12).

The larger LVEDV after endurance training is associated with an increased stroke volume and decreased heart rate for a given submaximal exercise intensity. It also contributes to a greater stroke volume at peak exercise, an important adaptation that improves peak cardiac output and VO$_{2max}$.

Contradictory information exists as to whether the stroke volume and heart rate responses at rest are cause and effect (7). For example, the lower heart rate response is also accompanied by increased parasympathetic innervation of the heart, and reductions in resting and exercise heart rates have been documented without increases in stroke volume (7). We believe that both the increase in stroke volume and a greater parasympathetic innervation contribute to the lower resting heart rates observed with training.

Blood Pressure

When systolic or diastolic blood pressure (or both) is chronically elevated at rest, it is called *hypertension*, or high blood pressure. Values measured over several examination visits that exceed 140 mmHg and 90 mmHg are generally classified as systolic and diastolic hypertension, respectively. The important role that preventing and treating hypertension, and the diseases it contributes to, are discussed in chapter 19. It is important to note; however, that regular aerobic-type exercise training can improve blood pressure in patients with mild to moderate hypertension (43, 47). More about the role of exercise training in helping treat hypertension is discussed in chapter 19 as well. More information about the physiology of blood pressure and how it is measured is provided in Up Close 7.2.

Blood

Endurance training increases the volume of plasma in blood. Simultaneous increases in red blood cell counts and hemoglobin also occur, but their concentrations relative to the volume of blood are lower because of the diluting effect of the relatively larger increase in plasma volume (fig. 7.16).

The increase in plasma volume is known to occur without a large training stimulus. For example, just one session of intense intermittent cycle ergometry exercise performed at 85% VO$_{2max}$ induced a 10% increase in plasma volume after 24 h (12). This chronic increase was predominantly due to an increase in plasma albumin. The time course of further change in plasma volume during a training program is unknown; however, training-induced increases in plasma volume have been reported between 300 and 800 mL (9, 12).

FIGURE 7.15

The cardiac hypertrophy of endurance athletes is characterized by a large ventricular cavity with a normal thickness of the wall. On the other hand, the cardiac hypertrophy of nonendurance athletes is characterized by a thicker ventricular wall with a normal-sized ventricular cavity.

FIGURE 7.16

The changes in plasma volume, hematocrit, and hemoglobin concentration during endurance exercise training. The increased expansion of the plasma volume can decrease hematocrit and hemoglobin concentration, even though total red cell and total hemoglobin masses also increase with training.

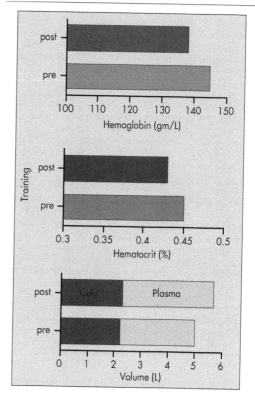

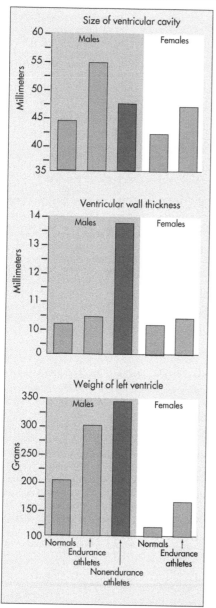

Source: Male data from Morganroth et al. (30): female data from Zeldis et al. (49).

An increased plasma volume increases venous return to the heart, increases ventricular preload, and thereby increases stroke volume for a given exercise intensity (9). The increased plasma volume also has thermoregulatory benefits, as will be detailed in chapter 17.

Skeletal Muscle Circulation

Anderson and Henriksson (1) performed histology and muscle biopsy tissue sections before and after training and revealed a 20% increase in capillary density. This finding occurred across fiber types and was associated with a 16% increase in VO_{2max} and a 40% increase in select mitochondrial enzyme activities. Increased capillary density would increase maximal muscle blood flow capacities, improve the distribution of blood flow within a muscle, and prolong the time that blood was exposed to the contracting muscle fibers *(capillary transit time)*. The latter two responses are probably the more meaningful, as increased oxygen extraction is known to occur after training, even when maximal cardiac output is not increased (7).

UP CLOSE 7.2

Blood Pressures in the Cardiovascular System

The pressure within the cardiovascular system is termed **blood pressure**. Knowledge of how exercise alters blood pressure has important medical applications, as excessive blood pressure causes the heart to work harder—as it maintains blood flow throughout the body. Chronic exposure to increased arterial blood pressure can damage the heart, blood vessels of the heart, and even certain organs of the body (e.g., kidney).

Arterial blood pressure is represented by three pressures: systolic, mean, and diastolic. After accounting for differences in hydrostatic pressure, it is often assumed that all arterial blood pressure values are the same. However, this is not true. There is no one systolic blood pressure within the arterial systemic circulation at any point in time (14, 32). Systolic blood pressures of the ascending aorta are lower than those of peripheral arteries (e.g., brachial, radial, femoral) (14), whereas diastolic and mean blood pressures are similar in most arteries (14). The more distal an artery is from the heart, the greater the systolic blood pressure (32). These differences in systolic blood pressure are due to complex interactions between fluid flow and the elastic properties of arteries. Despite the differences in the systolic and diastolic blood pressures between central and peripheral arteries, mean blood pressures are similar because of differences in the shape of the blood pressure waveform (mean arterial blood pressure is equal to the integrated area under the blood pressure waveform).

Despite the variability in systolic blood pressures within the arteries of the systemic circulation, a common method used to noninvasively measure blood pressure is sphygmomanometry, which can be completed manually (by a technician), or automatically (by computerized mechanical devices). During sphygmomanometry, the brachial artery is occluded by the inflation of a pressure cuff placed around the upper arm. As pressure is slowly released from the cuff, a stethoscope is used to hear *(auscultation)* the change in sounds (**Korotkoff sounds**) generated by the turbulent flow of blood within the artery. The Korotkoff sounds are interpreted as follows:

- Korotkoff sound I occurs when blood first rushes through the previous occlusion. The corresponding pressure = systolic blood pressure
- Korotkoff sound IV occurs when blood has a sudden decrease in resistance to flow through the artery. The corresponding pressure = diastolic blood pressure
- Korotkoff sound V is when sound is no longer audible. Although commonly used, it is incorrect to use the corresponding pressure to represent diastolic blood pressure.

Even though manual sphygmomanometry is used routinely to measure blood pressure at rest and during exercise, this method is not without error. Because the accuracy of the method is based on the detection of sounds, there is an increased likelihood for erroneous values to be detected as exercise intensity increases. In fact, the detection of diastolic blood pressure by manual sphygmomanometry is known to underestimate true values because of the difficulty in detecting the fourth Korotkoff sound (14).

A Summary of the Benefit of Cardiovascular Adaptations to Endurance Training

The chronic cardiovascular adaptations to endurance training can be observed at rest, and benefit both maximal and submaximal exercise performance (fig. 7.17). Maximal exercise performance results from an improvement in VO_{2max}. Improvement in submaximal performance results from a combined lowering of the relative intensity at a given work rate, as well as the raising of the lactate threshold (chapter 6). The most notable chronic training adaptation to cardiovascular function during submaximal exercise is a lower heart rate (48).

Adaptations from Training for Short-Term Intense Exercise and Muscular Strength

Generally, far less cardiovascular adaptation occurs from chronic resistance training (or weight lifting). However, the type of resistance training is important in determining the magnitude of potential cardiovascular improvement. Pellicia and colleagues (33) and Urhausen and Kindermann (45)

reported that bodybuilders had significantly less total heart volume than endurance-trained athletes. However, with more prolonged resistance training programs involving fewer and shorter rest intervals, (i.e., circuit training), endurance-related cardiovascular adaptation was evident.

Generally, the minimal cardiovascular and muscle metabolic adaptations that develop from resistance training prevent significant increases in VO_{2max}. Interestingly, resistance exercise combined with endurance training, especially for relatively untrained individuals, seems to contribute to initial increases in VO_{2max} (15). This may be because of the low muscle mass of untrained individuals. Resistance training may improve muscle recruitment and hypertrophy, thereby allowing improved exercise tolerance during incremental exercise.

blood pressure the pressure generated by the heart that moves blood through the circulatory system; pressure exerted by blood against the inside walls of blood vessels

Korotkoff sounds the sounds heard by auscultation during the measurement of blood pressure by sphygmomanometry

FIGURE 7.17

A summary of the chronic adaptations of the cardiovascular system after exposure to training for long-term endurance. Adaptations are related to their effects during both maximal and submaximal exercise.

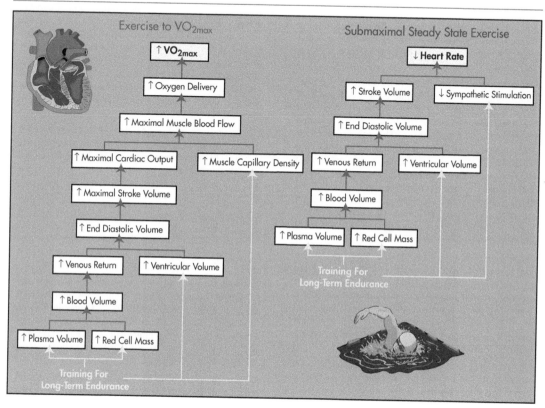

SUMMARY

- The **cardiovascular system** is composed of blood, the heart, and the vasculature within which blood is pumped throughout the body. Within the cardiovascular system are the systemic and pulmonary circulations. Within the **systemic circulation** are local circulation beds, such as those of the head and brain (*cranial* circulation), lungs (*pulmonary* circulation), liver (*hepatic* circulation), kidney (*renal* circulation), abdominal viscera and intestinal tract (*splanchnic* circulation), skin (*cutaneous* circulation), and *skeletal muscle* circulation.

- **Blood** is the liquid medium that circulates within the vascular system. Blood can be divided into cellular and noncellular components, and functions to transport gases, nutrients, and waste products; clot and decrease injury severity; and aid in acid-base buffering, immune functions, tissue repair, and thermoregulation.

- The cell content of blood constitutes approximately 45% of the total blood volume, and this measure is termed **hematocrit.** Hematocrit is lower in females than males, and will vary with hydration status. Blood consists of several types of cells, including white blood cells (*leukocytes*), red blood cells (**erythrocytes**), or cell fragments known as *platelets*. During the synthesis of erythrocytes (*erythropoiesis*) hemoglobin is synthesized.

- An increased production of erythrocytes can result in elevated red blood cell counts, and this condition is termed **polycythemia.** Conversely, an inadequate intake of dietary iron, excessive bleeding, or exaggerated erythrocyte destruction can result in a lowered red blood cell count, or **anemia.**

▪ The liquid component of blood is termed *plasma*. When blood is drawn from the body the clotting process forms fibrinogen, and the remaining fluid component of blood is termed *serum*. The presence of electrolytes and proteins in plasma generates an osmotic force to attract and retain water within the vasculature. This osmotic force is best reflected by the number of particles in solution, which is termed **osmolality.**

▪ The cycle of blood flow through the heart and vasculature is referred to as the **cardiac cycle.** The volume of blood in each ventricle at the end of diastole is referred to as *end-diastolic volume* (EDV), and exerts a stretch on the ventricular myocardium. This stretch can be interpreted as a load and is referred to as **preload.** The greater the EDV and the greater the stretch, the faster is the resultant ventricular myocardial contraction; this relationship is known as the *Frank-Starling law* of the heart. Catecholamine stimulation of the myocardium has a positive **inotropic** effect on the heart, which means a shift in the Frank-Starling curve upwards and to the left.

▪ Blood is ejected from the ventricles during ventricular contraction, or *ventricular systole*. During ventricular systole, not all blood is ejected from each ventricle. The volume of blood pumped from each ventricle per beat is termed **stroke volume,** and when expressed relative to the EDV is known as the **ejection fraction.** The ejection fraction for a healthy heart at rest approximates 0.6, or 60%, but can increase to 80% during exercise.

▪ The product of stroke volume and heart rate quantifies the volume of blood pumped by the heart per unit time, and is referred to as **cardiac output** (Q).

$$Q(L/min) = SV(L) \times HR (b/min)$$

▪ At rest, the normal value for cardiac output approximates 5 L/min, but may increase in excess of 35 L/min during exercise intensities at or close to VO_{2max}.

▪ The **Fick equation** is based on simple physiological principles. The extraction of oxygen is dependent on blood flow (Q), and the amount of oxygen extracted from blood which is usually expressed as the arterial-venous oxygen difference (a-$vO_2\Delta$).

$$VO_2 = Q \times a\text{-}vO_2\Delta$$

▪ Contraction of smooth muscle surrounding an arteriole will decrease the diameter of the lumen, increase resistance to blood flow, and thereby decrease flow—a process termed **vasoconstriction.** Conversely, smooth muscle relaxation around an arteriole will increase the diameter, decrease resistance, and increase blood flow—a process termed **vasodilation.**

▪ Heart rate and oxygen consumption increase rapidly during the onset of exercise. The heart rate response during incremental exercise is not completely linear. In many individuals, only a small portion of the heart rate curve is linear, with heart rates above an individually specific value revealing a curvilinear relationship with intensity. Stroke volume increases as exercise intensity increases from rest to approximately 50% VO_{2max} in relatively untrained individuals and thereafter plateaus. In trained individuals, stroke volume continues to increase up to VO_{2max}, which coincides with significant increases in maximal cardiac output and VO_{2max}.

▪ The increasing cardiac output that occurs during exercise has the potential to increase blood pressure. The potential for such blood pressure increases can be explored with the following equation:

$$Q = P_m / PVR$$

where

$$P_m = \text{mean blood pressure}$$
$$PVR = \text{peripheral vascular resistance.}$$

Under resting conditions, Q approximates 6 L/min, and P_m approximates 95 mmHg. Thus, PVR approximates 15.8 units. With exercise to VO_{2max}, Q may increase to 25 L/min, and P_m may increase to 110 mmHg. At this increased P_m, and to accommodate such an increase in Q, PVR must have decreased to approximately 4.5 units, more than a threefold decrease.

▪ **Blood pressure** can be measured indirectly using sphygmomanometry. Sphygmomanometry involves the placement of a cuff around a limb, inflation of the cuff to a pressure than causes the complete occlusion of an artery, and the detection of sounds (**Korotkoff sounds**) from an artery (auscultation) caused by the return of blood flow as the cuff pressure is allowed to slowly decrease.

▪ During acute effect of exercise, there is a shift of some fluid from the vascular compartment, which decreases the volume of plasma and blood. This fluid loss causes the hematocrit and plasma metabolite concentrations to increase, which is termed **hemoconcentration.**

▪ We can tolerate the increased metabolic demand of intense exercise because the systemic circulation is regulated to *redistribute blood flow* to the more metabolically active skeletal muscle tissue. In addition, the acute metabolic adaptations that occur in skeletal muscle result in an *increased extraction of oxygen* from the capillary blood, causing an increased a-$vO_2\Delta$. Increased blood flow to a given tissue bed is termed **hyperemia.**

▪ The gradual increase in heart rate and decrease in stroke volume during prolonged endurance exercise is called

cardiovascular drift. The increase in heart rate shortens the time for ventricles to fill, thus the lower stroke volume.

▪ Endurance training increases the volume of plasma in blood. An increased plasma volume increases venous return to the heart, increases ventricular preload, and thereby increases stroke volume for a given exercise intensity. Less cardiovascular adaptation occurs during resistance training compared with endurance training. Generally, the more continuous and less intense the resistance training, the more likely some cardiovascular adaptation will occur.

STUDY QUESTIONS

1. List the components of the cardiovascular system, and briefly explain why their function is important during exercise.

2. What are normal values for blood volume, plasma volume, hemoglobin concentration, and hematocrit? How do these values change with endurance training?

3. How does heart rate, stroke volume, and cardiac output change during incremental exercise to VO_{2max}? Are responses different after endurance training? If so, how?

4. Explain differences in the cardiovascular responses between exercise performed with the upper body and lower body.

5. Describe the typical response of systolic, mean, and diastolic blood pressures during exercise.

6. Why is the body's ability to redistribute blood flow (cardiac output) important for exercise tolerance?

7. Why are there minimal cardiovascular adaptations to chronic resistance training?

APPLICATIONS

1. Explain the cardiovascular benefits of ingesting fluid during prolonged exercise, especially in hot or humid climates.

2. Why is the body's regulation of blood flow redistribution important for increasing oxygen delivery to muscle and maximizing VO_{2max}?

3. Would the chronic peripheral adaptations of the cardiovascular system help individuals recovering from a myocardial infarction (i.e., heart attack)? Explain.

4. Individuals who have a heart transplant do not have any neural regulation of the heart, and a diminished potential for increasing myocardial contractility. How might these changes alter their ability to exercise? Include the role of heart rate, stroke volume, and cardiac output.

REFERENCES

1. Anderson, P., and J. Henriksson. Capillary supply of the quadriceps femoris muscle of man: Adaptive response to exercise. *J. Physiol.* 270:677–690, 1977.

2. Anderson, P., and B. Saltin. Maximal perfusion of skeletal muscle in man. *J. Physiol.* 366:233–249, 1985.

3. Barklay, J. K., and W. N. Stainsby. The role of blood flow in limiting maximal metabolic rate in muscle. *Med. Sci. Sports Exerc.* 7(2):116–119, 1975.

4. Barklay, J. K. A delivery-independent blood flow effect on skeletal muscle fatigue. *J. Appl. Physiol.* 61(3):1084–1090, 1986.

5. Brechue, W. F., J. K. Barklay, D. M. O'Drobinak, and W. N. Stainsby. Difference between VO_2 maxima of twitch and tetanic contractions are related to blood flow. *J. Appl. Physiol.* 71(1):131–135, 1991.

6. Burge, C. M., M. F. Carey, and W. R. Payne. Rowing performance, fluid balance, and metabolic function following dehydration and rehydration. *Med. Sci. Sports Exerc.* 25(12):1358–1364, 1993.

7. Clausen, J. P. Effect of physical training on cardiovascular adjustments to exercise in man. *Physiol. Rev.* 57(4):779–815, 1977.

8. Coyle, E. F., and J. Gonzalez-Alonso. Cardiovascular drift during prolonged exercise: New perspectives. *Exer. Sports Sci. Rev.* 29:86–92, 2001.

9. Coyle, E. F., M. K. Hemmert, and A. R. Coggan. Effects of detraining on cardiovascular responses to exercise: Role of blood volume. *J. Appl. Physiol.* 60(1):95–99, 1986.

10. Cox, M. L., J. B. Bennett III, and G. A. Dudley. Exercise training-induced alterations of cardiac morphology. *J. Appl. Physiol.* 61(3):926–931, 1986.

11. Ehsani, A. A., J. M. Hagberg, and R. C. Hickson. Rapid changes in left ventricular dimensions and mass in response to physical conditioning and deconditioning. *Am. J. Cardiol.* 42:52–56, 1978.

12. Gillen, C. M., R. Lee, G. W. Mack, C. M. Tomaselli, T. Nishiyasu, and E. R. Nadel. Plasma volume expansion in humans after a single intense exercise protocol. *J. Appl. Physiol.* 71(5):1914–1920, 1991.

13. Gledhill, N., D. Cox, and R. Jamnik. Endurance athlete's stroke volume does not plateau: Major advantage is diastolic function. *Med. Sci. Sports Exerc.* 26(9):1116–1121, 1994.

14. Griffin, S. E., R. A. Robergs, and V. H. Heyward. Blood pressure measurement during exercise: A review. *Med. Sci. Sports Exerc.*, 29(1):149–159, 1997.

15. Hickson, R. C., B. A. Dvorak, E. M. Gorostiaga, T. T. Kurowski, and C. Foster. Potential for strength and endurance training to amplify endurance performance. *J. Appl. Physiol.* 65:2285–2290, 1988.

16. Hofmann, P., V. Bunc, H. Leitner, R. Pokan, and G. Gaisl. Heart rate threshold related to lactate turn point and steady state exercise on a cycle ergometer. *Eur. J. Appl. Physiol.* 58:303–306, 1988.

17. Iversen, P. O., M. Standa, and G. Nicolaysen. Marked regional heterogeneity in blood flow within a single skeletal muscle at rest and during exercise hyperaemia in the rabbit. *Acta Physiol. Scand.* 136:17–28, 1989.

18. Johnson, P. C., P. D. Wagner, and D. F. Wilson, 1996. Regulation of oxidative metabolism and blood flow in skeletal muscle. *Med. Sci. Sports Exerc.* 28(3):305–314, 1996.

19. Joyner, M. J., R. L. Lennon, D. J. Wedel, S. H. Rose, and J. T. Shepherd. Blood flow to contracting muscles: Influence of increased sympathetic activity. *J. Appl. Physiol.* 68(4): 1453–1457, 1990.

20. Kellog, D. L. Jr., J. M. Johnson, and W. A. Kosiba. Selective abolition of adrenergic vasoconstrictor responses in the skin by local iontophoresis of bretylium. *Am. J. Physiol.* 257(26): H1599–H1606, 1989.

21. Kellog, D. L. Jr., L. M. Johnson, and W. A. Kosiba. Baroreflex control of the cutaneous active vasodilator system in humans. *Circ. Res.* 66:1420–1426, 1990.

22. Keteyian, S. J., C. R. C. Marks, A. B. Levine, T. Kataoka, F. Fedel, and T. B. Levine. Cardiovascular responses to submaximal arm and leg exercise in cardiac transplants. *Med. Sci. Sports Exerc.* 26:420–424, 1994.

23. Keteyian, S. J., C. R. C. Marks, C. A. Brawner, A. B. Levine, T. Kataoka, and T. B. Levine. Responses to arm exercise in patients with compensated heart failure. *J. Cardiopulmonary Rehabil.* 16:366–371, 1996.

24. Kenney, W. L., and J. M. Johnson. Control of skin blood flow during exercise. *Med. Sci. Sports Exerc.* 24(3):303–312, 1992.

25. Kiens, B., B. Saltin, L. Walloe, and J. Wesche. Temporal relationship between blood flow changes and release of ions and metabolites from muscles upon single weak contractions. *Acta Physiol. Scand.* 136:551–559, 1989.

26. Knight, D. R., et al. Relationship between body and leg VO_2 during maximal cycle ergometry. *J. Appl. Physiol.* 73(3): 1114–1121, 1992.

27. Krip, B., N. Gledhill, V. Jamnik, and D. Warburton. Effect of alterations in blood volume on cardiac function during maximal exercise. *Med. Sci. Sports. Exerc.* 29(11):1469–1476, 1997.

28. Martin, D. G., E. W. Ferguson, S. Wigutoff, T. Gawne, and E. B. Schoomaker. Blood viscosity responses to maximal exercise in endurance-trained and sedentary female subjects. *J. Appl. Physiol.* 59(2):348–352, 1985.

29. Miles, D. S., M. H. Cox, and J. P. Bomze. Cardiovascular responses to upper body exercise in normals and cardiac patients. *Med. Sci. Sports Exerc.* 21(5):S126–S131, 1989.

30. Morganroth, J., B. Maron, W. Henry, and S. Epstein. Comparative left ventricular dimensions in trained athletes. *Ann Intern Med.* 82:521–524, 1975.

31. Montain, S., and E. F. Coyle. Influence of graded dehydration on hyperthermia and cardiovascular drift during exercise. *J. Appl. Physiol.* 73(4):1340–1350, 1992.

32. O'Rourke, M. F. What is blood pressure? *Am. J. Hyperten.* 3:308–310, 1993.

33. Pellicia, A., B. J. Maron, A. Spataro, M. A. Proschan, and P. Spirito. The upper limit of physiologic cardiac hypertrophy in highly trained elite athletes. *N. Eng. J. Med.* 324(5):295–301, 1991.

34. Pendergast, D. R. Cardiovascular, respiratory, and metabolic responses to upperbody exercise. *Med. Sci. Sports Exerc.* 21(5):S121–S125, 1989.

35. Pokan, R., et al. Heart rate deflection related to lactate performance curve and plasma catecholamine response during incremental cycle ergometer exercise. *Eur. J. Appl. Physiol.* 70:175–179, 1995.

36. Robergs, R. A., M. V. Icenogle, T. L. Hudson, and E. R. Greene. Temporal disparity in arterial blood flow to contracting muscle. *Med. Sci. Sports Exerc.* 29(8):1021–1027, 1997.

37. Rowell, L., D. S. O'Leary, and D. L. Kellogg Jr. Integration of cardiovascular control systems in dynamic exercise. In L. B. Rowell and J. T. Shephard (eds.), *Handbook of physiology.* American Physiology Society, New York, 1996, chap. 17.

38. Rubal, B. J., A.-R. Al-Muhailani, and J. Rosentsweig. Effects of physical conditioning on the heart size and wall thickness of college women. *Med. Sci. Sports. Exerc.* 19(5):423–429, 1987.

39. Sawka, M. N., A. J. Young, K. B. Pandolf, R. C. Dennis, and C. R. Valeri. Erythrocyte, plasma, and blood volume of healthy young men. *Med. Sci. Sports Exerc.* 24(4):447–453, 1992.

40. Schumacker, P. T., and R. W. Samsel. Analysis of oxygen delivery and uptake relationships in the Krogh tissue model. *J. Appl. Physiol.* 67(3):1234–1244, 1989.

41. Spriet, L. L., N. Gledhill, A. B. Froese, and D. L. Wilkes. Effect of graded erythrocythemia on cardiovascular and metabolic responses to exercise. *J. Appl. Physiol.* 61(5):1942–1948, 1986.

42. Stainsby, W. N., W. F. Brechue, D. M. O'Drobinak, and J. K. Barclay. Effects of ischaemic and hypoxic hypoxia on VO_2 and lactic acid output during tetanic contractions. *J. Appl. Physiol.* 68:574–579, 1991.

43. Tipton, C. M. Exercise, training, and hypertension: An update. *Exer. Sports Sci. Rev.* 18:447–505, 1991.

44. Tokmakidis, S. P., and L. A. Leger. Comparison of mathematically determined blood lactate and heart rate "threshold" points and relationship with performance. *Eur. J. Appl. Physiol.* 64:309–317, 1992.

45. Urhausen, A., and W. Kindermann. One and two-dimensional echocardiography in body builders and endurance-trained subjects. *Int. J. Sports Med.* 10:139–144, 1989.

46. Walloe, L., and J. Wesche. Time course and magnitude of blood flow changes in the human quadriceps muscles during and following rhythmic exercise. *J. Physiol.* 405:257–273, 1988.

47. Wilmore, J. H., P. R. Stanforth, J. Gagnon, T. Rice, S. Mandel, A. S. Leon, D. C. Rao, J. S. Skinner, and C. Bouchard. Cardiac output and stroke volume changes with endurance training: The Heritage Family Study. *Med. Sci. Sports Exerc.* 33: 99–106, 2001.

48. Wilmore, J. H., P. R. Stanforth, J. Gagnon, T. Rice, S. Mandel, A. S. Leon, D. C. Rao, J. S. Skinner, and C. Bouchard. Heart rate and blood pressure changes with endurance training: The Heritage Family Study. *Med. Sci. Sports Exerc.* 33:107–116, 2001.

49. Zeldis, S. M., J. Morganroth, and S. Rubler. Cardiac hypertrophy in response to dynamic conditioning in female athletes. *J. Appl. Physiol.* 44(6):849–852, 1978.

RECOMMENDED READING

Barklay, J. K., and W. N. Stainsby. The role of blood flow in limiting maximal metabolic rate in muscle. *Med. Sci. Sports Exerc.* 7(2):116–119, 1975.

Ehsani, A. A., J. M. Hagberg, and R. C. Hickson. Rapid changes in left ventricular dimensions and mass in response to physical conditioning and deconditioning. *Am. J. Cardiol.* 42:52–56, 1978.

Gillen, C. M., R. Lee, G. W. Mack, C. M. Tomaselli, T. Nishiyasu, and E. R. Nadel. Plasma volume expansion in humans after a single intense exercise protocol. *J. Appl. Physiol.* 71(5): 1914–1920, 1991.

Knight, D. R. et al. Relationship between body and leg VO$_2$ during maximal cycle ergometry. *J. Appl. Physiol.* 73(3): 1114–1121, 1992.

Pellicia, A., B. J. Maron, A. Spataro, M. A. Proschan, and P. Spirito. The upper limit of physiologic cardiac hypertrophy in highly trained elite athletes. *N. Eng. J. Med.* 324(5):295–301, 1991.

Robergs, R. A., M. V. Icenogle, T .L. Hudson, and E. R. Greene. Temporal disparity in arterial blood flow to contracting muscle. *Med. Sci. Sports Exerc.* 29(8):1021–1027, 1996.

Saltin, B., R. Boushell, N. Secher, and J. Mitchell. Exercise and circulation in health and disease. Human Kinetics, Champaign, 1998.

Segal, S. S., and D. T. Kurjiaka. Coordination of blood flow control in the resistance vasculature of skeletal muscle. *Med. Sci. Sports Exerc.* 27(8):1158–1164, 1995.

Spriet, L. L., N. Gledhill, A. B. Froese, and D. L. Wilkes. Effect of graded erythrocythemia on cardiovascular and metabolic responses to exercise. *J. Appl. Physiol.* 61(5):1942–1948, 1986.

Toner, M. M., E. L. Glickman, and W. D. McArdle. Cardiovascular adjustments to exercise distributed between the upper and lower body. *Med. Sci. Sports Exerc.* 22(6):773–778, 1990.

Wagner, P. D. New ideas on limitations to VO$_{2max}$. *Exerc. Sport Sci. Rev.* 28:10–14, 2000.

Pulmonary Adaptations to Exercise

t the start of exercise, two of the first sensations we experience are increases in the frequency and depth of breathing. The rapidity of these responses is not surprising, because once we start to exercise we need to rapidly provide oxygen to the working muscles to minimize the oxygen deficit. Unless ventilation increases in concert with increases in cardiac output, an inadequate volume of air will be available in the lungs to replenish oxygen and remove carbon dioxide from the blood. To understand these changes, and the alteration in blood oxygen and carbon dioxide content as blood circulates around the body, the student must learn the basic physical principles that govern relationships among gas volume, pressure, solubility, and diffusion. Once these principles are understood, the importance of pulmonary physiology during exercise, as well as the changes in pulmonary function when exercising at altitude or when lung function is impaired (e.g., asthma, emphysema), can be fully appreciated. This chapter will present the basic anatomy of the lung, the physiology of gas exchange, the transport of gases in blood, and a summary of the research that has documented the magnitude of changes in lung function during different exercise conditions (acute) and in response to exercise training (chronic).

OBJECTIVES

After studying this chapter you should be able to:

- Identify the anatomical structure and components for the conducting zone and respiratory zone of the lungs.
- Identify the terms used for the different components of the total lung volume.
- Provide estimates of the volumes for the components of the total lung volume.
- Explain the procedures involved in spirometry testing.
- Calculate lung volumes from a spirometry tracing.
- Identify and describe the different instruments and methods used in pulmonary function testing.
- Describe the differences between ventilation, alveolar ventilation, and respiration.
- Explain how oxygen and carbon dioxide are transported in the blood.
- Explain the differences between the Bohr and Haldane effects and the factors that cause them.
- Identify the contributions that skeletal muscle, blood, carbon dioxide, bicarbonate, ventilation, and buffers make to the regulation of acid-base balance.
- Explain the complexity of neural and humoral controls of ventilation.
- Describe the range of ventilation possible from rest to maximal exercise.
- Explain the relationship between ventilation and exercise intensity and how to detect the ventilation threshold.
- Explain the metabolic theory that connects the ventilation threshold to the lactate threshold.
- List the chronic adaptations of the pulmonary system that occur in response to exercise training, and appreciate their role(s) in improving exercise tolerance/performance.

KEY TERMS

conducting zone	pneumotachometer	Bohr effect
respiratory zone	oximetry	carbonic anhydrase
pores of Kohn	residual volume	Haldane effect
pulmonary circulation	helium dilution	myoglobin
anatomical dead space	nitrogen washout	ventilatory threshold
tidal volume	ventilation	hypoxemia
spirometry	compliance	exercise-induced hypoxemia
kymograph	alveolar ventilation	asthma
spirometer	surfactant	pulmonary transit time
vital capacity	respiration	
	blood-gas interface	
	hemoglobin	

The Basic Anatomy of Lung and Pulmonary Circulation

*T*he two lungs of the body are located within the thoracic cavity. Air is directed to and from the lungs by the *trachea*, which is a long tube supported by cartilage that extends from the larynx to the diverging bronchi and bronchioles of the lungs (fig. 8.1). The trachea and each of the left and right *bronchi* have circumferentially layered smooth muscle, and are structurally supported by numerous C-shaped rings of cartilage. Collectively, the mouth and nasal passages, trachea, bronchi, and *bronchioles* make up the **conducting zone** of the lungs (Personal Trainer 8.1), whereas the *respiratory bronchioles, alveoli ducts,* and *alveoli,* which are the sites of gas exchange and responsible for the largest lung gas volumes, are referred to as the **respiratory zone** (fig. 8.2). The respiratory zone of the lung is the location of lung inflation, and as the category name suggests, is the site of gas exchange, or *respiration.*

The average diameter of an alveolus is approximately 0.25 mm, the average membrane thickness of the respiratory structures is 0.5 μm, and there are approximately 300 million respiratory bronchioles that diverge into numerous alveoli. The alveoli and respiratory bronchioles are connected by openings or holes in their membranes, termed **pores of Kohn.** Originally it was believed that these holes allowed air to flow from one alveolus to another; however, recent research has shown that the pores are normally filled with fluid, and are responsible for the distribution of water and surfactant throughout the respiratory zone (2). Collectively, the respiratory bronchioles and alveoli make up a surface area of approximately 70 square meters, which is a phenomenally large area for gas exchange, given that it is contained within the thoracic cavity.

Blood from the heart is pumped through the pulmonary arteries to the lungs, and blood is directed back to the left side of the heart via the pulmonary veins. The circulation of blood to and through the lung is termed the **pulmonary circulation.** The pulmonary circulation has a much lower blood pressure than the systemic circulation (25/8 compared to 120/80 mmHg at rest; see chapter 7). The respiratory zone of the lung is engorged with a rich blood supply (fig. 8.2). A dense capillary bed surrounds the structures of the respiratory zone, providing almost as much surface area of blood as that of the respiratory membranes. Obviously, optimal respiration would require a similarity between lung inflation and blood perfusion, and this concept is expressed by the ventilation perfusion ratio (V_E/Q).

Lung Volumes and Capacities

The conducting zone of the lung is often referred to as **anatomical dead space,** since it does not have a respiratory function. The anatomical dead space makes up an average volume of 150 mL, although this value varies directly with body size.

The remaining volumes of the lung (fig. 8.3) are subdivisions of the total lung capacity and essentially comprise the *residual volume* and *vital capacity.* Vital capacity is the maximal volume of air that can be exhaled from the lungs. It is measured as the volume reacting from air displaced during a maximal inspiratory effort followed by a forced expiration. Vital capacity can be divided into inspiratory and expiratory components using a technique called *spirometry.* Normal resting breathing involves the inspiration and expiration of

---

FIGURE 8.1

The respiratory system is located within the thoracic cavity and is connected to the facial openings of the nose and mouth by the trachea and pharynx.

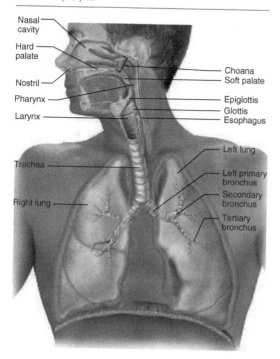

Nasal cavity
Hard palate
Nostril
Pharynx
Larynx
Choana
Soft palate
Epiglottis
Glottis
Esophagus
Left lung
Trachea
Left primary bronchus
Secondary bronchus
Right lung
Tertiary bronchus

---

conducting zone the zone of the lung where no respiration (gas exchange) occurs

respiratory zone the zone of the lung where respiration (gas exchange) occurs

pores of Kohn the holes within alveoli that allow fluid and surfactant to spread across the alveoli membranes

pulmonary circulation the blood and vessels that connect the heart and the lungs

anatomical dead space the volume of air within the conducting zone of the lung

FIGURE 8.2

Lungs structure can be divided into two zones. *(a)* The conducting zone is composed of airways that direct air to and from the regions of the lungs involved in gas exchange and the external environment (nose and mouth to alveoli). *(b and c)* The respiratory zone consists of the regions of the lungs involved in gas exchange, which are made up of highly vascularized inflatable structures, termed alveoli. *(c)* The walls of the alveoli are very thin and in close proximity to the blood vessels, which contain the red blood cells and blood gases.

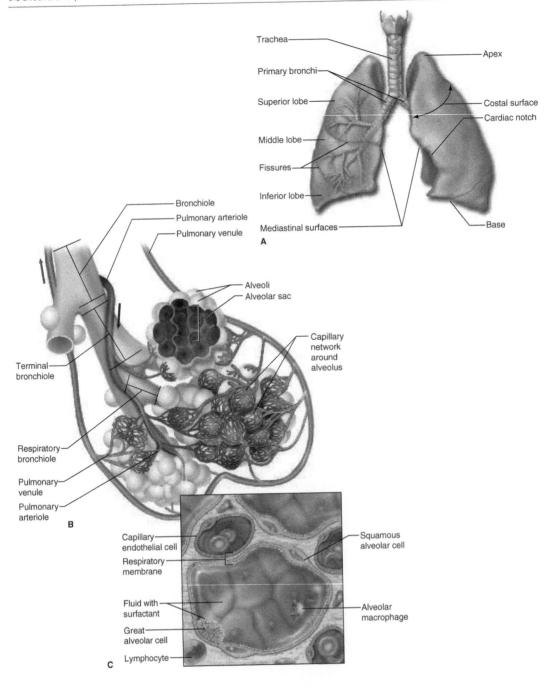

PERSONAL TRAINER 8.1

Do Nasal Strips Improve Ventilation and Exercise Performance?

Because of your interest in health and fitness, you might be asked about the benefit of wearing nasal strips. After all, these strips are worn by professional athletes, and television has provided ample coverage on professional and elite athletes who use them. Why are these strips worn? Do these strips offer any advantage to an athlete? Should these strips be recommended to the recreational athlete?

First of all, let's look at some background information. Because of the narrow passages of the conducting zone of the lung, there is the possibility that resistance to air flowing into the nose and mouth might limit the volume of air we can ventilate in and out of the lungs each minute. Based on this hypothesis, there is a product used by many athletes that functions to further open the nostrils of the nose to decrease resistance to airflow during nasal breathing. This product adheres to the outer surface of the nostrils, and small springs within the nasal strip function to slightly flare the nostrils.

Several studies have been completed in an attempt to verify manufacturer claims that the nasal strips will increase ventilation during exercise and improve sports performance (57, 59). Vermoen and associates (59) measured resistance to airflow through the nose, with and without nasal strips, while subjects breathed through the nose at rest, and during

increased inspiratory and expiratory efforts. Use of the nasal strips did not decrease nasal resistance to airflow. However, the volume of air ventilated through the nose in 1 s during inspiration was larger when nasal strips were worn.

More important, and despite the increase in the rate of inspired airflow with nasal strips, Thomas and colleagues (57) showed that nasal strips did not result in an increased capacity to generate mechanical power during intense exercise. This latter result is not surprising, because when individuals transition from rest to exercise there is a progressive decreased dependency on nasal breathing and an increased reliance on oral breathing. *The greater the exercise intensity, the greater the contribution of oral ventilation to total ventilation.* This transition occurs because there is less resistance to airflow when breathing through the mouth than the nose (oronasal breathing), and during exercise this transition in breathing occurs subconsciously. Consequently, the fact that nasal strips might increase the rate of airflow through the nose may only be beneficial for athletes who have an impaired ability to breathe through their mouth, such as those athletes who wear mouth guards. Unfortunately, more research is needed to verify that nasal strips benefit these athletes.

---

500 mL of air, termed the **tidal volume,** and it is the sum of the tidal volume and breathing frequency that determines *ventilation.*

Pulmonary Function Testing: Equipment and Methods

Pulmonary function tests (table 8.1) and testing equipment have become quite sophisticated in the last decade. Equipment used to test pulmonary function can cost less than $100 for portable instruments that measure flow rates, to more than $20,000 for whole-body plethysmographs or computerized lung volume and airflow systems. In this chapter, several important instruments that are used in the testing of athletes, as well as the routine clinical testing of patients, will be presented and their measurements explained.

Volume-Displaced Spirometer

In the early 1800s, John Hutchinson discovered that lung volumes could be accurately measured by having subjects breathe into a system that records volume displacements on paper. John Hutchinson's early experiments led to the development of the technique which we now call **spirometry.** Even today, the spirometer remains one of the basic tools for evaluating pulmonary function.

FIGURE 8.3

The volumes of the lung can be measured by spirometry. The total lung capacity (TLC) includes a volume that cannot be exhaled from the lung (residual volume, RV), and a volume that represents the maximal ability for lung inflation (vital capacity, VC). During normal resting breathing, an average of 500 mL of air is inspired and expired, and is termed the tidal volume (V_T).

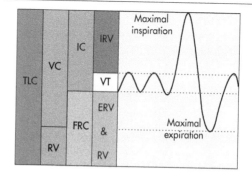

---

tidal volume the volume of air ventilated into and out of the lungs with each breath

spirometry (spi-rom'e-tri) the measurement of human lung volumes and functional capacities with a spirometer

TABLE 8.1

Examples of specific pulmonary function tests and the purpose(s) for which they are performed

TESTS	PURPOSES
Lung Volumes and Capacities	
Vital capacity	Functional lung volume
Residual lung volume	Body composition assessment
	Evaluation of lung damage
Lung Mechanics	
Lung and chest compliance	Evaluation of airway damage
Airway closure	Evaluation of airway damage
Lung Dynamics	
Flow rates	Evaluation of lung damage
	Evaluation of ventilatory muscle power
Airway closure	Evaluation of integrity of small airways
Gas Exchange	
Ventilation—perfusion	Assessment of regional distributions of lung ventilation and perfusion
	Estimation of physiological dead space
Gas diffusion	Assessment of edema, lung damage
Blood gas measurement	Evaluation of functional gas exchange
Pulse oximetry (hemoglobin saturation)	Evaluation of alveolar to arterial oxygen diffusion

Source: Adapted from Chusid (9).

A spirometer (fig. 8.4) consists of (1) an upright metal cylinder that is open at the top, (2) a second cylinder approximately ½ in smaller in diameter, which is closed at the top except for two holes (which are exit holes for the tubes that run from the inside of the spirometer to the outside), and (3) a plastic cylinder (often called a bell), which is open at the bottom. The first and second cylinders create a space which is filled with water. The bell sits in the water between the first and second cylinders. When the bell rests in the water, an airtight seal is made between the bell and the water, and when air is forced into or out of the spirometer, the bell will move either upward or downward.

When a subject breathes into the spirometer (exhales), the bell moves up because air is forced into the closed system. The air exhaled into the system is mixed throughout by a fan, and CO_2 is absorbed by soda lime contained in a canister inside the bell. During inhalation, air is removed from the closed system, which causes a vacuumlike effect because of the airtight seal, and the bell moves downward.

The oxygen removed from the air in the system by the body is added by an inflow of pure oxygen at a rate that equals VO_2. Thus spirometry is also a means to measure VO_2, and this method is termed *closed-circuit spirometry.* However, as CO_2 is removed and not measured, VCO_2 is not known and therefore RER (respiratory exchange ratio) and an accurate estimate of energy expenditure cannot be calculated.

The movement of the bell upward and downward represents the volume of air entering and exiting the lungs. When the bell is connected to a pen, the movements of the bell can be recorded on a rotating drum called a **kymograph.** Once the volume conversion of the bell is known (mL/mm), volume (ATPS) can be calculated. The various lung volumes and capacities at rest are illustrated in tables 8.2 and 8.3. They provide values for these measurements and indicate which lung volumes change during exercise. Table 8.4 provides prediction equations for many of these measurements.

Bellows-Type Spirometer

Another type of volume-displacement system for measuring lung volumes is the bellows-type **spirometer,** often termed a *spirograph* or *vitalograph.* The bellows-type spirometer consists of collapsible bellows that fold and unflod in response to inhalation and exhalation. When a subject exhales into the spirometer, the bellows expand and record the volume of air on paper. Thus the displacement of the bellows by a volume of air is transferred to either a mechanical recording or an electrical recording on a computer. Typically, an individual will exhale as hard and as fast as possible into a vitalograph, and **vital capacity** and expired flow rates can be computed from the calibrated paper used on the instrument.

Flow-Sensing Spirometers

A more sophisticated type of spirometer calculates lung volumes by directly measuring the flow of air. A **pneumotachometer** measures the rate of flow of air during inhalation and exhalation (fig. 8.5). Airflow during exhalation is based on the difference between the pressure of air entering the pneumotach against resistance (usually a small mesh screen) (P_1), and the pressure of air on the other side of the resistance (P_2). The greater the flow of air into the pneumotach, the greater the resistance, and the greater the pressure difference, and thus the greater the volume of air moving through the pneumotach.

The pressure difference ($P_1 - P_2$) is measured continuously with a special pressure-sensing transducer, and the signal is then transmitted to a computer, which then integrates the signal and transforms flow rates into volumes per unit time. Volumes can be calculated from the flow measurements because volume (mL) = flow (mL/s) × time (s). Pneumotach spirometers are frequently used when conducting

FIGURE 8.4

A Collins spirometer used for quantifying lung volumes and capacities. Air is directed into and from the spirometer by pipes and low-resistance tubing that connect the system to the outside air or to the subject. Vertical displacement of the floating bell during inspiration and expiration is marked on paper on the kymograph (rotating bell). Each millimeter rise or fall of the bell represents a given volume of gas, which depends on the volume conversion factor for the bell expressed in ATPS conditions.

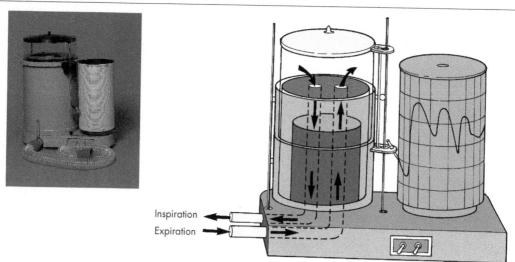

Inspiration ←

Expiration →

cardiopulmonary testing because of their small size and high sensitivity and accuracy.

Breathing Valves

There are two types of breathing valves commonly used in pulmonary function testing: free-breathing and multiple one-way directional valves (fig. 8.6). A free-breathing valve is commonly seen on a volume-displacement spirometer, because it allows the subject to be switched from breathing room air (open-circuit) to breathing gas contained in a spirometer (closed-circuit). The most common directional valve apparatus used in exercise testing is the Daniel's valve. This valve apparatus actually contains two one-way valves that direct inspired air into the mouth and expired air to a sampling hose.

The difficulty with a valve apparatus for placement in the mouth is the stimulus this gives to increase ventilation. Thus, when testing ventilation using a mouthpiece valve apparatus, subjects need to be given a familiarization period (usually 2 to 3 min of quiet breathing through the mouthpiece) before actual data collection is begun. To minimize hyperventilation, face masks are also available that have multiple one-way valves to direct inspired and expired air.

Pulse Oximetry

Oximetry involves the indirect determination of the percentage of hemoglobin that is bound with oxygen (S_aO_2). Oximetry is a commonly used (noninvasive) method in

hospitals and also during exercise testing to assess blood oxygenation. One of the newest methods of oximetry during exercise testing is the pulse oximeter (23, 43, 49). Pulse oximeters measure the change in infrared light transmission through a finger or the earlobe to calculate arterial saturation. Such a principle is based on the color change in oxyhemoglobin at different oxygen saturations. The pulse oximeter has been shown to be fairly accurate in exercise testing (23, 43, 49). A drop in arterial oxygenation under normal barometric pressure conditions is an indication of respiratory failure or, when used during exercise, it is able to detect a inadequate pulmonary function indicated by exercise-induced hypoxemia.

kymograph (ki′mo-graf) the rotating drum component of an instrument (e.g., spirometer) that is used to record wavelike modulations (e.g., ventilation)

spirometer (spi-rom′e-ter) a device used to measure lung volumes

vital capacity the maximal volume of air that can be exhaled from the lungs in one expiratory effort

pneumotachometer (nu′mo-ta-kom′e-ter) an instrument for measuring the instantaneous flow during ventilation

oximetry (ok′sim′e-tri) indirect measurement of the oxygen saturation of hemoglobin in blood

TABLE 8.2

Pulmonary lung volumes and capacities measured by spirometry and their changes during exercise

VOLUME CAPACITY	ABBREVIATION	DESCRIPTION	CHANGE DURING EXERCISE
Residual volume	RV	Volume of air remaining in the lungs after maximum exhalation; cannot be determined with spirometry	Slight increase
Expiratory reserve volume	ERV	Maximum volume of air exhaled from end-expiratory level	Slight decrease
Functional residual capacity	FRC	Sum of RV and ERV; cannot be determined with spirometry	Slight increase
Tidal volume	V_T	Volume of air inhaled and exhaled with each breath during quiet breathing	Increase
Inspiratory reserve volume	IRV	Maximum volume of air inhaled from end-inspiratory level	Decrease
Inspiratory capacity	IC	Sum of IRV and V_T	Increase
Vital capacity	VC	Maximum volume of air exhaled from the point of maximum inspiration	Slight decrease
Total lung capacity	TLC	Sum of all volume compartments of the lung	Slight decrease
Forced vital capacity	FVC	Forced vital capacity performed with maximally forced expiratory effort	Decrease
Forced expiratory volume in 1 sec	FEV_1	Volume of air expired in 1 s	
Maximum voluntary ventilation	MVV	Volume of air expired in a specified period during repetitive maximum respiratory effort	Slight decrease

Adapted from Buono et al. (6).

TABLE 8.3

Values for lung volumes* for healthy men and women

MEASURE	MALES	FEMALES
V_T	400–500	350–450
IRV	3100	1900
ERV	1200	900
RV	1200	1000
	[Age (yrs) × 0.0115] + [height (cm) × 0.019] − 2.24	[Age (yrs) × 0.03] + [height (cm) × 0.0387] − [body surface area (mm²) × 0.73] − 2.24
TLC	6000	4200

*Lung volumes (mL, BTPS); VT = tidal volume; IRV = inspiratory reserve volume; ERV = expiratory reserve volume; RV = residual volume; TLC = total lung capacity.

Sources: RV equations are from Boren et al. (5) for men and O'Brien and Drizd (42) for women.

Residual Lung Volume

Residual volume (RV) is the volume of air remaining in the lungs after a maximal exhalation (see fig. 8.3). RV represents the difference between TLC and VC. RV, which is a subdivision of FRC (functional residual capacity), must be measured, and is important for the accurate calculation of body density measured by hydrostatic weighing. In addition, among individuals with chronic obstructive lung disease, residual volume is increased because of premature airway closure (30, 51). There are a variety of methods used to indirectly measure RV. Most researchers use either a closed-circuit **helium dilution** or open-circuit **nitrogen washout** method.

Ventilation

The term **ventilation** is synonymous with the process of breathing, but is very different than the process of respiration, which will be described in later sections. *Ventilation involves the movement of air into and from the lungs by the process of bulk flow.* During inspiration and expiration, the lung compartments are opened to the external environment and, therefore, to the pressure, temperature, and humidity of atmo-spheric air. A pressure differential between the air within the lung and the atmospheric air is generated by the muscles of ventilation. During inspiration, the lungs are expanded because of contraction of the muscles of inspiration, causing the pressure in the lungs to decrease, and allowing air to move from the atmosphere into the lungs. During expiration, the contraction of the muscles of expiration force the lung volume to decrease, raising the pressure and forcing

TABLE 8.4

Equations to predict pulmonary capacities

PULMONARY CAPACITIES	MEN	WOMEN
	< 25 years	**< 20 years**
FVC	$(0.05 \times H)$ $+ (0.078 \times A)$ $- 5.508$	$(0.033 \times H)$ $+ (0.092 \times A)$ $- 3.469$
FEV₁	$(0.046 \times H)$ $+ (0.045 \times A)$ $- 4.808$	$(0.027 \times H)$ $- (0.085 \times A)$ $- 2.703$
FEV₁%	$103.64 - (0.087 \times H)$ $- (0.14 \times A)$	$107.38 - (0.111 \times H)$ $- (0.109 \times A)$
	> 20 years	**> 25 years**
FVC	$(0.065 \times H)$ $+ (0.029 \times A)$ $- 5.459$	$(0.037 \times H)$ $+ (0.022 \times A)$ $- 1.774$
FEV₁	$(0.052 \times H)$ $+ (0.027 \times A)$ $- 4.203$	$(0.027 \times H)$ $- (0.021 \times A)$ $- 0.794$
FEV₁%	$103.64 - (0.087 \times H)$ $- (0.14 \times A)$	$107.38 - (0.111 \times H)$ $- (0.109 \times A)$
MVV	$(1.15 \times H)$ $- (1.27 \times A) + 14$	$(0.55 \times H)$ $- (0.72 \times A) + 50$

FVC = forced vital capacity; FEV₁ = forced expired volume in 1 S; FEV₁% = FEV₁ expressed as percent of FVC; MVV = maximal voluntary ventilation; H = height (cm); A = age (yr).

Sources: Adopted from Comroe et al. (10), Knudson et al. (33) and Taylor et al. (55).

FIGURE 8.5

Advances in electronics have developed the pneumotach, which measures flow rates by sensing pressure differences between air before and after crossing a resistance membrane. Devices like the pneumotach can record airflow changes during inspiration and expiration. Computer processing of the signal can convert flow rates into ventilation volumes per unit time.

air from the lungs to the atmosphere. These events are incredibly important during exercise, when ventilation can increase airflow through the lung from a mere 6 L/min at rest to over 150 L/min during maximal exercise. During maximal voluntary breathing, ventilation may exceed 200 L/min (22, 52).

Large changes in lung ventilation occur in as little as a few seconds, and result from increases in breathing frequency and/or tidal volume.

8.1 Ventilation (V_E) (L/min)
= frequency (br/min) × tidal volume (L)

For example, at rest,

$$V_E = 12 \text{ br/min} \times 0.5 \text{ L} = 6 \text{ L/min}$$

and at maximal exercise

$$V_E = 60 \text{ br/min} \times 3.0 \text{ L} = 180 \text{ L/min}$$

The speed at which the lungs can be inflated and deflated is remarkable, and occurs because of the low resistance of the alveoli to inflation and deflation. The property of being able to increase size or volume with only small changes in pressure is termed **compliance**. Thus the lungs must be highly compliant to be able to be inflated and deflated from 6 L/min to up to 200 L/min all with minimal effort (table 8.5).

residual volume the volume remaining in the lungs after a forced maximal exhalation

helium dilution the method used to measure the functional residual capacity (FRC) of the lung that is based on the dilution of a known amount of helium

nitrogen washout an alternative method for measuring the residual volume of the lung

ventilation (vent'-l-á-shen) the movement of air into and out of the lungs by bulk flow

compliance (kom'pli-ens) the property of the ease with which an object can increase volume for a given pressure differential

FIGURE 8.6

Two examples of a Daniel's valve setup. Two one-way valves direct inspired air into the mouth and expired air away from the subject. Typically, expired air is collected and analyzed for expired gas fractions and volume.

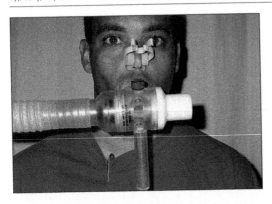
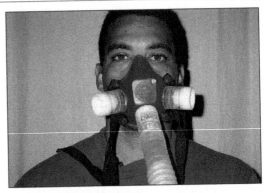

TABLE 8.5

Pulmonary ventilation at rest and during exercise

CONDITION	V_E (L/min)	=	f (br/min)	×	V_T (L/br)
Rest	6		12		0.5
Mild exercise	72		32		2.25
Maximal exercise	160		48		3.33

Volumes in BTPS conditions.

TABLE 8.6

Effect of changes in breathing patterns on alveolar ventilation

BREATHING	V_T (L/min)	f (br/min)	V_E (L/min)	V_A (L/min)
Shallow and rapid	0.24	25	6	2.25
Normal resting	0.5	12	6	4.2
Slow and deep	1.0	6	6.0	5.1

Ventilatory volumes in BTPS and assuming a constant DS (0.15 L).

Alveolar Ventilation

Because of the anatomical dead space, which hold ~150 mL or 0.15 L, not all of the air inspired actually reaches the respiratory zone and experiences gas exchange. Of the normal 500 mL tidal volume, 350 mL of "fresh" air reaches the respiratory zone, but this value varies based on the size of the individual and therefore the size of the tidal volume. The volume of "fresh" air that reaches the respiratory zone of the lung is termed **alveolar ventilation** (V_A) (table 8.6). *The greater the depth of breathing, the less impact the anatomical dead space has on alveolar ventilation.*

For example, for two conditions with identical minute ventilation (V_E):

Normal breathing:

8.2a
$$V_A = 12 \text{ br/min} \times (1.0 - 0.15 \text{ L})$$
$$= 12 \times 0.85 = 10.2 \text{ L/min}$$

Rapid shallow breathing:

8.2b
$$V_A = 60 \text{ br/min} \times (0.2 - 0.15 \text{ L})$$
$$= 60 \times 0.05 = 3.0 \text{ L/min}$$

The Importance of Surfactant

The presence of **surfactant** *makes it easier to inflate alveoli.* At normal lung volumes, when the alveoli are not overly inflated and the membrane circumference is small, there is a relatively high surfactant concentration covering the membranes of the alveoli. Surfactant functions to lower the surface tension of the alveoli, thereby decreasing the resistance to inflation and increasing compliance.

During inflation, the size of the alveoli surface area increases, and the concentration of surfactant decreases, so that *at higher lung volumes the resistance to inflation increases.* The latter event is not disastrous because it promotes a more even inflation of neighboring alveoli and respiratory bronchioles, and provides some elastic recoil force during the start of expiration.

Respiration

The three main gases of air are nitrogen, oxygen, and carbon dioxide. All three gases diffuse between the alveolar air and blood, but as gaseous nitrogen is not metabolized

The partial pressures of oxygen and carbon dioxide in air and alveoli when at sea level. Because of the removal of oxygen and the release of carbon dioxide by the body, and the saturation of air with water vapor, alveoli partial pressures of oxygen and carbon dioxide are very different from atmospheric air.

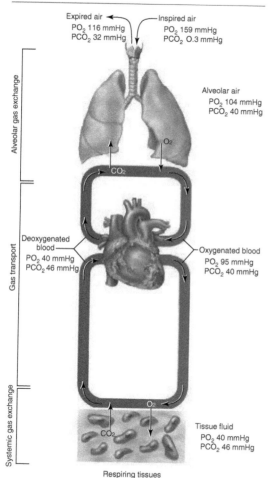

Expired air — Inspired air
PO_2 116 mmHg PO_2 159 mmHg
PCO_2 32 mmHg PCO_2 0.3 mmHg

Alveolar air
PO_2 104 mmHg
PCO_2 40 mmHg

O_2

CO_2

Deoxygenated blood
PO_2 40 mmHg
PCO_2 46 mmHg

Oxygenated blood
PO_2 95 mmHg
PCO_2 40 mmHg

O_2

CO_2

Tissue fluid
PO_2 40 mmHg
PCO_2 46 mmHg

Respiring tissues

Alveolar gas exchange

Gas transport

Systemic gas exchange

within the body (see chapter 3), only the latter two gases are of interest for normal physiological conditions. The process of gas exchange, or **respiration,** involves the movement of oxygen and carbon dioxide down pressure gradients that exist between pulmonary capillary blood and the air of the alveoli, and between capillary blood of the systemic circulation and the cells perfused by this blood. Consequently, the locations of respiration can be either in the lung, which is referred to as *external respiration,* or at the level of the systemic tissues, which is referred to as *internal respiration.*

External Respiration

The processes of external respiration result in the movement of gases between alveolar air and the pulmonary capillary blood. This exchange occurs via diffusion through a fluid medium that contains several membranes. The success of this diffusion depends on the characteristics of the gases for diffusion in an aqueous environment, and on the nature of the diffusion medium within the lung.

Gas Partial Pressures in Atmospheric and Alveolar Air

Dry atmospheric air contains 20.93% oxygen, 79.03% nitrogen, 0.03% carbon dioxide, and extremely small percentages of certain rare gases such as argon that make up the remaining 0.01%. When air contains moisture, or water vapor, the water vapor molecules force the gas molecules to disperse, resulting in an increased volume of air. For constant volumes of gas, the presence of water vapor occupies a pressure within the total gas pressure, and the pressures of the gases are lower than if no water was present. As described in appendix D, the water vapor pressure of air depends on relative humidity and the temperature of the gas.

Figure 8.7 presents the partial pressures of gases in air under standard conditions, in atmospheric air at a coastal location, and indicates how these gas pressures change in the alveoli. After accounting for the relative humidity (RH) and temperature of the atmospheric gas sample (at 55% RH and at 22° C, P_{H_2O} equals 18 mmHg), the actual pressure occupied by the true gases decreases from 747 to 729 mmHg. Within the alveoli, the pressure remains equal to atmospheric pressure, but as the air is warmed to 37° C and completely humidified (100% RH), the partial pressure of water vapor increases to 47 mmHg. Consequently, the pressure remaining for the true gases is 700 mmHg.

Diffusion of Gases

Once air is in the alveoli, it is subject to gas diffusion between the alveoli and blood, or vice versa. The factors that govern the direction and magnitude of diffusion are as follows:

- The diffusion capacity of each of the gases
- The gas partial pressure gradient between the alveoli and blood

alveolar ventilation the component of ventilation that reaches the respiratory zone of the lungs

surfactant (sir-fak'-tant) the lipoprotein molecule found over alveolar membranes that functions to decrease surface tension and improve compliance

respiration (res'p-ra'shen) gas exchange

UP CLOSE 8.1

Factors That Influence the Rate of Gas Diffusion in the Lung

For a gas to diffuse from one region to another, there must be a difference in gas partial pressure. If there is a difference, then the gas will move along this gradient until there is an even distribution of the gas, termed an *equilibrium*. Thus, for the lung, oxygen and carbon dioxide move along each of their partial pressure gradients between the pulmonary arterial blood and alveolar gas until these partial pressures equilibrate.

Not all gases move along a partial pressure gradient in a similar manner. For example, lung gas diffusion is complicated because there is more than just open air between the pulmonary arterial blood and alveolar gas. This anatomical distance, termed the **blood-gas interface**, consists of blood plasma, pulmonary capillary membranes, interstitial fluid, and alveolar membranes (fig. 8.8) that can interfere with gas

diffusion. For the normal lung, the most important of these components is the liquid of the plasma and interstitial fluid. If a gas is relatively insoluble in water, it will not diffuse rapidly through the blood-gas interface for a given partial pressure gradient.

Compared to carbon dioxide, oxygen is a relatively insoluble gas with a 20.3-fold lower solubility. Despite the small thickness of alveolar membranes and the large surface area of the respiratory zone (70 m^2), both of which make the lung suited to gas diffusion, the poor solubility of oxygen causes it to have a relatively low capacity for diffusion. Thus, even though the lung partial pressure gradients of oxygen is greater than 10-fold larger than for carbon dioxide, their different water solubility results in a more rapid equilibration for carbon dioxide than for oxygen.

FIGURE 8.8

The fluid and membranes that determine the distance between the alveolar air and the blood of the pulmonary capillary make up what is referred to as the "blood-gas interface." The physical principles that influence the diffusion of a gas across this interface depend on the solubility and diffusion coefficients for the respective gas.

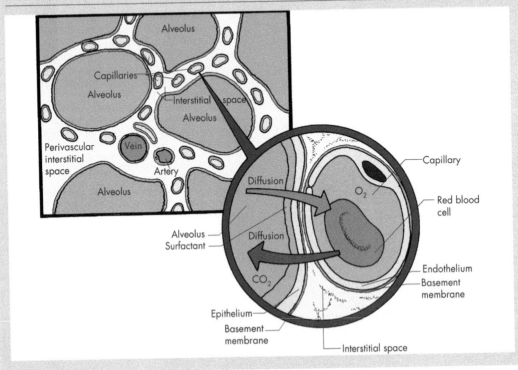

- The characteristics of the medium through which diffusion occurs

These factors are discussed in Up Close 8.1.

Transport of Oxygen and Carbon Dioxide in the Blood

To understand how gas partial pressures affect the volume of gases in blood, knowledge of how blood transports oxygen and carbon dioxide must be acquired.

Oxygen Transport

Oxygen is transported in blood bound to a specialized protein, **hemoglobin,** which is located on the surface of red blood cells. The blood hemoglobin concentration is influenced by gender, nutrition, and disease, with reference values provided in table 8.7. A given hemoglobin molecule can bind four oxygen molecules, and *when fully saturated with oxygen, 1 g of hemoglobin can bind 1.34 mL of oxygen.* For example, when the hemoglobin concentration equals 150 g/L, the following calculations result in the maximal volume of oxygen that can be transported in arterial blood:

8.3

Blood oxygen carrying capacity
$$= [Hb] \times O_2/g\ Hb \times [Hb] - O_2\ saturation$$
$$= 150\ g\ Hb/L \times 1.34\ mL\ O_2/g \times 0.98$$
$$= 197\ mL\ O_2/L$$

The slightly incomplete $Hb - O_2$ saturation at 98% is due to a combination of (1) diffusion limitation resulting from an average inequality between the lungs' ventilation and perfusion, (2) a *pulmonary arterial-to-venous shunt* where blood from the bronchioles drains into the pulmonary veins without passing through the pulmonary capillaries of the respiratory zone, and (3) a *cardiac shunt* involving the drainage of coronary venous blood into the left ventricle. These three deficiencies result in a minor reduction in the average arterial oxy-hemoglobin saturation to 98%.

Another small source of oxygen transport in blood is the volume of dissolved oxygen. Because of the low solubility of oxygen, this store is minimal and amounts to 0.003 mL of oxygen for every mmHg of gas partial pressure, or approximately 0.3 mL of oxygen at sea level where PO_2 approximates 104 mmHg.

Oxygen-Hemoglobin Saturation

At sea level, the normal alveolar partial pressure of oxygen (P_AO_2) approximates 104 mmHg. For conditions that lower P_AO_2, such as altitude or air pollution, the partial pressure gradient between the alveoli and blood would decrease. Based on the low-diffusion coefficient of oxygen, this can be disastrous for the exchange of oxygen between alveolar gas and blood, preventing the ability to equilibrate P_AO_2 and the arterial partial pressure of oxygen (P_aO_2) (58). It is important to understand how a

TABLE 8.7

Representative concentrations of hemoglobin and oxygen carrying capacity of the blood in males and females, after blood doping, and when anemic

POPULATION/CONDITION	[Hb] (g/100 mL)	mL O_2/L BLOOD*
Males	14.0	183.8
Females	12.0	157.6
Blood doping	18.0	236.4
Anemia	< 10.0	< 131.3

*Assumes 98% Hb saturation and a blood pH of 7.4

decrease in the partial pressure gradient for oxygen will affect the saturation of hemoglobin, and therefore the oxygen-carrying capacity of the blood.

Figure 8.9 illustrates the oxy-hemoglobin dissociation curve, which essentially describes the change in hemoglobin saturation with a decrease in P_aO_2. For P_aO_2 values that range from 100 to 80 mmHg, there are only minimal reductions in the saturation of hemoglobin. As P_aO_2 decreases from 80 to 60 mmHg, hemoglobin saturation decreases from 94.9% to 89.3%. For P_aO_2 values below 60 mmHg, dramatic decreases in hemoglobin saturation occur, which can result in large decreases in arterial oxygen transport.

Additional Factors That Alter Oxy-Hemoglobin Saturation

Apart from a decreased saturation when the P_aO_2 is reduced, increased dissociation of oxygen and hemoglobin occurs at given PO_2 values by increases in each of blood temperature, PCO_2, and 2,3-bisphosphoglycerate (2,3-BPG, previously abbreviated as 2,3-DPG), and decreases in blood pH.

The molecule 2,3-BPG is a by-product of glycolysis in the red blood cell, and its production increases during conditions of low PO_2 (hypoxia). The 2,3-BPG produced by the red blood cell binds to the deoxygenated form of hemoglobin and therefore assists the unloading of oxygen from hemoglobin (37, 40). However, there is no evidence that 2,3-BPG increases during exercise at low to moderate altitude. The ability to aid the "unloading" of oxygen from hemoglobin during an acute bout of exercise is dependent on additional factors (40). Specifically, temperature, PCO_2, and pH are conditions that change at the level of the tissues, and the direction of these changes combine to decrease the affinity between oxygen and hemoglobin causing a greater unloading of oxygen. The effects of temperature, pH, and PCO_2 on adjusting the oxy-hemoglobin dissociation curve

blood-gas interface the anatomical distance that a gas diffuses across

hemoglobin (he'mo-glo'-bin) the protein within red blood cells that contains four heme (iron)-containing groups that each can bind oxygen

FIGURE 8.9

A comparison between oxy-hemoglobin and oxy-myoglobin dissociation curves. For oxygen, the resulting curve is called the oxy-hemoglobin dissociation curve. The curve is moved down and to the right during conditions that increase blood temperature, PCO_2, acidosis, and 2,3-bisphosphoglycerate. As myoglobin retains greater saturation by oxygen at a given partial pressure, it is believed that oxygen moves from hemoglobin to myoglobin within cells. Details of how oxygen moves from myoglobin to within the mitochondria are unclear.

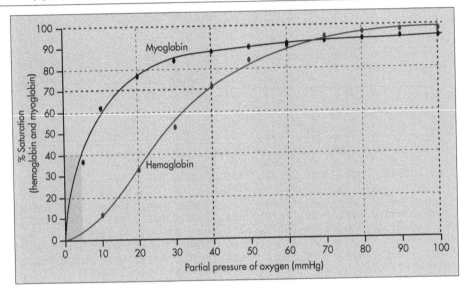

down and to the right is termed the **Bohr effect** in recognition of the scientist who first observed the phenomenon (3, 52).

Carbon Dioxide Transport

The volume of carbon dioxide stored in the body (blood and tissues) is approximately 10-fold greater than oxygen stores (32), and is transported in the blood in several forms (fig. 8.10).

Although carbon dioxide has a greater solubility than oxygen, the majority of CO_2 is not dissolved in plasma or the red blood cell, but reacts with water and is converted to carbonic acid via the **carbonic anhydrase** catalyzed reaction. This reaction occurs in red blood cells and the inner walls of the vascular endothelium in the lung. Carbonic acid then dissociates to bicarbonate (HCO_3^-) and a free proton (H^+). The bicarbonate ions are transported in the plasma, and under normal acid-base conditions the proton is bound to deoxygenated hemoglobin. The ability of hemoglobin to bind both carbon dioxide and protons is important for acid-base regulation of the blood (see Up Close 8.2).

The exchange in hemoglobin binding for carbon dioxide and oxygen is based on the change in partial pressure of oxygen. When the partial pressure of oxygen increases, the affinity between hemoglobin and carbon dioxide decreases and carbon dioxide is forced from hemoglobin. This PO_2

effect on the blood's ability to store carbon dioxide is termed the **Haldane effect** (58).

Internal Respiration

The exchange of gases at the cellular level is influenced by each of the Bohr and Haldane effects. In the tissues the partial pressure of oxygen is low (< 5 mmHg during intense exercise) because of the reduction of oxygen in the electron transport chain, and the partial pressure of carbon dioxide is high because of metabolic production of CO_2. The additional characteristics of an increased temperature and low pH favor the dissociation of oxygen from hemoglobin, and because of the Haldane effect, the affinity between hemoglobin and carbon dioxide increases.

The unloading of oxygen from hemoglobin is also aided by the molecule **myoglobin.** Myoglobin is found within skeletal muscle fibers and is a similar protein to hemoglobin in that it binds oxygen (36). At the cellular level of the circulation where oxygen is consumed and the partial pressure of oxygen in blood decreases, there is a sharp decrease in the affinity between oxygen and hemoglobin. For oxygen partial pressures less than 60 mmHg, myoglobin has a higher affinity for oxygen than does hemoglobin (see fig. 8.10), which allows a unidirectional transfer of oxygen from hemoglobin to myoglobin within the muscle fibers (3, 63). *Myoglobin can therefore be viewed as a "go-between," transferring oxygen*

FIGURE 8.10

Carbon dioxide is transported in the blood dissolved in plasma and in the red blood cell, bound to hemoglobin and plasma proteins, and as bicarbonate (HCO_3^-).

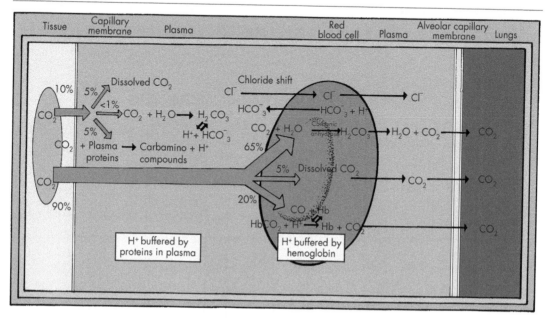

molecules between hemoglobin and the mitochondria within the muscle fiber. The drastic decrease in affinity between oxygen and myoglobin below an oxygen partial pressure of 10 mmHg is interesting because the intramuscular PO_2 can get below 10 mmHg during intense exercise. At these low PO_2 values, there is a much higher capacity for oxygen to be released from myoglobin for use in mitochondrial respiration. Having more myoglobin would increase the reservoir of oxygen stored within muscle fibers, and also increase the ability of muscle to continue mitochondrial respiration during intermittent periods of *hypoxia* (low P_aO_2) or *ischemia* (reduced blood flow).

Acute Adaptations of Pulmonary Function During Exercise

The start of exercise is characterized by immediate increases in ventilation. The factors that regulate this increase are numerous and complex, involving neural and blood (humoral) factors. Nerves from the central as well as peripheral nervous systems respond to stimuli to cause increases in the frequency and depth of breathing, thus increasing ventilation. Additional changes in blood, such as increases in partial pressures of carbon dioxide, increased temperature, increased acidosis, and even decreases in partial pressures of oxygen provide the stimuli to

nerves or neural tissue involved in increasing ventilation. The rapid and refined nature of ventilatory control result in characteristic responses of ventilation to different types and intensities of exercise.

Ventilation During Transitions from Rest to Steady-State Exercise

As with oxygen consumption, the increase in ventilation during the transition to an increased steady-state exercise intensity is abrupt, exponential, and proportional to the change in intensity (fig. 8.12). Steady-state ventilation is attained earlier than is steady-state VO_2 for a given bout of exercise. As previously explained, the increase in ventilation

Bohr effect the decrease in the hemoglobin to oxygen affinity with an increase in temperature, PCO_2 and acidosis

carbonic anhydrase conversion of CO_2 and water to become carbonic acid

Haldane effect the decrease in the affinity between hemoglobin and carbon dioxide with an increase in the partial pressure of oxygen

myoglobin (mi'o-glo-bin) intramuscular protein that contains one heme (iron)-containing group that enables the binding of oxygen

UP CLOSE 8.2

Blood Acid-Base Balance

Acidosis is quantified by the pH scale, where pH equals the negative logarithm of the hydrogen ion concentration (fig. 8.11)

$$pH = -\log[H^+] \quad \text{or} \quad [H^+] = 10^{-pH}$$

Normal arterial blood pH equals 7.4, and normal muscle pH equals 7.0. Multiple factors combine to determine each of blood and muscle pH during given nutrition or exercise conditions. The main determinants of pH are as follows:

- The rate of acid production, or proton release from metabolism
- The concentration of blood bicarbonate (HCO_3^-) and other weak acids and bases
- The partial pressure of carbon dioxide
- Ventilation of the lung
- The excretion or absorption of acid and base by the kidney

Because reactions of the body occur in an aqueous environment, the characteristics of water are also important in determining pH.

Blood Bicarbonate

The bicarbonate molecule can bind a H^+ to form carbonic acid, as described in the text for carbon dioxide transport in the blood. When protons are released from metabolism, they are removed from the muscle cells and bind with bicarbonate, and eventually form added carbon dioxide and water.

$$CL_T^- H^+ + Na^+HCO_3^- \Leftrightarrow Na^+CL^- + H_2CO_3$$
$$CA$$
$$H_2CO_3 \Leftrightarrow CO_2 + H_2O$$

The production of carbon dioxide from the bicarbonate buffering of acid accounts for the increase in RER above 1.0 during intense or non-steady-state exercise. In addition, the added production of carbon dioxide increases the partial pressure of carbon dioxide in the blood. Consequently, conditions of metabolic acidosis are accompanied by increases in the CO_2 content of venous blood (P_vCO_2) and, as will be discussed in the control of ventilation, severe acidosis may also cause slight increases in the CO_2 content of arterial blood (P_aCO_2).

Because there is a large volume of CO_2 in the body fluids, there is a large source of carbon for the formation of HCO_3^-. Due to the removal of carbon dioxide from the lungs, large increases in carbon dioxide are prevented, and the metabolic

FIGURE 8.11

The pH scale, with examples of solutions from everyday life and known changes in blood and muscle pH during exercise.

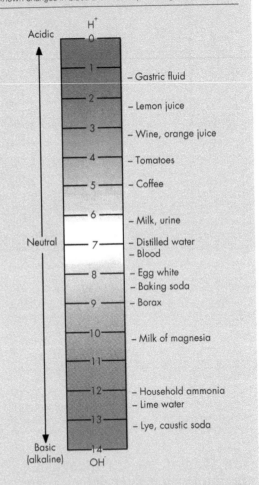

production of CO_2 allows for the reestablishment of normal blood bicarbonate and pH. *The bicarbonate-carbon dioxide system relies on ventilation for proper function as a buffer system.*

is because of increases in tidal volume and breathing frequency.

Despite the rapid increase in ventilation at the onset of exercise, there is still a slight increase in P_aCO_2 (64), which

indicates that increased ventilation still remains inadequate to remove the sudden increase in CO_2 production by the body. Nevertheless, numerous studies have shown that both ventilation and perfusion of the lungs increase during

FIGURE 8.12

The increase in (a) ventilation during the transition to an increased steady-state exercise intensity is abrupt, exponential, and similar in profile to the change in (b) oxygen consumption.

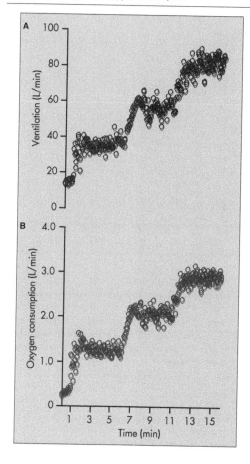

Ventilation During Incremental Exercise

The increases in ventilation and oxygen consumption during incremental cycle ergometry exercise are presented in figure 8.13. The variables V_E/VO_2 and V_E/VCO_2 are the *ventilatory equivalents* for oxygen and carbon dioxide, respectively, and are obtained by dividing V_E by VO_2 or VCO_2. During the initial intensities, ventilation increases linearly with intensity and VO_2. After an individually specific intensity, the increase in V_E is larger than the increase in VO_2, and by definition there is an abrupt increase in V_E/VO_2. Depending on the protocol used, there is a short time delay (usually 2 min) before V_E/VCO_2 also increases, and this time delay has been explained by the body's large storage capacity for CO_2 and the initial similarity between increased ventilation and VCO_2 at the point of the ventilation threshold (5).

The Ventilatory Threshold

The exercise intensity at which there is a simultaneous deviation from linearity in ventilation and an increase in V_E/VO_2 is termed the **ventilatory threshold** (VT) (4, 7, 19, 34, 41, 61, 65). Other measures can also be used to detect this point, such as an exponential increase in VCO_2 or RER (respiratory exchange ratio), and an abrupt increase in blood acidosis. However, Caizzeo and colleagues (7) have demonstrated that the *joint V_E and V_E/VO_2 criteria are most sensitive in detecting the VT*.

Another method for VT determination is called the V-slope method. Beaver and colleagues (4) introduced this procedure in 1986, which requires a plot of VCO_2 (y-axis) versus VO_2 (x-axis) (fig. 8.14). The logic behind this approach was based on the assumption that the increased CO_2 produced from acid buffering by bicarbonate would be better detected by graphing the increase in VCO_2 relative to VO_2. Methods that plot changes in ventilation, or are influenced by ventilation, can be influenced by individual differences in the multiple determinants of ventilation during incremental exercise. Nevertheless, the V-slope procedure has not been adequately validated by comparison to blood lactate thresholds (53). Furthermore, evidence indicates that all methods of VT detection are influenced by the exercise protocol, method of detection, and evaluator (53, 66). It appears that no single method of VT detection is without error.

The traditional explanation of the VT is that as exercise intensity increases, the abrupt increase in metabolic acidosis that occurs after the lactate threshold causes an increase in blood acidosis and P_aCO_2. Both the acidosis and the increased P_aCO_2 stimulate the chemoreceptors to induce increased ventilation. This mechanism has been interpreted by many physiologists as evidence that the lactate and ventilatory thresholds occur at the same exercise intensity (37).

exercise, become more evenly distributed throughout the lung (8, 11, 16, 32), and improve V_E/Q—all of which improves the process of external respiration.

Ventilation during submaximal exercise at given loads is also known to differ for different types of exercise (21, 45). Arm or upper-body exercise causes a relatively larger ventilation compared to cycling; static exercise also causes ventilation to be larger than dynamic exercise. Data from Paek and McCool (44) indicate that tidal volumes, inspiratory times, and end-expiratory lung volumes may also differ between different types of exercise; however their data were normalized to ventilation and not metabolic load (VO_{2max}). Finally, posture during exercise is also known to affect ventilation, which is important when studying different positions of the upper body during cycling.

> **ventilatory threshold** the metabolic intensity associated with an increase in the ventilatory equivalent for oxygen (V_E/VO_2)

FIGURE 8.13

The increase in ventilation, changes in the ventilatory equivalents for carbon dioxide (V_E/VCO_2) and oxygen (V_E/VO_2), and increase in oxygen consumption during incremental cycle ergometry exercise.

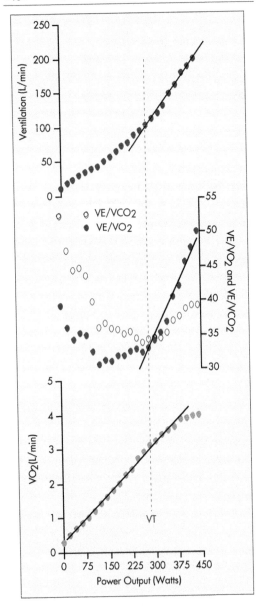

FIGURE 8.14

An illustration of the V-slope method. The ventilation threshold (VT) is detected at the intersection of the change in slope for the VCO_2 and VO_2 relationship.

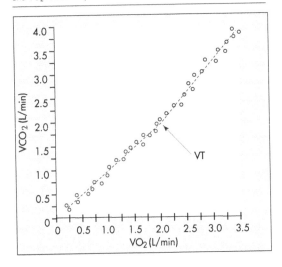

Researchers have concluded that the two measures are identical (7, 13, 61, 62, 65); however, others have concluded that the two measures can differ under certain conditions, and that the two criteria should not be used interchangeably (1, 20, 21, 22, 41). Factors that can cause the two measures to deviate are as follows:

1. Altered carbohydrate nutrition
2. Different exercise test protocols
3. Enzyme deficiency diseases
4. Methodological errors in detecting each threshold
5. Exercise training
6. Increasing altitude (hypoxia)
7. Altered states of sympathetic stimulation (20, 21, 22, 41)

Gladden and colleagues (22) have estimated that the variation in relative exercise intensity between the LT and VT may be larger than 8% of VO_{2max}, which would be significant when using the measures to prescribe a training exercise intensity.

The Mechanics and Metabolic Costs of Ventilation During Exercise

Both the frequency of ventilation and tidal volume increase during increases in exercise intensity. During intense exercise, when ventilation is already high, tidal volume plateaus and further increases in ventilation result from an augmented frequency of breathing. The demands of rapid and deep inflation and deflation of the lungs adds to the work of the muscles of inspiration and expiration.

This increased muscle work of ventilation during increasing exercise intensities demands a meaningful proportion of

Is the Ventilation Threshold Identical to the Lactate Threshold?

Numerous studies have been conducted to compare the lactate and ventilatory thresholds (19, 21, 37, 41, 61).

cardiac output, as well as contributes to whole-body oxygen consumption. Dempsey and colleagues (26–29) have estimated that the repeated contraction of the muscles of ventilation (incorrectly referred to as "respiratory muscles") during exercise close to VO_{2max} demands about 14–15% of both maximal cardiac output and VO_2. This is a significant blood flow and oxygen consumption cost to support exercise. Interestingly, when the work of breathing is reduced during exercise to VO_{2max} by the use of a assist ventilator, muscle VO_{2max} increases, and suggests that the metabolic demands of ventilation may in fact compromise the ability of the working muscles to receive blood flow and oxygen during intense exercise (24, 26, 29). Such compromised physiology has also been shown to be detrimental to exercise performance characterized by sustained exercise to fatigue at 90% VO_{2max} (24). In short, the need to ventilate the lungs at high rates during intense exercise is a meaningful stress on the body that detracts from the body's abilities to supply blood and oxygen to the active skeletal muscles used during exercise.

Do the Muscles of Ventilation Fatigue During Exercise?

The large increase in the work of breathing could cause respiratory muscle fatigue during maximal exercise. However, results indicate that for endurance-trained individuals, the ability to rapidly ventilate the lungs is not compromised during exercise to VO_{2max} (32). However, whether untrained individuals have near-optimal respiratory muscle and ventilatory function during fatiguing exercise remains to be researched. Interestingly, even highly trained athletes can show improved lung function during exercise after 5 weeks of training the muscles of ventilation using inspiratory resistance (54).

Some exercises, such as swimming and deep-water exercise, have the upper body submerged in water, which provides an increased external pressure (compression) to the thoracic cavity. This would theoretically decrease the work of expiration, but potentially increase the work of inspiration. Whether these changes would cause respiratory muscle fatigue and affect the effectiveness of ventilation is unclear. Ventilation and external respiration during swimming are also compromised by forced entrainment of ventilation during specific intervals during a stroke. Although not thoroughly researched, such entrainment causes inspiration and expiration times to be longer but less frequent. It remains unclear how lung function and blood gases and acid-base balance are affected by these constraints in trained or relatively untrained swimmers.

Exercise-Induced Hypoxemia

The partial pressure (P_aO_2) and concentration of oxygen (CaO_2) in arterial blood remain stable in most individuals during all intensities of exercise. However, high altitude can reduce P_aO_2 because of the lowered partial pressure of oxygen, or *hypoxia*, resulting in a reduced CaO_2, or **hypoxemia.** Interestingly, numerous reports have documented hypoxemia during exhausting exercise at sea level in individuals with healthy lungs (14, 16, 17, 45, 46, 48).

FIGURE 8.15

The decrease in the partial pressure of oxygen in arterial blood (P_aO_2) (hypoxemia) during incremental exercise in individuals with different VO_{2max} capacities. For individuals with larger values for VO_{2max}, there are greater reductions in P_aO_2, which indicate inadequacies in lung function.

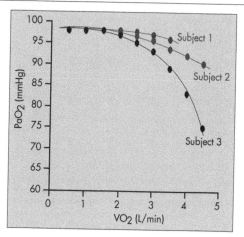

In 1984 it was observed that highly trained endurance athletes experience significant reductions in C_aO_2 at or near VO_{2max} at sea level, and this condition was termed **exercise-induced hypoxemia** (15). Figure 8.15 reveals the change in the partial pressure of oxygen in arterial blood (P_aO_2) in individuals of different cardiorespiratory endurance fitness during an incremental exercise test to volitional fatigue. The more endurance trained the athlete, the larger the reduction in P_aO_2, which indicates that for these individuals the lungs are not functioning optimally during intense exercise. Powers and colleagues (45, 46, 48) showed that at sea level, exercise-induced hypoxemia occurs in approximately 50% of well-trained endurance athletes during exercise at intensities above 80% VO_{2max}.

More recently, Dempsey and colleagues (38) showed that women seem to demonstrate more ventilatory limitations than men due to smaller lung volumes and maximal flow rates. Such conditions, in turn, lead to an earlier onset (lower VO_2) of exercise-induced hypoxemia in females than males (25).

As the healthy lung was always thought to function optimally during exercise, the initial explanation for sea level exercise-induced hypoxemia was an imbalance between

hypoxemia (hi-pox-see'-mia) a decrease in blood oxygen content caused by hypoxia

exercise-induced hypoxemia a decrease in arterial hemoglobin saturation during exercise

CLINIC UPDATE 8.1

Asthma, Exercise-Induced Bronchoconstriction, and Exercise

Asthma is an obstructive disorder of the lung that has been difficult to define (39, 50). However, the U.S. Department of Health and Human Services (18) has developed a working definition that recognizes asthma as a lung disease with the following characteristics:

1. Airway obstruction that is reversible (although sometimes not completely) with treatment
2. Airway inflammation
3. Increased airway responsiveness to a variety of stimuli

The airway obstruction is caused by the combination of smooth muscle contraction and inflammation of the tissue surrounding the trachea and bronchioles. This response causes constriction of the large and small airways and a dramatic increase in the resistance to airflow in the conducting zone of the lungs. Some individuals who have mild asthma may be asymptomatic, with their condition detected only with pulmonary function testing (spirometry and peak expiratory flow rate), whereas others with a more severe asthma experience concurrent episodes of cough and wheezing (18). It has been estimated that 10 million individuals in the United States have asthma, that the incidence of the disorder is increasing, and that up to 25% of the population in the United States has experienced asthma at least once in their lives (18, 36).

Exercise is known to increase the irritability of the bronchial network and increase the likelihood for asthma. However, unlike true asthma, asthma caused by exercise is not accompanied by inflammation, and has therefore been termed *exercise-induced bronchoconstriction*. Exercise-induced bronchoconstriction (EIB) results from irritation of the bronchial lining because of alterations in moisture and temperature caused by the increased airflow. EIB usually does not occur

until after exercise, reaching a peak severity after 5 to 10 min of recovery, and becoming completely resolved after 30 min of recovery (fig. 8.16) (18). For individuals with EIB, graded exercise tests are often used to evaluate the onset of the condition or whether certain medications are effective in prevention.

There is some research evidence for the decreased occurrence of EIB when exercise is performed in a warm and humid environment. Consequently, exercise such as swimming is highly recommended, and exercise in cold or dry conditions is to be avoided for individuals susceptible to both EIB and asthma. When medications are used, the inhalation of a bronchodilator immediately prior to exercise, and the use of corticosteroids as a preventive strategy can totally prevent asthma and EIB during and after exercise. Consequently, individuals who are susceptible to asthma and EIB should not refrain from exercise participation. For example, during the 1984 Olympic games, 67 athletes were asthmatics, and many of these individuals received medals (18, 39, 50, 56).

FIGURE 8.16

The changes in FEV_1 (L) (forced expired volume in 1 s) following a bout of exercise by an individual with exercise-induced bronchoconstriction. Note that the most severe restrictions to breathing occur after 5 min of recovery. 1: baseline lung function; 2: exercise; 3: initial rapid increase in FEV_1, post-exercise; 4: lowest FEV, usually measured 5–10 min postexercise; 5: FEV returns to normal by 20 min postexercise.

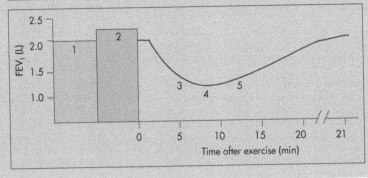

cardiac output and maximal effective pulmonary blood flow. It was assumed that endurance athletes were trained to the point where their central blood volume and maximal cardiac output had exceeded the ability of their lungs to maintain pulmonary blood flow at a velocity required to equilibrate P_AO_2 and P_aO_2. The velocity of blood flow in the pulmonary capillaries is important, because a high velocity would decrease the time for a given red blood cell within the blood-gas interface, termed the **pulmonary transit time,** and risk inequilibration. The time required

for equilibration between P_AO_2 and P_aO_2 in the healthy lung is believed to be 350 to 400 ms (60). Current research indicates that there is probably sufficient time for equilibration between P_AO_2 and P_aO_2, even in highly trained endurance athletes (60). Consequently, research is currently being pursued to better quantify how other factors could explain the hypoxemia, such as a mild pulmonary edema, or an imbalance in V_E/Q.

Discussion of asthma and exercise-induced bronchoconstriction is presented in Clinic Update 8.1.

Chronic Adaptations

The lungs and pulmonary circulation do not express the degree of long-term adaptation to exercise as was evident for neuromuscular function and skeletal muscle energy metabolism. Efforts have been made to verify whether respiratory muscles can adapt to exercise training and improve lung function during exercise (47). However, although respiratory muscles can adapt to exercise, it appears that their function remains near optimal, and there are no signs to support superior lung function in the trained compared to untrained state.

Numerous studies have shown that the ventilatory threshold improves with endurance training (13, 20, 62). Because the causes for this improvement are more determined by muscular and cardiovascular function, it would be prudent to review the section on lactate threshold in chapter 5.

---

asthma (az'mah) a condition of the lungs associated with a narrowing of the bronchial airways in response to an irritant

pulmonary transit time the time it takes for a red blood cell to pass through the respiratory zone of the lung

---

SUMMARY

- The mouth and nasal passages, trachea, bronchi and bronchioles make up the **conducting zone** of the lungs, whereas the respiratory bronchioles, alveoli ducts, and alveoli, which are the sites of gas exchange and responsible for the largest lung gas volumes, are referred to as the **respiratory zone** of the lung. The conducting zone of the lung is often referred to as the **anatomical dead space,** because it does not have a respiratory function. The anatomical dead space makes up an average volume of 150 mL, although this value will vary in a positive relationship with body size.

- The alveoli and respiratory bronchioles are connected by openings or holes in their membranes, termed **pores of Kohn.** The respiratory bronchioles and alveoli make up a surface area of approximately 70 square meters.

- The circulation of blood to and through the lung is termed the **pulmonary circulation.** The pulmonary circulation has a much lower blood pressure than the systemic circulation (25/8 compared to 120/80 mmHg at rest). The respiratory zone of the lung is engorged with a rich blood supply, providing almost as much surface area of blood as that of the respiratory membranes.

- The vital capacity is the maximal volume of air that can be exhaled from the lungs. It can be divided into inspiratory and expiratory components using the method of *spirometry.* Normal resting breathing involves the inspiration and expiration of 500 mL of air, termed the **tidal volume.**

- In the early 1800s, John Hutchinson discovered that lung volumes could be accurately measured by having subjects breathe into a system that could record volume displacements on paper. John Hutchinson's early experiments lead to the development of the technique we now call **spirometry.**

- The movement of the spirometry bell upward and downward represents the volume of air entering and exiting the lungs. When the bell is connected to a pen, the movements of the bell can be recorded on a rotating drum called a

  kymograph. Once the volume conversion of the bell is known (mL/mm), volume (ATPS) can be calculated.

- Another type of volume-displacement system for measuring lung volumes is the bellows-type **spirometer,** often termed a *spirograph* or *vitalograph.* The bellows-type spirometer consists of collapsible bellows that fold and unfold in response to inhalation and exhalation. Typically, an individual will exhale as hard and as fast as possible into a vitalograph, and **vital capacity** and expired flow rates can be computed from the calibrated paper used on the instrument.

- A more sophisticated type of spirometer calculates lung volumes by directly measuring the flow of air. A **pneumotachometer** measures the rate of flow of air during inhalation and exhalation. Pneumotach spirometers are becoming increasingly used when conducting cardiopulmonary testing because of their small size, and high sensitivity and accuracy.

- **Oximetry** involves the indirect determination of the percentage of hemoglobin that is combined with oxygen. Oximetry is a commonly used (noninvasive) method in hospitals and also during exercise testing to assess blood oxygenation. one of the newest methods of oximetry during exercise testing is the pulse oximeter.

- Research has shown that prior submaximal and maximal exercise reduces vital capacity and FEV$_1$ within 30 min of recovery, and increases residual volume. It has been recommended that exercise should not be performed for up to 12 h prior to pulmonary function measurements.

- **Residual volume** (RV) is the volume of air remaining in the lungs after a maximal exhalation. RV represents the difference between TLC and VC. RV, which is a subdivision of FRC, must be measured, and is important for the accurate calculation of body density measured by hydrostatic weighing. In addition, for individuals with chronic obstructive lung disease, residual volume is increased because of premature airway closure. Most researchers use either a closed-circuit **helium dilution** or open-circuit **nitrogen washout** method.

▪ The product of the tidal volume and breathing frequency determines **ventilation.** *Ventilation involves the movement of air into and from the lungs by the process of bulk flow.* Ventilation can increase airflow through the lung from a mere 6 L/min at rest to over 150 L/min during maximal exercise. Of the normal 500 mL tidal volume, 350 mL of "fresh" air reaches the respiratory zone. The volume of "fresh" air that reaches the respiratory zone of the lung is termed **alveolar ventilation** (V_A). *The greater the depth of breathing, the less impact the anatomical dead space has on alveolar ventilation.*

▪ The property of being able to increase size or volume with only small changes in pressure is termed **compliance.** Thus, the lungs have very high compliance. *The presence of surfactant makes it easier to inflate alveoli.* Surfactant functions to lower the surface tension of the alveoli, thereby decreasing the resistance to inflation, and increasing compliance.

▪ The process of gas exchange, or **respiration,** involves the movement of oxygen and carbon dioxide down pressure gradients that exist between pulmonary capillary blood and the air of the alveoli, and between capillary blood of the systemic circulation and the cells perfused by this blood.

▪ Once air is in the alveoli it is subject to gas diffusion between the alveoli and blood, or vice versa. The factors that govern the direction and magnitude of diffusion are (1) the diffusion capacity of each of the gases, (2) the gas partial pressure gradient between the alveoli and blood, and (3) the characteristics of the medium through which diffusion occurs.

▪ The anatomical distance that a gas diffuses across is termed the **blood-gas interface,** and in the lung consists of blood plasma, pulmonary capillary membranes, interstitial fluid, and alveolar membranes that can interfere with gas diffusion. Compared to carbon dioxide, oxygen is a relatively insoluble gas with a 20.3-fold lower solubility.

▪ Oxygen is transported in blood bound to a specialized protein, **hemoglobin,** which is located on the surface of red blood cells. The blood hemoglobin concentration is influenced by gender, nutrition, and disease. A given hemoglobin molecule can bind four oxygen molecules, and *when fully saturated with oxygen, 1 g of hemoglobin can bind 1.34 mL of oxygen.*

▪ At sea level, the normal P_AO_2 approximates 104 mmHg. For P_aO_2 values that range from 100 to 80 mmHg, there are minimal reductions in the saturation of hemoglobin. As P_aO_2 decreases from 80 to 60 mmHg, hemoglobin saturation decreases from 94.9% to 89.3%, and for P_aO_2 values below 60 mmHg, dramatic decreases in hemoglobin saturation occur, which can result in large decreases in arterial oxygen transport.

▪ Increased dissociation of oxygen and hemoglobin occurs at given PO_2 values by increases in each of blood temperature, PCO_2, and 2,3-bisphosphoglycerate (2,3-BPG, previously abbreviated as 2,3-DPG), and decreases in blood pH. Temperature, PCO_2, and pH are conditions that change at the level of the tissues, and the direction of these changes combine to decrease the affinity between oxygen and hemoglobin causing greater unloading of oxygen. The adjustment of the oxy-hemoglobin dissociation curve down and to the right is termed the **Bohr effect.**

▪ The majority of CO_2 is converted to carbonic acid via the **carbonic anhydrase** catalyzed reaction that occurs on the surface of red blood cells and inner walls of the vascular endothelium. Carbonic acid then dissociates to bicarbonate (HCO_3^-) and a free proton (H^+). The bicarbonate ions are transported in the plasma and under normal acid-base conditions the proton is bound to deoxygenated hemoglobin. When the partial pressure of oxygen increases, the affinity between hemoglobin and carbon dioxide decreases and carbon dioxide is forced from hemoglobin. This PO_2 effect on the blood's ability to store carbon dioxide is termed the **Haldane effect.**

▪ Acidosis is quantified by the pH scale, where pH equals the negative logarithm of the hydrogen ion concentration ($pH = -\log [H^+]$ or $[H^+] = 10^{-pH}$). Normal arterial blood pH equals 7.4, and normal muscle pH equals 7.0. The main determinants of pH are (1) the rate of acid production, (2) the concentration of blood bicarbonate (HCO_3^-) and other weak acids and bases, (3) the partial pressure of carbon dioxide, (4) ventilation of the lung, and (5) the excretion or absorption of acid and base by the kidney.

▪ The unloading of oxygen from hemoglobin is also aided by the molecule **myoglobin.** Myoglobin is found within skeletal muscle fibers and is a similar protein to hemoglobin in that it binds oxygen. *Myoglobin can be viewed as a "go-between," transferring oxygen molecules between hemoglobin and the mitochondria within the muscle fiber.*

▪ Steady-state ventilation is attained earlier than is steady-state VO_2 for a given bout of exercise. The variables V_E/VO_2 and V_E/VCO_2 are the *ventilatory equivalents* for oxygen and carbon dioxide, respectively, and are obtained by dividing the VO_2 or VCO_2 into V_E. The exercise intensity at which there is a simultaneous deviation from linearity in ventilation and an increase in V_E/VO_2 is termed the **ventilatory threshold** (VT). The estimated variation in the relative exercise intensity between the VT and LT may be larger than 8% of VO_{2max}, which would be significant when using the measures to prescribe a training exercise intensity.

▪ **Asthma** is an obstructive disorder of the lung that is responsive to pharmacological treatment. The asthma-like condition caused by exercise has been termed exercise-induced bronchoconstriction (EIB). A lowering of blood P_aO_2 is called hypoxemia. During incremental exercise to VO_{2max}, approximately 50% of highly trained endurance athletes experience significant reductions in C_aO_2 at sea level, and this condition is termed **exercise-induced hypoxemia.** As the altitude above sea level increases, exercise-induced hypoxemia increases in occurrence and severity. The velocity of blood flow in the pulmonary capillaries may be influential in causing exercise-induced hypoxemia. A high pulmonary blood flow velocity decreases the time a given red blood cell is within the blood-gas interface, termed the **pulmonary transit time,** and risks inequilibration.

STUDY QUESTIONS

1. What are the two zones of the lung and how do their functions differ?

2. What is surfactant, where is it located within the lung, and what are its functions?

3. From a spirogram tracing, calculate IRV, TV, VC (vital capacity), ERV, and TLC.

4. If the FVC of a subject is 5.75L (ATPS), the room and water temperature is 21.50°C and PB is 715 mm Hg, convert FVC (ATPS) to a BTPS volume (see Appendix B).

5. Why are lung volumes reported in BTPS conditions?

6. What are typical resting values for a normal, healthy subject for the following:
   a. Lung volumes (BTPS)—IC, ERV, VC, RV, FRC and TLC
   b. Ventilation (BTPS)—V_T, f, and V_E
   c. Pulmonary dynamics—FVC, FEV_1, and MVV

7. The following are values for pulmonary measurements (volume$_{ATPS}$):

   Dead space = 165 mL; vital capacity = 5.4 L

   Resting V_E = 6 L/min, breathing frequency = 12/min

   Exercise V_E = 76 L/min, breathing frequency = 45/min

   Maximal exercise V_E = 185 L/min

   For rest and exercise, calculate V_T. For maximal exercise, calculate what the V_T and breathing frequency would probably be if a person used only 60% of the vital capacity per breath during maximal exercise.

8. How does air move into and from the lung?

9. Why is compliance of the lung important to ventilation at rest and during exercise?

10. Calculate the oxygen transported in the blood every minute for the following conditions:
    a. [Hb] = 135 g/L, P_aO_2 = 98 mmHg, Q = 5 L/min
    b. [Hb] = 135 g/L, P_aO_2 = 95 mmHg, Q = 5 L/min
    c. [Hb] = 135 g/L, P_aO_2 = 98 mmHg, Q = 25 L/min
    d. [Hb] = 135 g/L, P_aO_2 = 95 mmHg, Q = 25 L/min
    When cardiac output is considered, do small changes in hemoglobin concentration or hemoglobin saturation result in large changes in blood oxygen transport? How would small decreases in [Hb] or P_aO_2 influence the ability to exercise at moderate to high intensities?

11. Are the Haldane and Bohr effects simply a reversal of each other? Explain.

12. Why is gas solubility important to diffusion between the alveoli and blood?

13. Explain the importance of CO_2 to blood acid-base balance?

14. How does ventilation change during incremental exercise, and what factors are believed to cause these changes?

15. Is the ventilation threshold identical to the lactate threshold? Explain.

16. What is exercise-induced hypoxemia, what type of individuals mainly experience it, and why does it occur?

APPLICATIONS

1. Why would lung damage (e.g., emphysema) increase residual volume?

2. Individuals who suffer from exercise-induced bronchospasm have a reduced FEV_1 during recovery from exercise. Explain how FEV_1 is measured. What other pulmonary function tests would detect increased airway resistance?

3. You are asked by an asthma sufferer why exercise seems to exacerbate the condition. What is your response, and what types of exercise would you recommend?

4. Many clinical exercise tests are conducted that use the ventilation threshold as an index of skeletal muscle metabolism and the lactate threshold. Is this a correct and accurate practice? Explain.

5. If there is 3 mL of O_2 dissolved in plasma for every 1 L of blood at sea level, calculate the amount of O_2 dissolved in blood plasma when breathing pure oxygen

at sea level. During this condition, how much extra oxygen circulates around the body when cardiac output is 20 L/min? Do you think this is a meaningful change? Why?

6. During periods between play in American football, many players sit on a bench and breath pure oxygen. This is done with the assumption that it will improve the recovery from intense exercise. However, breathing pure oxygen is known to depress ventilation. How

would this practice influence the recovery from acidosis, and could it be doing more harm than good? Explain your answer.

7. Tests that measure lung compliance and elasticity were not covered in this chapter. Nevertheless, how would conditions of lung damage (e.g., emphysema) affect lung compliance, and what would be the functional consequences of this condition?

REFERENCES

1. Anderson, G. S., and E. C. Rhodes. The relationship between blood lactate and excess CO_2 in elite cyclists. *J. Sports Sciences* 9:173–181, 1991.

2. Bastacky, J. B., and J. Goerke. Pores of Kohn are filled in normal lungs: Low-temperature scanning electron microscopy. *J. Appl. Physiol.* 73(1):88–95, 1992.

3. Baumann, R., H. Bartels, and C. Bauer. Blood oxygen transport. In L. E. Farhi and S. M. Tenney (eds.), *Handbook of physiology: Sec. 3: The respiratory system. Vol. 1: Gas exchange.* American Physiological Society, Bethesda, MD, 1987, pp. 147–172.

4. Beaver, W., K. Wasserman, and B. Whipp. A new method for detecting anaerobic threshold by gas exchange. *J. Appl. Physiol.* 60(6):2020–2027, 1986.

5. Boren, H. G., R. C. Kory, and J. C. Synder. The Veteran's Administration Army cooperative study of pulmonary function. II: The lung volume and its subdivisions in normal men. *Am. J. Med.* 41:96–114, 1966.

6. Buono, M. J., S. H. Constable, A. R. Morton, T. C. Rotkis, P. R. Stanforth, and J. H. Wilmore. The effect of an acute bout of exercise on selected pulmonary function measurements. *Med. Sci. Sports Exerc.* 13(5):290–293, 1981.

7. Caiozzeo, V. J., et al. A comparison of gas exchange indices used to detect the anaerobic threshold. *J. Appl. Physiol.* 53(5):1184–1189, 1982.

8. Capen, R., L., W. L. Hanson, L. P. Latham, C. A. Dawson, and W. W. Wagner, Jr. Distribution of pulmonary transmit times in recruited networks. *J. Appl. Physiol.* 69(2):473–478, 1990.

9. Chusid, E. L. Pulmonary function testing: An overview. In E. L. Chusid, (ed.), *The selective and comprehensive testing of adult pulmonary function.* Futra, Mount Kisco, NY, 1983.

10. Comroe, J. H., R. E. Foster, A. B. Dubois, W. A. Briscoe, and E. Carlsen. *The lung.* Year Book Medical Publishers, Chicago, 1962.

11. Cordain, L., A. Tucker, D. Moon, and J. M. Stager. Lung volumes and maximal respiratory pressures in collegiate swimmers and runners. *Res. Quart. Exerc. Sport.* 61(1):70–74, 1990.

12. Cotton, D. J., F. Taher, J. T. Mink, and B. L. Graham. Effect of volume history on changes in DL_{CO}^{SB} – 3EQ with lung volume in normal subjects. *J. Appl. Physiol.* 73(2):434–439, 1992.

13. Cox, N. J. M., C. L. A. van Herwaarden, H. Folgering, and R. A. Binkhorst. Exercise and training in patients with chronic obstructive lung disease. *Sports Medicine* 6(3):180–192, 1988.

14. Davis, J. A., P. Vodak, J. Wilmore, J. Vodak, and P. Kurtz. Anaerobic threshold and maximal aerobic power for three modes of exercise. *J. Appl. Physiol.* 41(4):544–550, 1976.

15. Dempsey, J. A., P. G. Hanson, and K. S. Henderson. Exercise-induced arterial hypoxemia in healthy persons at sea level. *J. Physiol.* 355:161–175, 1984.

16. Dempsey, J. A., B. D. Johnson, and K. W. Saupe. Adaptations and limitations in the pulmonary system during exercise. *Chest.* 97 (Suppl. 3):81S–87S, 1990.

17. Dempsey, J. A., G. Mitchell, and C. Smith. Exercise and chemoreception. *Am. Rev. Resp. Dis.* 129:31–34, 1984.

18. Dempsey, J. A., E. Virdruk, and G. Mitchell. Pulmonary control systems in exercise: Update. *Federation Proc.* 44:2260–2270, 1985.

19. Dempsey, J. A. Is the lung built for exercise? *Med. Sci. Sports Exerc.* 18(2):143–155, 1986.

20. Department of Health and Human Services. *Guidelines for the diagnoses and management of asthma.* Publication No. 91-3042. National Institutes of Health, 1991.

21. Farrell, S. W., and J. L. Ivy. Lactate acidosis and the increase in V_E/VO_2 during incremental exercise. *J. Appl. Physiol.* 62(4):1551–1555, 1987.

22. Gaesser, G. A., and D. C. Poole. Lactate and ventilatory thresholds: Disparity in time course of adaptations to training. *J. Appl. Physiol.* 61(3):999–1004, 1986.

23. Girandola, R., R. Wiswell, J. Mohler, G. Romero, and W. Barnes. Effects of water immersion on lung volumes: Implications for body compositional analysis. *J. Appl. Physiol.* 43(2):276–279, 1977.

24. Gladden, L. B., J. W. Yates, R. W. Stremel, and B. A. Stamford. Gas exchange and lactate anaerobic thresholds: Inter- and intraevaluator agreement. *J. Appl. Physiol.* 58(6):2082–2089, 1985.

25. Grucza, R., Y. Miyamoto, and Y. Nakazonto. Kinetics of cardiorespiratory response to rhythmic-static exercise in men. *Eur. J. Appl. Physiol.* 61:230–236, 1990.

26. Guyton, A. C. *Textbook of medical physiology,* 8th ed. Saunders, Philadelphia, 1991.

27. Hagberg, J. M., E. F. Coyle, J. E. Carroll, J. M. Miller, W. M. Martin, and M. H. Brooke. Exercise hyperventilation in patients with McArdle's disease. *J. Appl. Physiol.* 52(4): 991–994, 1982.

28. Hansen, J. E. and R. Casaburi. Validity of ear oximetry in clinical exercise testing. *Chest* 91:333–337, 1987.

29. Hickman, J. B., E. Blair and R. Frayser. An open circuit helium method for measuring functional residual capacity and defective intrapulmonary gas mixing. *J. Clin. Invest.* 33:1277–1282, 1954.

30. Hutchinson, J. Lecture on vital statistics, embracing an account of a new instrument for detecting the presence of disease in the system. *Lancet* 1:567, 594, 1844.

31. Johnson, B. D., K. W. Saupe, and J. A. Dempsey. Mechanical constraints on exercise hyperpnea in endurance athletes. *J. Appl. Physiol.* 73(3):874–886, 1992.

32. Jones, N. L. *Blood gases and acid-base physiology,* 2d ed. Thieme Medical Publishers, New York, 1987.

33. Knudsen, R. J., R. C. Slatin, M. D. Lebowitz, and B. Burrows. The maximal expiratory flow-volume curve. Normal standards, variability, and effects of age. *Am. Rev. Resp. Dis.* 113:587–600, 1976.

34. Koike, A., D. Weiler-Ravell, D. K. McKenzie, S. Zanconato, and K. Wasserman. Evidence that the metabolic acidosis threshold is the anaerobic threshold. *J. Appl. Physiol.* 68(6):2521–2526, 1990.

35. Lehninger, A. L. Principles of biochemistry. Worth Publishers, New York, 1982.

36. Loat, C. E. R., and E. C. Rhodes. Relationship between the lactate and ventilatory thresholds during prolonged exercise. *Sports Medicine* 15(2):104–115, 1993.

37. Mahler, D. A. Exercise-induced asthma. *Med. Sci. Sports Exerc.* 25(5):554–561, 1993.

38. Mairbaurl, H., W. Schobersberger, W. Hasibeder, G. Schwaberger, G. Gaesser, and K. R. Tanaka. Regulation of 2,3-DPG and Hb-O_2-affinity during acute exercise. *Eur. J. Appl. Physiol.* 55:174–180, 1986.

39. Meneely, G. R., C. O. T. Ball, and R. C. Kory. A simplified closed circuit helium dilution method for the determination of the residual volume in the lungs. *Am. J. Med.* 28:824–831, 1960.

40. Morris, J. F. Spirometry in the evaluation of pulmonary function. *West . J. Med.* 125(2):110–118, 1976.

41. Neary, P. J., J. D. MacDougall, R. Bachus, and H. A. Wenger. The relationship between lactate and ventilatory thresholds: Coincidental or cause and effect? *Eur. J. Appl. Physiol.* 54:104–108, 1985.

42. O'Brien, R. J., and T. A. Drizd. Roentgenographic determination of total lung capacity: Normal values from a national population survey. *Am. Rev. Resp. Dis.* 128:949–952, 1983.

43. O'Krory, J. A., R. A. Loy, and J. R. Coast. Pulmonary function changes following exercise. *Med. Sci. Sports Exerc.* 24(12):1359–1364, 1992.

44. Paek, D., and D. McCool. Breathing patterns during varied activities. *J. Appl. Physiol.* 73(3):887–893, 1992.

45. Powers, S. K., and J. Williams. Exercise-induced hypoxemia in highly trained athletes. *Sports Medicine* 4:46–53, 1987.

46. Powers, S. K., et al. Incidence of exercise induced hypoxemia in the elite endurance athlete at sea level. *Eur. J. Appl. Physiol.* 58:298–302, 1988.

47. Powers, S. K., J. Lawlor, J. A. Dempsey, S. Dodd, and G. Landry. Effects of incomplete pulmonary gas exchange on VO_{2max}. *J. Appl. Physiol.* 66(6):2491–2495, 1989.

48. Powers, S. K., et al. Endurance-training-induced cellular adaptations in respiratory muscles. *J. Appl. Physiol.* 68(5):2114–2118, 1990.

49. Powers, S. K., D. Martin, M. Cicale, N. Collop, D. Huang, and D. Criswell. Exercise induced hypoxemia in athletes: Role of inadequate hyperventilation. *Eur. J. Appl. Physiol.* 65:37–42, 1992.

50. Powers, S. K., D. Martin, and S. Dodd. Exercise-induced hypoxemia in elite endurance athletes: Incidence, causes and impact on VO_{2max}. *Sports Medicine* 16(1):14–22, 1993.

51. Rebuk, A. S., K. R. Chapman, and A. D'Urzo. The accuracy and response characteristics of a simplified ear oximeter. *Chest* 83:860–864, 1983.

52. Roberts, J. A. Exercise-induced asthma in athletes. *Sports Medicine* 6(4):193–196, 1988.

53. Ruegg, W. R., and G. P. Reynolds. A procedure for the measurement of lung volumes by helium dilution. *Analyzer* 10:18–22, 1980.

54. Seeley, R. R., T. D. Stephens, and P. Tate. *Anatomy and physiology.* Times Mirror/Mosby College Publishing, St. Louis, 1989.

55. Shimizu, M., et al. The ventilatory threshold: Method, protocol, and evaluator agreement. *Am. Heart J.* 122:509–516, 1991.

56. Taylor, A. E., K. Rehder, R. E. Hyatt, and J. C. Parker. *Clinical respiratory physiology.* Saunders, Philadelphia, 1989.

57. Thomas, D. Q., B. A. Bowdoin, D. D. Brown, and S. T. McCaw. Nasal strips, and mouth pieces do not affect power output during anaerobic exercise. *Res. Q. Exerc. Sport.* 69(2):201–204, 1998.

58. Torre-Bueno, J. R., P. D. Wagner, H. A. Saltzman, G. E. Gale, and R. E. Moon. Diffusion limitation in normal humans during exercise at sea level and simulated altitude. *J. Appl. Physiol.* 58(3):989–995, 1985.

59. Vermoen, C. J., A. F. Verbraak, and J. M. Bogaard. Effect of nasal dilator on nasal patency during normal and forced nasal breathing. *Int. J. Sports Med.* 19(2):109–113, 1998.

60. Warren, G., K. J. Cureton, W. F. Middendorf, C. A. Ray, and J. A. Warren. Red blood cell pulmonary transit time during exercise in athletes. *Med. Sci. Sports Exerc.* 23(12):1353–1361, 1991.

61. Wasserman, K., and M. B. McIlroy. Detecting the threshold of anaerobic metabolism in cardiac patients during exercise. *Am. J. Cardiol.* 14:844–852, 1964.

62. Wasserman, K., B. J. Whipp, S. N. Koyal, and W. L. Beaver. Anaerobic threshold and respiratory gas exchange during exercise. *J. Appl. Physiol.* 35(2):236–243, 1973.

63. Wasserman, K., B. J. Whipp, and R. Casaburi. Respiratory control during exercise. In N. S. Cherniak and J. G. Widdicombe (eds.), *Handbook of Physiology: Sec. 3: The respiratory system. Vol. 2: Control of breathing.* American Physiological Society, Bethesda, MD, 1986, pp. 595–620.

64. Weissman, M. L., P. W. Jones, A, Oren, N. Lamarra, B. J. Whipp, and K. Wasserman. Cardiac output increase and gas exchange at the start of exercise. *J. Appl. Physiol.* 52(1):236–244, 1982.

65. West, J. B. *Respiratory physiology: The essentials.* 3d ed. Williams & Wilkins, Philadelphia, 1985.

66. Whipp, B. J., and S. Ward. Physiological determinants of pulmonary gas exchange kinetics during exercise. *Med. Sci. Sports Exerc.* 22(1):62–71, 1990.

67. Yeh, M. P., R. M. Gardner, T. D. Adams, F. G. Yanowitz, and R. O. Crappo. "Anaerobic threshold": Problems of determination and validation. *J. Appl. Physiol.* 55(4):1178–1186, 1983.

RECOMMENDED READINGS

Caiozzeo, V. J., et al. A comparison of gas exchange indices used to detect the anaerobic threshold. *J. Appl. Physiol.* 53(5):1184–1189, 1982.

Cummiskey, I. Exercise-induced asthma: An overview. *Am. J. Med. Sci.* 322(4):200–203, 2001.

Dempsey, J. A., and P. D. Wagner. Exercise-induced arterial hypoxemia. *J. Appl. Physiol.* 87(6):1997–2006, 1999.

Dempsey, J. A., B. D. Johnson, and K. W. Saupe. Adaptations and limitations in the pulmonary system during exercise. *Chest* 97(Suppl. 3):81S–87S, 1990.

Harms, C. A., M. A. Babcock, S. R. McClaran, D. F. Pegelow, G. A. Nickele, W. B. Nelson, and I. A. Dempsey. Respiratory muscle work compromises leg blood flow during maximal exercise. *J. Appl. Physiol.* 82(5):1573–1583, 1997.

Harms, C. A., and J. A. Dempsey. Cardiovascular consequences of exercise hyperpnea. *Exerc. Sport. Sci. Rev.* 27:37–62, 1999.

Harms, C. A., S. R. McClaran, G. A. Nickele, D. F. Pegelow, W. B. Nelson, and I. A. Dempsey. Exercise-induced arterial hypoxaemia in healthy young women. *J. Physiol.* 507 (Pt 2):619–628, 1998.

Harms, C. A., S. R. McClaran, G. A. Nickele, D. F. Pegelow, W. B. Nelson, and J. A. Dempsey. Effect of exercise-induced arterial 02 desaturation on VO_{2max} in women. *Med. Sci. Sports. Exerc.* 32(6):1101–1108, 2000.

Harms, C. A., T. I. Wetter, S. R. McClaran, D. F. Pegelow, G. A. Nickele, W. B. Nelson, P. Hanson, and I. A. Dempsey. Effects of respiratory muscle work on cardiac output and its distribution during maximal exercise. *J. Appl. Physiol.* 85(2):609–618, 1998.

Harms, C. A., T. J. Wetter, C. M. St. Croix, D. F. Pegelow, and J. A. Dempsey. Effects of respiratory muscle work on exercise performance. *J. Appl. Physiol.* 89(1):131–138, 2000.

Johnson, B. D., K. W. Saupe, and J. A. Dempsey. Mechanical constraints of exercise hyperpnea in endurance athletes. *J. Appl. Physiol.* 73(3):874–886, 1992.

Langdeau, J. B., and L. P. Boulet. Prevalence and mechanisms of development of asthma and airway hyperresponsiveness in athletes. *Sports Medicine* 31(8):601–616, 2001.

Loat, C. E. R., and E. C. Rhodes. Relationship between the lactate and ventilatory thresholds during prolonged exercise. *Sports Medicine* 15(2):104–115, 1993.

Mairbaurl, H., W. Schobersberger, W. Hasibeder, G. Schwaberger, G. Gaesser, and K. R. Tanaka. Regulation of 2,3-DPG and Hb-O_2-affinity during acute exercise. *Eur. J. Appl. Physiol.* 55:174–180, 1986.

McClaran, S. R., C. A. Harms, D. F. Pegelow, and I. A. Dempsey. Smaller lungs in women affect exercise hyperpnea. *J. Appl. Physiol.* 84(6):1872–1881, 1998.

Mahler, D. A. Exercise-induced asthma. *Med. Sci. Sports Exerc.* 25(5):554–561, 1993.

O'Brien, R. J., and T. A. Drizd. Roentgenographic determination of total lung capacity: Normal values from a national population survey. *Am. Rev. Resp. Dis.* 128:949–952, 1983.

O'Krory, J. A., R. A. Loy, and J. R. Coast. Pulmonary function changes following exercise. *Med. Sci. Sports Exerc.* 24(12): 1359–1364, 1992.

Powers, S. K., and J. Williams. Exercise-induced hypoxemia in highly trained athletes. *Sports Medicine* 4:46–53, 1987.

Sonetti, D. A., T. J. Wetter, D. F. Pegelow, and J. A. Dempsey. Effects of respiratory muscle training versus placebo on endurance exercise performance. *Respir. Physiol.* 127(2–3): 185–199, 2001.

Thole, R. T., R. E. Sallis, A. L. Rubin, and G. N. Smith. Exercise-induced bronchospasm prevalence in collegiate cross-country runners. *Med. Sci. Sports. Exerc.* 33(10):1641–1646, 2001.

Wasserman, K., B. J. Whipp, S. N. Koyal, and W. L. Beaver. Anaerobic threshold and respiratory gas exchange during exercise. *J. Appl. Physiol.* 35(2):236–243, 1973.

West, J. B. *Respiratory physiology: The essentials,* 3d ed. Williams & Wilkins, Philadelphia, 1985.

20

Laboratory Assessment of Human Performance

■ Objectives

By studying this chapter, you should be able to do the following:

1. Discuss the factors that determine the effectiveness of a physiological test of athletic performance.
2. Define "specificity of $\dot{V}O_2$ max."
3. Explain the difference between $\dot{V}O_2$ max and $\dot{V}O_2$ peak.
4. Discuss the physiological rationale for the assessment of the lactate threshold in the endurance athlete.
5. Describe methods for the assessment of anaerobic power.
6. Discuss the techniques used to evaluate muscular strength.

■ Outline

■ Key Terms

critical power
dynamic
dynamometer

isokinetic
power test

Quebec 10-second test
Wingate test

In general, there have been two principal approaches to the assessment of physical performance: (1) field tests of general physical fitness, which include a variety of measurements requiring basic performance demands, and (2) laboratory assessments of physiological capacities such as maximal aerobic power ($\dot{V}O_2$ max), anaerobic power, and exercise economy. It can be argued that physical fitness testing is important for an overall assessment of general conditioning, particularly in terms of evaluating student progress in a physical education conditioning class (1, 68). However, the use of these test batteries does not provide the detailed physiological information needed to assess an athlete's current level of conditioning or potential weaknesses. Therefore, more specific laboratory tests are required to provide detailed physiological information about performance in specific athletic events. This chapter will discuss tests designed to measure physical work capacity and performance in athletes. Specifically, much of this chapter will focus on both laboratory and field tests to evaluate the maximum energy transfer capacities discussed in chapters 3 and 4. The performance tests described in this chapter differ from the exercise tests described in chapter 15 in several ways. Recall that the exercise tests described in chapter 15 were targeted toward assessing cardiorespiratory fitness in healthy adults entering or actively engaged in a regular "health-related" exercise program. In contrast, the exercise tests described in this chapter are targeted toward measurement of performance in athletes actively engaged in competitive sports. Let's begin with a discussion of the theory and ethics of laboratory assessment of performance.

LABORATORY ASSESSMENT OF PHYSICAL PERFORMANCE

Physiological Testing: Theory and Ethics

Designing laboratory tests to assess physical performance requires an understanding of those factors that contribute to success in a particular sport or athletic event. In general, physical performance is determined by the individual's capacity for maximal energy output (i.e., maximal aerobic and anaerobic processes), muscular strength, coordination/economy of movement, and psychological factors (e.g., motivation and tactics) (32, 79). Figure 20.1 illustrates a simple model of the components that interact to determine the quality of physical performance. Many types of athletic events require a combination of several of these factors for an outstanding performance to occur. However, often one or more of these factors plays a dominant role in determining ath-

Figure 20.1 Factors that contribute to physical performance. See text for details.

letic success. In golf, there is little need for a high-energy output, but proper coordination is essential. Sprinting 100 meters requires not only good technique, but a high anaerobic power output. In distance running, cycling, or swimming, a high capacity for aerobic energy-yielding processes is essential for success. Again, laboratory evaluation of performance requires an understanding of those factors that are important for optimal performance in a particular athletic event. Thus, a test that stresses the same physiological systems required by a particular sport or athletic event would be a valid means of assessing physical performance.

A key concern in the performance of "athletic" laboratory testing is maintaining respect for the athlete's human rights. Therefore, laboratory testing should be performed only on athletes who are volunteers and have given written consent prior to testing. Further, prior to testing, the exercise scientist has the responsibility of informing the athlete about the purpose of the tests and the potential risks or discomfort associated with laboratory testing.

WHAT THE ATHLETE GAINS BY PHYSIOLOGICAL TESTING

Laboratory measurement of physical performance can be expensive and time consuming. An obvious question arises: What does the athlete gain by laboratory testing? A testing program can benefit the athlete and coach in at least three major ways:

1. Physiological testing can provide information regarding an athlete's strengths and weaknesses in his/her sport; this information can be used as baseline data to plan individual exercise training programs. As discussed above, athletic success in

most sports involves the interaction of several physiological components (Figure 20.1). In the laboratory, the exercise scientist can often measure these physiological components separately and provide the athlete with information about which physiological components require improvement in order for the athlete to raise his/her level of athletic performance. This information becomes the foundation for an individual exercise prescription that concentrates on the identified areas of weakness (53).

2. Laboratory testing provides feedback to the athlete about the effectiveness of a training program (53). For example, comparing the results of physiological tests performed before and after a training program provides a basis for evaluating the success of the training program (5).

3. Laboratory testing educates the athlete about the physiology of exercise (53). By participation in laboratory testing, the athlete learns more about those physiological parameters that are important to success in his/her sport. This is important because athletes with a basic understanding of elementary exercise physiology will likely make better personal decisions concerning the design of both exercise training and nutritional programs.

WHAT PHYSIOLOGICAL TESTING WILL NOT DO

Laboratory testing of the athlete is not a magical aid for the identification of future Olympic gold medalists (53). Although laboratory testing can provide valuable information concerning an athlete's strengths and weaknesses, this type of testing has limitations in that it is difficult to simulate in the laboratory the physiological and psychological demands of many sports. Therefore, it is difficult to predict athletic performance from any single battery of laboratory measurements. Performance in the field is the ultimate test of athletic success, and laboratory testing should be considered primarily a training aid for coach and athlete (53).

COMPONENTS OF EFFECTIVE PHYSIOLOGICAL TESTING

For laboratory testing to be effective, several key factors need consideration (53):

1. The physiological variables to be tested should be relevant to the sport. For example, measurement of maximal handgrip strength in a distance

runner would not be relevant to the athlete's event. Therefore, only those physiological components that are important for a particular sport should be measured.

2. Physiological tests should be valid and reliable. Valid tests are tests that measure what they are supposed to measure. Reliable tests are tests that are reproducible. Based on these definitions, the need for tests that are both valid and reproducible is clear (20). (See A Closer Look 20.1.)

3. Tests should be as sport-specific as possible. For instance, the distance runner should be tested while running (i.e., treadmill), and the cyclist should be tested while cycling.

4. Tests should be repeated at regular intervals. One of the main purposes of laboratory testing is to provide the athlete with systematic feedback concerning training effectiveness. To meet this objective, tests should be performed on a regular basis.

5. Testing procedures should be carefully controlled. The need to rigidly administer the laboratory test relates to the reliability of tests. For tests to be reliable, the testing protocol should be standardized. Factors to be controlled include the instructions given to the athletes prior to testing, the testing protocol itself, the calibration of instruments involved in testing, the time of the day for testing, prior exercise, diet standardization, and other factors such as sleep, illness, hydration status, or injury.

6. Test results should be interpreted to the coach and athlete clearly. This final step is a key goal of effective laboratory testing.

IN SUMMARY

■ Designing laboratory tests to assess physical performance requires an understanding of those factors that contribute to success in a particular sport. Physical performance is determined by the interaction of the following factors: (a) maximal energy output, (b) muscular strength, (c) coordination/economy of movement, and (d) psychological factors such as motivation and tactics.

■ To be effective, physiological tests should be (a) relevant to the sport; (b) valid and reliable; (c) sport specific; (d) repeated at regular intervals; (e) standardized; and (f) interpreted to the coach and athlete.

A CLOSER LOOK 20.1

Reliability of Physiological Performance Tests

For a physiological test of human performance to be useful, the test must be reliable. That is, the test results must be reproducible. Several factors influence the reliability of physiological performance tests. These include the caliber of athletes tested, the type of ergometer used during the test, and the specificity of the test.

Physiological tests of performance are more reliable when highly trained and experienced athletes are tested (38). The explanation for this observation appears to be that these athletes are highly motivated to perform and that they are better able to pace themselves in a reproducible manner during a performance test. That is, high-caliber athletes may have a better "feel" for pace, and their perceptions of fatigue are less variable than those of less-experienced athletes (38).

It is clear that some ergometers are more unvarying than others in providing a constant resistance. For instance, an ergometer that maintains its calibration and delivers a constant power output during a test would result in a more reproducible test of human performance than an ergometer that provides variable power outputs during the test.

Although controversy exists, it is believed that exercise tests with a movement pattern and exercise intensity that mimics the actual sporting event are more reliable than tests that do not imitate the event (38, 39). For example, testing racing cyclists on a cycle ergometer at an exercise intensity close to the intensity of competition should be a more reliable performance test than testing these athletes on other types of ergometers, such as treadmills.

DIRECT TESTING OF MAXIMAL AEROBIC POWER

Let's begin our discussion of the laboratory assessment of human performance by describing tests to measure the maximal oxygen uptake ($\dot{V}O_2$ max) of athletes. Exercise testing to determine $\dot{V}O_2$ max dates back to studies conducted more than 80 years ago by the British scientist A.V. Hill. Indeed, A.V. Hill coined the term "$\dot{V}O_2$ max" in the early 1920s (3). *Maximal oxygen uptake* was first mentioned in chapter 4 and is defined as the highest oxygen uptake that an individual can obtain during exercise using large muscle groups (1). By necessity, the type of exercise performed to determine $\dot{V}O_2$ max must use large muscle groups (e.g., legs). Although several tests to estimate $\dot{V}O_2$ max exist (12, 24, 89), the most accurate means of determination is by direct laboratory measurement. Direct measurement of $\dot{V}O_2$ max is generally performed using a motorized treadmill or cycle ergometer, and open-circuit spirometry is used to measure pulmonary gas exchange (see chapter 1). However, $\dot{V}O_2$ max has also been measured during both free and tethered swimming, cross-country skiing, bench stepping, ice skating, and rowing (8, 12, 54, 57, 64, 95).

Historically, the measurement of $\dot{V}O_2$ max has been considered the test of choice for predicting success in endurance events such as distance running (11, 16, 27, 28, 34, 45, 53, 63, 101). For example, relative $\dot{V}O_2$ max (i.e., $\dot{V}O_2$ max expressed in ml · kg^{-1} · min^{-1}) has been shown to be the single most important factor in predicting distance running success in a heterogeneous (i.e., different $\dot{V}O_2$ max) group of athletes (17, 18, 28). The logical explanation for this finding is that because distance running is largely an aerobic event (see chapters 4 and 19), those individuals with a high $\dot{V}O_2$ max should have an advantage over individuals with lower aerobic capacities. However, as one would expect, the correlation between $\dot{V}O_2$ max and distance running performance is low in a homogeneous (i.e., similar $\dot{V}O_2$ max) group of runners (15, 75). These observations suggest that although a high $\dot{V}O_2$ max is important in determining distance running success, other variables are important as well. Therefore, measurement of $\dot{V}O_2$ max is only one in a battery of tests that should be used in evaluating physical work capacity in endurance athletes.

Specificity of Testing

As stated previously, running on a treadmill and pedaling a cycle ergometer are the two most common forms of exercise used to determine $\dot{V}O_2$ max. However, much evidence exists to suggest that a test to determine $\dot{V}O_2$ max should involve the specific movement used by the athlete in his or her event (7, 8, 69). For example, if the athlete being tested is a runner, it is important that $\dot{V}O_2$ max be assessed during running. Likewise, if the athlete being evaluated is a trained cyclist, the exercise test should be performed on the cycle ergometer. Further, specific testing procedures have been established for cross-country skiers and swimmers as well (54, 57, 64).

A LOOK BACK—IMPORTANT PEOPLE IN SCIENCE

Robert Bruce Was a Pioneer in the Development of the Graded Exercise Test

Robert Arthur Bruce (1916–2004) was born in the Boston suburb of Somerville, Massachusetts. He earned his B.S degree from Boston College and completed his medical school training in 1943 at the University of Rochester. After finishing his medical residency in 1946, he joined the faculty at the University of Rochester. Dr. Bruce later (1950) became the chief of cardiology at the University of Washington Medical School, where he remained until his retirement from academic medicine in 1987.

Early in his career, Dr. Bruce recognized that an exercise test could play an important role in the clinical evaluation of cardiac patients. He published his first paper on exercise testing in 1949 and concluded that a standardized exercise test provides key diagnostic information about cardiac patients. Dr. Bruce continued to explore exercise testing protocols for patient testing, and in 1963 he conceived and validated a multistage exercise protocol that was designed to evaluate the patient's exercise performance and provide important diagnostic information from the measurement of heart rate, blood pressure, and ECG changes during exercise. Subsequently the standard Bruce Exercise Test evolved into its present form with seven 3-minute

stages. This test became known as the "Bruce Protocol" and is one of the most widely used treadmill protocols in North America to evaluate cardiac patients.

Dr. Bruce developed his exercise test for patient populations in the clinical laboratory. Nonetheless, the Bruce graded exercise test was the conceptual model behind many of the current graded exercise tests that are used in the exercise physiology laboratory to evaluate both $\dot{V}O_2$ max and the lactate threshold in athletes. Because of his research accomplishments in the area of clinical exercise testing, Dr. Bruce has been labeled as a pioneer of the cardiac stress test.

Exercise Test Protocol

Although the first exercise tests to determine $\dot{V}O_2$ max were performed in the 1920s, rigorous studies to optimize laboratory exercise tests were not performed until the 1940s and 1950s. An early leader in the development of graded exercise tests was Dr. Robert Bruce, a cardiologist at the University of Washington (See A Look Back—Important People in Science).

A test to determine $\dot{V}O_2$ max generally begins with a submaximal "warm-up" load that may last 3 to 5 minutes. After the warm-up period, the power output can be increased in several ways: (1) the work rate may be increased to a load that in preliminary experiments has been shown to represent a load near the predicted maximal load for the subject, (2) the load may be increased stepwise each minute until the subject reaches a point at which the power output cannot be maintained, or (3) the load may be increased stepwise every 2 to 4 minutes until the subject cannot maintain the desired work rate. When any one of these procedures is carefully followed, it yields approximately the same $\dot{V}O_2$ max as the others (1, 49, 73, 104), although an exercise protocol that does not exceed 10 to 12 minutes seems preferable (10, 49).

The criteria to determine if $\dot{V}O_2$ max has been obtained were discussed in chapter 15. Because of the importance of this measure, some important issues will be reviewed here. The primary criterion to determine if $\dot{V}O_2$ max has been reached during an

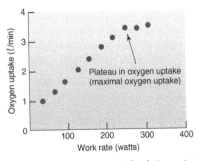

Figure 20.2 Changes in oxygen uptake during an incremental cycle ergometer test designed to determine $\dot{V}O_2$ max. The observed plateau in $\dot{V}O_2$ with an increase in work rate is considered to be the "gold standard" for validation of $\dot{V}O_2$ max.

incremental exercise test is a plateau in oxygen uptake with a further increase in work rate (94). This concept is illustrated in figure 20.2. Unfortunately, when testing untrained subjects, a plateau in $\dot{V}O_2$ is rarely observed during an incremental exercise test. Does this mean that the subject did not reach his or her $\dot{V}O_2$ max? This possibility exists, but it is also possible that the subject reached his or her $\dot{V}O_2$ max at the last work rate but could not complete another exercise stage; therefore, a plateau in $\dot{V}O_2$ was not observed. In light of this possibility, several investigators have suggested that the validity of a $\dot{V}O_2$ max test be determined from not one but several criteria. In chapter 15 it was discussed that a blood lactate concentration of >8 mmoles $\cdot$ liter^{-1} during the last stage of exercise could be used as one of the criteria to determine if $\dot{V}O_2$ max had been obtained. However, to avoid the difficulty of taking blood samples and subsequent analysis for lactate levels, investigators have proposed additional criteria that do not involve blood sampling. For example, Williams et al. (100) and McMiken and Daniels (58) have proposed that a $\dot{V}O_2$ max test be judged as valid if any two of the following criteria are met: (1) a respiratory exchange ratio of ≥ 1.15, (2) a heart rate during the last exercise stage that is ± 10 beats per minute within the subject's predicted maximum heart rate, or (3) a plateau in $\dot{V}O_2$ with an increase in work rate.

Determination of Peak $\dot{V}O_2$ in Paraplegic Athletes

Again, by definition, $\dot{V}O_2$ max is the highest $\dot{V}O_2$ that can be attained during exercise using large muscle groups (1). However, subjects with injuries to or paralysis of their lower limbs can have their aerobic fitness evaluated through arm ergometry, which substitutes arm cranking for cycling or running. Given the aforementioned definition of $\dot{V}O_2$ max, the highest $\dot{V}O_2$ obtained during an incremental arm ergometry test is not referred to as $\dot{V}O_2$ max, but is called the peak $\dot{V}O_2$ for arm exercise.

The protocols used to determine peak $\dot{V}O_2$ during arm ergometry are similar in design to the previously mentioned treadmill and cycle ergometer protocols (84, 86). Evidence suggests that in subjects who are not specifically arm trained, a higher peak $\dot{V}O_2$ is obtained during arm ergometry if the test begins at some predetermined load that represents approximately 50% to 60% of peak $\dot{V}O_2$ during arm work (97). A logical explanation for these findings is that an "accelerated" incremental arm testing protocol that rapidly reaches a high power output might limit muscular fatigue early in the test, allowing the subject to reach a higher power output and therefore obtain a higher peak $\dot{V}O_2$.

In an effort to provide a more specific form of testing for paraplegics who are wheelchair racing athletes, some laboratories have modified a wheelchair by connecting the wheels to a cycle ergometer in such a way that the resistance to turn the wheels can be adjusted in the same manner as the load is altered on the cycle ergometer (81). This allows wheelchair athletes to be tested using the exact movement that they use during a race; therefore, it is superior to using arm ergometry to evaluate peak $\dot{V}O_2$ in this population.

IN SUMMARY

- The measurement of $\dot{V}O_2$ max requires the use of large muscle groups and should be specific to the movement required by the athlete in his or her event or sport.
- A $\dot{V}O_2$ max test can be judged to be valid if two of the following criteria are met: (a) respiratory exchange ratio $>1:15$, (b) HR during the last test stage that is ± 10 beats per minute within the predicted HR max, and/or (c) plateau in $\dot{V}O_2$ with an increase in work rate.
- Arm crank ergometry and wheelchair ergometry are commonly used to determine the peak $\dot{V}O_2$ in paraplegic athletes.

LABORATORY TESTS TO PREDICT ENDURANCE PERFORMANCE

Exercise physiologists, coaches, and athletes have actively searched for a single laboratory test that can predict success in endurance events. Numerous tests have been developed in an effort to predict athletic performance. In this section, we describe two well-developed laboratory tests—lactate threshold and critical power—that are useful in predicting endurance performance. Also, another laboratory test to predict performance, called "peak running velocity," is introduced in Research Focus 20.1. Let's begin with a discussion of the lactate threshold.

Use of the Lactate Threshold to Evaluate Performance

Numerous studies have provided evidence that some measure of the maximal steady-state running speed is useful in predicting success in distance running events from 2 miles to the marathon (19, 25, 26, 48–50, 52, 74, 91, 92). The most common laboratory measurement to estimate this maximal steady-state speed is the determination of the lactate threshold. Recall that the lactate threshold represents an exercise intensity wherein blood lactate levels begin to systematically increase. Because fatigue is associated with high levels of blood and muscle lactate, it is logical that the lactate threshold would be related to endurance performance in events lasting longer than 12 to 15 minutes (51). Although much of the research examining the role of the lactate threshold in predicting endurance performance has centered around distance running, the same principles apply to predicting performance in endurance cycling, swimming, and cross-country skiing.

RESEARCH FOCUS 20.1

Measurement of Peak Running Velocity to Predict Performance in Distance Running

The lactate threshold and critical power measurements have generally been used to predict performance in endurance events lasting longer than 20 minutes (e.g., 10-kilometer run). In an effort to develop a laboratory or field test to predict performance in endurance events lasting fewer than 20 minutes (e.g., 5-kilometer run), researchers have developed a test called "peak running velocity" (42, 66, 67, 85). The test is easy to administer and can be performed on a treadmill or track. For example, the measurement of peak running velocity on a treadmill involves a short test of progressively increasing the treadmill speed every 30 seconds (0% grade) until volitional fatigue. Peak running velocity (meters · second[-1]) is defined as the highest speed that can be maintained for more than 5 seconds' duration (85).

How well does peak running velocity predict performance? In a

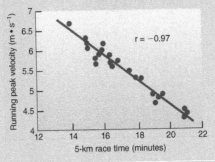

FIGURE 20.3   Relationship between running peak velocity and finish time of a 5-kilometer (km) race. Data from reference (77).

well-designed study, researchers demonstrated that peak running velocity was an excellent predictor of success in a 5-kilometer run (85). This point is illustrated by the strong correlation between peak running velocity and 5-kilometer race time (see figure 20.3). Surprisingly, similar findings have been reported for longer running events (e.g., 10–90 kilometer) as well (46, 67). Although additional research is required to fully investigate the application of this test to athletic performance, peak running velocity appears to be a promising laboratory or field test to predict endurance performance.

Direct Determination of Lactate Threshold

Similar to the assessment of $\dot{V}O_2$ max, the determination of the lactate threshold requires athletes to be tested in a manner that simulates their competitive movements (i.e., specificity of testing). Testing protocols to determine the lactate threshold generally begin with a 2- to 5-minute warm-up at a low work rate followed by a stepwise increase in the power output every 1 to 3 minutes (76, 92, 95, 98, 99, 104). In general, the stepwise increases in work rate are small in order to provide better resolution in the determination of the lactate threshold (104).

To determine the blood concentration of lactate, blood samples are obtained at each work rate from a catheter (an indwelling tube) placed in an artery or vein in the subject's arm or from a small puncture of the fingertip. After the test, these blood samples are chemically analyzed for lactate, and the concentration at each exercise stage is then graphed against the oxygen consumption at the time the sample is removed. This concept is illustrated in figure 20.4. How is the lactate threshold determined? Recall that the formal definition of the lactate threshold is the point after which there is a systematic and continuous rise in blood lactate concentration. Although several techniques are available, the simplest and most common

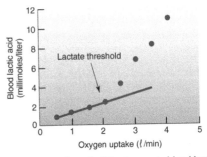

Figure 20.4   Typical graph of the changes in blood lactic acid concentrations during an incremental exercise test. The sudden rise in blood lactic acid is called the "lactate threshold."

procedure is to allow two independent investigators to subjectively pick the lactate "breakpoint" by visual inspection of the lactate/$\dot{V}O_2$ plot (22, 76, 98). If the two investigators disagree as to where the threshold occurs, a third investigator is used to arbitrate.

In practice, the lactate "break point" can often be chosen by using a ruler and drawing a straight line through the lactate concentrations at the first several work rates. The last point on the line is considered the lactate threshold (figure 20.4). The obvious advantage of this technique is its simplicity. The disadvantage is that not all investigators agree that this procedure yields valid and reliable results (76). In light of this concern, several researchers have proposed that complex computer programs be used to more accurately predict the lactate threshold, or that an arbitrary lactate value (e.g., 4 mM) be used as an indication of the lactate threshold (31, 51).

Prediction of the Lactate Threshold by Ventilatory Alterations   A technique to estimate the lactate threshold that does not require blood withdrawal has obvious appeal to both investigators and experimental subjects. This need for a noninvasive method to determine the lactate threshold has led to the widespread use of ventilatory and gas exchange measures to estimate the lactate threshold. Recall from chapter 10 that the rationale for the use of the "ventilatory threshold" as a "marker" of the lactate threshold is linked to the belief that the increase in blood lactate concentration at the lactate threshold stimulates ventilation via hydrogen ion influence on the carotid bodies. Although there are several noninvasive techniques in use today (4, 13, 87), the least complex procedure to estimate the lactate threshold by gas exchange is to perform an incremental exercise similar to the previously discussed test used to determine the lactate threshold. Upon completion of the test, the minute ventilation at each work rate during the test is graphed as a function of the oxygen uptake. Figure 20.5 illustrates this procedure. Similar to the determination

of the lactate threshold, the usual procedure is to allow two independent researchers to visually inspect the graph and subjectively determine the point where there is a sudden increase in ventilation (figure 20.5). The point at which ventilation increases rapidly is considered the ventilatory threshold and is used as an estimate of the lactate threshold. The error in predicting the lactate threshold from the ventilator threshold is estimated to range from 12–17% (36). Therefore, some authors have criticized this technique for a lack of precision (36, 76). Nonetheless, this procedure has been shown to be useful in predicting success in endurance events (29, 75).

Measurement of Critical Power

Another laboratory measurement that can be used to predict performance in endurance events is critical power. The concept of **critical power** is based upon the notion that athletes can maintain a specific submaximal power output without fatigue (35, 42, 46). Figure 20.6 illustrates the critical power concept for running performance. In this illustration, running speed is plotted on the y-axis, and the time that the athlete can run at this speed prior to exhaustion is plotted on the x-axis. Critical power is defined as the running speed (i.e., power output) at which the running speed/time curve reaches a plateau. Therefore, in theory, the critical power is considered the power output that can be maintained indefinitely (44). In practice, however, this is not the case. In fact, most athletes fatigue within 30 to 60 minutes when exercising at their critical power (35).

Critical power can be determined in the laboratory by having subjects perform a series of five to seven timed exercise trials to exhaustion. This is

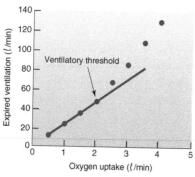

Figure 20.5   Example of the ventilatory threshold determination. Note the linear rise in ventilation up to an oxygen uptake of 2.0 liters/minute—above which ventilation begins to increase in an alinear fashion. This break in linearity of ventilation is termed the "ventilatory threshold" and can be used as an estimate of the lactate threshold.

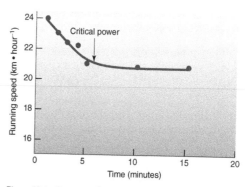

Figure 20.6   Concept of critical power.

generally accomplished over several days of testing. The results are graphed, and critical power is determined by subjective assessment of the point where the power/time curve begins to plateau or by using a mathematical technique (see references (35, 41, 46) for details). Although figure 20.6 illustrates the critical power measurement for running, the same principle of measurement can be applied to other endurance sports (e.g., cycling, rowing, etc.) (35, 40).

How well does critical power predict performance? Several studies have shown that critical power is significantly correlated with performance in endurance events lasting 3 to 100 minutes (e.g., r = 0.67 − 0.85) (35, 40, 42, 46). Therefore, critical power is a useful laboratory predictor of success in endurance sports.

Is critical power a better predictor of success in endurance events than other laboratory measures such as the lactate threshold or $\dot{V}O_2$ max? The answer remains controversial because many investigators report that $\dot{V}O_2$ max is the best single predictor of endurance performance success (17, 18, 28). However, in events lasting approximately 30 minutes, the lactate threshold, $\dot{V}O_2$ max, and critical power appear to be similar in their abilities to predict performance (46). This is not surprising, considering that critical power is dependent upon both $\dot{V}O_2$ max and the lactate threshold. Indeed, critical power is highly correlated to both $\dot{V}O_2$ max and the lactate threshold (46, 62). In other words, a subject with a high $\dot{V}O_2$ max and lactate threshold will also possess a high critical power. See Jones et al. (2010) in the Suggested Readings for more details on the critical power concept.

IN SUMMARY

- Common laboratory tests to predict endurance performance include measurement of the lactate threshold, critical power, and peak running velocity. All these measurements have been proven useful in predicting performance in endurance events.
- The lactate threshold can be determined during an incremental exercise test using any one of several exercise modalities (e.g., treadmill, cycle ergometer, etc.). The lactate threshold represents an exercise intensity at which blood lactate levels begin to systematically increase.
- Critical power is defined as the running speed (i.e., power output) at which the running speed/time curve reaches a plateau.
- Peak running velocity (meters · second^{-1}) can be determined on a treadmill or track and is defined as the highest speed that can be maintained for more than 5 seconds.

TESTS TO DETERMINE EXERCISE ECONOMY

The topic of exercise economy was first introduced in chapter 1. The economy of a particular sport movement (e.g., running or cycling) has a major influence on the energy cost of the sport and consequently interacts with $\dot{V}O_2$ max in determining endurance performance (15, 21, 51, 61). For example, a runner who is uneconomical will expend a greater amount of energy to run at a given speed than will an economical runner. With all other variables being equal, the more economical runner would likely defeat the less economical runner in head-to-head competition. Therefore, the measurement of exercise economy would seem appropriate when performing a battery of laboratory tests to evaluate an athlete's performance potential.

How is exercise economy evaluated? Conceptually, exercise economy is assessed by graphing energy expenditure during a particular activity (e.g., running, cycling, etc.) at several speeds. In general, the energy costs of running, cycling, or swimming can be determined using similar methods. Let's use running as an example to illustrate this procedure. The economy of running is quantified by measuring the steady-state oxygen cost of running on a horizontal treadmill at several speeds. The oxygen requirement of running is then graphed as a function of running speed (9, 37). Figure 20.7 illustrates the change in $\dot{V}O_2$ in two runners at a variety of running speeds. Notice that at any given speed, runner B requires less oxygen and therefore expends less energy than runner A (i.e., runner B is more economical than runner A). A marked difference in running economy between athletes can have an important impact on performance.

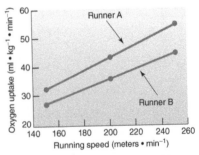

Figure 20.7 An oxygen cost-of-running curve for two subjects. Note the higher $\dot{V}O_2$ cost of running at any given running speed for subject A when compared to subject B. See text for details.

ESTIMATING SUCCESS IN DISTANCE RUNNING USING THE LACTATE THRESHOLD AND RUNNING ECONOMY

Over the past 15 to 20 years, many investigators have tried to apply laboratory tests to predict performance in a variety of sports [see reference (71) for examples]. The sport that has received the most attention is distance running. Theoretically, the prediction of potential performance in any endurance sport involves the use of similar laboratory measurements ($\dot{V}O_2$ max, economy of movement, etc.). We will use distance running as an example of how a sport scientist or coach might use laboratory measurements to estimate an athlete's performance in a particular event. Let's begin our discussion with a brief overview of the physiological factors that contribute to distance running success. As previously mentioned, the best test for determining an endurance runner's potential is $\dot{V}O_2$ max. However, other factors modify the pace that can be maintained for races of different lengths. For example, anaerobic energy contributes significantly to the ability to maintain a specified pace during shorter distance runs (e.g., 1,500 meters) (11, 51). In longer runs (5,000 to 10,000 meters), running economy and the lactate threshold may play important roles in determining success (25, 75, 92). To predict endurance performance, we must determine the athlete's maximal race pace that can be maintained for a particular racing distance.

To illustrate how performance in distance running might be estimated, consider an example of predicting performance in a 10,000-meter race. We begin with an assessment of the athlete's running economy and then perform an incremental treadmill test to determine $\dot{V}O_2$ max and the lactate threshold. The test results for our runner are graphed in figure 20.8. How do we determine the maximal race pace from the laboratory data? Numerous studies have shown that a close relationship exists between the lactate or ventilatory threshold and the maximal pace that can be maintained during a 10,000-meter race (25, 75, 92). For instance, it appears that well-trained runners can run 10,000 meters at a pace that exceeds their lactate threshold by approximately 5 m · min⁻¹ (37, 72). With this information and the data from figure 20.8, we can now predict a finish time for an athlete. First, we examine figure 20.8, part b, to determine the $\dot{V}O_2$ at the lactate threshold. The lactate threshold occurred at a $\dot{V}O_2$ of 40 ml · kg⁻¹ · min⁻¹, which corresponds to a running speed of 200 m · min⁻¹ (part a of figure 20.8). Assuming that the athlete can exceed this speed by 5 m · min⁻¹, the projected average race pace for a 10,000-meter run would be 205 m · min⁻¹. Therefore, an estimate of the athlete's finish time could

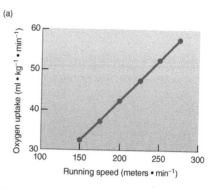

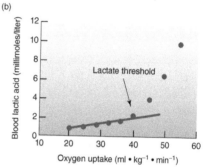

Figure 20.8 Incremental exercise test results for a hypothetical runner. These test results can be used to predict performance in an endurance race. See text for details.

be obtained by dividing 10,000 meters by his predicted running speed (m · min⁻¹):

Estimated finish time = 10,000 m ÷ 205 m · min⁻¹
= 48.78 min

Although theoretical predictions of performance, such as the example presented here, can generally estimate performance with a reasonable degree of precision, a number of outside factors can influence racing performance. For example, motivation and race tactics play an important role in distance running success. Environmental conditions (heat/humidity, altitude, etc.) also influence an athlete's ultimate performance (see chapters 19 and 24). For information on the ability of laboratory testing to predict future champions, see The Winning Edge 20.1.

IN SUMMARY

- Success in an endurance event can be predicted by a laboratory assessment of the athlete's movement economy, $\dot{V}O_2$ max, and lactate threshold. These parameters can be used to determine the maximal race pace that an athlete can maintain for a given racing distance.

THE WINNING EDGE 20.1

Exercise Physiology Applied to Sports—Can Laboratory Testing of Young Athletes Predict Future Champions?

Numerous articles in popular magazines have proclaimed the ability of laboratory testing in children to predict future athletic champions. For example, it has been argued that determination of skeletal muscle fiber type (via a muscle biopsy) in youth athletes can be used to predict the future athletic success of these individuals. The truth is that there are no laboratory measurements that accurately predict the "ultimate" athletic ability of anyone. Indeed, athletic success depends on numerous physiological and psychological factors, many of which are difficult, if not impossible, to measure in the laboratory. As mentioned earlier, the primary benefits of laboratory testing of athletes are to provide the individual with information about his or her strengths and weaknesses in a sport, to offer feedback about the effectiveness of the conditioning program, and to educate the athlete about the physiology of exercise (2). For more details on testing elite young athletes see Barker et al. (2011) in the Suggested Readings.

DETERMINATION OF ANAEROBIC POWER

For the assessment of anaerobic power, it is essential that the test employed use the muscle groups involved in the sport (i.e., specificity) and involve the energy pathways used in the performance of the event. Although several classification schemes have been proposed (6, 33), tests to assess maximal anaerobic power can be generally classified into (1) ultra short-term tests designed to test the maximal capacity of the "ATP-PC system," and (2) short-term tests to evaluate the overall anaerobic capacity, which measures the maximal capacity for ATP production by both the ATP-PC system and anaerobic glycolysis. Remember that events lasting fewer than 10 seconds are believed to principally use the ATP-PC system to produce ATP, while events lasting 30 to 60 seconds utilize anaerobic glycolysis as the major bioenergetic pathway to synthesize ATP. This principle is illustrated in figure 20.9 and should be remembered when designing tests to evaluate an athlete's anaerobic power for a specific sport.

Tests of Ultra Short-Term Maximal Anaerobic Power

Several practical "field tests" have been developed to assess the maximal capacity of the ATP-PC system to produce ATP over a very short time period (e.g., 1 to 10 seconds) (55). These tests are generally referred to as **power tests.** Recall from chapter 1 that power is defined as:

$$Power = (F \times D) \div T$$

where F is the force generated, D is the distance over which the force is applied, and T is the time required to perform the work.

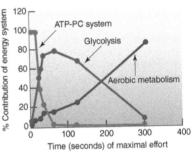

Figure 20.9 The percent contribution of the ATP-PC system, anaerobic glycolysis, and aerobic metabolism as a function of time during a maximal effort.

Jumping Power Tests For many years, tests such as the standing broad jump and vertical jump have been used as field tests to evaluate an individual's explosive anaerobic power. The standing broad jump is the distance covered in a horizontal leap from a crouched position, whereas the vertical jump is the distance between the standing reach height and the maximum jump-and-touch height. Both tests probably fail to adequately assess an individual's maximal ATP-PC system capacity because of their brief duration. Moreover, neither test is considered a good predictor of running success in a short dash (e.g., 40–100 yards) (80, 88). Nonetheless, the vertical jump test is considered valuable in predicting vertical leaping ability of athletes and is widely used by coaches in professional football, soccer, and basketball as one of the many performance tests used to evaluate athletic potential.

Running Power Tests for American Football The 40-yard dash has been a popular test to evaluate power output in football players for many years. The athlete generally performs two to three timed 40-yard dashes with full recovery between efforts. The fastest time recorded is considered an indication of the individual's power output. Although a 40-yard dash is a rather specific test of power output for football players, there is little evidence that a 40-yard run in a straight line is a reliable predictor of an athlete's success at a particular position. Perhaps a shorter run (e.g., 10–20 yards), with several changes in direction, might provide a more specific test of power output in football players (57).

Stuart and colleagues (90) have proposed a fitness test for football players that is designed to evaluate the athlete's ability to perform repeated short bursts of power. The test is conducted in the following way. After a brief warm-up, the athlete performs a series of ten timed 40-yard dashes (maximum effort), with a 25-second recovery between dashes. The 25-second recovery period is designed to simulate the elapsed time between plays in a football game. The athletes' time for each 40-yard dash is graphed as a function of the trial number. This procedure is illustrated in figure 20.10 where line A represents data from a well-conditioned athlete and line B is data from a less-fit athlete. Notice that both lines A and B have negative slopes (fatigue slope). This demonstrates that each of the two athletes is slowing down with each succeeding 40-yard trial. Athletes who are highly conditioned will be able to maintain faster 40-yard dash times over the ten trials when compared to less-conditioned athletes, and therefore will have a less-negative fatigue slope. In an effort to establish a set of standards for this test, Stuart and co-workers have proposed that athletes be classified into one of four groups on the basis of the maximal

TABLE 20.1	Classification of Fitness Levels for Football Players on the Basis of a Series of 40-Yard Dash Times

Level	Category	Percentage of Maximal Velocity Maintained*
1	Superior	>90%
2	Good	85%–89%
3	Sub-par	80%–84%
4	Poor	<79%

*The "percentage of the maximal velocity maintained" is calculated by averaging the velocity of the last three trials and dividing by the average velocity over the first three trials. This ratio is then expressed as a percentage. See text for further details.

running velocity percentage that can be maintained over the final three 40-yard dash trials (see table 20.1). At present, levels 1 and 2 are considered acceptable levels of fitness for football players of any position, whereas levels 3 and 4 are labeled as subpar and poor fitness standards, respectively.

Running Tests for Soccer Soccer (called football outside of North America) remains the most popular sport in many countries around the world. Therefore, it is not surprising that numerous performance tests have been developed for soccer players (14, 60, 77, 78). Included in these performance tests are both tests of motor skills required for soccer and fitness tests. The design of a fitness test for soccer is complicated by the fact that soccer is a complex game requiring intermittent bursts of maximal running followed by periods of walking and/or running slowly. Therefore, soccer is a sport that utilizes both anaerobic and aerobic bioenergetic pathways to produce the required ATP. One of the most widely used field tests to determine both performance and metabolic responses of soccer athletes is the Loughborough Intermittent Shuttle Test developed at Loughborough University in England (65). This shuttle run test is designed to simulate the activity pattern of soccer players during a 90-minute match and consists of intermittent shuttle running (i.e., running back and forth) between markers placed 20 meters apart. The Loughborough intermittent shuttle test is performed with the subjects completing the following runs:

- 3 × 20 meters at walking pace
- 1 × 20 meters at maximal running speed with 4-second recovery
- 3 × 20 meters at a running speed corresponding to 55% of individual $\dot{V}O_2$ max
- 3 × 20 meters at a running speed corresponding to 95% of individual $\dot{V}O_2$ max

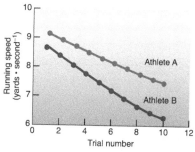

Figure 20.10 Illustration of the use of a series of timed 40-yard dashes to determine the anaerobic fitness of football players. In this illustration, athlete A shows a small but constant decline in running speed with each additional dash. In contrast, athlete B shows a large systematic decline in speed across dash trials. Therefore, athlete A is considered to be in better condition than athlete B. See text for details.

This block of exercise is repeated continuously for 90 minutes. In practice, the 20-meter distance is marked on the ground (or floor), and walking and running speeds are dictated by audio signals produced from a computer. Sprint times for the maximal 20-meter runs are recorded throughout the test by infrared photoelectric cells and represent one of the measured performance variables. That is, soccer players with the highest fitness levels will be able to maintain a higher percentage of their maximal sprint speed throughout the shuttle test. Further, the total distance covered during the test is also measured as a performance variable. During this shuttle test, it is estimated that 22% of the total exercise time is spent at or above 95% $\dot{V}O_2$ max, whereas the activity level for the remainder of the test is 55% $\dot{V}O_2$ max or below (65). Complete details of the numerous tests used to evaluate soccer performance are beyond the scope of this chapter, and the reader is referred to Castagna et al. (2010), Mirkov et al. (2008), and Psotta et al. (2011) in the Suggested Readings for more details about performance testing of soccer players.

Cycling Power Tests The **Quebec 10-second test** was developed to assess ultra short-term anaerobic power in cyclists (88). The technical error of this test is small, and the procedure is highly reliable (6). The test is performed on a friction-braked cycle ergometer that contains a photocell capable of measuring flywheel revolutions; the number of flywheel revolutions and resistance against the flywheel are electrically relayed to a microcomputer for analysis. The design of the test is simple. After a brief warm-up, the subject performs two all-out 10-second cycling trials separated by a rest period. The initial resistance on the cycle flywheel is determined by the subject's weight (about 0.09 kg per kg of body weight). Upon a verbal start command by the investigator, the subject begins pedaling at 80 rpm, and the load is rapidly adjusted within 2 to 3 seconds of the desired load. The subject then pedals as fast as possible for 10 seconds. Strong verbal encouragement is provided throughout the test. After a 10-minute rest period, a second test is performed and the results of the two tests averaged. The test results are reported in peak joules per kg of body weight and total joules per kg of body weight.

In addition to the evaluation of cyclists, the Quebec 10-second test has been used to test ultra short-term anaerobic power in nonathletes, runners, speed skaters, biathletes, and body builders. For complete details of these results, see Bouchard et al. (6).

Tests of Short-Term Anaerobic Power

As illustrated in figure 20.9, the ATP-PC system for production of ATP during intense exercise is important for short bursts of exercise (1 to 10 seconds),

whereas glycolysis becomes an important metabolic pathway for energy production in events lasting longer than 15 seconds. In an effort to evaluate the maximal capacity for anaerobic glycolysis to produce ATP during exercise, several short-term anaerobic power tests have been developed. Like other performance tests, anaerobic power tests should involve the specific muscles used in a particular sport.

Cycling Anaerobic Power Tests Researchers at the Wingate Institute in Israel have developed a maximal effort cycling test **(Wingate test)** designed to determine both peak anaerobic power and mean power output over the 30-second test. This test has been shown to be highly reproducible (43) and offers an excellent means of evaluating anaerobic power output in cyclists. The test is administered in the following manner. The subject performs a short, 2- to 4-minute warm-up on the cycle ergometer at an exercise intensity sufficient to elevate heart rate to 150 to 160 beats · min^{-1}. After a 3- to 5-minute rest interval, the test begins with the subject pedaling the cycle ergometer as fast as possible without resistance on the flywheel. After the subject reaches full pedaling speed (e.g., 2 to 3 seconds), the test administrator quickly increases the flywheel resistance to a predetermined load. This predetermined load is an estimate (based on body weight) of a workload that would exceed the subject's $\dot{V}O_2$ max by 20% to 60% (see table 20.2). The subject continues to pedal as

TABLE 20.2	The Resistance Setting for the Wingate Test Is Based on the Subject's Body Weight
Subject's Body Weight (kg)	Resistance Setting on the Flywheel (kg)
20–24.9	1.75
25–29.9	2.0
30–34.9	2.5
35–39.9	3.0
40–44.9	3.25
45–49.9	3.5
50–54.9	4.0
55–59.9	4.25
60–64.9	4.75
65–69.9	5.0
70–74.9	5.5
75–79.9	5.75
80–84.9	6.25
>85	6.5

From B. Noble, *Physiology of Exercise and Sport*. Copyright © 1986. The C.V. Mosby Company, St. Louis MO. Reprinted by permission.

rapidly as possible, and the pedal rate is recorded every 5 seconds during the test. The highest power output over the first few seconds is considered the peak power output and is indicative of the maximum rate of the ATP-PC system to produce ATP during this type of exercise. The decline in power output during the test is used as an index of anaerobic endurance and presumably represents the maximal capacity to produce ATP via a combination of the ATP-PC system and glycolysis. The decrease in power output is expressed as the percentage of peak power decline. The peak power output obtained during a Wingate test occurs near the beginning of the test, and the lowest power output is recorded during the last 5 seconds of the test. The difference in these two power outputs (i.e., highest power output minus lowest power output) is then divided by the peak power output and expressed as a percentage. For instance, if the peak power output was 600 watts and the lowest power output during the test was 200 watts, then the decline in power output would be computed as:

$$(600 - 200) \div 600 = .666 \times 100\% = 67\%$$

The 67% decline in power output means that the athlete decreases his or her peak power output by 67% over the 30-second exercise period.

Since the introduction of the Wingate test in the early 1970s, a number of modifications to the original protocol have been proposed (23, 30, 43, 70, 82). An Australian team of sport scientists (30) has developed a new test for the measurement of anaerobic power on a cycle ergometer that involves 60 seconds of maximal exercise and uses a variable resistance loading. The test design permits the measurement of both peak anaerobic power (i.e., peak ATP-PC system power) and mean (glycolytic) power output over the 60-second maximal exercise bout. The test is designed as follows. The subject performs a 5-minute warm-up at a low work rate (e.g., 120 watts). After a 2-minute recovery, the subject begins pedaling as fast as possible with no load against the cycle flywheel. When peak pedaling speed is obtained (i.e., 3 seconds), the investigator quickly increases the load on the flywheel to 0.095 kg resistance per kg of body weight. The subject continues to pedal as fast as possible at this load for 30 seconds; at the 30-second point, the load on the flywheel is reduced to 0.075 kg resistance per kg of body weight for the remainder of the test. The subject's power output during the test is continuously monitored electronically and work output is recorded as peak power output (joules per kg per second) and mean power output (joules per kg per second) during the entire test.

The rationale for the variable load is that although a high resistance is required to elicit maximal anaerobic power, such a resistance is too great for a supramaximal test of 60 seconds' duration (30). By reducing the resistance midway through the test, the workload becomes more manageable, which enables the subject to complete a maximal effort test for the entire 60-second period. The advantage of this test over the Wingate test is that the variable resistance design permits the measurement of peak anaerobic power and maximal anaerobic power over 60 seconds' duration. This type of test would be useful for athletes who compete in events lasting between 45 and 60 seconds. Note that while this test maximally taxes both the ATP-PC system and glycolysis, because of the test duration, the aerobic system is also activated (see chapters 3 and 4). Therefore, although the energy required to perform 60 seconds of maximal exercise comes primarily (e.g., 70%) from anaerobic pathways, the aerobic energy contribution may reach 30%.

Running Anaerobic Power Tests Maximal distance runs from 35 to 800 meters have been used to evaluate anaerobic power output in runners (83, 93, 103). Because such factors as running technique and motivation influence the performance of these types of power tests, the development of appropriate norms has been difficult. Nevertheless, this type of test can be used effectively to determine improvement within individuals as a result of a training regimen. One example of a valid and reliable running anaerobic test is the "running anaerobic sprint test" (RAST) (102). This running anaerobic sprint test is easy to administer and has been reported to be reliable and a good predictor of success in sprint races (103). A brief overview of the test is as follows. Subjects perform a series of six 35-meter maximal sprints with a 10-second recovery between run. Each sprint is timed, and peak power is calculated (power = (body mass × distance²)/time³) for each of the individual sprints. Mean power is then calculated as the average of the peak power of the six runs. The mean power output from this test has been shown to be a moderately good predictor of running performance at 100, 200, and 400 meters (103).

Sport-specific Tests Ultra short-term and short-term sport-specific anaerobic tests can be developed to meet the needs of team sports or individual athletic events not previously discussed here. The tests could attempt to measure the peak power output in a few seconds or measure mean power output during a period of 10 to 60 seconds, depending upon the energy demands of the sport.

Tests could be developed for tennis, basketball, ice skating, swimming, and so on. In some cases, time or distance covered would be the dependent variable measured rather than a direct measurement of power output (6). This type of sport-specific test provides the coach and athlete with direct feedback about the athlete's present level of fitness; subsequent periodic testing can be used to evaluate the success of training programs.

IN SUMMARY

- Anaerobic power tests are classified as (a) ultra short-term tests to determine the maximal capacity of the ATP-PC system and (b) short-term tests to evaluate the maximal capacity for anaerobic glycolysis.
- Ultra short-term and short-term power tests should be sport-specific in an effort to provide the athlete and coach with feedback about the athlete's current fitness level.

EVALUATION OF MUSCULAR STRENGTH

Muscular strength is defined as the maximum force that can be generated by a muscle or muscle group (1). The measurement of muscular strength is a common practice in the evaluation of training programs for football players, shot-putters, weight lifters, and other power athletes. Strength testing can be used to monitor training progress or the rehabilitation of injuries (56). Muscular strength can be assessed by using one of four methods: (1) isometric testing, (2) free-weight testing, (3) isokinetic testing, and (4) variable resistance testing. Before we discuss these methods of strength measurement, let's consider some general guidelines for the selection of a strength-testing method.

Criteria for Selection of a Strength-Testing Method

The criteria for selecting a method of strength testing include the following factors (80): specificity, ease of data acquisition and analysis, cost, and safety. Given the importance of proper strength-test selection, a brief discussion of each of these factors is warranted.

Specificity of strength testing considers the muscles involved in the sport movement, the movement pattern and contraction type, and the velocity of the contraction. For example, the measurement of sport-specific strength should use the muscle groups involved in the activity. Further, the testing mode should simulate the type of contraction used in the sport (isometric vs. dynamic). If the contraction used in the sport is dynamic, further consideration should

be given to whether the contraction is concentric or eccentric. A final level of specificity is the velocity of shortening. There is a degree of velocity specificity in strength training; speed and power athletes perform better on high-velocity power tests than on low (96). Therefore, there is a justification for trying to make the velocity of test contractions similar to those used in the sport.

Factors such as convenience and time required for strength measurements are important considerations when measurements are made on a large number of athletes (47). Currently, a number of companies market strength measurement devices that are interfaced with computer analysis packages. These devices greatly reduce the time required for strength measurement and analysis.

Much of the commercially available computerized equipment for strength measurement is expensive. The high cost of this equipment may prevent its purchase by physical therapy, exercise science, or athletic programs with small budgets. In these cases, the physical therapist, exercise scientist, or coach must choose the best available option within his/her budget.

A final concern for the selection of a strength-testing method is the safety of the technique. Safety should be a key concern for any measurement of strength. Clearly, strength-measurement techniques that put the athlete at high risk of injury should be avoided.

Isometric Measurement of Strength

Measurement of isometric strength requires a device that permits testing of the sport-specific muscle groups. These devices are commercially available from numerous sources. Most of the isometric testing devices available today are computerized instruments that are capable of measuring isometric force in a variety of muscle groups. Figure 20.11 illustrates one of these devices being used to measure leg strength during a knee extension. As the subject generates maximal isometric force, the computerized tensiometer (tension-measuring device) measures the force produced, and this information is recorded and displayed on an electronic panel on the instrument.

The measurement of isometric strength is typically performed at several joint angles. Isometric testing at each joint angle usually consists of two or more trials of maximal contractions (contraction duration of approximately 5 seconds), and the best of these trials is considered to be the measure of strength.

Advantages of isometric testing using computerized equipment include the fact that these tests are generally simple and safe to administer. For example, computerized measurement of isometric strength has been used in physical therapy to evaluate training progress in injured limbs. It has been argued that

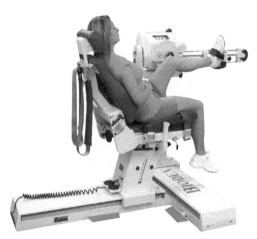

Figure 20.11 Use of a commercially available tensiometer to measure static force during a knee extension. Photo courtesy of Biodex Medical Systems, Inc.

since the isometric tensiometer can be used to measure static strength at many different joint angles with a low risk of injury, this technique might be more effective in evaluating strength gains during therapeutic training than conventional weight-lifting tests (57). Disadvantages of isometric testing include the high cost of some commercial devices and the fact that many sport activities involve dynamic movements. Further, because strength differs over the full range of joint movement, isometric measurements must be made at numerous joint angles; this increases the amount of time required to perform a test.

Free-Weight Testing of Strength

The term *isotonic* means constant tension. This term is often applied to conventional weight-lifting exercise because the weight of the barbell or dumbbell remains constant as the weight is lifted over the range of movement. In a strict sense, application of the term *isotonic* to weight lifting is not appropriate because the actual force or torque applied to the weight does not remain constant over the full range of movement. Acceleration and deceleration of the limbs during a weight-lifting movement often cause variation in the force applied. Therefore, in place of the term isotonic, the term **dynamic** is now commonly used to describe this type of muscle activity when exercising with a constant external resistance, such as free weights or weight stacks on machines where the resistance remains constant throughout the range of motion. The most common measure of dynamic strength is the one-repetition maximum, but tests involving three to six repetitions have been employed.

The one-repetition maximum (1-RM) method of evaluating muscular strength involves the performance of a single, maximal lift. This refers to the maximal amount of weight that can be lifted during one complete dynamic repetition of a particular movement (e.g., bench press). To test the 1-RM for any given muscle group, the subject selects a beginning weight that is close to the anticipated 1-RM weight. If one repetition is completed, the weight is increased by a small increment and the trial repeated. This process is continued until the maximum lifting capacity is obtained. The highest weight moved during one repetition is considered the 1-RM. The 1-RM test can be performed using free weights (barbells) or an adjustable resistance exercise machine. For more details of the 1-RM test, see Powers et al. (2006) in the Suggested Readings.

Because of safety concerns, some physical therapists and exercise scientists have recommended that a dynamic test consisting of three or six repetitions be substituted for the 1-RM test. The rationale is that the incidence of injury may be less with a weight that can be lifted a maximum of three or six times compared to the heavier weight that can be lifted during a 1-RM contraction.

In addition to the use of free weights or machines, maximal dynamic strength can be measured using dynamometers. A **dynamometer** is a device capable of measuring force. Hand-grip dynamometers have been used to evaluate grip strength for many years. Dynamometers operate in the following way. When force is applied to the dynamometer, a steel spring is compressed and moves a pointer along a scale. By calibrating the dynamometer with known weights, one can determine how much force is required to move the pointer a specified distance on the scale. Figure 20.12 illustrates the use of a hand-grip dynamometer to assess grip strength.

The advantages of dynamic strength testing include low cost of equipment and the fact that force is dynamically applied, which may simulate sport-specific movements. The disadvantages of free-weight testing using a 1-RM technique include the possibility of subject injury and the fact that it does not provide information concerning the force application over the full range of motion. This point will be discussed again in the next section.

Isokinetic Assessment of Strength

Over the past several years, many commercial computer-assisted devices to assess dynamic muscular force have been developed. The most common type of computerized strength measurement device on the market is an isokinetic dynamometer, which provides variable resistance. The term **isokinetic** means moving at a constant rate of speed. A variable-resistance isokinetic dynamometer is an electronic-mechanical

Figure 20.12   Use of the typical hand-grip dynamometer. Photo courtesy of Lafayette Instrument Company.

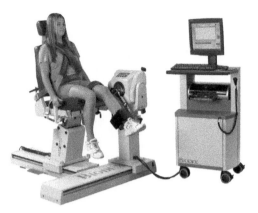

Figure 20.13   Use of a commercially available computer-assisted isokinetic dynamometer to measure strength during a knee extension. Photo courtesy of Biodex Medical Systems, Inc.

instrument that maintains a constant speed of movement while varying the resistance during a particular movement. The resistance offered by the instrument is an accommodating resistance, which is designed to match the force generated by the muscle. A force transducer inside the instrument constantly monitors the muscular force generated at a constant speed and relays this information to a computer, which calculates the average force generated over each time period and joint angle during the movement. An example of this type of instrument is pictured in figure 20.13.

A typical computer printout of data obtained during a maximum-effort leg extension on a computerized isokinetic dynamometer is illustrated in figure 20.14. This type of strength assessment provides a great deal more information than that supplied by a 1-RM test. The force curve pictured in figure 20.14 illustrates that the subject generates the smallest amount of force early in the movement pattern and the greatest amount of force during the middle portion of the movement. The 1-RM test provides only the final outcome, which is the maximum amount of weight lifted during this particular movement. That is, a 1-RM test does not provide information about the differences in force generation over the full range of movement. Therefore, a computer-assisted isokinetic instrument appears to offer advantages over the more

traditional 1-RM test. Further, isokinetic strength testing has been shown to be highly reliable (59).

Variable-Resistance Measurement of Strength

Several commercial companies market weight machines that vary the resistance (weight) during dynamic muscular contractions. The measurement of strength using a variable-resistance device is similar in principle to isotonic tests using 1-RM or three to six repetitions, with the exception that the variable-resistance machine creates a variable resistance over the range of movement. This variable resistance is typically achieved via a "cam," which in theory is designed to vary the resistance according to physiological and mechanical factors that determine force generation by muscles over the normal range of movement.

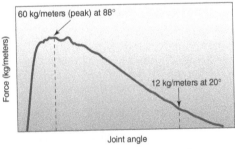

Figure 20.14   Example of a computer printout from a computer-assisted isokinetic dynamometer during a maximal-effort knee extension.

Potential advantages of these devices include the fact that most sport movement patterns are performed using variable forces, and the design of these machines makes adjustment of weight easy; therefore, little time is required for measurement. A disadvantage of these machines is the high cost; this is compounded by the fact that several individual machines are often required to measure strength in different muscle groups. For more details on the evaluation of muscular strength, see Baechle and Earle (2008) in the Suggested Readings.

IN SUMMARY

- Muscular strength is defined as the maximum force that can be generated by a muscle or muscle group.
- Evaluation of muscular strength is useful in assessing training programs for athletes involved in power sports or events.
- Muscular strength can be evaluated using any one of the following techniques: (a) isometric, (b) free-weight testing, (c) isokinetic, or (d) variable-resistance devices.

STUDY QUESTIONS

1. Discuss the rationale behind laboratory tests designed to assess physical performance in athletes. How do these tests differ from general physical fitness tests?
2. Define maximal oxygen uptake. Why might relative $\dot{V}O_2$ max be the single most important factor in predicting distance running success in a heterogeneous group of runners?
3. Discuss the concept of "specificity of testing" for the determination of $\dot{V}O_2$ max. Give a brief overview of the design of an incremental test to determine $\dot{V}O_2$ max. What criteria can be used to determine the validity of a $\dot{V}O_2$ max test?
4. Briefly, explain the technique employed to determine the lactate threshold and the ventilatory threshold.
5. Describe how the economy of running might be evaluated in the laboratory.
6. Discuss the theory and procedures involved in predicting success in distance running.
7. Explain how short-term maximal anaerobic power can be evaluated by field tests.
8. Describe how the Wingate test is used to assess medium-term anaerobic power.
9. Provide an overview of the 1-RM technique to evaluate muscular strength. Why might a computer-assisted dynamometer be superior to the 1-RM technique in assessing strength changes?
10. Discuss the advantages and disadvantages of each of the following types of strength measurement: (1) dynamic, (2) free weights, (3) isokinetic, and (4) variable resistance.

SUGGESTED READINGS

Baechle, T. R., and R. W. Earle. 2000. *Essentials of Strength Training and Conditioning.* Champaign, IL: Human Kinetics.

Bentley, D.J., J. Newell, and D. Bishop. 2007. Incremental exercise test design and analysis: Implications for performance diagnostics in endurance athletes. *Sports Medicine.* 37(7):575–86.

Castagna C., V. Manzi, F. Impellizzeri, M. Weston, and J. C. Barbero Alvarez. 2010. Relationship between endurance field tests and match performance in young soccer players. *J Strength Cond Res* 24:3227–33.

Currell K., and A. E. Jeukendrup. 2008. Validity, reliability and sensitivity of measures of sporting performance. *Sports Med* 38:297–316.

Mirkov D., A. Nedeljkovic, M. Kukolj, D. Ugarkovic, and S. Jaric. 2008. Evaluation of the reliability of soccer-specific field tests. *J Strength Cond Res* 22:1046–50.

Powers, S., S. Dodd, and E. Jackson. 2009. *Total Fitness and Wellness.* San Francisco:Pearson.

Reiman, M., and R. Manske. 2009. *Functional Testing in Human Performance.* Champaign: Human Kinetics.

Van Praag, E. Anaerobic fitness tests: What are we measuring? *Medicine and Science in Sports and Exercise* 50:26–45, 2007.

Zagatto A. M., W. R. Beck, and C. A. Gobatto. 2009. Validity of the running anaerobic sprint test for assessing anaerobic power and predicting short-distance performances. *J Strength Cond Res* 23:1820–27.

REFERENCES

1. **Åstrand P, and Rodahl K.** *Textbook of Work Physiology.* New York: McGraw-Hill, 1986.
2. **Barker AR, and Armstrong N.** Exercise testing elite young athletes. *Med Sport Sci* 56: 106–125, 2011.
3. **Bassett DR, Jr., and Howley ET.** Limiting factors for maximum oxygen uptake and determinants of endurance performance. *Med Sci Sports Exerc* 32: 70–84, 2000.
4. **Beaver WL, Wasserman K, and Whipp BJ.** A new method for detecting anaerobic threshold by gas exchange. *J Appl Physiol* 60: 2020–2027, 1986.
5. **Bentley DJ, Newell J, and Bishop D.** Incremental exercise test design and analysis: implications for performance diagnostics in endurance athletes. *Sports Med* 37: 575–586, 2007.
6. **Bouchard C.** Testing anaerobic power and capacity. In: *Physiological Testing of the High Performance Athlete,* edited by MacDougall J, Wenger H, and Green H. Champaign: Human Kinetics, 1991, p. 175–222.
7. **Bouckaert J, and Pannier J.** Specificity of $\dot{V}O_2$ max and blood lactate determinations in runners and cyclists. *International Archives of Physiology and Biochemistry* 93: 30–31, 1984.
8. **Bouckaert J, Pannier JL, and Vrijens J.** Cardiorespiratory response to bicycle and rowing ergometer exercise in oarsmen. *Eur J Appl Physiol Occup Physiol* 51: 51–59, 1983.
9. **Bransford DR, and Howley ET.** Oxygen cost of running in trained and untrained men and women. *Med Sci Sports* 9: 41–44, 1977.

10. **Buchfuhrer MJ, Hansen JE, Robinson TE, Sue DY, Wasserman K, and Whipp BJ.** Optimizing the exercise protocol for cardiopulmonary assessment. J Appl Physiol 55: 1558–1564, 1983.

11. **Bulbulian R, Wilcox AR, and Darabos BL.** Anaerobic contribution to distance running performance of trained cross-country athletes. Med Sci Sports Exerc 18: 107–113, 1986.

12. **Burke EJ.** Validity of selected laboratory and field tests of physical working capacity. Res Q 47: 95–104, 1976.

13. **Caiozzo VJ, Davis JA, Ellis JF, Azus JL, Vandagriff R, Prietto CA, and McMaster WC.** A comparison of gas exchange indices used to detect the anaerobic threshold. J Appl Physiol 53: 1184–1189, 1982.

14. **Castagna C, Manzi V, Impellizzeri F, Weston M, and Barbero Alvarez JC.** Relationship between endurance field tests and match performance in young soccer players. J Strength Cond Res 24: 3227–3233, 2010.

15. **Conley DL, and Krahenbuhl GS.** Running economy and distance running performance of highly trained athletes. Med Sci Sports Exerc 12: 357–360, 1980.

16. **Costill D.** A scientific approach to distance running. Los Altos: Track and Field News Press 1979.

17. **Costill DL.** Metabolic responses during distance running. J Appl Physiol 28: 251–255, 1970.

18. **Costill DL.** The relationship between selected physiological variables and distance running performance. J Sports Med Phys Fitness 7: 61–66, 1967.

19. **Costill DL, Thomason H, and Roberts E.** Fractional utilization of the aerobic capacity during distance running. Med Sci Sports 5: 248–252, 1973.

20. **Currell K, and Jeukendrup AE.** Validity, reliability and sensitivity of measures of sporting performance. Sports Med 38: 297–316, 2008.

21. **Daniels J, and Daniels N.** Running economy of elite male and elite female runners. Med Sci Sports Exerc 24: 483–489, 1992.

22. **Davis JA, Rozenek R, DeCicco DM, Carizzi MT, and Pham PH.** Comparison of three methods for detection of the lactate threshold. Clin Physiol Funct Imaging 27: 381–384, 2007.

23. **Dotan R, and Bar-Or O.** Load optimization for the Wingate Anaerobic Test. Eur J Appl Physiol Occup Physiol 51: 409–417, 1983.

24. **Ebbeling CB, Ward A, Puleo EM, Widrick J, and Rippe JM.** Development of a single-stage submaximal treadmill walking test. Med Sci Sports Exerc 23: 966–973, 1991.

25. **Farrell PA, Wilmore JH, Coyle EF, Billing JE, and Costill DL.** Plasma lactate accumulation and distance running performance. Med Sci Sports 11: 338–344, 1979.

26. **Foster C.** Blood lactate and respiratory measurement of the capacity for sustained exercise. In: Physiological Assessment of Human Fitness, edited by Maud P, and Foster C. Champaign: Human Kinetics, 1995, p. 57–72.

27. **Foster C.** $\dot{V}O_{2\,max}$ and training indices as determinants of competitive running performance. Journal of Sports Sciences 1: 13–27, 1983.

28. **Foster C, Daniels J, and Yarbough R.** Physiological correlates of marathon running and performance. Australian Journal of Sports Medicine 9: 58–61, 1977.

29. **Gaskill SE, Ruby BC, Walker AJ, Sanchez OA, Serfass RC, and Leon AS.** Validity and reliability of combining three methods to determine ventilatory threshold. Med Sci Sports Exerc 33: 1841–1848, 2001.

30. **Gastin P, Lawson D, Hargreaves M, Carey M, and Fairweather I.** Variable resistance loadings in anaerobic power testing. Int J Sports Med 12: 513–518, 1991.

31. **Grant S, McMillan K, Newell J, Wood L, Keatley S, Simpson D, Leslie K, and Fairlie-Clark S.** Reproducibility of the blood lactate threshold, 4 mmol.l(-1) marker, heart rate and ratings of perceived exertion during incremental treadmill exercise in humans. Eur J Appl Physiol 87: 159–166, 2002.

32. **Green H.** What do tests measure? In: Physiological Testing of the High Performance Athlete, edited by MacDougall J, Wenger H, and Green H. Champaign: Human Kinetics, 1991.

33. **Green S.** Measurement of anaerobic work capacities in humans. Sports Med 19: 32–42, 1995.

34. **Hagan RD, Smith MG, and Gettman LR.** Marathon performance in relation to maximal aerobic power and training indices. Med Sci Sports Exerc 13: 185–189, 1981.

35. **Hill DW.** The critical power concept: a review. Sports Med 16: 237–254, 1994.

36. **Hopker JG, Jobson SA, and Pandit JJ.** Controversies in the physiological basis of the 'anaerobic threshold' and their implications for clinical cardiopulmonary exercise testing. Anaesthesia 66: 111–123, 2011.

37. **Hopkins P, and Powers SK.** Oxygen uptake during submaximal running in highly trained men and women. Am Correct Ther J 36: 130–132, 1982.

38. **Hopkins WG, Hawley JA, and Burke LM.** Design and analysis of research on sport performance enhancement. Med Sci Sports Exerc 31: 472–485, 1999.

39. **Hopkins WG, Schabort EJ, and Hawley JA.** Reliability of power in physical performance tests. Sports Med 31: 211–234, 2001.

40. **Housh DJ, Housh TJ, and Bauge SM.** The accuracy of the critical power test for predicting time to exhaustion during cycle ergometry. Ergonomics 32: 997–1004, 1989.

41. **Housh TJ, Cramer JT, Bull AJ, Johnson GO, and Housh DJ.** The effect of mathematical modeling on critical velocity. Eur J Appl Physiol 84: 469–475, 2001.

42. **Hughson RL, Orok CJ, and Staudt LE.** A high velocity treadmill running test to assess endurance running potential. Int J Sports Med 5: 23–25, 1984.

43. **Jacobs I.** The effects of thermal dehydration on performance of the Wingate Anaerobic Test. International Journal of Sports Medicine 1: 21–24, 1980.

44. **Jones AM, Vanhatalo A, Burnley M, Morton RH, and Poole DC.** Critical power: implications for determination of $\dot{V}O_2$ max and exercise tolerance. Med Sci Sports Exerc 42: 1876–1890, 2010.

45. **Kenney WL, and Hodgson JL.** Variables predictive of performance in elite middle-distance runners. Br J Sports Med 19: 207–209, 1985.

46. **Kolbe T, Dennis SC, Selley E, Noakes TD, and Lambert MI.** The relationship between critical power and running performance. J Sports Sci 13: 265–269, 1995.

47. **Kraemer W, and Fry A.** Physiological Assessment of Human Fitness, edited by Maud P, and Foster C. Champaign, IL: Human Kinetics, 1995, p. 115–138.

48. **LaFontaine TP, Londeree BR, and Spath WK.** The maximal steady state versus selected running events. Med Sci Sports Exerc 13: 190–193, 1981.

49. **Lawler J, Powers SK, and Dodd S.** A time-saving incremental cycle ergometer protocol to determine peak oxygen consumption. Br J Sports Med 21: 171–173, 1987.

50. **Lehmann M.** Correlations between laboratory testing and distance running performance in marathoners of similar ability. International Journal of Sports Medicine 4: 226–230, 1983.

51. **Londeree B.** The use of laboratory test results with long distance runners. Sports Medicine 3: 201–213, 1986.

52. **Lorenzo S, Minson CT, Babb TG, and Halliwill JR.** Lactate threshold predicting time trial performance: impact of heat and acclimation. *Journal of Applied Physiology* In press: 2011.

53. **MacDougall J, and Wenger H.** The purpose of physiological testing. In: *Physiological Testing of the High Performance Athlete*, edited by MacDougall J, Wenger H, and Green H. Champaign: Human Kinetics, 1991.

54. **Magel JR, and Faulkner JA.** Maximum oxygen uptakes of college swimmers. *J Appl Physiol* 22: 929–933, 1967.

55. **Margaria R, Aghemo P, and Rovelli E.** Measurement of muscular power (anaerobic) in man. *J Appl Physiol* 21: 1662–1664, 1966.

56. **Mayhew T, and Rothstein J.** Measurement of muscle performance with instruments. In: *Measurement of Muscle Performance with Instruments*, edited by Rothstein J. New York: Churchill Livingstone, 1985, p. 57–102.

57. **McArdle W, Katch F, and Katch V.** *Exercise Physiology: Energy, Nutrition, and Human Performance.* Baltimore: Lippincott Williams & Wilkins, 2001.

58. **McMiken DF, and Daniels JT.** Aerobic requirements and maximum aerobic power in treadmill and track running. *Med Sci Sports* 8: 14–17, 1976.

59. **Meeteren J, Roebroeck ME, and Stam HJ.** Test-retest reliability in isokinetic muscle strength measurements of the shoulder. *J Rehabil Med* 34: 91–95, 2002.

60. **Mirkov D, Nedeljkovic A, Kukolj M, Ugarkovic D, and Jaric S.** Evaluation of the reliability of soccer-specific field tests. *J Strength Cond Res* 22: 1046–1050, 2008.

61. **Morgan DW, and Craib M.** Physiological aspects of running economy. *Med Sci Sports Exerc* 24: 456–461, 1992.

62. **Moritani T, Nagata A, deVries HA, and Muro M.** Critical power as a measure of physical work capacity and anaerobic threshold. *Ergonomics* 24: 339–350, 1981.

63. **Murase Y, Kobayashi K, Kamei S, and Matsui H.** Longitudinal study of aerobic power in superior junior athletes. *Med Sci Sports Exerc* 13: 180–184, 1981.

64. **Mygind E, Larsson B, and Klausen T.** Evaluation of a specific test in cross-country skiing. *J Sports Sci* 9: 249–257, 1991.

65. **Nicholas CW, Nuttall FE, and Williams C.** The Loughborough Intermittent Shuttle Test: a field test that simulates the activity pattern of soccer. *J Sports Sci* 18: 97–104, 2000.

66. **Noakes TD.** Implications of exercise testing for prediction of athletic performance: a contemporary perspective. *Med Sci Sports Exerc* 20: 319–330, 1988.

67. **Noakes TD, Myburgh KH, and Schall R.** Peak treadmill running velocity during the $\dot{V}O_2$ max test predicts running performance. *J Sports Sci* 8: 35–45, 1990.

68. **Noble B.** *Physiology of Exercise and Sport.* St. Louis: C. V. Mosby, 1986.

69. **Pannier JL, Vrijens J, and Van Cauter C.** Cardiorespiratory response to treadmill and bicycle exercise in runners. *Eur J Appl Physiol Occup Physiol* 43: 243–251, 1980.

70. **Parry-Billings M.** The measurement of anaerobic power and capacity: studies on the Wingate Anaerobic Test. *Snipes* J9: 48–58, 1986.

71. **Peronnet F, and Thibault G.** Mathematical analysis of running performance and world running records. *J Appl Physiol* 67: 453–465, 1989.

72. **Pollock ML.** Submaximal and maximal working capacity of elite distance runners. Part I: cardiorespiratory aspects. *Ann N Y Acad Sci* 301: 310–322, 1977.

73. **Pollock ML, Bohannon RL, Cooper KH, Ayres JJ, Ward A, White SR, and Linnerud AC.** A comparative analysis of four protocols for maximal treadmill stress testing. *Am Heart J* 92: 39–46, 1976.

74. **Pollock ML, Jackson AS, and Pate RR.** Discriminant analysis of physiological differences between good and elite distance runners. *Res Q Exerc Sport* 51: 521–532, 1980.

75. **Powers S.** Ventilatory threshold, running economy, and distance running performance of trained athletes. *Research Quarterly for Exercise and Sport* 54: 179–182, 1983.

76. **Powers SK, Dodd S, and Garner R.** Precision of ventilatory and gas exchange alterations as a predictor of the anaerobic threshold. *Eur J Appl Physiol Occup Physiol* 52: 173–177, 1984.

77. **Psotta R, Bunc V, Hendl J, Tenney D, and Heller J.** Is repeated-sprint ability of soccer players predictable from field-based or laboratory physiological tests? *J Sports Med Phys Fitness* 51: 18–25, 2011.

78. **Rampinini E, Bishop D, Marcora SM, Ferrari Bravo D, Sassi R, and Impellizzeri FM.** Validity of simple field tests as indicators of match-related physical performance in top-level professional soccer players. *Int J Sports Med* 28: 228–235, 2007.

79. **Reiman M, and Manske R.** *Functional Testing in Human Performance.* Champaign: Human Kinetics, 2009.

80. **Sale D.** Testing strength and power. In: *Physiological Testing of the High Performance Athlete*, edited by MacDougall J, Wenger H, and Green H. Champaign: Human Kinetics, 1991, p. 21–106.

81. **Sawka MN, Foley ME, Pimental NA, Toner MM, and Pandolf KB.** Determination of maximal aerobic power during upper-body exercise. *J Appl Physiol* 54: 113–117, 1983.

82. **Schenau G.** Can cycle power output predict sprint running performance? *European Journal of Applied Physiology* 63: 255–260, 1991.

83. **Schnabel A, and Kindermann W.** Assessment of anaerobic capacity in runners. *Eur J Appl Physiol Occup Physiol* 52: 42–46, 1983.

84. **Schwade J, Blomqvist CG, and Shapiro W.** A comparison of the response to arm and leg work in patients with ischemic heart disease. *Am Heart J* 94: 203–208, 1977.

85. **Scott BK, and Houmard JA.** Peak running velocity is highly related to distance running performance. *Int J Sports Med* 15: 504–507, 1994.

86. **Shaw DJ, Crawford MH, Karliner JS, DiDonna G, Carleton RM, Ross J, Jr., and O'Rourke RA.** Arm-crank ergometry: a new method for the evaluation of coronary artery disease. *Am J Cardiol* 33: 801–805, 1974.

87. **Sherrill DL, Anderson SJ, and Swanson G.** Using smoothing splines for detecting ventilatory thresholds. *Med Sci Sports Exerc* 22: 684–689, 1990.

88. **Simoneau JA, Lortie G, Boulay MR, and Bouchard C.** Tests of anaerobic alactacid and lactacid capacities: description and reliability. *Can J Appl Sport Sci* 8: 266–270, 1983.

89. **Storer TW, Davis JA, and Caiozzo VJ.** Accurate prediction of $\dot{V}O_2$ max in cycle ergometry. *Med Sci Sports Exerc* 22: 704–712, 1990.

90. **Stuart M, Powers S, and Nelson J.** Development of an anaerobic fitness test for football players. In: Unpublished observations.

91. **Tanaka K, and Matsuura Y.** Marathon performance, anaerobic threshold, and onset of blood lactate accumulation. *J Appl Physiol* 57: 640–643, 1984.

92. **Tanaka K, Matsuura Y, Kumagai S, Matsuzaka A, Hirakoba K, and Asano K.** Relationships of anaerobic threshold and onset of blood lactate accumulation with endurance performance. *Eur J Appl Physiol Occup Physiol* 52: 51–56, 1983.

93. **Taunton JE, Maron H, and Wilkinson JG.** Anaerobic performance in middle and long distance runners. *Can J Appl Sport Sci* 6: 109–113, 1981.

94. **Taylor HL, Buskirk E, and Henschel A.** Maximal oxygen intake as an objective measure of cardio-respiratory performance. *J Appl Physiol* 8: 73–80, 1955.

95. **Thoden J.** Testing aerobic power. In: *Physiological Testing of the High Performance Athlete*, edited by MacDougall J, Wenger H, and Green H. Champaign: Human Kinetics, 1991, p. 107–174.

96. **Thorland WG, Johnson GO, Cisar CJ, Housh TJ, and Tharp GD.** Strength and anaerobic responses of elite young female sprint and distance runners. *Med Sci Sports Exerc* 19: 56–61, 1987.

97. **Walker R, Powers S, and Stuart MK.** Peak oxygen uptake in arm ergometry: effects of testing protocol. *Br J Sports Med* 20: 25–26, 1986.

98. **Wasserman K, Whipp BJ, Koyl SN, and Beaver WL.** Anaerobic threshold and respiratory gas exchange during exercise. *J Appl Physiol* 35: 236–243, 1973.

99. **Weltman A, Snead D, Stein P, Seip R, Schurrer R, Rutt R, and Weltman J.** Reliability and validity of a continuous incremental treadmill protocol for the determination of lactate threshold, fixed blood lactate concentrations, and $\dot{V}O_{2max}$. *Int J Sports Med* 11: 26–32, 1990.

100. **Williams JH, Powers SK, and Stuart MK.** Hemoglobin desaturation in highly trained athletes during heavy exercise. *Med Sci Sports Exerc* 18: 168–173, 1986.

101. **Wyndham CH, Strydom NB, van Rensburg AJ, and Benade AJ.** Physiological requirements for world-class performances in endurance running. *S Afr Med J* 43: 996–1002, 1969.

102. **Zacharogiannis E, Pardisis G, and Tziortzis S.** An evaluation of tests of anaerobic power and capacity. *Med Sci Sports Exerc* 36: S116, 2004.

103. **Zagatto AM, Beck WR, and Gobatto CA.** Validity of the running anaerobic sprint test for assessing anaerobic power and predicting short-distance performances. *J Strength Cond Res* 23: 1820–1827, 2009.

104. **Zhang YY, Johnson MC, II, Chow N, and Wasserman K.** Effect of exercise testing protocol on parameters of aerobic function. *Med Sci Sports Exerc* 23: 625–630, 1991.